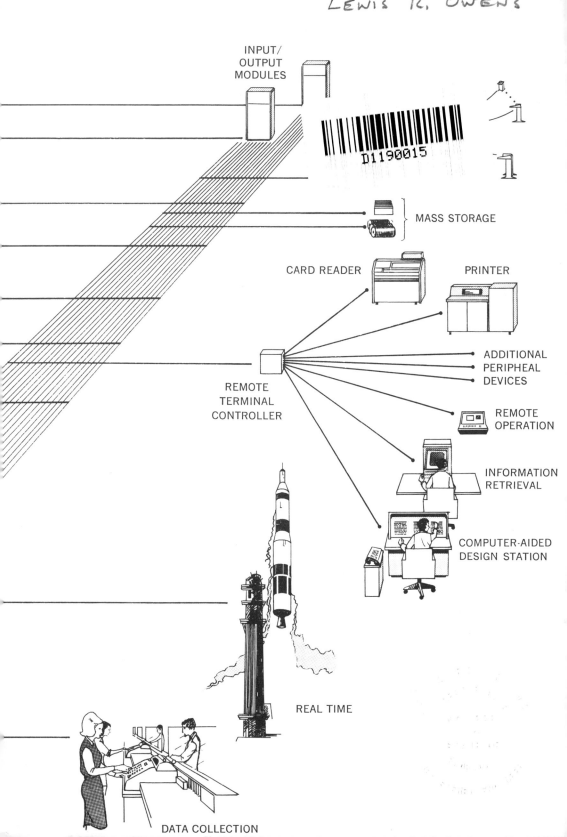

INPUT/ OUTPUT MODULES

D1190015

MASS STORAGE

CARD READER

PRINTER

REMOTE TERMINAL CONTROLLER

ADDITIONAL PERIPHEAL DEVICES

REMOTE OPERATION

INFORMATION RETRIEVAL

COMPUTER-AIDED DESIGN STATION

REAL TIME

DATA COLLECTION

DIGITAL COMPUTER PRINCIPLES

DIGITAL COMPUTER PRINCIPLES

second edition

BURROUGHS CORPORATION

Technical Training Department
Defense, Space, and Special Systems Group
Paoli, Pennsylvania

McGraw-Hill Book Company

New York   St. Louis   San Francisco   London
Sydney   Toronto   Mexico   Panama

DIGITAL COMPUTER PRINCIPLES

Library of Congress Catalog Card Number: 69-13599

09232

2 3 4 5 6 7 8 9 0 MAMM 7 6 5 4 3 2 1 0

To our families

Preface

This book is intended to provide an explanation of the basic principles of digital computers and the manner in which the basic building blocks are combined to provide small- and large-scale computing systems.

The text has undergone extensive revision and reorganization for the second edition. All references to vacuum-tube circuitry have been dropped, and the introductory chapter on basic semiconductor device theory has been deleted. A more detailed analysis of computer organization has been presented, and new material on system control concepts and integrated circuits added.

The book is divided into three parts:

I   Computer Fundamentals (Chapters 1 through 9)
II   Computer and Peripherals (chapters 10 through 14)
III Programming and System Concepts (Chapters 15 through 18)

Part I provides an exposure to the fundamental concepts which govern the operation of the digital computer. It includes an introduction to computers, logic, numbering systems, Boolean algebra, magnetic device fundamentals, and transistor switching characteristics. The chapter on computer circuits presents circuit analyses of the basic circuits used in digital computers, while the chapter on computer elements shows how the basic circuits are combined to provide larger functional groupings.

Part II deals with the computer and the peripheral devices which are connected to it. The chapter on the basic computer presents the data flow within the computer and the interfaces which exist among the major functional areas. A separate chapter is devoted to memory systems used with computing systems.

The chapters on peripheral devices and display systems provide an insight into the range of input/output devices used with the computing system, as well as into some of the operating characteristics of each device. Computer organization is discussed in a chapter which shows how the functional computer areas have been developed within the modularity concept.

Part III provides an introduction to programming and discusses some of the more advanced concepts used in computing system control. Assemblers and compilers, program debug, multiprogramming, and multiprocessing are included in the topics covered.

The text reorganization allows the reader to begin with the basic computer and advance through time to the present state of the art. Should he choose not to delve into multiprogramming or multiprocessing, his introduction to and understanding of the basic computer is satisfied in earlier chapters.

To the reader already familiar with computers, Parts II and III offer a review and an introduction to advanced computer concepts and the direction in which the field is moving.

Appendix material, such as appeared in the first edition, has been incorporated into the text, and the index serves to direct the reader to the explanation of the more commonly used computer terms.

Bernard L. Zaber, *Manager*
Technical Training Department

Contents

DIGITAL COMPUTER PRINCIPLES

I

COMPUTER
FUNDAMENTALS

chapter one

Introduction to Computers

Throughout the ages, man's progress has been measured by the implements he has invented to ease his mental and physical burdens. Perhaps the greatest invention has been the written word—with this, man has been able to record his discoveries and pass them on to future generations. In much of his scientific research, man has relied upon mathematical computations to predict the outcome of his numerous experiments and to test an abundance of new ideas. This probably has been the greatest stimulus to production of the outstanding developments in the field of automatic computation and electronic data processing in the last decade.

Electronic computers have made possible scientific and industrial advances that were unattainable only a decade ago. The mathematics required to orbit the sun with a satellite, or soft-land a space probe on the surface of the moon, for example, would tax the capabilities of teams of mathematicians for an entire lifetime. Now, with the aid of the electronic computer, the conquest of space is rapidly becoming a reality.

Computers are employed wherever repetitious calculations or the processing of voluminous data become necessary. Computers find their greatest applications in the commercial, scientific, and military fields. They are used in many varied projects, such as mail sorting, engineering design calculations, air traffic control, airline reservations, on-line banking, and educational applications. The beneficial aspects of computers include speed, accuracy, and the reduction of manpower in clerical and routine jobs, as well as in highly complex operations.

The digital computer is a member of a family of machines known as electronic data processors, which range in size from the desk-size computer used in banking applications to the room-size machines used in air traffic control. Digital computers solve mathematical problems by performing simple arithmetic operations.

Although a limited number of computers use subtraction, the majority use addition as the basic arithmetic operation. Computers perform subtraction, multiplication, division, and square root extraction by modification of the addition process. Following a sequence of instructions known as a *program*, a computer can solve problems in algebra, geometry, and calculus in a fraction of the time required by a human mathematician. Because they are capable of performing thousands of basic arithmetic operations each second, digital computers can relieve the scientist of lengthy numerical calculations and free his mind for more creative activities. Since the computer is a product of man's ingenuity, it can be only as versatile as its designers and programmers make it, and as reliable as the computer technician keeps it through his maintenance activities.

Data is applied to digital computers in the form of electric pulses of two discrete levels; hence this type of machine is highly adaptable to numerical calculations. The information is represented by the number of pulses and the spacing between them. There must be an intermediate device, between the operator and the data-manipulating portions of the computer, that will translate the information from numerical data to pulse data. Punched cards and punched paper tape are examples of input media. This intermediate step is necessary since the computer can arrive at a solution in a fraction of the time it takes to insert the information, and the medium must therefore be prepared well in advance. The computer then accepts the information from the medium as it is required, usually at a high rate of speed. After computations have been performed, the results are translated into a form that a human operator can read and understand.

This chapter presents a brief history of digital computers and the events that led to their present stage of development, an account of computer applications, and a description of the basic elements of computers. More detailed information is presented in the chapters that follow.

History of Digital Computers

Early man counted on his fingers and measured size and quantity with parts of his anatomy, such as the foot, hand, and palm. Another unit of measure based on the human body is the cubit (the length of the forearm from the elbow to the end of the middle finger). The familiar decimal system used for expressing quantity originated with the use of the fingers (digits) of the hand for computation; hence the word *digital* is used to describe any device which uses numbers to express quantity.

Eventually, the human hand proved inadequate for counting the quantities man needed to express, and he resorted to such devices as scratches in stones, notched sticks, and knotted string. The earliest known device made with a provision for denoting carries was the *abacus*, which originated in the Far East about 600 B.C. The abacus is a wooden frame with beads strung on wire columns (Fig. 1·1). Each column of beads represents an order, or place, in the decimal system, such as units, tens, hundreds, and thousands. The abacus is still used in some parts of the world, and

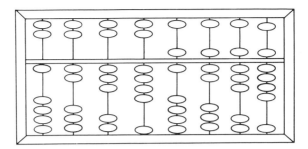

FIG. 1-1 Abacus.

skilled operators can manipulate it at a speed comparable to that of a desk calculator.

The next significant contribution to the field of computation was made in 1614 by John Napier, who invented and published tables of logarithms. Working with John Briggs, Napier was able to convert the logarithms to the base of 10 and introduce the use of the decimal point in this method of calculation. These logarithms were used by William Oughtred of England, who inscribed them on ivory in originating the slide rule. In 1617 Napier devised a system of computation known as "Napier's bones," which consists of manipulation of numbered squares of bone arranged to form whole numbers and fractions.

About 1642 Blaise Pascal constructed the first desk-calculator type of adding machine (Fig. 1·2). This device used gears with 10 teeth to represent numbers from 0 through 9. In its original form the machine performed addition and subtraction. It was later modified by other scientists to perform multiplication by repeatedly adding a given number for the required number of times. The principle of using repeated addition and subtraction is currently used in electronic computers to multiply and divide large numbers.

FIG. 1·2 Pascal's calculator

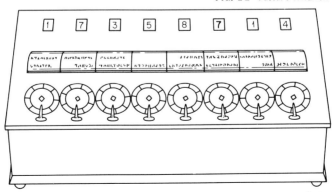

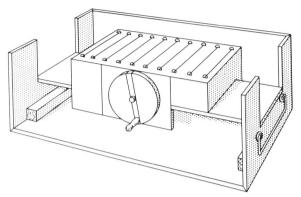

FIG. 1·3 Stepped reckoner.

Baron von Leibnitz constructed a machine called a *stepped reckoner* (Fig. 1·3) in the latter part of the seventeenth century. This machine was gear-operated, and it provided a carry from one order to the next. The various calculating machines just discussed were the forerunners of modern adding machines.

These machines, although able to speed the calculation process, had a major limitation to their full utilization. It was still necessary for man to introduce the data during various steps of the operation and to manually operate the device. The introduction of errors was possible during different phases of the calculation, and these devices were capable of faster operating speeds than were utilized by man. Thus the true capacity of even these primitive devices was not realized because of the human intervention required.

During the early part of the nineteenth century, Charles Babbage proposed a solution to this problem when he attempted to build a calculator that would solve problems and print answers. Babbage envisioned a machine that could automatically follow stored instructions and store a thousand numbers of 50 digits each. For an input to this analytical engine, Babbage planned to adapt the punched card that Joseph Marie Jacquard had invented in 1801 for the control of looms. Babbage's machine was never completed because the British government withdrew its support and because the machine tools of the day were incapable of the precision required to construct the components. Babbage's ideas were advanced for the technology of that time, and they included many of the features found in modern computers.

Charles Xavier Thomas of Alsace invented the first successful calculating machine in 1820. This machine, which was widely sold, contained units for setting, counting, and registering. In Europe Arthur Burkhardt began manufacturing in 1878 a Thomas type of machine known as the *arithmometer*. In 1875 Frank Stephen Baldwin and W. T. Odhner each designed a calculating machine that modified the stepped reckoner so that a variable number of teeth protruded from the periphery of the wheel. The thin Odhner wheel made possible a more compact design, which has been used in several more recent adding-machine designs. In 1850 D. D. Parmalee obtained a patent for the first key driven adding machine in the United States. It could add only a single column of digits at a time. It was not until after the turn of the century that Dorr Eugene Felt introduced parallel operation of keys and carry.

Although E. D. Barbor incorporated a printing device with an adding machine in 1872, the first commercially practical adding-listing machine was invented by William Seward Burroughs, who was granted a patent on it in 1888. The company for which Burroughs worked (the Boyer Machine Company) received a contract to produce 50 of the calculating machines (Fig. 1·4). Thus the business machine industry was established. However, it was not until special motors were developed in 1920 that desk calculators could be electrified.

FIG. 1·4 Burroughs' first adding machine.

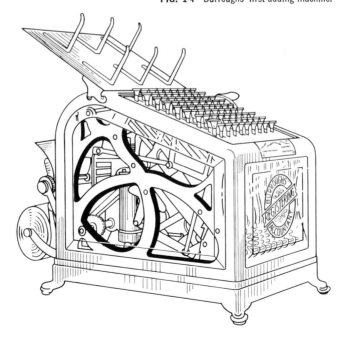

Development of Electromechanical and Electronic Computers

The first special-purpose relay computer was originated in 1940 by the Bell Telephone Laboratories. Many of the components developed by the telephone and telegraph industry were suitable for computing-machine construction. A special-purpose computer is one designed to perform a specific job and no other, so that it has limited applications. The first general-purpose computer, the Mark I, or automatic sequence-controlled calculator, was developed jointly by Harvard University and International Business Machines Corporation. Designed by Dr. Howard Aiken of the Harvard faculty, this computer used electromagnetic relays and punched cards.

While the debt of the computer industry to the communications industry is great, it owes an even greater debt to the pulse techniques developed in connection with radar during World War II. During this period when industry turned to automation, applied mathematics gained momentum. In fact, the general development of electronic computers had its real beginning in government projects during World War II.

Perhaps the greatest single advance in automatic computing came in 1945 when Dr. John von Neumann introduced the idea of storing the computer's instructions internally. Previous computers had been controlled by means of plugboard wiring or instructions stored in some external medium such as punched paper tape or cards. The new development in storage was first used in the design of the electronic discrete variable automatic computer (EDVAC). The computer was developed in 1946 by the Moore School of Engineering of the University of Pennsylvania for use by the United States Army at Aberdeen Proving Grounds in Maryland. In this machine the program of instructions was inserted directly into the memory so that an instruction was immediately accessible when the previous one had been performed.

The electronic numerical integrator and computer (ENIAC) was developed by J. W. Mauchly and J. P. Eckert of the University of Pennsylvania for the Ordnance Department of the United States Army. Completed in 1946, this machine represented both an advance and a step backward from the technological level of the EDVAC. The ENIAC was the first computer to be completely electronic in internal operation. However, it had no stored program, utilizing instead a complex external switching arrangement.

These computers were followed in rapid succession by others that featured improvements in speed, storage, and reliability. A. W. Burks, Dr. John von Neumann, and Dr. H. H. Goldstine developed a whole family of computers that used electrostatic memories. These computers were developed largely for military, scientific, and statistical purposes in various government projects. Soon after the end of World War II, such leaders in the computing machine field as the International Business Machines Corporation, Burroughs Corporation, National Cash Register Company, and Remington Rand Company (now Sperry Rand Corporation) developed electronic computers for general purposes. The UNIVAC, built in 1951 by Remington Rand, was the first mass-produced electronic computer.

Modern computers use transistors, integrated circuits, and miniature magnetic elements for compactness and reliability. They compute with speeds and accuracies that far outstrip the capabilities of the human brain. Today computers and other electronic data processors not only relieve man of many tedious tasks but also help him to better understand his environment.

Description of a Typical Computer

Basically, electronic digital computers are composed of six units (see Fig. 1·5): input, memory, arithmetic, output, control, and program. The following paragraphs briefly describe these units.

Input unit. The purpose of the input unit is to accept the initial input data from the input peripheral devices and provide the interface with the computing system. This input data is required for problem solution and must be prepared in a form that the computer can understand. The information is then said to be encoded into machine language. Typical input peripheral devices are punched-card readers, tape readers (paper or magnetic), and keyboards. The input and output devices are often slower in operation than the rest of the computer, which makes it necessary to store unworked and partly processed data in the memory unit.

FIG. 1·5 Basic computer units.

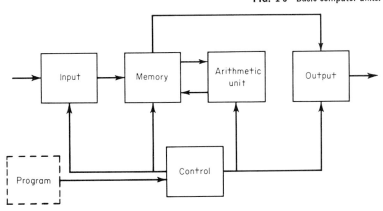

Memory unit. To solve a complex problem, the memory must hold (store) the steps for solution and the initial input data and, later, the intermediate and final results. All information that enters or leaves the computer passes through this unit.

Digital computers utilize magnetic-core or thin-film type of memory, although other types now in development may supersede these.

Arithmetic unit. The arithmetic unit performs all mathematical computations upon receiving instructions from the control unit. These operations take place sequentially. If multiplication is required, the unit obtains the result by repeated addition. The arithmetic unit receives its inputs from the memory unit and, after carrying out the appropriate calculation, sends the answers back to the same unit. The design of modern arithmetic units permits exacting, high-speed data computation requirements to be met.

Output unit. The output unit accepts final results from the storage unit and provides the interface between the computing systems and the peripheral devices. Common output peripheral devices are card punches, magnetic-tape units, paper-tape punches, printers, and CRT display devices.

Control unit. The control unit actuates the other units and controls the data flow between them to solve a problem. It accepts the problem and directs the order of operation in a step-by-step sequence.

Program. The program consists of a group(s) of instructions that describes a job(s) to be performed under control of the control unit. It should be noted that the program is not a hardware element but directions stored in memory (as explained in Chap. 10). It is shown here as a separate block to illustrate its overall control of the system.

Manual Problem Solving

The manner in which an electronic digital computer solves a problem may be illustrated by first analyzing the manner in which a typical business problem is solved manually. The corresponding steps taken by a computer to solve this problem will then be described.

The problem selected for analysis is that of computing and recording an employee's pay and deductions. The method of solution follows.

Step 1.   If this is the first time that the accountant has prepared a payroll for this particular firm, he consults a procedure manual or else obtains instructions from his fellow workers on the system in use.

Step 2. The next step is to accumulate the basic factors of the problem, namely, hours worked, hourly rate, overtime, tax deduction tables, employee tax status, and any other applicable deductions.

Step 3. The accountant then carries out the proper arithmetic calculations with a pencil and paper or with a desk calculator.

Step 4. The final results are then transferred to the regular company payroll form.

Computer Problem Solving

An electronic digital computer solves this payroll problem in a manner closely paralleling that of the accountant. The method follows.

Step 1. In digital computer procedure the loading of the program into the memory unit by way of the input unit corresponds to the accountant's obtaining the proper instructions for his job.

Step 2. The loading of raw data into the computer's memory unit through the input units corresponds to the accumulating by the accountant of the basic factors of the problem (hours worked, etc.).

Step 3. In this step the computer calculates the desired payroll data, guided always in a step-by-step manner by the control unit. The memory unit serves three functions: it holds raw data until the arithmetic unit is ready for it, it holds partially processed data, and it holds the final answers.

Step 4. When the output unit is switched on, it prints out or otherwise records the final answers on a sheet of paper, a punched card, or a tape.

This payroll problem illustrates a highly useful characteristic of a digital computer, namely, that it can solve any problem, no matter how complex, by a sequence of simple, logical steps.

The payroll problem is only one of many now being solved by computers. The chapters that follow will cover all the basic decision and storage elements of computers in detail and will show how these elements are connected to form the operational units described in this chapter.

Applications

It has been previously stated that computers are employed widely in the commercial, scientific, and military fields. The commercial field is the largest of the three. Nearly all large businesses use computers and data processors for calculating payrolls and billings, for processing inventories, and for reducing huge piles of statistics to comprehensible terms.

Data processors are used in the New York Stock Exchange to (1) inform stockbrokers of stocks available, (2) determine whether stock values are increasing or decreasing, and (3) compute Dow-Jones averages to show prevailing market tendencies. Large transportation companies use data processors to direct trains and airplanes along the most favorable routes. Flight plans and passenger reservations are recorded and updated.

Banking applications. The increasing use of checks and other banking services has resulted in the growth of banks' clerical staffs to almost unmanageable proportions and work loads are continually increasing. Computers are being used to solve part of this problem by taking the checks after the teller has typed in the amount, sorting the checks into the proper bins at the rate of thousands per hour, and recording the transactions on permanent records.

The American Bankers' Association, working with engineers and printers, has developed a standardized set of symbols for the numbers 0 through 9, along with four other symbols meaning "transit number," "on us," "amount," and "dash." These 14 symbols include all the information required for banking that is completely automatic except for writing the amount on the check. The numbers or symbols used for processing are written in magnetic ink across the bottom of each check.

When the check is moved through the sensing (reading) mechanism of the processing machine, these magnetized digits produce magnetic flux variations that can be converted into the proper symbols. This data is recorded in the memory, where it will be available for further processing or for activating sorting equipment for proper disposition of the check.

Many banks have also installed computer systems that allow the bank clerk to have immediate access to any customer account. This makes it possible for deposit-withdrawal accounting to be recorded directly into the computer for immediate disposition.

Other commercial applications. Manufacturing plants use computers for the control of industrial tools and processes, machine loading, and production scheduling. Accounting and sales applications include payroll and royalty computations, sales analysis, inventory control, and cost accounting. Among the many uses that engineers have found for computers are highway and canal cut-and-fill calculations, instrument-response studies, and gas-plant design.

Another commercial application is the automatic airline reservations system. Here, a central computer accepts information from thousands of reservation clerks at airports and offices throughout the country. This system allows reservations to be made, recorded, and confirmed in a matter of seconds.

Scientific applications. Businesses and institutions in scientific fields use digital computers and data processors for developing and testing new alloys and compounds, finding weak and strong areas of newly designed devices, and determining the effects of natural forces on man and his machines. Computers used for these purposes do not solve complete problems, but they do reduce the boredom and the time involved in solving the simple, repetitious portions of the problems. Many scientific institutions reduce the cost of operating their computers by solving problems for companies that can neither afford nor justify the cost of a full-time computer. Further examples of scientific applications of computers are molecular-vibration studies, optical-ray tracing, and high-energy-physics research. Among the many scientific applications of digital computers are physical, mathematical, chemical, astronomical, and biological research.

In hospitals and medical clinics, computers are being used to aid doctors in making the proper diagnoses from available symptoms.

Computers are also used in the field of education, where their information-processing capacities make it possible to adapt mechanical teaching routines to the needs and the past performance of the individual student.

Additional computer use is found in the launch and flight control of various weather and communication satellites, as well as in many types of deep-space probes.

The future of the digital computer in science is even more promising, for the computer makes feasible scientific exploration in many new areas.

Military applications. The armed forces also use many digital computers and data processors to supply materials to combat units, detect hostile aircraft and ships, and conduct retaliatory attacks at peak efficiency. Digital computers are used to determine cargo storage areas in ships and airplanes, considering both weight distribution and convenience, and they calculate the quantities of supplies required for combat units. Data processors are employed in early-warning-radar systems to arrange information in a form easily interpreted by the officers who assign and direct missiles and aircraft to the target. Compact, airborne digital computers are used in supersonic aircraft for aiming rockets at targets and in intercontinental ballistic missiles for guidance. The launch and control of such missile systems as the Minuteman and Polaris are under control of computers. Computers are also used aboard ships and submarines to calculate positional data. Thus, the computer can be used in both offensive and defensive military applications.

Another utilization of the computer is in automatic message-processing and switching centers for worldwide communications control.

The computer uses presented in this chapter are representative of the

many ways in which digital computers and data processors have been employed in commercial, scientific, and military applications. As technology
expands, more and more uses for computers will be found in these and other
fields.

In the fields of science and industry there has been a growing need for
high-speed computing devices. Long, tedious calculations that take months
to perform have impeded to a considerable extent the progress of scientific
research and development. Time-consuming computations that might take
a human being years to perform can be accomplished in a matter of minutes
with modern, high-speed computers.

Automatic electronic digital computers are relatively new, dating back
to about 1944. Since then, more than 200 types of computers have been
built. Of the two general types of digital computers, special purpose and
general purpose, the general purpose has become more prevalent. The main
advantage of the general-purpose computer is that it can solve many
different problems by inserting a program relating to the given problem into
the memory. The special-purpose computer, on the other hand, being hard-
wired program controlled, can perform only one job without modifications
to its fixed program. Computers range in size from small desk calculators
to those used in high-capacity data processing systems.

This chapter has surveyed the history and application of digital computers in the commercial, military, and scientific fields. The operation of
computers and typical computer problem-solving methods have been
described in simplified form. The potential of these machines is unlimited.
The future of those trained and experienced in the computer field appears
bright.

QUESTIONS

1·1   What advantages do computers offer over conventional methods of
      problem solving?
1·2   What are the two major classifications of digital computers? Which
      type is more prevalent? Why?
1·3   Draw a block diagram showing the six basic units of a digital com-
      puter and briefly describe the function of each unit.
1·4   Can a digital computer solve any type of problem? What are the
      factors involved?
1·5   List some applications for which computers are used.
1·6   What is the basic arithmetic operation used by the computer?
1·7   In what form is data applied to a digital computer?
1·8   What did John Napier contribute to the computer field?
1·9   Who invented the first desk calculator and what operations did it per-
      form?

1·10 In what way was the calculator Charles Babbage attempted to build like the computer of today?

1·11 What was perhaps the greatest single advance in automatic computing?

1·12 Name two types of memories used in computer systems.

chapter two

Computer Logic

A first glance at the circuitry of a digital computer has the tendency to reinforce the assumption of the observer that this machine is a giant brain containing masses of exotic circuits, the operation of which is beyond the comprehension of the average technician. It is the purpose of this chapter to dispel this assumption, to show that this is not the case. By definition, a computer is a mechanical or electronic machine which is capable of performing sequences of reasonable operations upon information — mainly arithmetic and logical operations. The term "computer logic" indicates the manner in which the basic computer elements are connected to provide the reasoning and decision-making activity of the computer. A simplified mathematical expression of computer logic termed *Boolean algebra* has been adopted by the digital computer industry; this system of mathematics removes the computer from design-equation level and simplifies the operational analysis to the point where it can be comprehended readily by well-informed laymen. A more extensive treatment of Boolean algebra is given in Chap. 4.

As the material in this book is assimilated, the seemingly intricate operations will become clear and sometimes surprisingly simple. A computer is constructed from only a few types of basic circuits, modified to suit a particular need (compactness, circuit reliability, stability, etc.). These circuits are then grouped together to process information. The purpose of this chapter is not to give a complete theory of computer operation but to acquaint the reader with computer language, computer components, and the logical symbols used.

Basic Principles of Computer Design

Computer design is divided into two areas, logical design and electrical design. Logical design involves the use of mathematical logic to provide equations for all the operations a computer must perform. Electrical design provides electric circuits corresponding to the logical equations. The four basic requirements for computer design are as follows:

1. A system of numbers that can be easily adapted by the machine to perform arithmetic operations.
2. A system of mathematics that can determine and describe all the operations to be performed by a computer.
3. A means of representing all commands, information, and numbers in a computer by electrical quantities.
4. A system of electric circuits to execute operations to be performed by a computer.

Each of these requirements will be discussed.

Number Systems for Computers

The arithmetic operations of a digital computer are dependent upon counters for computations and data synchronization and upon gating devices for decision making. The early computers, such as the Harvard Mark I calculator constructed by the International Business Machines Corporation in 1944, used many standardized calculator parts. This electromechanical computer used relays and mechanical counters, and it had a storage capacity of 1728 decimal digits. The basic time cycle of the machine was 300 msec for the addition of two numbers. Its mechanical drive was a 4-hp motor. The total assembly weighed approximately 5 tons.

The high driving power required and the speed limitations of relays and mechanical counters, caused by inertia, led to the utilization of vacuum tubes and then transistors for counting and temporary storage and to the

TABLE 2-1 Binary Representation of Decimal Digits

Decimal number	Binary equivalent	
	8421	Position value
0	0000	
1	0001	
2	0010	
3	0011	
4	0100	
5	0101	
6	0110	
7	0111	
8	1000	
9	1001	
10	1010	

abandonment of the decimal system of numeration in the computers that followed. The 10 digits used in the decimal system were too cumbersome for a computer of reasonable size. In order to use the decimal system, either 10 storage devices or a device with 10 distinct levels was required for each order. Since a signal of two discrete levels is less subject to deterioration than a multilevel signal, modern digital computers operate with the binary (two-value) system. The binary system uses only two digits, 0 and 1. The equivalent counts in the binary system for the decimal numbers 0 through 10 are shown in Table 2·1. The binary 1 can be represented by a conducting transistor and the binary 0 can be represented by a cutoff transistor. In the binary system, five transistors could represent a decimal value of 31 (binary 11111 = decimal 31). A complete explanation of the binary system is given in Chap. 3, Number Systems.

Although the binary system is cumbersome for pencil-and-paper manipulation, the fact that only two digits are involved makes this system ideal for computer manipulation.

Mathematical Logic for Computers

The most widely used system of mathematics for describing the logical sequences of operation a computer must perform is Boolean algebra, which was developed by George Boole, a philosopher and mathematician who wished to express philosophical logic in mathematical terms. Boolean algebra is not an algebra involving customary numerical values; rather, it is an algebra of *classes*. Only two of the classes in Boolean algebra are of importance in computer design. These are the *universal* class, in which everything is a member $(1 + 0 = 1)$, and the *empty* class, in which nothing is a member $(1 \times 0 = 0)$.

The concept of classes in its pure sense, however, is of importance only to the mathematician and the philosopher. For computer design purposes, the important factor is that only two discrete values are involved: a quantity either exists or does not exist.

In a computer, the empty class is mechanized by what is termed an AND gate. The simple switch-and-lamp configuration shown in Fig. 2·1 illustrates the function of an AND gate.

FIG. 2·1   (a) Switches performing the AND function; (b) truth table.

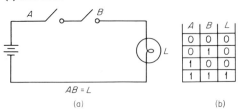

A	B	L
0	0	0
0	1	0
1	0	0
1	1	1

$AB = L$

(a)   (b)

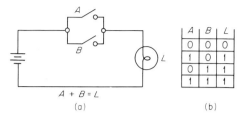

A	B	L
0	0	0
1	0	1
0	1	1
1	1	1

$A + B = L$

(a)

(b)

FIG. 2-2 (a) Switches performing the OR function; (b) truth table.

If the lamp L is to light, series switches A and B must be closed at the same time. The Boolean expression for this function uses the multiplication sign and can be expressed in either of three forms: $A \times B = L$, $AB = L$, or $A \cdot B = L$, read as "A AND B equals L." If a closed switch were to represent a 1, or "true," condition and the open switch were to represent a 0, or "false," condition, a table could be constructed showing all possible conditions of the two variables. Such a table is called a *truth table*. Truth tables are useful when a large number of variables is used.

The universal class is mechanized by an OR gate. The switch-and-lamp configuration is again used to illustrate the OR function as shown in Fig. 2-2. The truth table for this function is also shown. If either of the parallel switches (A or B) is closed, the lamp will light. The Boolean expression for the OR function is $A + B = L$, read as "A OR B equals L."

The diagrams illustrate the important AND and OR functions in their purest form. In actual computer circuitry, these gates are composed of diodes or of amplifying devices such as transistors. The AND gate is the actual "decision" element in a computer and the OR gate is the "mixer" element.

The following example shows how computer operations are expressed in Boolean notation. In Chap. 1, two of the main computer units described were the arithmetic unit and the memory unit. Quite often it is desired to transfer a sum from the arithmetic unit to the memory unit. There are two conditions that must exist before the transfer may occur:

1. The addition process must be complete.
2. A position must be available in the memory unit to accommodate the sum.

To express these conditions for transfer in Boolean notation, let T designate the transfer command, signal C indicate that addition is complete, and signal P indicate that a position exists in the memory. The equation for transfer is written as follows:

$$C \cdot P = T$$

This equation states that a transfer command will occur when addition is completed and a position is available in the memory. The dot in the equation indicates that an AND circuit is used.

Consider another example, using the OR circuit. Prior to any arithmetic operation, the arithmetic unit must be cleared. Let C designate the CLEAR command, signal A indicate an ADD instruction, S indicate a SUBTRACT instruction, M indicate multiplication, and D indicate division. The equation for the CLEAR command is written as follows:

$$C = A + S + M + D$$

Boolean algebra expresses all the logical operations performed in a computer in terms of the existence or nonexistence of specific conditions. A more detailed description of Boolean algebra is given in Chap. 4.

Representing Information by Electrical Quantities

Boolean algebra and the binary number system have one important common characteristic: only two discrete quantities exist in each system. In Boolean algebra these quantities are "present" and "not present," and in binary arithmetic they are 1 and 0.

Since, in each case, only two values are used, an electric pulse is the most suitable means of representing these values. Although there are a number of constant-level signals used in a computer, the majority of numbers, commands, and information contained in the computer is in the form of pulses, which are the internal language of the machine. Depending upon their use, the width and timing of these pulses will vary over a considerable range.

Pulse characteristics. An electric pulse is either a voltage or a current that undergoes an almost instantaneous change in amplitude from one constant level to another. Pulse characteristics are shown in Fig. 2·3. The time between the leading edge of one pulse and the leading edge of the following pulse is known as the *pulse repetition time* (PRT). The *pulse repetition frequency* (PRF) is the reciprocal of the PRT. For example, if the time between pulses is 0.002 sec, the PRF is 1/0.002 or 500 pulses per second (pps).

The pulses shown in Fig. 2·3 are idealized. An actual pulse seen on an oscilloscope would appear similar to the pulse shown in Fig. 2·4. Pulse-amplifying and -shaping circuits are used in the computer so that the ideal waveshape is approached.

Pulses perform a variety of functions in a digital computer: they provide basic timing, indicate information, and control the sequence of operation of the computer. Each function will now be discussed.

FIG. 2·3 Pulse characteristics.   **FIG. 2·4** Actual pulse waveforms.

Timing pulses. The speed of computer operation is dependent upon the PRF of the basic timing pulses. A digital computer is a sequential machine in that all tasks performed by it are accomplished in a sequence of basic, and often repetitive, operations. Each operation a computer performs is performed in coincidence with a timing pulse.

Timing pulses are generated by a stable pulse-generating circuit, or *timing oscillator.* The width of the timing pulse is short, usually about 0.05 μsec. Timing pulses are often called *clock pulses.* Typical computer clock rates may vary between 1 and 20 MHz.

Information pulses. Information in a computer includes coded data such as numbers, letters, and symbols. This information is represented in the computer by a configuration of 1's and 0's. For example, decimal 10 is represented as binary 1010. The pulse representation of this number is shown in Fig. 2·5.

Each 1 and 0 in the number is a BInary digiT, often contracted to *bit.* A bit is the smallest unit of information, that is, a Yes or a No. The bits are used to form machine characters.

Characters. A character can be a decimal digit 0 to 9, a letter A to Z in either uppercase or lowercase, a punctuation mark, or a symbol. Characters are the basic pieces of intelligible machine information, and they are usually of fixed length. For example, a character length may be six bits. The pulses shown in Fig. 2·5 illustrate a four-bit machine character, representative of the decimal number 10. The same configuration could also be used to represent either the letter J or a symbol; this is determined by the character code used by the computer.

FIG. 2·5 Pulse representation of binary 1010.

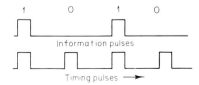

Words. Machine characters are used to construct computer words. The number of characters in a word differs for various computers (a computer word may be composed of eight characters or a total of 48 bits per word). The arithmetic unit of the computer usually operates on words rather than on a single character or bit, although a special operation may call for a character or bit of a word to be isolated for a particular function. An analogy may be drawn between the machine character and a written letter and between the machine word and a spoken word. In both cases, an elemental unit of a language (character) is used to compose a unit of intelligence that has meaning. The characters represent letters, numbers, and symbols.

Blocks. In the majority of digital computers it is expedient to process information in larger units than the word. Since the internal storage capacity of a computer is limited, voluminous and seldom-used information, such as records and accounts, are generally stored externally in storage devices such as magnetic tapes, drums, and disks. Since thousands, and in some cases millions, of words can be stored on these devices, they are usually preferred for permanent bulk storage because of the low cost per character stored and the fairly short access time (in the order of microseconds to milliseconds). Before the external data is actually needed by the computer, the device is actuated by signals from the computer to search for the required information. Information is applied to the computer in units of several words each, termed *blocks*. A block could contain from one word to thousands of words. The blocks of information are thus transferred to internal storage, to which the computer has a shorter access time (in the order of microseconds). Figure 2·6 illustrates a segment of an information block of 20 four-character words using four-bit characters.

More details on block information selection from external storage are presented in later chapters.

FIG. 2·6 Typical information block.

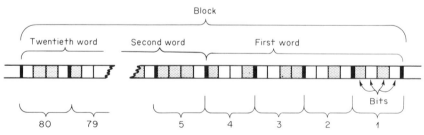

Computer Logic

The digital computer is a complex machine in its entirety; however, it is still no more than an aggregate of simple devices that perform a few basic operations. The two most commonly used devices are *bistable switching circuits* and *gates*.

A bistable device is one having two stable states of conduction or being. A typical example of a bistable device is an ordinary push-button light switch. When the switch is pushed to the ON position, it makes a rapid transition from the OFF state to the ON state and "remembers" that position until it is depressed again to the OFF position. A rapid transition is highly desirable in bistable switching circuits because it determines the maximum speed at which the computer can operate.

The two types of gates used in computers are the *linear gate* and the *logical gate*. The linear gate is defined as one from which the output is an approximate replica of at least one of the inputs. The logical gate is defined as one in which the output is a pulse which may have no resemblance to any of the inputs, except that the pulse occurs during an interval selected by the control voltages. The term *logical* is applied to these gates because the input-output characteristics of these circuits are suggestive of logical operations. Computer operations are implemented by bistable switching circuits, by gates, or by a combination of these items. Gates and switching circuits are generally used in conjunction with other devices such as delay lines, multivibrators, inverters, and amplifiers to control the movement of pulse information throughout the machine. The function and the representative symbol of each type of basic computer circuit are described in the following paragraphs. The emphasis will not be upon the electrical characteristics, but rather on how the circuit performs its function. The electrical operation of each type of circuit will be described in detail in another chapter of this book.

Bistable elements. Information in a computer is indicated in the form of words consisting of 1's and 0's. A bistable element, an element capable of indicating a 1 or a 0, must be used to indicate each bit in a word. The relay was the bistable element used in earlier computers, and it is still useful in many applications today. Figure 2·7 shows the simplified diagram of a relay. A relay is a switch that operates electromagnetically. The relay closes or opens a circuit if the current through its exciting coil is started or stopped. If the operating switch is closed, current flows through the coil, energizing the electromagnet and drawing the armature upward to the contact.

If the relay contact is closed, a 1 could be indicated; if the relay contact

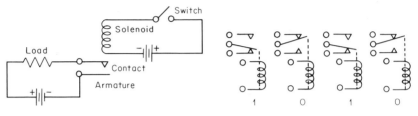

FIG. 2·7 Simple relay.   FIG. 2·8 Relays indicating 1010.

is open, a 0 could be indicated. Of course, the opening and closing of the switch are controlled by other relays or control elements.

Since words rather than individual bits are processed in a computer, the bistable elements are grouped together as a unit to accommodate a word. This is the reason that words contain a fixed number of characters. For example, four relays would be required to hold the character 1010. In Fig. 2·8 the positions of the relay contacts are shown as they would appear when the character 1010 is indicated.

A typical relay has a life expectancy of nearly a billion cycles and operates in the order of milliseconds. The operational speed of the electromechanical relay restricted the computational speed of the relay-equipped computer to the range of hundreds of cycles per second. To overcome speed limitations, the relays were supplanted with high-speed electronic switches.

Flip-flop. The most commonly used bistable element in computers is the bistable multivibrator usually referred to as a *flip-flop.* This device has two stable states; that is, a designated output may appear at one side (first stable state) or at the other side (second stable state). This characteristic allows each of the stable states to represent one of the symbols used in the binary system; thus, one of the stable states is used to represent a 1 and is referred to as the ONE state. The other stable state (side) represents a 0 and is referred to as the ZERO state. The symbol for a flip-flop is shown in Fig. 2·9. In order to store a 1, the flip-flop is set or placed in the ONE state and to store a 0, it is reset or placed in the ZERO state. Some flip-flops have internal gating circuitry which allows the flip-flop to take the opposite state on an input trigger. A detailed discussion of the electrical characteristics and operation of the flip-flop is contained in Chap. 7.

Magnetic cores. The development of magnetic materials possessing high retentivity and a nearly square hysteresis loop has made it possible to construct magnetic cores for use as bistable switching devices. Their small physical size and their ability to store binary information at the expense of very little energy make these core devices ideally suited for computer data-storage applications. The core can be regarded as storing a 1 when mag-

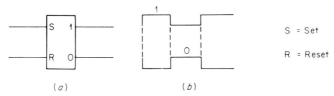

FIG. 2-9 Flip-flop. (a) Logical symbol; (b) waveforms.

netized by sufficient current in a given direction and storing a 0 when magnetized in the opposite direction. When the core is "read," it is set to the 0 state. The magnetic core finds its greatest use in memory systems.

Thin film. Another type of magnetic storage device is the thin-film spot. It possesses the same magnetic properties as the magnetic core but is both smaller in size and normally faster in switching speed than the core. The film, like the core, can store a 1 by magnetization in one direction and a 0 by magnetization in the opposite direction. When the film is read, it is placed in the 0 state. The detailed operation of magnetic cores and thin-film spots is explained in Chap. 5.

Logical gates. Computer operation is characterized by decision-making, mixing of signals, comparison of signals, and other types of execution and control. Several basic logic gates can be implemented to satisfy these needs. These gates are explained in the following discussions. It should be noted that the truth tables used in these discussions (and elsewhere in this chapter) will use 1's and 0's for explanation purposes rather than the "true-false" or "high-low" convention. The "true" or "1" in a computer may be represented by either a positive or negative level, determined by the electrical configuration used. The purpose of this chapter is to show the input-output relationship of the various gates from a logical approach; hence, mention of electrical levels and polarities has been omitted.

AND *gate.* The AND gate is used to detect the coincidence of several input signals; that is, the output will be present only when all inputs are present. The symbol for the AND gate and the truth table which represents its operational conditions are shown in Fig. 2·10. As can be seen in Fig. 2·10, when

FIG. 2·10 AND gate. (a) Logical symbol; (b) truth table.

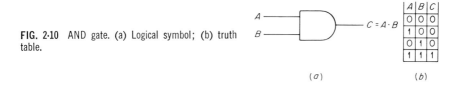

A	B	C
0	0	0
1	0	0
0	1	0
1	1	1

$C = A \cdot B$

(a)   (b)

both the A and the B inputs are present, output C is satisfied and can be used for some control purpose. The truth table illustrates all combinations of signals A and B. It can be seen that output C is satisfied under only one of the combinations of input signals, the presence of all inputs (two in this example).

OR *gate.* The OR gate provides a mixing function in a computer; that is, if one or more of several inputs to the gate are present, the output will be present (see Fig. 2·11). It can be seen from the truth table that any combination of inputs except the absence of A and B will produce an output at point C. In this manner the gate acts as a mixer device in that C is generated if either A or B or both (all) are present.

Exclusive-OR *gate.* The exclusive-OR gate provides a comparison function. It is capable of detecting opposite conditions of its inputs. An output will be produced when only one or the other of the two inputs is present. The logic symbol and truth table for the exclusive-OR gate are shown in Fig. 2·12. The truth table shows that output C will be generated if either input A or B is present (only one input), but not if both A and B (more than one) are present or absent. This type of gate is useful in error-checking circuits.

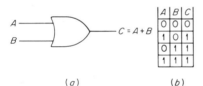

A	B	C
0	0	0
1	0	1
0	1	1
1	1	1

FIG. 2·11   OR gate. (a) Logical symbol; (b) truth table.

(a) (b)

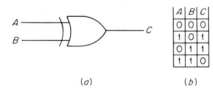

A	B	C
0	0	0
1	0	1
0	1	1
1	1	0

FIG. 2·12   Exclusive-OR gate. (a) Logical symbol; (b) truth table.

(a) (b)

FIG. 2·13   NAND gate. (a) Logical symbol; (b) equivalent; (c) truth table.

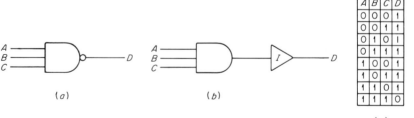

A	B	C	D
0	0	0	1
0	0	1	1
0	1	0	1
0	1	1	1
1	0	0	1
1	0	1	1
1	1	0	1
1	1	1	0

(a) (b) (c)

NAND *gate.* The term NAND gate is a contraction of the terms NOT AND gate and is sometimes labeled as such. This gate performs the equivalent of two circuits, an AND gate and an inverter. The logic symbol, equivalent circuit, and a truth table for a typical NAND gate are shown in Fig. 2·13. Output D is present for all input combinations except when A, B, and C are all present. The absence of at least one of the inputs results in output D.

NOR *gate.* The term NOR is a contraction of the terms NOT OR gate. The NOR, like the NAND gate, is a gate which feeds an inverter state. The logic symbol, equivalent circuit, and the truth table for a NOR gate are shown in Fig. 2·14. The input-output relationship of the NOR gate is the opposite of the NAND gate. Output D will be present only when all inputs to the gate are absent. If one or more of the inputs are present, the desired output is absent.

Amplifier. When logical building blocks are connected in various combinations to perform logical operations, the output pulses from these devices decrease in amplitude and their waveforms become distorted. The output from a gate or a flip-flop is usually applied to several other elements as inputs. These devices may not provide enough power to drive all the necessary inputs. Circuits are interspersed between logical blocks to reshape the pulses and to provide driving power and isolation between stages. Pulse amplifiers and buffer amplifiers are used throughout a computer system for these purposes. Although amplifiers provide no logical function, they are necessary for reliable electrical operation of computers. The symbol for the amplifier is shown in Fig. 2·15.

FIG. 2·14 NOR gate. (a) Logical symbol; (b) equivalent; (c) truth table.

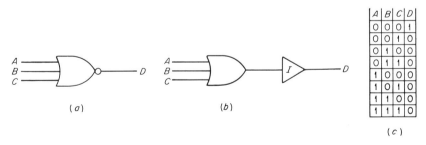

A	B	C	D
0	0	0	1
0	0	1	0
0	1	0	0
0	1	1	0
1	0	0	0
1	0	1	0
1	1	0	0
1	1	1	0

(a)   (b)   (c)

FIG. 2·15 Amplifier.

(a)   (b)

FIG. 2·16 Inverter. (a) Logical symbols; (b) example of use.

Inverter. Quite often it becomes necessary to invert the polarity of a signal or level. Inversion may become necessary to perform a logical function or to obtain the correct level to perform an electrical operation. Inversion is usually performed by an amplifier stage whose output is 180° out of phase with the input or by a phase-inverting transformer. The logical symbol for the inverter and an example of its use are shown in Fig. 2·16. In the example of Fig. 2·16 it is desired to produce an output D when a situation F exists and a situation E does not exist. This is expressed as $D = F \cdot \bar{E}$. With a "true" at input F and a "false" at input E (converted to a "true" via the inverter stage), the AND gate is satisfied and output D is produced.

Delay devices. It is often necessary to delay data or information pulses as they are routed through the computer system without affecting the widths of the pulse(s) or the timing between pulses. It may be necessary at times to increase or decrease the width of a pulse. These functions can be accomplished by the use of a delay element. Examples of delay devices in use are the quartz, lumped-constant, magnetostrictive, and glass delay lines and the monostable multivibrator. Of the delay lines, the magnetostrictive and the glass are more widely used. A typical application of these delay circuits is in providing accurate timing for memory systems. A brief explanation of these devices follows.

Quartz delay line. A quartz delay line consists of two crystals placed on the sides of a container of quartz. An electric pulse is applied to the input crystal causing it to vibrate and create a mechanical wave of energy that traverses the quartz to the output crystal. The delay encountered depends upon the delaying properties of quartz and, to some extent, upon how it is cut. The output crystal, upon reception of the energy pulse, vibrates and produces an electric pulse at the output side.

Lumped-constant delay line. The lumped-constant delay line is composed of a group of inductors and capacitors. The amount of time required for a pulse to traverse each inductor-capacitor section depends upon the values of the components. The desired delay is accomplished by correct choice of components and the required number of sections. For very short delays (100 nsec, for example) like those encountered in thin-film memory timing, only the inductors are required; the distributed capacitance existing between the windings provides the shunt capacitance.

Magnetostrictive delay line. A magnetostrictive delay line consists of an input transducer (coil), a length of metal wire (such as nickel), and an output transducer (coil). If an electric pulse is applied to the input coil, the coil will produce a magnetic field. The magnetic field in turn will cause a physical change in the crystal structure of the metal wire (magnetostriction effect) creating a mechanical wave of energy. The energy pulse travels down the wire to the output transducer which converts the mechanical energy back into an electric pulse. The amount of delay is determined by the length of the wire and may vary from microseconds up to several milliseconds. The delay may be adjusted by moving the input transducer along the wire.

Glass delay line. The glass delay line competes with the magnetostrictive as one of the more widely used delay lines. The glass type operates in a higher frequency range and is used for shorter delay periods. Like other similar delay lines, it is composed of an input transducer, an output transducer, and a delay medium of glass which is sometimes in the form of a rod. The input transducer converts an electric pulse into mechanical energy which traverses the length of the glass. The output transducer converts the energy wave back into an electric pulse, delayed by an amount determined by the length of the rod. Figure 2·17a shows how the word 1101 may be delayed for a period of 4000 μsec using a delay line. Observe that even though each bit in the word has been delayed for 4000 μsec, the pulse widths and the time between pulses are unaffected. Figure 2·17b indicates the symbol used for the delay line.

Monostable multivibrator. A more commonly used delay device is the monostable multivibrator which is usually referred to as a *single-shot circuit.* Once the single shot is supplied with an input trigger, it will produce one

FIG. 2·17 Delays. (a) Binary word delayed 4000 μsec; (b) delay symbol.

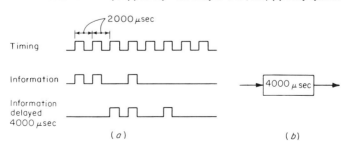

complete output pulse, the width of which is controlled by a time constant circuit within the single shot. By using a series of single shots, various delays can be obtained. This is accomplished by using the trailing edge of one single shot to trigger another single shot. An example of this is shown in Fig. 2·18. This device is normally used to delay a single pulse rather than a train of pulses or a word.

An analysis of the circuit operation of the devices discussed in this chapter is presented in subsequent chapters.

Logical diagrams. Since most logical elements in computers are used repetitively and since the input and output characteristics are known, each element can be represented by its particular logical symbol. By showing the connections between symbols, the complete operation of the computer can be traced. An example of the logical diagram is shown in Fig. 2·19.

A logical diagram and the Boolean equations that describe computer operations are the most useful means of analyzing the complete operation of a computer. Notice that no voltage levels are shown on the logical diagram. The primary concern is merely to show the logical sequence of operation. Another diagram may be provided to show input and output levels along with the location of pulse and buffer amplifiers and other necessary circuitry.

FIG. 2·18 Delay device. (a) Monostable multivibrator; (b) combined-delay; (c) delay timing.

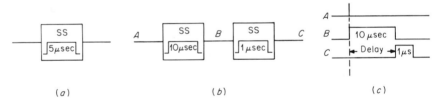

FIG. 2·19 Logical diagram.

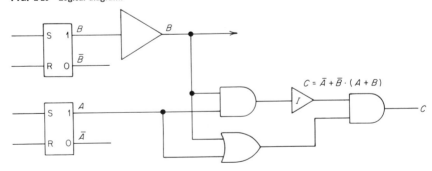

A diagram such as this is very useful in troubleshooting in order to isolate a fault to a specific block.

SUMMARY

The purpose of this chapter has been to describe the basic requirements of computer design, to show how pulses are used to perform logical operations, and to describe the basic types of pulse circuits required to perform computer operations. The basic circuits are called *building blocks* and are used repetitively to perform the various logical operations. Logical diagrams employing symbolic representations of the basic blocks may be used to trace the complete operation of the computer without considering the electrical characteristics of each circuit.

None of the explanations given in this chapter has been complete. Rather, an overall view has been given describing the essential topics to be discussed in the book. Number systems, Boolean algebra, pulse circuits, and logical operations will be discussed in detail in subsequent chapters.

QUESTIONS

2·1   What system of numeration was used by the first electromechanical computers? Why was it later abandoned?

2·2   Develop a table showing the binary equivalents of decimal numbers 1 through 10.

2·3   What are the two basic logical gates used in digital computers? Which is the decision-making gate and which is the mixing gate? Make up a truth table showing all possible input and output conditions of a two-input gate of each basic type.

2·4   What is the purpose of computer timing pulses? Information pulses?

2·5   Briefly explain the following terms: bit, character, word, block.

2·6   List components which could be used as bistable elements in digital computers.

2·7   What is the purpose of a logical diagram?

2·8   What was the major disadvantage of the use of relays as bistable elements?

2·9   What is the most commonly used bistable element?

2·10 What is the difference between storing a ONE and a ZERO in a magnetic core?

2·11 What is the advantage of using the thin-film spot rather than the magnetic core as a storage device?

2·12 Draw the logical diagram for the equation $C = A \cdot B + D + E$.

2·13 What type of gate can be used to satisfy the equation $C = \bar{A} \cdot B + A \cdot \bar{B}$?

2·14 What type of logical gate is suited for use in error-checking circuits?

2·15 What is the equivalent circuit for a NAND gate?

2·16 If output D is "true" only when inputs A, B, and C are "false," what logical gate is used to represent this condition?

2·17 Draw a logical diagram to represent a 1-μsec pulse delayed 50 μsec.

Number Systems

Bistable devices for counting and storing pulses are used extensively throughout digital computers and data processors. These devices produce outputs of two levels which are equivalent to either 1 or 0. This mode of counting can be expressed by the binary number system. Therefore, in order to grasp the concept of computer operation, it is necessary to become familiar with computer number systems. Although digital computers can and do utilize several number systems, the most commonly used system is the binary because of the nature of the electronic and electromechanical components available to digital computer designers. This chapter describes the basic principles of number systems, with emphasis on the binary, binary coded decimal, and hexadecimal systems.

This chapter is divided into four sections:

1. History
2. Binary system
3. Fixed-point machine arithmetic
4. Floating point and error checking

SECTION 1   HISTORY

Quantity is perhaps one of the most abstract concepts that civilizations have had occasion to develop. Comprehension of the significance of numbers such as 10, 5, or 20 is relatively easy. However, comprehension of the true value of numbers on the order of billions is difficult. The history of number systems is the history of man's efforts to find a notation that would overcome this difficulty and also simplify the rules for manipulating numbers arithmetically.

Making a single vertical mark for each item to be counted was probably the first approach to systematic counting or record keeping. This is known as a *tally system*, and it was soon found to be too cumbersome for the representation of large numbers. An improvement came with the making of four vertical marks, with a diagonal fifth mark to complete a set of five items.

Many believe this was the beginning of a crude form of decimal counting, and it is attributed to the fact that we have five fingers on each hand and five toes on each foot. The decimal system of counting by tens naturally evolved from this and from the fact that we have two hands and two feet.

The greatest forward step in the development of the decimal system came with the adoption of Arabic symbols and positional notation. The Arabic symbols 0, 1, 2, 3, 4, 5, 6, 7, 8, and 9 are easy to write and recognize visually, compared with other symbols that might be used, such as Roman numerals. When written in the above order, each Arabic symbol has a value of one more than the symbol preceding. These symbols, and the idea of giving each symbol yet another value depending on its relative position, brought about the concept of the decimal system.

Fundamental Concepts

In the decimal system or any other number system each symbol has a dual value. When standing alone, each symbol has a fixed value assigned to it; but when combined with other symbols, each has a varying value assigned to it depending on its relative position. When two or more symbols are combined to represent a single quantity, each symbol is referred to as a digit, and the position of each symbol is referred to as a digit position. The digit position at the extreme right is the one of least value, or lowest order, with the value of each digit position increasing by a power of 10 (or by the base of the numbering system in use) to the left. Thus, the digit of highest order, or the most significant digit (MSD), appears at the extreme left; and the digit of lowest order, or the least significant digit (LSD), appears at the extreme right. This order, rather than the reverse thereof, was chosen because in English-speaking countries it is customary to read from left to right. With this convention, and the proceeding order of digit positions, the MSD meets the eye first, making numbers easier to read.

As an illustration of positional notation, consider the number 5287. The notation 5287 really means

$$5000 \ + \ 200 \ + \ 80 \ + \ 7 \ = 5287$$
$$5 \times 10^3 + 2 \times 10^2 + 8 \times 10^1 + 7 \times 10^0 = 5287$$

TABLE 3·1 Positive Powers of 10 and Decimal Equivalents

Thousands	Hundreds	Tens	Units
1000	100	10	1
10^3	10^2	10^1	10^0

The concept of units, tens, hundreds, and thousands has been in use for a long time, but few have considered its real significance. Note that each position of a digit has a base value of a power of 10 according to Table 3·1. The presence of a 0 as a digit within a number merely means that the power of 10 represented by its positional location is not used. For example, the number 402 means

$$4 \times 10^2 + 0 \times 10^1 + 2 \times 10^0 = 402$$
$$400 \quad + \quad 0 \quad + \quad 2 \quad = 402$$

Thus far, only decimal integers or whole numbers with the decimal point assumed to be to the right of the LSD have been considered. When a decimal fraction is written, each digit position to the right of the decimal point has a negative power of 10 assigned in ascending negative powers of 10 to the right. For example, the number 0.6834 can be expressed as

$$
\begin{aligned}
0.6834 &= 6 \times 10^{-1} + 8 \times 10^{-2} + 3 \times 10^{-3} + 4 \times 10^{-4} \\
&= \tfrac{6}{10} + \tfrac{8}{100} + \tfrac{3}{1000} + \tfrac{4}{10,000} \\
&= 6(0.1) + 8(0.01) + 3(0.001) + 4(0.0001) \\
&= (0.6000) + (0.0800) + (0.0030) + (0.0004) \\
&= 0.6 \qquad 8 \qquad 3 \qquad 4
\end{aligned}
$$

The mixed decimal number 529.78 really means

$$5 \times 10^2 + 2 \times 10^1 + 9 \times 10^0 + 7 \times 10^{-1} + 8 \times 10^{-2}$$
$$500 \quad + \quad 20 \quad + \quad 9 \quad + \quad 0.70 \quad + \quad 0.08$$

In writing 529.78, the decimal point is used merely as a reference to show where the positive powers of 10 end and the negative powers begin.

In the decimal system, 10 is called the *base*, or *radix*, of the system. In any number system employing a single radix, the radix of the system is equal to the number of different symbols that can be used in any digit position. For example, in the decimal system there are 10 Arabic symbols that can be used in any digit position. The octal system uses eight symbols (0, 1, 2, 3, 4, 5, 6, 7) and the hexadecimal system uses sixteen (0, 1, 2, 3, 4, 5, 6, 7, 8, 9, A, B, C, D, E, F). These symbols have the same significance as in the decimal system in that they represent no units, one unit, two units, three units, etc., respectively. In the octal system, there are no symbols representing eight or more units so the values 8 or 9 cannot exist as single digits. The radix of the octal system is 8 because there are eight unique symbols. For example, the octal number 213 means:

$$2 \qquad 1 \qquad 3$$
$$2 \times 8^2 + 1 \times 8^1 + 3 \times 8^0$$
$$2 \times 64 + 1 \times 8 + 3 \times 1$$
$$128 \quad + \quad 8 \quad + \quad 3 \quad = 139$$

In addition to the number systems employing a single radix, such as the decimal and octal systems, number systems having more than one radix have been used in digital computers. That is, it is possible to construct number systems in which certain digit positions have one radix and other digit positions have a different radix. Number systems employing other special rules have also been constructed. Some of these will be discussed later.

For applications other than in digital computers, the choice of a number system depends on economy and ease of reading. Since recognizing the magnitude of quantities written in decimal has become customary, it is difficult to recognize the same magnitudes written in some other notation. For everyday use, then, only the decimal system is employed. In general, however, a system having a smaller radix will also have a simpler addition and multiplication table. That is, it would be easier to do arithmetic computations with a system having a smaller radix because it would not be necessary to memorize as large an addition or multiplication table; hence, such a system would be more economical from that point of view. On the other hand, with a system having a smaller radix, a larger number of digits is required to represent a given quantity than would be required with a system having a larger radix; hence, the smaller-radix system would be less economical from that point of view. For general application, then, the choice of a number system is not a simple one.

In digital computer applications, the choice of a number system depends primarily on the physical components available to the computer designer. Electronic devices capable of assuming 10 discrete stable states could be constructed to count units. The basic counting capability could then be increased by increasing the number of these tens-counters, but the use of these devices necessitates voltage levels of 10 distinct values. Incorporation of these levels into a pulse system presents problems not only of design but also of expense and space. This is primarily due to the "all-or-nothing" quality of pulse signals. Because of this, the smaller-radix number systems — in particular, the binary system — have been found to be most economical in computer applications.

Most computers are limited in respect to the size of the numbers that can be handled; this usually varies between systems. A number taken in this context usually represents a basic unit of information and is called a *machine word* or *computer word*. A word in a large-scale general-purpose digital computer ranges from 24 to 64 digits (usually binary digits).

Letters of the alphabet, decimal numbers, and special characters such as a question mark may be represented in the computer by special codes called *alphameric characters*. These characters consist of a binary-code variation that is usually a submultiple of the machine word size. These special systems will be discussed under the general heading of binary coded-decimal systems.

Another important term used in number systems is *modulo*. Modulo, or *modulus*, is a term indicating the maximum capacity of a counter or the machine word capacity of a computer. For example, the largest number that a three-stage decimal counter can contain is 999. This would be called a modulo 1000 counter (000 through 999). If an attempt were made to count 1314 times, the counter would contain an erroneous count of 314. A counter cannot recognize the difference between numbers which differ only by an integral multiple of its modulus. The *modulo sum* of two numbers is a sum with respect to a modulus while ignoring the carry. For example, the sum of 6 and 7 is 13 but the modulo sum is 3 (the modulus is 10 in this example).

There are several ways that a number may be represented in a computer. One of the most important is the sign and magnitude representation. A positive decimal number is written as 724. This really can be considered +724 but the plus sign is normally understood. The negative form would be −724. The MSD position of the number in a computer using binary could be utilized to represent the sign of the number. A binary point (the same as a decimal point in the decimal system) would be located to the right of the least significant digit for an integer machine and to the left of the most significant digit position for a fractional machine. As an example, the number +5 in binary would be represented as

0101

and the number −5 could be represented as

1101

The MSD written as a 1 signifies a negative number. Note that the digit position assigned to indicate the positive or negative form of the number serves only that function and does not assume or indicate a positional value. (1101 is a negative 5 and not 13.)

QUESTIONS: SECTION 1

3·1   Define radix.

3·2   Define positional notation.

3·3   What is the advantage of the use of the binary numbering systems in computers?

3·4   Illustrate the correct positional notation of the following numbers:
63213 base 10
637 base 8
1010 base 2
342 base 5
931.78 base 10

3·5   Define alphameric characters.

3·6   Define the term modulo (modulus).

3·7   What is the modulo sum of the numbers 7 and 8? The modulus?

3·8   Show the numbers −5 and +7 in binary, using the sign convention discussed.

SECTION 2   BINARY SYSTEM

System of notation. The binary system employs only one of two symbols (0 or 1) in any digit position. Therefore, 2 is the radix, or base, of the system.

The binary system is sometimes called true binary to distinguish it from binary coded systems such as binary coded decimal.

In the binary system the symbols 0 and 1 have the same significance as in the decimal system. That is, they represent no units and one unit, respectively; the positional location of a binary digit has the same significance as in the decimal system, except that the base is 2 instead of 10. The positive and negative powers of 2 and their decimal equivalents are listed in Table 3·2.

The presence of a 1 in any digit position of a binary number indicates that the corresponding power of 2 is to be used in expressing a quantity. A 0 indicates that the power of 2 is not required. For example, the binary number 11011 means

$$1 \times 2^4 + 1 \times 2^3 + 0 \times 2^2 + 1 \times 2^1 + 1 \times 2^0$$
$$1 \times 16 + 1 \times 8 + 0 \times 4 + 1 \times 2 + 1 \times 1$$
$$16 \ + \ 8 \ + \ 0 \ + \ 2 \ + \ 1 \ = 27$$

The binary number 11011 is equivalent to the decimal number 27. This example illustrates not only the method of representing a quantity in binary notation but also the most convenient method of converting a binary number to its decimal equivalent.

TABLE 3-2   Positive and Negative Powers of 2 with Decimal Equivalents

2^n decimal equivalent	n	2^{-n} decimal equivalent
1	0	
2	1	0.5
4	2	0.25
8	3	0.125
16	4	0.062 5
32	5	0.031 25
64	6	0.015 625
128	7	0.007 812 5
256	8	0.003 906 25
512	9	0.001 953 125
1 024	10	0.000 976 562 5
2 048	11	0.000 488 281 25
4 096	12	0.000 244 140 625
8 192	13	0.000 122 070 312 5
16 384	14	0.000 061 035 156 25
32 768	15	0.000 030 517 578 125
65 536	16	0.000 015 258 789 062 5
131 072	17	0.000 007 629 394 531 25
262 144	18	0.000 003 814 697 265 625
524 288	19	0.000 001 907 348 632 812 5
1 048 576	20	0.000 000 953 674 316 406 25
2 097 152	21	0.000 000 476 837 158 203 125
4 194 304	22	0.000 000 238 418 579 101 562 5
8 388 608	23	0.000 000 119 209 289 550 781 25
16 777 216	24	0.000 000 059 604 644 775 390 625

When fractional quantities are represented in binary notation, the same general rules apply as in decimal notation. For example, the binary number 0.1101 means

$$1 \times 2^{-1} + 1 \times 2^{-2} + 0 \times 2^{-3} + 1 \times 2^{-4}$$
$$\tfrac{1}{2} \quad + \quad \tfrac{1}{4} \quad + \quad 0 \quad + \quad \tfrac{1}{16}$$
$$0.5000 + 0.2500 + \quad 0 \quad + 0.0625 = 0.8125$$

When binary is converted to decimal it is, perhaps, easier to write and sum the powers of 2 by columns. For example, the binary number 10011 might be converted to decimal as follows:

$$1 = 1 \times 2^4 = 16$$
$$0 = 0 \times 2^3 = 0$$
$$0 = 0 \times 2^2 = 0$$
$$1 = 1 \times 2^1 = 2$$
$$1 = 1 \times 2^0 = \underline{1}$$
$$19 = \text{sum}$$

The even shorter notation following might be used:

$$1 = 16$$
$$0 = 0$$
$$0 = 0$$
$$1 = 2$$
$$1 = \underline{1}$$
$$19 = \text{sum}$$

Methods of Conversion

The use of systems with a base of other than 10 poses some problems in ready interpretation of the values of the numbers involved. An understanding of the techniques used in converting numbers expressed in one base to an equivalent value expressed in another base is extremely useful. A brief discussion of some of the conversion methods applicable to the binary and decimal systems is presented below.

Decimal to binary integer. To convert a decimal integer to a binary number, the repeated-division-by-2 method is used. In this method the decimal number is successively divided by 2, the quotients being placed directly beneath the dividend and the remainders opposite the quotients. The equivalent binary number is composed of the remainders, with the last remainder being the MSD. In the three examples shown in Table 3·3, the decimal numbers 26, 18, and 32 are converted to binary by this method.

In Example 1 in Table 3·3, the decimal number 26 is divided by 2, yielding a quotient of 13 and a remainder of 0. The quotient 13 is recorded and, opposite it, the remainder 0. Next, the quotient 13 is divided by 2, yielding the quotient 6 and the remainder 1. The quotient 6 is recorded and, opposite it, the remainder 1. This process is continued until a quotient of 0

TABLE 3·3   Repeated-division-by-2 Conversion from Decimal to Binary

1. *Quotients*	*Remainders*	2. *Quotients*	*Remainders*	3. *Quotients*	*Remainders*
26		18		32	
13	0 (LSD)	9	0 (LSD)	16	0 (LSD)
6	1	4	1	8	0
3	0	2	0	4	0
1	1	1	0	2	0
0	1 (MSD)	0	1 (MSD)	1	0
				0	1 (MSD)
26 =	11010	18 =	10010	32 =	100000

is obtained. The remainders are then written in horizontal succession, beginning with the one at the bottom of the column and going to the top. This is the binary number sought.

When the division process is performed, it is necessary to remember that 1 divided by 2 yields a quotient of 0 and a remainder of 1.

This is the most used method of converting a decimal integer to binary, since even large decimal integers can be converted with little effort and without tables.

Binary to decimal integer. To convert a binary integer to its decimal equivalent, the repeated-multiplication-by-2 method is used. In this method the most significant digit is doubled if the next digit is a 0, or doubled and a 1 added if the next digit is a 1. This result is doubled or doubled and a 1 added, depending upon the value (1 or 0) of the next digit in the descending order of digits in the binary number. This process is continued until the operation indicated by the least significant digit has been performed. Table 3·4 contains examples of this conversion process for the binary numbers 110101, 101010, and 110001.

In Example 1 in Table 3·4, the MSD is doubled and a 1 added (result = 3) since the next digit is 1. The result (3) is then doubled and

TABLE 3·4 Repeated-multiplication-by-2 Conversion from Binary to Decimal

1. Binary digits	Result		2. Binary digits	Result
MSD 1			MSD 1	
$1 = (1 \times 2) + 1 = 3$			$0 = (1 \times 2) + 0 = 2$	
$0 = (3 \times 2) + 0 = 6$			$1 = (2 \times 2) + 1 = 5$	
$1 = (6 \times 2) + 1 = 13$			$0 = (5 \times 2) + 0 = 10$	
$0 = (13 \times 2) + 0 = 26$			$1 = (10 \times 2) + 1 = 21$	
LSD $1 = (26 \times 2) + 1 = 53$			LSD $0 = (21 \times 2) + 0 = 42$	
$110101 = 53$			$101010 = 42$	

3. Binary digits	Result
MSD 1	
$1 = (1 \times 2) + 1 = 3$	
$0 = (3 \times 2) + 0 = 6$	
$0 = (6 \times 2) + 0 = 12$	
$0 = (12 \times 2) + 0 = 24$	
LSD $1 = (24 \times 2) + 1 = 49$	
$110001 = 49$	

a 0 added (result = 6) since the operation-controlling digit is 0. This process is continued until the operation controlled by the LSD is performed with the cumulative result representing the decimal equivalent of the binary number.

Decimal to binary fraction. While a decimal integer is converted to binary form by successively *dividing* by 2, a decimal fraction is converted by successively *multiplying* by 2. The successive products are placed directly beneath the multiplicand. If at any time a product has an integer part, the integer part is ignored when performing the next multiplication-by-2. This is continued until the fractional part of any product is 0 or, in the case of a nonterminating binary fraction, until the required number of binary digits is obtained. The binary fraction is then the integer part of each successive product, with the first integer part being the MSD of the binary fraction. In the three examples in Table 3·5 the decimal fractions 0.8125, 0.7893, and 0.218 are converted to binary by using the described method.

In Example 1 in Table 3·5 the decimal number 0.8125 is multiplied by 2, yielding a product of 1.6250. The integer part (1) is recorded, and the fractional part (0.625) is multiplied by 2, yielding the product 1.2500. The integer part (1) of this product is recorded, the fractional part (0.2500) is multiplied by 2, and so on, until the product 1.0000 is obtained. Since the fractional part of the product 1.0000 is 0, it indicates that the process is complete and, also, that the required binary number is a terminating binary

TABLE 3·5 Repeated-multiplication-by-2 Conversion of Fractions from Decimal to Binary

1. Product	Integer part	2. Product	Integer part	3. Product	Integer part
0.8125		0.7893		0.218	
1.6250	1	1.5786	1	0.436	0
1.2500	1	1.1572	1	0.872	0
0.5000	0	0.3144	0	1.744	1
1.0000	1	0.6288	0	1.488	1
		1.2576	1	0.976	0
		0.5152	0	1.952	1
		1.0304	1	1.904	1
				1.808	1
				1.616	1
				1.232	1
				0.464	0
0.8125 = 0.1101		0.7893 = 0.1100101+		0.218 = 0.00110111110+	

fraction. Then after the binary point, the integer parts are written in horizontal succession, beginning with the one at the top and going to the bottom. This is the required binary fraction. The same process is used in Examples 2 and 3, except that in these examples the resultant binary number is not a terminating fraction, as indicated by the plus ($+$) sign at the end. The assumption is made that in Examples 2 and 3, seven and eleven binary places are required, respectively; hence, the multiplication process is carried out until that number of binary digits is obtained in each case.

Binary to decimal fraction. The repeated-division-by-2 method is used to convert binary fractions to their decimal equivalents. In this method, the least significant binary digit is divided by 2 if the next significant digit is 0, or divided by 2 and 1 added if the next significant digit is 1. This first result is divided by 2 with the next-order digit determining whether or not the 1 is added. This process of dividing the result by 2 with the ascending-order digits controlling the operation continues until the 0 digit to the left of the binary point effects the final result. Table 3·6 provides examples of this conversion process for the binary fractions 0.0101, 0.1011, and 0.1100. In Example 1 of Table 3·6 the LSD (1) is divided by 2 with a 0 added since the controlling bit is a 0 with the operation result 0.5. This value is divided by 2 and a 1 is added since the significant digit for this operation is a 1 (result $= 1.25$). This sequence continues until the result of the final opera-

TABLE 3·6   Repeated-division-by-2 Conversion of Fractions from Binary to Decimal

1. *Binary digit*		*Result*	2. *Binary digit*		*Result*
LSD 1			LSD 1		
0 $= (1 \div 2)$	$+ 0 = 0.5$		1 $= (1 \div 2)$	$+ 1 = 1.5$	
1 $= (0.5 \div 2)$	$+ 1 = 1.25$		0 $= (1.5 \div 2)$	$+ 0 = 0.75$	
0 $= (1.25 \div 2)$	$+ 0 = 0.625$		1 $= (0.75 \div 2)$	$+ 1 = 1.375$	
0. $= (0.625 \div 2)$	$+ 0 = 0.3125$		0. $= (1.375 \div 2)$	$+ 0 = 0.6875$	
	0.0101 $= 0.3125$			0.1011 $= 0.6875$	

3. *Binary digit*		*Result*
LSD 0		
0 $= (0 \div 2)$	$+ 0 = 0$	
1 $= (0 \div 2)$	$+ 1 = 1.0$	
1 $= (1 \div 2)$	$+ 1 = 1.5$	
0. $= (1.5 \div 2)$	$+ 0 = 0.75$	
	0.1100 $= 0.75$	

tion (controlled by the digit to the left of the binary point) is generated. This number is the decimal fractional representation of the binary fraction.

Mixed-number conversion. The procedures for conversion discussed above may be used to convert mixed numbers from decimal to binary and from binary to decimal. When a decimal mixed number is converted to its binary equivalent, the integer and fractional parts are converted separately by using the above methods, and the separate results are then combined. For example, to convert the decimal mixed number 528.27 to binary, the integer part (528) and the fractional part (0.27) are converted separately as shown in Table 3·7. Combining the results gives 1000010000 + 0.010001 as the binary equivalent of 528.27.

To convert from binary to decimal, the appropriate procedures may be selected for the conversion of the integer and fractional portions of the number.

Binary arithmetic operations. Arithmetic operations can be performed using binary numbers. As in any other numbering system, certain rules govern the operations involved and the sequences to be followed. These conventions are discussed below.

Binary addition. The mechanics of binary addition are the same as those for decimal addition. When the limit of any digit position is reached and one more unit is added, counting in the same digit position must begin again at 0 with a carry of 1 to the next higher-order digit position. In the

TABLE 3·7 Conversion of Mixed Numbers to Binary

	Integer part			*Fractional part*	
	528			0.27	
	264-0			0.54-0	
	132-0			1.08-1	
Division-by-	66-0		Multiplication-	0.16-0	
2 method	33-0		by-2 method	0.32-0	Integers
	16-1			0.64-0	
	8-0	Remainders		1.28-1	
	4-0				
	2-0				
	1-0				
	0-1				
=	1000010000			= 0.010001+	

TABLE 3·8 Summary of Rules for Binary Addition

---

1. 0 plus 0 equals 0 with no carry.
2. 0 plus 1 equals 1 with no carry.
3. 1 plus 0 equals 1 with no carry.
4. 1 plus 1 equals 0 with a carry of 1.

---

binary system there are only two symbols, 0 and 1. The limit of any digit position is therefore reached when a 1 is present. Adding one more unit to that digit position then results in a sum of 0 and a carry of 1 into the next higher-order digit position. The rules for binary addition are summarized in Table 3·8.

Four examples of binary addition follow:

1.	1000	2.	1010	3.	1101	4.	1111
	111		101		1001		111
	1111		1111		10110		10110

Examples 1 and 2 are self-explanatory since there are no carries. In Example 3 if the lowest-order digits are added, 1 plus 1 equals 0 with a carry of 1 into the next higher-order digit position. Adding the next higher-order digits, 0 plus 0 equals 0 plus a carry of 1 equals 1 with no carry. Adding the next higher-order digits, 1 plus 0 equals 1 with no carry. Adding the highest-order digits, 1 plus 1 equals 0 with a carry of 1 into the next higher-order digit position. Since there are no higher-order digits to be added, the last sum 0 is written with a 1 to the left of the 0 to indicate the final carry of 1 into the next higher-order digit position, and the addition is complete. In Example 4 if the lowest-order digits are added, 1 plus 1 equals 0 with a carry of 1 into the next higher-order digit position. Adding the next higher-order digits, 1 plus 1 equals 0 plus a carry of 1 equals 1 with a carry of 1 into the next higher-order digit position. Adding the next higher-order digits, again, 1 plus 1 equals 0 plus a carry of 1 equals 1 with a carry of 1 into the next higher-order digit position. Adding the highest-order digits, 1 plus 0 equals 1 plus a carry of 1 equals 0 with a carry of 1 into the next higher-order digit position. Since there are no higher-order digits to be added, the last sum 0 is written with a 1 to the left of the 0 to indicate the final carry into the next higher-order digit position, and the addition is complete.

These same rules of addition apply to binary fractions and mixed numbers. That is, the binary point of the augend is placed beneath the binary point of the addend, and the addition is then carried out according to the rules given.

Although three or more binary numbers can be summed simultaneously, as in summing a column of three or more decimal numbers, the propagation of carries becomes complex, and the process has little application in digital computers.

Binary subtraction. When direct decimal subtraction is performed, each digit of the subtrahend is subtracted from the corresponding digit in the minuend. If the digit in the subtrahend is larger than the corresponding digit in the minuend, then a 1 is borrowed from the next higher-order digit of the minuend, and that digit is reduced by 1. If, in borrowing, the next higher-order digit of the minuend is 0, then a 1 is borrowed from the next higher-order digit of the minuend that is not 0; that digit is reduced by 1, and the 0's thus skipped in the minuend are replaced by 9's. The same rules apply in performing direct binary subtraction, except that, in borrowing, the 0's that are skipped in the minuend are replaced by 1's. In decimal a unit which has a value of 10 is borrowed, while in binary a unit which has a value of 2 is borrowed. The rules for direct binary subtraction are summarized in Table 3·9.

It is wise in performing direct binary subtraction to remember that the binary number 10 is equivalent to 2 in decimal and that Rule 4 in Table 3·9 really means $10 - 1 = 1$.

1. 1101
    -1001
    0100 $= 100$

2. 1001
    -1000
    0001 $= 1$

The first two examples need no explanation since borrowing was not necessary. The two examples that involve borrowing are as follows:

3. 1011011
    -1001111
    0001100

Minuend after borrowing	1	0 0	10	10	1 1
Minuend before borrowing	1	0 1	1	0	1 1
Subtrahend	1	0 0	1	1	1 1
Remainder	0	0 0	1	1	0 0

4. 1100010
    -100100
    111110

Minuend after borrowing	0	10 1	1	10	1 0
Minuend before borrowing	1	1 0	0	0	1 0
Subtrahend		1 0	0	1	0 0
Remainder		1 1	1	1	1 0

TABLE 3-9 Summary of Rules for Binary Subtraction

1. 0 minus 0 equals 0 with no borrow.
2. 1 minus 1 equals 0 with no borrow.
3. 1 minus 0 equals 1 with no borrow.
4. 0 minus 1 equals 1 with a borrow of 1.

Example 3 illustrates the case where a 1 is borrowed from a digit (the fourth from the right), reducing that digit to 0; and then, because of that borrow, another borrow must be made from the next higher-order digit in order to perform the next subtraction.

Example 4 illustrates the case where a 1 is borrowed from a digit (the sixth from the right), reducing that digit to 0; but in the process of borrowing, 0 digits are skipped and are replaced by 1's in performing succeeding subtractions.

These same rules for direct binary subtraction apply when binary fractions and mixed numbers are involved. Again, the binary point of the subtrahend is placed beneath the binary point of the minuend, and the subtraction is then carried out according to the rules.

Because of the nature of the electronic components available to digital computer designers and the fact that subtraction is the reverse of addition, a relatively complex circuit is required if the computer is to perform both operations, while a relatively simple circuit is required if it is to perform only one of these operations. Therefore, in digital computers the arithmetic circuits are usually designed to perform addition only, and the operation of subtraction is reduced to one of addition by using numerical complements.

Binary multiplication. Binary multiplication is performed in the same manner as decimal multiplication. Table 3-10 summarizes the rules for binary multiplication.

To calculate the product of binary numbers, multiply the multiplicand by one digit of the multiplier at a time in the same manner as decimal numbers are multiplied. This results in a partial product for each digit of the multiplier, and each partial product is placed so that its lowest-order

TABLE 3-10 Summary of Rules for
            Binary Multiplication

1. 0 times 0 equals 0.
2. 0 times 1 equals 0.
3. 1 times 0 equals 0.
4. 1 times 1 equals 1.

digit is under the multiplier digit which caused it. The partial products are then added to obtain the complete product.

As an example, the product of 1110 and 101 is calculated as follows:

1110	Multiplicand
101	Multiplier
1110	First partial product resulting from operation by least significant multiplier digit (1).
0000	Second partial product resulting from operation by next multiplier digit (0). Note the positioning of the LSD of the newly generated partial product directly below the multiplier digit which caused it to be formed.
1110	Third partial product resulting from operation by third multiplier bit.
1000110	Product of the multiply operation. It should be noted that in the generation of the partial products, the rules of Table 3·10 were observed and that the rules of Table 3·8 were observed in the generation of the final product.

Octal notation. Although the binary numbering system is used almost exclusively as the computer number language, the octal numbering system has also come into widespread use in the computer industry. The length of the binary numbers has increased to the point where the numbers have become unwieldy to read and use in some of the manual operations involved in data preparation areas, for example, programming. The larger the radix of the system, the fewer symbols required to represent a given number. The octal system, with a radix of 8, requires fewer digits than the binary system to represent a given number. The octal system uses the symbols 0, 1, 2, 3, 4, 5, 6, and 7. These symbols represent the same units value as in the decimal system. Its selection (octal) to represent binary numbers in off-line operations is occasioned by the fact that the octal system is a direct multiple of the binary system. This relationship allows for conversion between systems by inspection. These relationships, as well as the octal-decimal relationships, are presented below.

Binary to octal. The conversion of a binary number to octal is accomplished as follows:

1. For binary-integer-to-octal conversion, begin at the binary point and, going to the left, block off the number into groups of three digits each. If the number of digits in the binary integer is not a multiple of 3, fill out the last group at the extreme left with 0's.

2. Replace each group (of three binary digits) with its equivalent octal digit.

Examples of this conversion process are shown for the binary numbers 111000101 and 1011010.

1. 111 000 101   2. (00)1 011 010
   7   0 5_8 1   3 2_8

In Example 1, the binary digits in the numbers to be converted were broken into three groups of 3. The octal equivalents of these groups are 705. It should be noted that a subscript of 8 is placed after the number to indicate the radix of the system in use. This identification is usually not indicated when the decimal system is used since the decimal system is normally assumed in use. However, since the 0 through 7 symbols are used in both the decimal and octal systems, this radix identification is necessary since $123_{10} \neq 123_8$. The subscripting of a binary number is not usually required.

The conversion in Example 2 is also made by the substitution of an octal symbol for each group of three binary digits. In this example, however, it was necessary to fill the leftmost group prior to the substitution.

Octal notation can also be used to represent binary fractional values. In the case of fractional values, the grouping of binary digits into groups of three begins at the binary point and moves to the right. A number length which is not a multiple of 3 must be filled before the substitution may take place. The substitution of an octal digit for each group is made and the binary point is retained as an octal point.

The binary fractional values 0.101100 and 0.0110101 are converted below.

1. 0.101 100   2. 0.011 010 1(00)
   0. 5 4_8 0. 3   2 4_8

Example 1 allows for a straightforward substitution of octal digits for binary groups of three. In Example 2, the significance of adding the fill 0's prior to the substitution becomes apparent since the 4 is the desired octal digit. Without the accepted convention of the fill, the last group could well assume the value of an octal 1(001) which is not the desired last grouping. As in the conversion of binary integers, the radix subscript is attached to the results of the conversion, and the binary point is retained as the octal point.

A binary mixed number may be converted to an octal form by applying the rules for integer conversion to the integer portion of the number, and by applying the rules for fractional conversion to the fractional portion of the number. The separation of integer and fraction is preserved by the retention of the binary (octal) point.

Octal to binary. The conversion of octal numbers to a binary form results from a direct substitution of a three-binary-digit group for each symbol of the octal number. This convention is followed for both the integer and fractional parts of the octal number to be converted. Consider the mixed number 705.324_8. Substitution of the octal digits with binary groupings results in:

```
7   0   5 . 3   2   4
111 000 101. 011 010 100
```

The example presented illustrates the benefits to be gained by octal representation of large binary numbers. The ease of conversion between the binary–octal and octal–binary systems is another advantage gained by the selection of the octal system (over any other large-radix system) to provide this representation.

Decimal to octal. Decimal-to-octal conversion may be accomplished through methods similar to those used in decimal-to-binary conversion. Conversion of a decimal number to octal may be useful as a short-cut method of decimal-to-binary conversion of large numbers.

The most convenient way of converting a decimal integer to octal is to divide the decimal integer successively by 8 and record the remainders as in the repeated-division-by-2 method for converting a decimal integer to binary. Table 3·11 gives examples of the conversion of the decimal numbers 492 and 7531 to octal.

Decimal to octal fraction. A decimal fraction may be converted to octal by successively multiplying the decimal number by 8 and recording the integer parts of the resulting products in a manner similar to that explained earlier for decimal- to binary-fraction conversion. Table 3·12 shows the conversion of the decimal fractions 0.597 and 0.9375.

TABLE 3·11   Repeated-division-by-8 Conversion from Decimal to Octal

Quotient	*Remainder*	*Quotient*	*Remainder*
492 $\div 8 \to 4$ LSD		7531 $\div 8 \to 3$ LSD	
61 $\div 8 \to 5$		941 $\div 8 \to 5$	
7 $\div 8 \to 7$ MSD		117 $\div 8 \to 5$	
0		14 $\div 8 \to 6$	
		1 $\div 8 \to 1$ MSD	
		0	
$492_{10} = 754_8$		$7531_{10} = 16553_8$	

TABLE 3-12   Repeated-Multiplication-by-8 Conversion of Fractions from Decimal to Octal

Product	Integer parts	Product	Integer parts
$0.597 \times 8 = 4.776$	4 MSB	$0.9375 \times 8 = 7.5000$	7 MSB
$0.776 \times 8 = 6.208$	6	$0.5000 \times 8 = 4.0000$	4
$0.208 \times 8 = 1.664$	1		
$0.664 \times 8 = 5.312$	5		
$0.312 \times 8 = 2.496$	2+		
$0.597_{10} \quad = 0.46152+_8$		$0.9375_{10} \quad = 0.74_8$	

Octal to decimal.   The same rules apply to octal-to-decimal conversion as apply to the conversion to decimal from any other number system. The symbol contained in each digit position is multiplied by the positional value and the total of these products is the decimal value of the number. For example, the number 516_8 means

$$5 \qquad 1 \qquad 6$$
$$5 \times 8^2 + 1 \times 8^1 + 6 \times 8^0$$
$$5 \times 64 + 1 \times 8 + 6 \times 1$$
$$320 \ + \ 8 \ + \ 6 \ = 334_{10}$$

The fractional number 0.436_8 means

$$4 \qquad 3 \qquad 6$$
$$4 \times 8^{-1} + 3 \times 8^{-2} + 6 \times 8^{-3}$$
$$\tfrac{4}{8} \quad + \quad \tfrac{3}{64} \quad + \quad \tfrac{6}{512}$$
$$0.50000 + 0.04687 + 0.01172 = 0.55859_{10}$$

Mixed-number conversion from octal to decimal results from performing integer and fractional conversion and retaining the octal point as the decimal point of the resultant number.

Binary Coded Decimal Systems

It has been shown that even though the binary system is the base system used in data processors, relationships have been established with other systems (e.g., octal) to serve a useful function in data processing. Most transactions in day-to-day operations are conducted in the decimal system. Computers operate in the binary system. A useful relationship has been established between the decimal and binary systems in a notation termed the binary coded decimal (BCD) system. In this system a direct relationship is established by assigning groups of four binary digits to represent the possible decimal symbols (0 through 9) which may appear in each of the positions of a number. For example, 932_{10} could be represented in BCD as

$$
\begin{array}{ccc}
9 & 3 & 2 \\
1001 & 0011 & 0010
\end{array}
$$

This translation is made in a BCD code which is most commonly used and is called the 8421 code. This code is known as a weighted code since the 8421 indicates the positional value of the digits, and a direct translation can be made to decimal. Table 3·13 illustrates but a few of the code combinations possible using four-bit codes.

An advantage of such codes is that although the groupings are handled as decimal numbers, the computer can operate on them as binary numbers. A disadvantage of this particular code (8421) becomes apparent when an operation such as subtraction is to be performed. Subtraction is performed by the addition of complements. Since the four bits used in the system are capable of representing 16 symbols (0–15) and only 10 symbols are used in the decimal system, machine-complementing of the BCD numbers 0 through 5(0000–0101) will result in the numbers 15–10(1111–1010), all of which are unacceptable BCD characters because they do not fall in the

TABLE 3·13 Four-bit BCD Codes

Binary	BCD				
Binary number	8421	2421	5211	$84\bar{2}\bar{1}$	Excess-3
0000	0000 = 0	0000 = 0	0000 = 0	0000 = 0	
0001	0001 = 1	0001 = 1	0001 = 1		
0010	0010 = 2	0010 = 2			
0011	0011 = 3	0011 = 3	0011 = 2		0011 = 0
0100	0100 = 4	0100 = 4		0100 = 4	0100 = 1
0101	0101 = 5		0101 = 3	0101 = 3	0101 = 2
0110	0110 = 6			0110 = 2	0110 = 3
0111	0111 = 7		0111 = 4	0111 = 1	0111 = 4
1000	1000 = 8		1000 = 5	1000 = 8	1000 = 5
1001	1001 = 9		1001 = 6	1001 = 7	1001 = 6
1010				1010 = 6	1010 = 7
1011		1011 = 5	1011 = 7	1011 = 5	1011 = 8
1100		1100 = 6			1100 = 9
1101		1101 = 7	1101 = 8		
1110		1110 = 8			
1111		1111 = 9	1111 = 9	1111 = 9	

allowed 0–9 range. This difficulty is overcome by the use of a BCD code known as the excess-3 code. (See Table 3·13.) To form the excess-3 code, 3 is added to the decimal number before translation to BCD, or it may be added to the BCD number. A meaningful 9's complement may then be obtained through the bit substitution (0 for 1's, 1 for 0's). $4_{10}(0100\ 8421$ BCD) when complemented becomes 11_{10}, which is not in the 0–9 allowable character range and is therefore illegal. If the 4_{10} is converted to excess-3, it becomes 7_{10} or 1010 in excess-3 code. When 1010 is complemented, it becomes $0101(2_{10})$ which is in the excess-3 BCD allowable symbol range. The excess-3 code is termed a *nonweighted code* since the sum of the bits does not equal the number represented.

Unlike the normal 8421 BCD code the excess-3 BCD is a self-complementing code. That is, any number in the character range (0–9) when complemented (9's complement) will yield a character that is also in the number range.

Some four-bit weighted codes are also self-complementing. One such code is the 2421. An examination of Table 3·13 illustrates this point.

Other coding schemes may be used to meet specific needs. For example, six-bit codes might be used for alphameric presentations where it is necessary to represent 36 symbols, the 10 decimal plus the 26 alphabetic symbols. A six-bit code allows for 64 combinations which would allow for special-symbol representation in addition to the alphamerics discussed above.

Gray Code

Another number system similar to binary is the Gray code, or *reflected binary system*. The outstanding feature of the Gray-code system is that successive integers differ from one another by only one digit. This is advantageous in analog-to-digital conversion equipment. The use of Gray code to perform arithmetical operations is quite complex; for this reason it is not in common use for this purpose. Since Gray code is used for input and output information, some method of conversion between Gray code and binary is needed. Table 3·14 shows the relationship between numbers in the decimal and binary systems and the Gray code.

Notice that the change from binary 0111 (7) to 1000 (8) requires a change from three 1's to only one. In the Gray-code system, there is a change of only one digit.

To convert a binary number to Gray code, write the MSD of the binary number as the MSD of the Gray-code number. The sum of the MSD and the first digit to its right, disregarding the carry if any, is the next digit of the Gray-code number. This process is continued until the least significant order is reached.

TABLE 3·14 Comparison of Decimal, Binary, and Gray-code Systems

Decimal	Binary	Gray code
0	0000	0000
1	0001	0001
2	0010	0011
3	0011	0010
4	0100	0110
5	0101	0111
6	0110	0101
7	0111	0100
8	1000	1100
9	1001	1101
10	1010	1111
11	1011	1110
12	1100	1010
13	1101	1011
14	1110	1001
15	1111	1000
16	10000	11000

As an example, the conversion from binary 1101 (13) to Gray code is as follows:

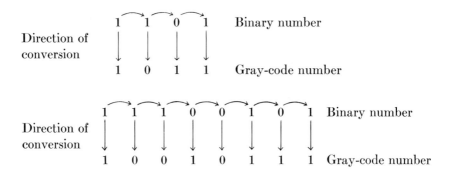

A Gray-code number can be converted to binary by a similar process. The MSD is again the same in both systems. The next binary digit is the sum of the corresponding Gray-code digit and the preceding binary digit, again disregarding a carry if it occurs.

The conversion of Gray-code 1110 (11) to binary is as follows:

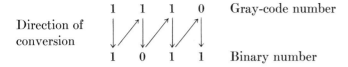

The following example illustrates conversion of Gray-code 10010111 (229) to its binary equivalent:

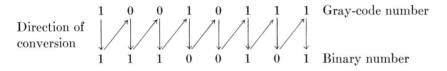

Hexadecimal Number System

The hexadecimal number system is another numbering system which is used in digital computers. The radix of the system is 16; therefore, 1 of 16 symbols may be used in each digit position of a number. The digit position values are increased by a power of 16 in moving from the LSD (16^0 power) to the more significant digit positions. Table 3·15 shows the symbols which are used to represent the range of decimal values.

The conversion from hexadecimal to decimal may be made according to the rules discussed for the other numbering systems. Hexadecimal arithmetic operations may be performed, and some computers are mechanized to perform these operations. The hexadecimal number $F1C_{16}$ is equal to

$$F \qquad 1 \qquad C_{16}$$
$$F(16^2) \quad + \; 1(16^1) \; + \; C(16^0)$$
$$F(256_{10}) \; + \; 1(16_{10}) \; + \; C(1_{10})$$
$$15_{10}(256_{10}) + \quad 16_{10} \quad + \; 12_{10}(1)$$
$$3840_{10} \quad + \quad 16_{10} \quad + \quad 12_{10} \quad = 3868_{10}$$

TABLE 3·15   Hexadecimal Symbols

Decimal	0	1	2	3	4	5	6	7	8	9	10	11	12	13	14	15
Hexadecimal	0	1	2	3	4	5	6	7	8	9	A	B	C	D	E	F

TABLE 3-16   Conversion from Decimal to Hexadecimal

1. $7_{10} = 7_{16} = (7 \times 16^0)$	2. $22_{10} = 16_{16} = (1 \times 16^1) + (6 \times 16^0)$

3. $\quad$ *Quotient* $\quad$ *Remainder* $\quad\quad 57 \div 16 \quad$ 9 LSD $\quad\quad\; 3 \div 16 \quad$ 3 MSD $\quad\quad\; 0$ $57_{10} = 39_{16} = (3 \times 16^1) + (9 \times 16^0)$	4. $\quad$ *Quotient* $\quad$ *Remainder* $\quad\quad 418 \div 16 \quad$ 2 LSD $\quad\quad\; 26 \div 16 \quad$ 10* $\quad\quad\;\; 1 \div 16 \quad$ 1 MSD $\quad\quad\;\; 0$ $418_{10} = 1A2_{16} = (1 \times 16^2) + (10 \times 16^1)$ $\quad\quad\quad\quad\quad\quad\quad\quad\quad\quad + \; (2 \times 16^0)$

*Note that in Example 4, the remainder of 10 had to be converted to the symbol A since 10 is not an acceptable symbol in hexadecimal.

The method of conversion from decimal to hexadecimal is the same method used for conversions from decimal to another number system, the repeated division by the radix of the system. In the case of the hexadecimal, the division is by 16. The remainders must be converted to hexadecimal equivalents if they range from 10 through 15. Several conversions are illustrated in Table 3·16.

An advantage of the hexadecimal system is that in a given number of digit positions, a larger number can be represented.

QUESTIONS: SECTION 2

3·9   What is the method used to convert decimal to binary integer? To binary fraction?

3·10   Provide the binary equivalents of the following decimal numbers:
6   23.21   107   257.8

3·11   Convert the following binary numbers to their decimal equivalents:
110101   111.101   010110   1111111.011

3·12   What are the rules for binary addition? Subtraction?

3·13   Add the following binary numbers:

(a) 1010	(b) 1000	(c) 110101	(d) 11111
0101	1001	000011	00001

3·14   Perform a binary subtraction on the following numbers:

(a) 1010	(b) 1011011	(c) 100000
−0011	−1001111	−000001

3·15   What is the advantage of octal over the binary number system?

3·16   Convert the following binary numbers to octal:
       101010   11011.110110   1100110.00101

3·17   Convert the following decimal numbers to octal:
       7   322   88

3·18   Multiply the following binary numbers:
       (a)   101   (b)   1010   (c)   0010
             011   101   0111

3·19   Convert the following numbers to binary:
       263_8 776_8 22_8 544.321_8

3·20   Convert the following octal numbers to decimal:
       263   776   22   544.321

3·21   What is the binary coded decimal system? Describe the difference
       between a weighted and nonweighted code.

3·22   Convert the following decimal numbers to BCD form using the 8421
       code.
       31   10   453

3·23   Convert the following decimal numbers to hexadecimal:
       57   421   5

3·24   Convert the following hexadecimal numbers to decimal:
       $B1C$ ABC $63E$

3·25   Convert the following numbers from binary to Gray code:
       1101   10111   10001   10101

3·26   Convert the following numbers from Gray code to binary:
       0110   1001   11111   101101

SECTION 3 FIXED-POINT MACHINE ARITHMETIC

Because of hardware limitations, the computing device cannot exercise the
flexibility in performing arithmetic operations which is available in paper-
and-pencil arithmetic. The arithmetic devices available for use in computers are adders and subtracters. The economics of hardware construction
dictate that one or the other of the devices be used. The adder is the more
commonly used arithmetic element. The choice of the adder does not limit
the arithmetic capability of the unit, however, since the adder can perform
subtraction, multiplication, and division through the use of the basic add
functions and a series of shifts. Subtraction, for example, is performed by
the addition of complements. Before discussing machine arithmetic operations, the conventions of the complement system are covered below.

Complements.   In the decimal system every number has two complements,
called the 10's complement and the 9's complement. The 10's and 9's com-

plements are essentially the same in that they serve the same purpose in digital computer applications and they differ by only 1 numerically; that is, the 9's complement of a number is 1 less than the 10's complement.

The 10's and 9's complements are most conveniently defined in terms of the arithmetic registers of a computer. In general, the 10's complement of a number N is $10^n - N$, where n is the number of digits that can be contained in the arithmetic registers of a computer. For the purposes of illustration, it is assumed that the arithmetic registers of a computer can contain 10 digits. The 10's complement of a number N is then $10^{10} - N$. According to this definition, then, the 10's complement of 325 is

$$10^{10} - 325 = 9999999675$$

or

$$
\begin{aligned}
10000000000 &= 10^{10} \\
-\ 0000000325 & \\
\hline
9999999675 &= \text{10's complement of 325}
\end{aligned}
$$

The 10's complement of 52973 is $10^{10} - 52973 = 9999947027$
or

$$
\begin{aligned}
10000000000 &= 10^{10} \\
-\ 0000052973 & \\
\hline
9999947027 &= \text{10's complement of 52973}
\end{aligned}
$$

Suppose now it is desired to subtract 325 from 400. The subtraction operation can be changed to one of addition by complementing the subtrahend and adding as follows:

$$
\begin{aligned}
0000000400 & \\
+\ 9999999675 &= \text{10's complement of 325} \\
\hline
10000000075 &= \text{remainder}
\end{aligned}
$$

The carry of 1 off-register into the eleventh digit position from the right could not be contained in a 10-digit register; in a computer having 10-digit registers, it would be lost, yielding a remainder of 0000000075, or 75. The carry of 1 off-register could, however, be detected by a computer, and it indicates that the remainder is positive and that no recomplementing is necessary. Had there been no carry off-register, it would have indicated that the remainder was negative and should be recomplemented. For example, if 400 is subtracted from 325 by complementing the subtrahend and adding, the remainder would be

$$
\begin{array}{l}
\ 0000000325 \\
+\ 9999999600 = \text{10's complement of 400} \\
\hline
\ 9999999925 = \text{10's complement of the remainder}
\end{array}
$$

The absence of a carry off-register to the left indicates that the remainder thus obtained should be recomplemented and have a negative sign attached to it. If this operation is performed, the remainder will be

$$
\begin{array}{l}
\ 1000000000 = 10^{10} \\
-\ 999999925 = \text{10's complement of the remainder} \\
\hline
\ 000000075 = \text{recomplemented remainder} = 75
\end{array}
$$

Attaching a negative sign to the final remainder makes -75 the correct result.

The above steps may be summarized as follows:

1. Compute the 10's complement of the subtrahend.
2. Add the 10's complement of the subtrahend to the minuend.
3. If there is a carry off-register, the result is positive and no recomplementing is necessary; otherwise, the result is negative and recomplementing is necessary.

Although there are numerous methods of performing both decimal addition and decimal subtraction using the 10's complement, they will not be described here since they would not serve the purpose of this discussion.

With respect to a computer having 10-digit registers, the 9's complement of a number N may be defined as $(10^{10} - 1) - N$, or $9999999999 - N$. That is, the 9's complement may be found by subtracting from 9 each digit of the number whose complement is required. For example, the 9's complement of 325 is $9999999999 - 925 = 9999999674$ or

$$
\begin{array}{l}
\ 9999999999 = 10^{10} - 1 \\
-\ 0000000325 \\
\hline
\ 9999999674 = \text{9's complement of 325}
\end{array}
$$

Suppose now it is desired to subtract 325 from 400, using the 9's complement. If the subtrahend is complemented and addition is performed, the result is

```
    0000000400
+ 9999999674 = 9's complement of 325
  10000000074 = remainder
```

Again, there is a carry of 1 off-register to the left, which again indicates that the remainder is positive; but since the 9's complement of a number is 1 less than the 10's complement, the remainder is 1 less than it should be. Therefore, to correct the remainder, the carry of 1 off-register to the left is added to the LSD of the remainder. This is called the *end-around carry* and it yields the correct remainder of 0,000,000,075, or 75. Had there been no carry off-register to the left, that, again, would have indicated that the remainder was negative and that recomplementing was necessary. However, since no carry off-register is equivalent to a carry off-register of 0, an end around carry of 0 might be performed in a computer, as in the case of a carry off-register of 1, to simplify the gating and, hence, the circuitry involved. Adding 0 to the LSD of the remainder would not affect the remainder, and the deficiency of 1 in the remainder would automatically be replaced when the final remainder is recomplemented.

Since end-around carry is normally used in digital computers, it would be well to illustrate the above rules more graphically. In the example below, 6907 is subtracted from 25863, as follows:

```
                        0000025863
                    +  9999993092  = 9's complement of 6907
Result is positive; add  10000018955  = uncorrected remainder
                         └──────────→ 1  = end-around carry
                        0000018956  = final remainder = 18956
```

In the example below, 25863 is subtracted from 6907, as follows:

```
                        0000006907
                    +  9999974136  = 9's complement of 25863
Result is negative; add  09999981043  = uncorrected remainder
                         └──────────→ 0  = end-around carry
                        9999981043  = final remainder
                        0000018956  = final remainder recomplemented
                                    = −18956
```

The preceding steps may be summarized as follows:

1. Compute the 9's complement of the subtrahend.
2. Add the 9's complement of the subtrahend to the minuend.
3. Perform an end-around carry of 1 or 0.
4. If there is an end-around carry of 0, recomplement the remainder and attach a negative sign; otherwise, omit this step.

The two methods described for subtracting in the decimal system by using the 10's and 9's complements may be applied to other number systems — in particular, the binary system. That is, the so-called "2's complement" and "1's complement" of a binary number are analogous to the 10's and 9's complements, respectively, of a decimal number.

Although subtracting in the decimal system by using the 6's complement instead of the 10's complement requires an extra step, that of an end-around carry, the end-around-carry method is usually used in a computer that utilizes the binary system because of the ease with which the 1's complement of a binary number can be computed, in contrast to computing the 2's complement.

In terms of the arithmetic register under discussion, the 2's complement of a binary number N is $2^{10} - N$. For example, the 2's complement of the binary number 0101000101 is $2^{10} - 0101000101$ or

$$10000000000 = 2^{10}$$
$$- 0101000101$$
$$\overline{1010111011} = \text{2's complement of } 0101000101$$

Suppose now it is desired to subtract 0101000101 from 0110010000. Complementing the subtrahend and adding gives a result of

$$0110010000$$
$$+ 1010111011 = \text{2's complement of } 0101000101$$
$$\overline{10001001011} = \text{remainder}$$

As in the case of adding a 10's complement in the decimal system, the carry of 1 off-register to the left indicates that the remainder is positive and no recomplementing is necessary. The correct remainder is, then, 0001001011, or 1001011. The above example is equivalent to

$$400 - 325 = 75$$

in decimal.

In terms of the computer under discussion, the 1's complement of a binary number is $(2^{10} - 1) - N$, where N is the number whose complement is required. The above expression is equivalent to $1111111111 - N$, or means the 1's complement of a binary number N may be found by subtracting each digit of N from 1; this in turn means that the 1's complement of a binary number may be found by changing all the 1's to 0's and all the 0's to 1's. For example, the 1's complement of 101000101 is $1111111111 - 0101000101 = 1010111010$ or

$$1111111111 = 2^{10} - 1$$
$$- \ 0101000101$$
$$1010111010 = \text{1's complement of } 0101000101$$

Note that if in the binary number 0101000101 all the 1's are changed to 0's and all the 0's to 1's, the result is the same as that obtained above, namely, 1010111010. Digital computers are able to compute complements of this type with ease through the use of NOT circuits, or inverters; hence this explains the reason for the almost exclusive use of the 1's complement in digital computer applications.

Since the computation of a 1's complement is such an elementary operation, no further examples will be given here. The next step is to give examples of the end-around-carry method of binary subtraction using the 1's complement.

Three examples of binary subtraction using this method will now be given. In the first example, 16 is subtracted from 25 as follows:

$$11001 = 25$$
$$- \ 10000 = \text{direct subtraction of 16}$$
$$1001 = 9$$

$$11001 = 25$$
$$+ \ 01111 = \text{1's complement of 16}$$
$$101000$$
$$\underline{\qquad 1} = \text{end-around carry}$$
$$1001 = \text{remainder} = 9$$

In the direct-subtraction method, there is no end-around carry involved, but in adding the complement of the subtrahend, an end-around carry must be performed to obtain the correct result.

In the second example, using larger numbers, 129 is subtracted from 256 as follows:

$$
\begin{array}{rl}
100000000 &= 256 \\
+\ 101111110 &= \text{1's complement of 129} \\
\hline
1001111110 & \\
1 &= \text{end-around carry} \\
\hline
001111111 &= 127
\end{array}
$$

The examples given thus far have illustrated the subtraction of a smaller number from a larger number. When a larger number is subtracted from a smaller number, the rules governing complementing and end-around carry apply. This is illustrated in the third example, in which 25 is subtracted from 16, yielding a remainder of -9 as follows:

$$
\begin{array}{rl}
10000 &= 16 \\
+\ 00110 &= \text{1's complement of 25} \\
\hline
10110 &= \text{1's complement of remainder}
\end{array}
$$

Since there is no carry off-register, the remainder must be recomplemented and have a negative sign attached to it; this makes the final remainder $-01001 = -9$.

Several subtraction problems should be solved by using both the direct method and the 1's complement method until facility that can come only through practice is acquired. The work can always be checked by using decimal equivalents.

Each of the computer-performed arithmetic operations will be discussed separately. However, before this analysis is undertaken, several characteristics of arithmetic units will be discussed, namely, the sign convention used and the placement of the binary point. The sign convention adopted for use in the examples to be presented is one which identifies positive numbers by a 0 in the first digit (sign bit) and negative numbers by a 1 in the sign bit. A four-bit machine will be used, composed of a sign and three magnitude bits. Examples of a positive and negative word are given in Table 3·17.

Notice the placement of the binary point in the words shown in Table 3·17. Since the point is located to the left of the most significant bit, the number is a binary fraction. Thus, the range of values that the arithmetic unit can handle lies between $+1$ and -1. Integers may be used as operators in a fractional machine after they have been scaled (scaling is discussed later). Whenever the numbers involved in an arithmetic operation are of

TABLE 3·17   Typical Arithmetic Word

	Positive	*Negative*

$+\tfrac{5}{8} = 0.101$ — Sign bit / Magnitude bits / Least significant / Most significant

$-\tfrac{5}{8} = 1.101$ — Sign bit / Magnitude bits / Least significant / Most significant

TABLE 3·18   Conversion of Signed-magnitude Numbers to Decimal

Positive	$\tfrac{5}{8}$ in signed magnitude $=$ 0 . 1 0 1
	Conversion to decimal $= +$. $\tfrac{1}{2} + 0 + \tfrac{1}{8} = +\tfrac{5}{8}$
Negative	$\tfrac{5}{8}$ in signed magnitude $=$ 1 . 1 0 1
	Conversion to decimal $= -$. $\tfrac{1}{2} + 0 + \tfrac{1}{8} = -\tfrac{5}{8}$

TABLE 3·19   Conversion of 1's Complement Number to Decimal

Negative $\tfrac{5}{8}$ in 1's complement	$= 1$. 0 1 0
Recomplement to signed magnitude	$= 1$. 1 0 1
Conversion to decimal	$= 1$. $\tfrac{1}{2} + 0 + \tfrac{1}{8} = -\tfrac{5}{8}$

such values that the result is equal to or greater than unity, the capacity of the machine is exceeded and overflow occurs.

Numbers are placed into and taken out of the arithmetic unit in their signed-magnitude form. The term *signed magnitude* means that the number carries its applicable sign (negative or positive) and the magnitude bits are in their true form; that is, the absolute value of a signed-magnitude number may be determined by a direct conversion of the magnitude bits from binary to decimal.

The result of any arithmetic operation, if negative, will be expressed in 1's complement form. This complementing is a result of the logical process used to perform the various operations. A 1's complement number retains the identifying sign bit but all 1's in the magnitude are represented by 0's and all 0's in the magnitude are represented by 1's. Before the absolute value of 1's complement number can be determined, the magnitude bits must be recomplemented, yielding a signed-magnitude number.

Addition. The process of addition can be resolved into two distinctly different logical functions. First, if the two numbers have like signs, they are added together, generating a sum equal to the compound total of the two. Second, if the numbers have unlike signs, the smaller of the two quantities must be subtracted from the larger, generating a sum which is equal to the difference in absolute values of the two quantities and prefixed with the sign of the larger.

The arithmetic unit selected for the examples to be given is designed so that all the arithmetic operations are performed by addition, that is, by combining two numbers so that the compound total of the two quantities will always be generated. The circuits that accomplish this function are called *full adders*.

Because the adders generate the compound total of the numbers which are introduced into them, the process of adding two positive numbers can be performed by passing both quantities directly to the adders in their signed-magnitude form. The sum output, thus generated by the adders as a result of these two inputs, is a signed-magnitude number equal to the compound total of the two quantities. Addition of two numbers having unlike signs, however, must yield a sum which is equal to the difference in absolute values of the two numbers. This can be accomplished by adding one of the numbers expressed in signed-magnitude form to the other expressed in 1's complement form. For this reason one of the quantities must be in 1's complement form upon being introduced into the adders as an input. The negative quantity is passed to the adders in 1's complement form and added with the positive quantity expressed in signed-magnitude form. The sum thus generated will be equal to the difference in absolute values and prefixed by the sign of the larger. Because of the logical process employed to determine the difference in absolute values of two numbers, the sum generated will be expressed in 1's complement form if negative and in signed-magnitude form if positive. Whenever two negative numbers are added, both quantities are passed to the adders in 1's complement form. The sum thus generated by the adders equals the compound total of the two quantities and is expressed in 1's complement form.

It is possible to exceed the capacity of the machine when adding two numbers having like signs, since the compound total generated may be greater than unity. Whenever the numbers being added have unlike signs, the possibility of overflow does not exist because the sum thus generated is equal to the difference in absolute values of the two quantities.

During every addition, the machine inspects the signs of the augend and the addend. If they are alike, an overflow can occur and a further inspection is made of the sum sign bit. If this sign bit is unlike the sign bits of the augend and the addend, an overflow condition is indicated.

Upon the instruction to execute an addition, one of the two operands is brought into the arithmetic unit from a memory unit and becomes the addend. The result generated on the previous arithmetic operation is stored in the arithmetic unit and becomes the augend during the execution of an ADD instruction. Examples are given in Table 3·20.

In Example 1, the operands are like-signed positive quantities. Therefore the numbers are both applied to the adders in the same form, signed magnitude, in order to generate a sum which is equal to the compound total of the two. Examination of the sign bits indicates that the addition is valid and overflow is not indicated.

TABLE 3·20 Machine Addition

Addition of positive-signed numbers

---

1. No overflow   *2. Overflow*

Addend	$0.100 = +\frac{1}{2}$	Addend	$0.101 = +\frac{5}{8}$
Augend	$0.010 = +\frac{1}{4}$	Augend	$0.100 = +\frac{1}{2}$
Sum	$0.110 = +\frac{3}{4}$	Sum	$1.001 = -\frac{3}{4}$

Addition of unlike-signed numbers

---

3. Negative addend   *4. Negative augend*

Addend	$1.001 = -\frac{3}{4}$	Addend	$0.101 = +\frac{5}{8}$
Augend	$0.100 = +\frac{1}{2}$	Augend	$1.101 = -\frac{1}{4}$
Sum	$1.101 = -\frac{1}{4}$	End-around carry	0.010 → 1
		Sum	$0.011 = +\frac{3}{8}$

Addition of negative-signed numbers

---

5. No overflow   *6. Overflow*

Addend	$1.101 = -\frac{1}{4}$	Addend	$1.010 = -\frac{5}{8}$
Augend	$1.011 = -\frac{1}{2}$	Augend	$1.001 = -\frac{3}{4}$
End-around carry	1.000 → 1	End-around carry	0.011 → 1
Sum	$1.001 = -\frac{3}{4}$	Sum	$0.100 = +\frac{1}{2}$

The absolute values of the operands in Example 2 are such that addition of the two will produce a sum which is greater than unity. Upon adding, a carry is propagated from the most significant bit into the sign place. If the machine were to consider the sum sign bit as having a value equal to 2^0 power, the sum would be correctly indicated above as $1\frac{1}{8}$. However, the machine would have no way of determining at this time or indicating in a later operation whether the sum is positive or negative. Therefore the sign bit is assigned the specific function of indicating the sign of the result. Since the sign bit is a ONE, the machine regards this result as a 1's complement negative $\frac{3}{4}$. Overflow will be indicated upon examination of the sign bits and the program may be modified accordingly.

The algebraic rule for addition of numbers having unlike signs is as follows: Subtract the larger from the smaller (that is, determine the difference in absolute values of the two quantities) and prefix the sign of the larger.

In Example 3 the positive augend, expressed in signed-magnitude form, is combined in the adders with the addend, expressed in 1's complement form, yielding a sum equal in value to the difference in absolute values of the two quantities. Notice that the sign affixed to the sum as a by-product of the addition is the same as that of the larger quantity. This process accomplishes the addition of numbers having unlike signs without violating the algebraic rule. However, if the sum generated is negative as in the preceding example, it is expressed in 1's complement form. This action is a result of the logical process used to accomplish the addition of unlike signed numbers but is advantageous, as will be illustrated in Example 4.

By assuming that Example 3 was the previous arithmetic operation, the sum generated in that example is used as the augend in the following operation, Example 4. Since negative operands are introduced into the adders in 1's complement form and a negative result is represented in 1's complement form, the negative sum generated in the previous example need not be changed before being applied to the adders. The addend is placed into the arithmetic unit in signed-magnitude form and introduced into the adders directly, since it is positive, as is the sign of the larger operand.

Addition of two like-signed negative numbers is accomplished by representing both numbers in the same form (1's complement), thus generating a sum which is equal to the compound total of the two. Because the sum of two negative quantities is always negative, except in the case of overflow, the sum is generated in 1's complement form. Overflow is possible upon adding like-signed negative quantities and is detected in the same manner as described previously.

Example 5 illustrates addition of negative-signed quantities. Assume that the augend is negative as a result of the previous arithmetic operation and exists in the arithmetic unit in 1's complement form. It is introduced into the adders in this same form. The negative addend is introduced into the adders in 1's complement form. Upon examination of the sign bits, overflow is not indicated, since the sum sign bit is the same as those of the augend and addend.

Example 6 illustrates what happens when two negative quantities are added, resulting in an overflow condition.

In Example 6 the numbers are both added in 1's complement form. The values of the operands, however, are of such values that the sum exceeds unity, and overflow is indicated by the sign digit at the time overflow is sensed for.

In the examples of Table 3·20 the logical processes used by the computer in performing the ADD operation were shown. The following rules indicate the forms in which the numbers are passed to the adders during the ADD operation.

1. Augend positive: Quantity used in signed-magnitude form.
2. Augend negative: The magnitude bits are used in their complemented form.
3. Addend positive: Quantity used in signed-magnitude form.
4. Addend negative: The magnitude bits are used in their complemented form.

Subtraction. From a mathematical point of view there is no difference between the addition of numbers having unlike signs and the subtraction of corresponding numbers having like signs.

Likewise from a mathematical point of view there is no difference between the addition of like-signed numbers and the subtraction of numbers having unlike signs. See Table 3·21 for these comparisons.

The addition of unlike-signed quantities, shown in Example 1*a*, yields a sum equal to the difference in absolute value of the two numbers. In Example 1*b*, the same result is obtained by subtracting like-signed quanti-

TABLE 3·21 Manual Subtraction Comparisons

EXAMPLE 1a	EXAMPLE 1b
To plus three-fourths add negative one-fourth	From plus three-fourths subtract plus one-fourth
$(+\frac{3}{4}) + (-\frac{1}{4}) = +\frac{1}{2}$	$(+\frac{3}{4}) - (+\frac{1}{4}) = +\frac{1}{2}$
EXAMPLE 2a	EXAMPLE 2b
To plus one-half add plus one-fourth	From plus one-half subtract negative one-fourth
$(+\frac{1}{2}) + (+\frac{1}{4}) = +\frac{3}{4}$	$(+\frac{1}{2}) - (-\frac{1}{4}) = +\frac{3}{4}$

ties, that is, by changing the sign of the subtrahend and proceeding as in addition.

The addition shown in Example 2a illustrates addition of like-signed quantities yielding a sum equal to the compound total of the two. Subtraction of corresponding unlike quantities shown in Example 2b is accomplished by changing the sign of the subtrahend and proceeding as in addition. The sum thus generated is equal in absolute value to the sum obtained in Example 2a and has the identical sign.

In view of the foregoing analysis of subtraction, it may be seen that the process of subtraction, like addition, can be resolved into two distinctly different logical functions. First, if the numbers have like signs, the process of subtraction must yield a difference which represents the difference in absolute values of the two numbers. Second, if the numbers have unlike signs, the process of subtraction must yield a sum which is equal to the compound total of the two numbers.

During every subtraction, the machine inspects the signs of the minuend and the subtrahend. If they are unlike, an overflow can occur and a further inspection is made of the sum sign bit. If this sign bit is unlike the sign bit of the minuend and the sign bit of the subtrahend (after change), an overflow condition is indicated.

As in the operation of addition, only one new operand is brought into the arithmetic unit upon initiating a SUBTRACT operation. This number becomes the subtrahend. The result obtained on the previous operation may be left in the arithmetic unit and becomes the minuend during a subtraction. This result, as mentioned previously, will be in signed-magnitude form if positive and in 1's complement form if negative.

In order to conform with the algebraic rule for subtraction, the sign bit of the subtrahend must always be complemented. The subtraction is then completed by proceeding as in addition. Thus after changing the sign of the subtrahend, the magnitude bits must be acted upon in the same manner as would an addend having the same sign during an addition.

To clarify the statements in the preceding paragraph, the manipulation of the subtrahend will be examined in greater detail. Gating logic in the arithmetic unit performs the necessary conversion before the number reaches the adders.

TABLE 3-22 Subtrahend Manipulation Prior to Arithmetic Operation

		1. Positive	2. Negative
(a)	Subtrahend into arithmetic unit	$0.100 = +\frac{1}{2}$	$1.100 = -\frac{1}{2}$
(b)	Subtrahend sign change	$1.100 = -\frac{1}{2}$	$0.100 = +\frac{1}{2}$
(c)	Subtrahend to adders	$1.011 = (+)-\frac{1}{2}$	$0.100 = +\frac{1}{2}$

Assume that the subtrahend placed in the arithmetic unit is a positive number, as shown in Example 1a of Table 3·22. The sign bit is changed as shown in Example 1b. In order to proceed as in addition, the subtrahend must now be acted upon in the same manner as would a negative addend during addition. Since a negative addend will have its magnitude complemented before being passed to the adders as an input, the magnitude bits shown in Example 1b are complemented and the number passed to adders as shown in Example 1c.

If the subtrahend placed in the arithmetic unit is a negative quantity, as shown in Example 2a, after changing the sign, as shown in Example 2b, it becomes a positive quantity. Since a positive addend is passed to the adders directly, no further complementing of the subtrahend is necessary in order to proceed as in addition. The subtrahend, therefore, is passed to the adders without further modification, as shown in Example 2c.

The algebraic rule for subtraction does not specifically mention what is to be done with the minuend, but by omission implies that it may be treated in the same manner as the augend. During an addition the result of

TABLE 3·23   Machine Subtraction

Subtraction of like-signed numbers

1. Positive		2. Negative	
Subtrahend	$0.101 = +\frac{5}{8}$	Subtrahend	$1.101 = -\frac{5}{8}$
Subtrahend to		Subtrahend to	
adders	$1.010 = -\frac{5}{8}$	adders	$0.101 = +\frac{5}{8}$
Minuend	$0.010 = +\frac{1}{4}$	Minuend	$1.101 = -\frac{1}{4}$
			0.010
Sum	$1.100 = -\frac{3}{8}$	End-around carry	$\hookrightarrow 1$
		Sum	$0.011 = +\frac{3}{8}$

Subtraction of unlike-signed numbers

3. No overflow		4. Overflow	
Subtrahend	$1.011 = -\frac{3}{8}$	Subtrahend	$0.101 = +\frac{5}{8}$
Subtrahend to		Subtrahend to	
adders	$0.011 = +\frac{3}{8}$	adders	$1.010 = -\frac{5}{8}$
Minuend	$0.010 = +\frac{1}{4}$	Minuend	$1.001 = -\frac{3}{4}$
Sum	$0.101 = +\frac{5}{8}$	End-around carry	0.011
			$\hookrightarrow 1$
		Sum	$0.100 = +\frac{1}{2}$

the previous operation becomes the augend and during a subtraction it becomes the minuend. Thus minuend and augend are merely names given to the same quantity depending upon the operation being performed; hence, the set of rules that applies to the augend is equally applicable to the minuend.

The following examples illustrating the SUBTRACT operation shown in Table 3·23 will not be accompanied by a detailed explanation in view of the analysis just presented.

By examination of the logical process employed in the computer for the performance of subtraction, the following four rules can be derived. Note that the rules for the minuend are identical with the rules for the augend given in a preceding portion of this chapter which described the ADD operation.

1. Minuend positive: Quantity used in signed-magnitude form.
2. Minuend negative: The magnitude bits of the quantity are complemented before being used.
3. Subtrahend positive: The sign bit and the magnitude bits are complemented before being used.
4. Subtrahend negative: The sign bit only is complemented before being used.

Multiplication. The MULTIPLY operation in any number system is merely a shortcut method of multiple successive additions. The process of arriving at the result is simplified by the use of shift sequences interspersed in the addition operations. The method shown below of arriving at the result of the multiplication of decimal 112 and decimal 23 is a sequence known to all.

$$
\begin{array}{r}
112 \\
23 \\
\hline
336 \\
224 \\
\hline
2576
\end{array}
$$

In arriving at the product, the value 112 was summed three times to generate the partial product 336. This partial product was the operation of $112(3 \times 10^0)$. The value 112 was then summed twice; however, the partial product generated was recorded shifted one place to the left. The operation involved was $112(2 \times 10^1)$. The shift took into account the positional value of the multiplier digit 2 which is in the 10^1 position. This shift allowed the second partial product to retain its true value in relation to the first partial product (which resulted from the operation caused by the digit in the

10^0 position). The addition of the partial products is 2576, which is the same value arrived at if 112 is added in 23 successive steps.

The above relationship is significant in that the add/shift convention is used in performing the MULTIPLY operation in the computing device. In the computer, the operation is performed as follows: (1) each bit of the multiplier is sensed and initiates the generation of a partial product which undergoes a shift, (2) the partial product resulting from the new bit sensing is added to the previously generated partial product before the shift, and (3) the processes of multiplier bit sensing, partial product generation, and new running partial product generation continue until all bits have been sensed and caused a final product to be generated.

When two binary numbers are multiplied, the product is formed by repeated addition of the multiplicand. As in every multiplication process each partial product must be shifted relative to the previous partial product before being added to it. This shift necessitates the use of additional storage space to accommodate the sum bits generated by the addition of the lowest order bits.

The problem of obtaining partial products in the binary system is comparatively simple because only two possibilities exist; if the multiplier bit is a 1, the multiplicand is added to the previous partial product, and if the multiplier bit is a 0, zeros are added to the previous partial product. For example, multiply 11011 by 101. Table 3·24 shows the multiplication process in manual and machine methods.

In Example 1, note that the multiplicand is used as a partial product if the controlling multiplier bit is 1; a partial product of 0's is generated if the multiplier bit is a 0. The partial products are retained and summed after the last partial product is generated.

A digital computer uses this method but implements it in a slightly different way. The partial products are summed as they are generated and then shifted as a running sum. The shift, however, is made to the right. This change in direction of the shift between manual and machine multiplication does not destroy the positional relationship concept developed earlier. Example 2 illustrates machine multiplication of the numbers used in the manual process of Example 1. Note that the number of additions and shifts performed is equal to the number of digits in the multiplier. The first addition performed is not shown; it actually occurs when the first partial product is brought down, when the addition of the multiplicand to all zeros is made. It is important to note that each partial product is added to only the running sum. With each shift to the right, an additional low-order digit becomes firm as a part of the final product. The final product of 135_{10} is achieved in both examples.

An example of the MULTIPLY operation using the four-bit fractional machine (sign and 3 magnitude bits) previously discussed is given below.

TABLE 3-24 Comparison of Manual and Machine Multiplication

1. *Manual*	2. *Machine*	
11011 = multiplicand = 27_{10}		11011 = 27_{10}
$\times$101 = multiplier = 5_{10}		$\times$00101 = 5_{10}
11011 = 1st partial product	1st partial product	11011
000000 = 2d partial product	1st partial product shifted	011011 $\rightarrow$
11011 = 3d partial product	2d partial product	00000
10000111 = final product = 135_{10}	Sum of 1st & 2d partial products	011011
	Running sum shifted	0011011 $\rightarrow$
	3d partial product	11011
	Running sum	10000111
	Running sum shifted	010000111 $\rightarrow$
	4th partial product	00000
	Running sum	10000111
	Running sum shifted	010000111 $\rightarrow$
	5th partial product	00000
	Running sum	010000111
	Running sum shifted	0010000111 $\rightarrow$
	Final product	0010000111 = 135_{10}

The following example applies to the multiply unrounded operation. When multiply unrounded is performed, the product is a double-length number. For example, if two numbers each having a sign and three magnitude bits are multiplied, the product will carry the appropriate sign and the magnitude will be six bits in length. Additional registers are provided to hold the least significant half of the product. In the example shown, this register initially holds the multiplier.

PROBLEM

Multiply plus three-fourths by plus five-eighths.

$\frac{3}{4} \times \frac{5}{8} = +\frac{15}{32} = 0.011110$

Initial Step of Multiplication

Multiplicand added = 0.110   Sense first multiplier bit

Initial partial
 product = 0.000   Multiplier = $+\frac{5}{8}$ = 0101

Discarded

Product sign stored   0.011   0010
 and not used during
 remaining steps.

The initial step in the multiplication process is shown above. The least significant bit of the multiplier is sensed to determine whether or not the multiplicand will be added. In this case the least significant multiplier bit is a 1, and therefore the magnitude bits of the multiplicand are added to the initial partial product which is zero. The sign bit of the multiplicand is half-added with the multiplier sign bit to generate the product sign Half-adding means that upon adding the sign bits, should a carry be generated, it will be discarded. For instance, if two negative numbers are multiplied, the sign bits (1's) are added generating a 0 sum and a 1 carry. The carry is discarded, and the sum (0) is used as the sign of the product. The sign thus generated follows the algebraic rule of signs for multiplication; that is, when numbers having like signs are multiplied the product sign is positive. The magnitude bits of the sum are shifted right one place upon the generation of each partial product as shown above. One bit of the partial product (the least significant) is stored at the right, together with the multiplier, which is also shifted right one place. The least significant multiplier bit is discarded on this shift since there is no further need for it.

Second Step of Multiplication

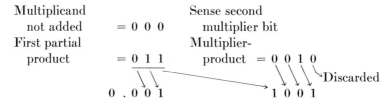

Multiplicand		Sense second
not added	= 0 0 0	multiplier bit
First partial		Multiplier-
product	= 0 1 1	product = 0 0 1 0

0 . 0 0 1   1 0 0 1

Discarded

The second step in the sequence for multiplication is illustrated above. The initial partial product was replaced by the first partial product, and the multiplier was replaced by the shifted-multiplier in which the second multiplier bit occupied the least significant position. Since this bit is a zero, the multiplicand is not added to the first partial product. Instead, the first partial product is added to zero, and the sum and multiplier are shifted to the right. The second multiplier bit is discarded on this shift. Two bits of the partial product are now stored at the right.

Third Step of Multiplication

Multiplicand		Sense last
added	= 1 1 0	multiplier bit
Second		Multiplier-
partial product	= 0 0 1	product = 1 0 0 1

0 . 0 1 1   1 1 0 0

Discarded

On the step shown above the last multiplier bit is sensed. Because this bit is a 1, the multiplicand is added to the second partial product. The shift right occurs as before, and the final product is complete.

The multiply unrounded operation and the particular values used in the preceding discussion were selected to simplify the explanation. The result of 0.0111100 is considered to be a double-precision result. Discarding the least significant half of the product would result in a single-precision result. In discarding the least significant half of the product, a rounding operation would probably take place; that is, a 1 in the MSD of the LS half of the product would affect the value of the LSD of the MS half of the product. The above product rounded would be $0.011 + 0.001$ or 0.100. The effects of rounding in this problem are significant. However, a rounding in, say, the 2^{-23} position of a 24-bit machine could be rather insignificant. The significance of this action is, of course, dependent upon the scaling factors involved.

More complex forms of multiplication have been evolved in modern computer systems in order to speed up the operation. An example of an improved method is the *multiple-digit method*. In the normal method, two numbers are multiplied by repeated sampling of consecutive multiplier digits and either adding and shifting or shifting.

With the multiple-digit method it is possible to speed the process by examining two multiplier digits at a time instead of just one and adding either all zeros, the multiplicand, twice the multiplicand, or three times the multiplicand, depending on the values of the two multiplier digits examined.

00 = add zeros
01 = add the multiplicand
10 = add twice the multiplicand
11 = add three times the multiplicand

The running partial product must be shifted two positions after each addition. As an example, 10101010 or 170_{10} will be multiplied by 10010011 or 147_{10}.

$$10101010 = 170_{10}$$
$$\times\ 10010011 = 147_{10}$$

multiplicand $= 10101010$
$2 \times$ multiplicand $= 101010100$
$3 \times$ multiplicand $= 111111110$

First partial product:	111111110	multiplier digits $= 3$
Second partial product:	000000000	multiplier digits $= 0$
Third partial product:	10101010	multiplier digits $= 1$
Fourth partial product:	101010100	multiplier digits $= 2$
Product:	110000110011110 $= 24,990_{10}$	

The advantage of speed gained in the method described above must be weighed against the increased costs involved in implementing such a system. The mechanics involved in the arithmetic process of multiplication, however, are the same.

Division. The basic division process consists of a series of attempts to subtract the divisor first from the dividend and, in subsequent steps, from the remainder. If the subtraction results in a remainder having a sign bit which is the same as that of the divisor, a quotient bit of ONE is generated. If the sign bit of the remainder is unlike that of the divisor, a quotient bit of ZERO is generated. If the restoring process of division is used and a quotient bit of ZERO is generated, the remainder must be restored in its original value in preparation for a second trial subtraction. The sign comparison is used to indicate whether a valid subtraction has occurred. The restoring process is time-consuming and may be eliminated by the use of the nonrestoring method of division.

To illustrate both the division processes, consider the examples in Table 3·25, where binary number Y is to be divided by binary number X. Since a fractional computer cannot utilize numbers whose absolute value is equal to or greater than unity, the condition is imposed that divisor X be larger than dividend Y in order that the magnitude of the quotient be smaller than unity.

Example 1 in Table 3·25 illustrates the restoring method of division. Because the divisor must be larger than the dividend, the first subtraction of the divisor (1*a*) will always result in an overdraw and the divisor (1*b*) must be added to the remainder in order to restore. This first step, however, is not wasted since the sign of the quotient is determined as a result of this

TABLE 3·25 Comparison of Restoring and Nonrestoring Methods of Division

1. *Restoring method*				2. *Nonrestoring method*			
	Dividend	$=$	Y		Dividend	$=$	Y
(*a*)	Divisor-subtract	$=$	$-X$	(*a*)	Divisor-subtract	$=$	$-X$
	Remainder	$=$	$Y - X$		Remainder	$=$	$Y - X$
(*b*)	Restore	$=$	$+X$	(*b*)	Shifted remainder	$=$	$2Y - 2X$
	Restored remainder	$=$	Y	(*c*)	Divisor-add	$=$	$+X$
(*c*)	Shifted remainder	$=$	$2Y$		Remainder	$=$	$2Y - X$
(*d*)	Divisor-subtract	$=$	$-X$				
	Remainder	$= 2Y - X$					

action. After the restoring step is completed, the restored remainder is effectively multiplied by the radix of the number system being used (1c). This is accomplished in the computer by shifting left. It is assumed that the shifted remainder $2Y$ is greater than the divisor X. The divisor is again subtracted (1d) and the remainder is $2Y - X$. Compare the number of steps required to obtain this remainder by the restoring method illustrated here with the number of steps required to obtain the same remainder by the nonrestoring process illustrated in Example 2.

The first step (2a) of the nonrestoring method is identical with the first step of the restoring method. Omitted in the nonrestoring process is the restoring step. Instead, the overdrawn remainder is shifted to the left, effectively multiplying the remainder by the radix (2b). The divisor is then added instead of subtracted from the shifted remainder (2c). The remainder obtained by this method is the same as that obtained by the restoring method. Note that by using the nonrestoring process, one step is saved. This saving of one step results each time an invalid subtraction of divisor from dividend (remainder) is made. This step (time) saving is significant if a 48-bit machine is considered or if double precision numbers are the operators in a division. An example of machine-performed division is given using the four-bit machine of the previous examples.

PROBLEM

Divide plus one-fourth by plus one-half.

$$+\tfrac{1}{4} \div +\tfrac{1}{2} = +\tfrac{1}{4} \times +\tfrac{2}{1} = +\tfrac{2}{4} \text{ or } +\tfrac{1}{2} = 0.100$$

Initial Step of Division

Dividend = 0. 0 1 0   Divisor = 0. 1 0 0

Like-sign bits

Dividend   = 0. 0 1 0 = $+\tfrac{1}{4}$

Divisor-subtract   = 1. 0 1 1 = $(-) + \tfrac{1}{2}$ 1's complement form

Remainder before shift   = 1. 1 0 1 = $-\tfrac{1}{4}$ ⎫ Magnitude in 1's comple-

Shifted remainder   = 1. 0 1 1 = $-\tfrac{1}{2}$ ⎭ ment

Quotient sign bit is positive, therefore

Q bit generated   = 0

On the initial step of division, as shown, the sign of the divisor is compared with the sign of the dividend. Whenever the signs are alike, as in this example, the divisor is subtracted from the dividend. The sign of the remainder before shift is compared with the true sign of the divisor to determine the value of the quotient bit. If the signs are unlike, the quotient bit generated will be a ZERO; if alike, the quotient bit generated will be a ONE. Thus the first quotient sign bit (Q bit) generated above is a ZERO. The process used by the computer in determining the sign of the quotient is in direct agreement with the algebraic rule for determining the sign of a quotient. Shifting the remainder to the left results in a remainder whose value is twice that of the remainder before shifting. Note that the divisor was subtracted from the dividend as in (2a) of the preceding example of the nonrestoring process and the dividend minus the divisor was shifted left to effectively double the remainder as in (2b). The Q bit is examined to set up the arithmetic unit for the following step. If the Q bit is a 0, the divisor is added to the shifted remainder on the next step. If the Q bit is a 1, the divisor is subtracted from the remainder on the next step. Since the Q bit is a 0, the divisor is added on the next step. This corresponds to (2c) of the nonrestoring process. The Q bits generated are stored in a secondary register, usually the one used to hold the multiplier bits and the least significant bits of the partial product during the MULTIPLY operation.

Second Step of Division

Remainder	$= 1.\ 0\ 1\ 1 = -\frac{1}{2}$	1's complement magnitude
Divisor-add	$= 0.\ 1\ 0\ 0 = +\frac{1}{2}$	
Remainder before shift	$= 1.\ 1\ 1\ 1 = -0$	Magnitude in 1's complement
Shifted remainder	$= 1.\ 1\ 1\ 1 = -0$	
Q bits generated	$=\ 0\ \ 0$	

On the second step in this particular example of division, as illustrated above, the divisor is added to the remainder generated in the preceding step. The resulting remainder is equal to -0. The shift left does not alter the remainder. This is correct since the shift effectively multiplies the remainder by 2 and any integer times zero is equal to zero. The sign of the remainder before shift is compared with the true sign of the divisor to determine the value of the second Q bit generated. Because the Q bit thus generated is a zero, the divisor will again be added to the remainder on the next step.

Third Step of Division

Remainder	$= 1.\ 1\ 1\ 1 = -0$ Magnitude in 1's complement
Divisor-add	$= 0.\ 1\ 0\ 0 = +\frac{1}{2}$

$$0\ \ 0\ 1\ 1$$

End-around carry $= \quad \longrightarrow 1$

Remainder before shift $= 0.\ 1\ 0\ 0 = +\frac{1}{2}$

Shifted remainder $= \boxed{1.\ 0\ 0\ 0} = +1$ Sign bit has 2^0 value

Q bits generated $= 0\ \ 0\ 1$

On the third step, above, the divisor is again added to the shifted remainder. The sign bit of the remainder before shift is positive. Shifting the remainder left places a 1 in the sign position. The shifted remainder, however, is considered to be positive if the remainder is positive before the shift occurs and the sign bit is considered by the machine to have the value of 2^0 power. This is possible since the sign is examined to set up the next operation before the shift occurs, and overflow is not being sensed for at this time. The shifted remainder is equal to $+1$. The sign of the remainder before shift is compared with the sign of the true divisor and a Q bit of 1 is generated. Since the Q bit just generated is a 1, the divisor will be subtracted from the remainder on the next step.

Fourth Step of Division

Remainder	$= 1.\ 0\ 0\ 0 = +1$
Divisor-subtract	$= 1.\ 0\ 1\ 1 = -\ (+\frac{1}{2})$ In 1's complement

$$0.\ 0\ 1\ 1$$

End-around carry $= \quad \longrightarrow 1$

Remainder before shift $= 0.\ 1\ 0\ 0 = +\frac{1}{2}$

Shifted remainder $= \boxed{1.\ 0\ 0\ 0} = +1$ Sign bit has 2^0 value

Q bits generated $+ 0\ \ 0\ 1\ 1$

One additional Q bit must be generated for roundoff purposes. The generation of this roundoff bit is accomplished in the same manner as the generation of the preceding bits. The quotient is then shifted from the secondary register into the position for input to the adders.

Fifth Step of Division

Remainder	$= 1.\ 0\ 0\ 0$	Sign bit has 2^0 value
Divisor-subtract	$= 1.\ 0\ 1\ 1 + \frac{1}{2}$	In 1's complement
	$0\ \ 0\ 1\ 1$	

End-around carry $\longrightarrow 1$

Remainder before shift $\quad 0.\ 1\ 0\ 0 + \frac{1}{2}$

Shifted remainder $\quad\boxed{1.\ 0\ 0\ 0}$ $\quad$ Sign bit has 2^0 value

Q bits generated $\quad= 0\ \ 0\ 1\ 1\ 1$

Q bits shifted for adder
 input $\qquad\qquad = 0\ \ 0\ 1\ 1 \qquad$ 1 roundoff bit

(Partial remainder discarded)

Last Step of Division — Roundoff

Unrounded quotient	$= 0.\ 0\ 1\ 1 = +\frac{3}{8}$	
1 added in LS place	$= 0.\ 0\ 0\ 1 = +\frac{1}{8}$	Roundoff bit
Final quotient	$= 0.\ 1\ 0\ 0 = +\frac{1}{2}$	

A 1 is added to the least significant bit of the unrounded quotient as shown. This addition is not performed unconditionally. The action taken on the roundoff cycle is determined by comparing the roundoff bit with the sign of the unrounded quotient. The roundoff is necessary in some cases because of the nonterminating nature of the quotient being generated. In the above example it is necessary to finalize the quotient which results from an "even" division. Roundoff is performed by adding a 1 if the quotient sign is positive and the roundoff bit is a 1, or by adding a 1 if the quotient sign is negative and the roundoff bit is a 0. Recall that negative values are expressed in 1's complement; hence a 0 is actually a 1 roundoff bit.

It should be noted that during a DIVIDE operation, it is possible to overflow if the divisor is smaller than the dividend. Sensing networks are included to detect this condition.

Decimal addition. Decimal mathematics may be performed in a binary computer by the use of binary coded decimal numbers. The addition of four bit positions at a time is accomplished with the possibility of carries between each BCD number. An example of a method which might be used is shown in Table 3·26. An 8421 BCD code is used to represent the numbers 795 and 683 in the example given.

TABLE 3-26 BCD Machine Addition

Manual addition	Machine addition			
	Thousands	Hundreds	Tens	Units
795_{10}		$\begin{matrix}1\\0\ 1\ 1\ 1 = 7\end{matrix}$	$1\ 0\ 0\ 1 = 9$	$0\ 1\ 0\ 1 = 5$
683_{10}		$0\ 1\ 1\ 0 = 6$	$1\ 0\ 0\ 0 = 8$	$0\ 0\ 1\ 1 = 3$
	(a)	$1\ 1\ 1\ 0 = 14_{10}$	$0\ 0\ 0\ 1 = 1_{10}$	$1\ 0\ 0\ 0 = 8_{10}$
	(b)	$0\ 1\ 1\ 0 = 6^*_{10}$	$0\ 1\ 1\ 0 = 6^*_{10}$	
1478_{10}	(c) $(00)1 = 1_{10}$	$0\ 1\ 0\ 0 = 4_{10}$	$0\ 1\ 1\ 1 = 7_{10}$	$1\ 0\ 0\ 0 = 8_{10}$

It should be noted that the result of the addition in (a) above is 14, 1, and 8, an obviously incorrect sum. This resulted from the straight binary addition in the machine in which the normal carries were added. In the addition, the modulus of the number system was exceeded in the tens and hundreds positions. The computer must be mechanized to sense these conditions and apply a correction factor. In the example the tens-position error is sensed by the generation of a carry-out of this position. In the hundreds position it is sensed by an illegal symbol representation (in this case 14). Any representation of a number other than the single digits 0 through 9 is illegal. Upon sensing of either of these conditions, a correction factor of 6 is added (b) to the positions in question to correct this modulus "overflow." In the example, the correction produced the sum 1478_{10}. The correction of 6_{10} is added to "fill" the excess positions required in stepping through the unused combinations available in the four digits used to represent the allowable decimal symbols. It should be noted that if the addition of the correction factor results in a carry, the carry should be added to the next higher order.

It can be seen that although BCD numbers may be used in arithmetic operations, additional sensing circuitry is necessary to ensure valid results from the computation.

QUESTIONS: SECTION 3

3-27 What is the relationship of the 9's complement to the 10's complement in the decimal system?

3-28 What is the 9's complement of 450_{10} (10-digit machine)?

3-29 Subtract 225 from 300 (assume 10-digit machine) using the 10's complement add method.

3·30 The 1's complement of a binary number can be found by the term $(2^n - 1) N$; what is an easier way?

3·31 What is the range of values that can be handled in an arithmetic unit when the binary point is to the left of the most significant magnitude bit of the word?

3·32 What process must integer numbers undergo to allow their use in a fractional machine?

3·33 When adding two numbers, is overflow possible? Explain.

3·34 Perform the following ADD operations as they are performed in a computer:

(a) 0.11001   (b) 1.1010   (c) 1.0010   (d) 0.1110
     0.00101   1.0101   0.1111   1.1111

3·35 Perform the following SUBTRACT operations as they are performed in a computer:

(a) 0.0001   (b) 1.1001   (c) 1.1000   (d) 0.0101   (e) 1.110
     0.0100   1.0110   0.0101   1.1010   0.101

3·36 Perform the following unrounded multiply problems in manual and machine form:

(a)   1011 (11_{10}) (b)   0.100 $(+\frac{1}{2})$
     $\times$0101 (5_{10}) $\times$0.101 $(+\frac{5}{8})$

3·37 Perform the following DIVIDE operations by the machine method:

$\frac{3}{8} \div \frac{1}{2}$ $0.100 \overline{)0.011}$

3·38 Perform the following additions after number conversion to the 8421 BCD code:

(a) 733_{10} (b) 476_{10}
     622_{10} 235_{10}

SECTION 4   FLOATING POINT AND ERROR CHECKING

Floating Point

In a fixed-point computer, the binary-point position is established during the design phase. If the binary point is located immediately to the right of the sign bit, the computer is considered to be a fractional machine; however, if the binary point is located to the right of the least significant bit, the computer is considered to be an integer machine. This does not mean that integers cannot be operated upon in the fractional machine or vice versa. It does mean, however, that the numbers must be converted to a form suitable for use in the machine. This preparation of the numbers to fit the machine is known as *scaling* and imposes a bookkeeping restriction on the programmer. He must be aware of the limitations the machine has of representing his numbers (available bit positions), and he must ensure that all numbers modified undergo the same scaling factors so that the relationships among the numbers used are not changed. He must also make the necessary adjustments after certain operations to ensure the retention of the originally established relationships. Assume, for example, that a signed six-bit decimal machine is in use. Numerical values of 32.72, 0.000185, and 127.5 are to be used as operators in the machine. To preserve the relationships which exist among the numbers, the storage and use of the numbers should be centered about the decimal point as shown in Example 1 of Table 3·27.

To preserve this relationship and allow direct use of the numbers requires a register length of nine bits. However, the computer in the example requires that the relationship be preserved within a span of six magnitude digits. This can be accomplished by scaling the numbers through the assignment of powers of 10 to each of the numbers as shown in Example 2.

In scaled form, the decimal points are aligned and six places are sufficient for all the numbers. It is necessary, however, to provide for storage of the power of 10 (exponent) as well as the magnitude digits. This storage is not shown here but will be discussed later. All input words can now be accepted by the computer, but the exponent is the indicator of the true value of the number.

When numbers are scaled, they are usually normalized; that is, the first nonzero digit appears immediately to the left of the decimal (binary) point for integers and to the right for fractions. The scaled, normalized fractional numbers are shown in Example 3. A significant point to note is that although the data has been entered, the positional relationships of the original numbers must be reestablished by expressing both numbers in the same scale factor prior to an operation. For example, to add the first number 0.327200×10^2 (32.72_{10}) to 0.127500×10^3 (127.5) requires that both

TABLE 3·27   Scaling and Normalizing

1. Original numerical relationship	2. Scaled	3. Normalized
S 1 2 3 4 5 6 7 8 9	S.1 2 3 4 5 6	S.1 2 3 4 5 6
3 2.7 2	$0.3\ 2\ 7\ 2\ 0\ 0 \times 10^2$	$0.3\ 2\ 7\ 2\ 0\ 0 \times 10^2$
0.0 0 0 1 8 5	$0.0\ 0\ 0\ 1\ 8\ 5 \times 10^0$	$0.1\ 8\ 5\ 0\ 0\ 0 \times 10^{-3}$
1 2 7.5	$0.1\ 2\ 7\ 5\ 0\ 0 \times 10^3$	$0.1\ 2\ 7\ 5\ 0\ 0 \times 10^3$

numbers be represented in the same power of 10. This can be achieved through a shift to the right as follows:

$$0.327200 \times 10^2 = \quad 0.032720 \times 10^3$$
$$+\ 0.127500 \times 10^3$$
$$\overline{+\ 0.160220 \times 10^3} = +\quad 160.22_{10}$$

The manipulations necessary to preserve the relationships must be initiated by the programmer. This procedure is tedious, time-consuming, and error-prone. To relieve the programmer of this task, a computer can be mechanized to automatically perform these internal bookkeeping and scaling operations. Such a computer is said to perform floating-point arithmetic.

In a fractional computer, a computer word was represented by sign and magnitude. An additional portion must be added to the computer word to indicate the scaling factor of the number. This additional portion is called the *exponent*, while the fractional magnitude is called the *mantissa*.

1		23
0	0 1 0 1 1	.0 1 1 0 0 1 0 1 1 1 0 0 1 1 0 0 1
Sign	Exponent	Mantissa

The computer word above illustrates how a typical floating-point word could be constructed. The computer word is designed to hold 23 binary digits. The first digit is interpreted as a sign of the mantissa (in this case positive). The next five digits are interpreted as the exponent. The last 17 bits are interpreted as the mantissa or magnitude. Note that the binary point is considered to exist to the left of the mantissa, which indicates fractional values for the mantissa.

The exponent shown above is 11 and indicates that the mantissa value is scaled $\times\ 2^{11}$. The computer word above is $+0.313462_8 \times 2^{11}$. For ease of reading, the value is expressed octally.

The system of notation shown in the example above can represent only numbers with positive exponents. The sign bit represents only the sign of the mantissa. If it were desired to utilize both positive and negative exponents, thereby increasing the power of the computer, an additional sign for the exponent could be added. The original computer word would become:

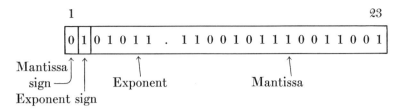

The computer word above represents $0.627144_8 \times 2^{-11}$. The octal notation for the word changed in the above example since the 23-bit word was retained and the mantissa length was changed from 17 to 16 bits to allow for a bit position assignment to represent exponent sign.

Automatic scaling will be accomplished by shifting the mantissa while counting the exponent up or down depending on the direction of shift and the signs of the mantissa and exponent. The shifting will continue until the most significant bit is not equal to 0. This is called *normalizing*, and the result is called the *normalized form*. The numbers are usually stored in the computer in the normalized form until actually used in an arithmetic operation. When a floating-point number is not in the normalized form, it is in either an overflow form or an underflow form. In the former case there are nonzero digits to the left of the binary point — in most uses these digits will be lost because there are normally no bit positions reserved for them. In the underflow form, zero digits occur to the right of the binary point. Both these conditions could be considered erroneous in some arithmetic computations.

Addition and subtraction. Before adding or subtracting numbers, their scale factors must be the same. The first operation performed is a comparison of the exponents of both numbers concerned. If the exponents are equal, the numbers have the same scale factor and can be added or subtracted. The comparison is usually accomplished by subtracting one exponent from the other and noting the size and value of the result. If a positive 0 resulted and the two numbers were of the same sign, the numbers were scaled by the same amount. An addition or subtraction can be performed. If a result other than 0 occurs, the larger exponent will be taken as the exponent of the sum or the difference. The number with the smaller exponent will be rescaled prior to the addition or subtraction by shifting the mantissa portion of the number. The addition or subtraction will then be performed. Finally, the sum or the difference is normalized.

Multiplication. When two floating-point numbers are multiplied, no rescaling is required prior to the operation. Multiplying of fractional mantissas always results in a smaller product. The algebraic rule of exponents states that when two numbers are multiplied, their exponents are added. Overflow cannot occur because of the fractions involved, but underflow will occur.

Division. When dividing fixed-point fractional numbers, care must be taken to ensure that the divisor is larger than the dividend. The converse will always yield an overflow result no matter how small the numbers are.

In floating-point division the same convention must be followed. If this relationship does not exist, the dividend must be rescaled. Since both the dividend and divisor are in normalized form, all digits in both fractional parts are significant digits with no leading zeros. The dividend may still be larger than the divisor in this case, however, and this situation can be readily remedied by shifting the dividend before division one position to the right. The corresponding exponent must be changed. The final exponent will be determined by subtracting the exponent value of the divisor from the exponent value of the dividend.

Error Detection and Correction

The normal operating sequences within a computing system require multiple high-speed data transfers and communication among the various units of the computing system. In order to ensure a high degree of reliability, methods have been devised to allow for constant data checking to detect errors, and in some cases, to recover from or correct the error.

Parity checking. The most common system of error detection in use involves the counting of the number of 1 bits in a computer word to determine if any were lost during transfer from one section of the computer to another. The method is known as parity checking and may involve either odd parity counts or even parity counts. When a word is placed in the computer, the number of 1 bits is counted. If the number is odd (when an odd parity is being used), parity is considered good and nothing further is done. If the number of 1 bits totals an even count, an extra bit equal to a 1 is tacked on, usually to the LSD end of the computer word, making the overall parity count odd. Several examples are shown below utilizing a 10-bit computer word.

Bit	1	2 3 4 5 6 7 8 9 10	P
Example 1	0.	1 0 1 1 0 0 1 1 0	0
Example 2	1.	1 1 1 0 0 1 0 1 0	1
Example 3	0.	1 1 0 0 0 1 0 1 0	1

In Example 1, the number of 1 bits is five; therefore, a zero parity bit is inserted since the odd-bit convention already exists. In Example 2, an even 1's count exists if the sign bit is considered in the counting. The sign bit is considered part of the data word, and Example 2 contains even 1's; therefore, a 1 parity bit is inserted to achieve the odd-parity count in the word. Example 3 represents another case in which a 1 bit must be added to achieve odd parity. If odd parity checking is in use, the total word, including the parity position, must total an odd number of 1's if valid data is to be indicated.

An even parity checking may be used and differs only in a word composition which results in an even number of 1's as a total 1's count.

Parity is not usually checked in every section of a computer. It is used where information transfers are critical, for example, transfers into and out of memory. The method of checking parity is very similar to the method of assigning parity. The following discussion concerns a system that utilizes an odd parity generation and checking scheme.

If a count of the 1 bits in a computer word yields an even number of bits and the parity bit is a 0, or if a count yields an odd number of bits with a parity bit of 1, an error condition exists. The action taken upon the detection of this condition depends upon the computer design. In most cases the computer halts because a parity error is usually considered a critical error. It is interesting to note that an error can indicate either an error in the computer word or an error in the parity bit itself. Note also that if an even number of bits had been lost, no error would have been detected. The odds against losing an even number of bits are quite high, but the condition has been known to occur.

Odd parity is usually used for the following reason. The 0 digit is often represented by the absence of a signal (0 volts). Odd parity assures that when an all-zeros computer word is transferred within a computer, at least one of the bits transferred (the parity bit) will be a 1 to indicate that the transfer had been made. This is helpful in determining if an entire transfer path is operative.

A computer word need not be restricted to a single parity bit. It may be desirable to provide a parity bit for each group of five bits. This would improve the odds against dropping an even number of bits and not detecting the error. This procedure, however, would involve additional hardware and is another aspect of the cost utility tradeoffs which are considered in computer design.

Parity checking in decimal system. A method of parity checking similar to the method employed for the binary system can be devised to error-check decimal numbers. The process becomes more involved because of the increased complexity of circuitry necessary to handle binary coded decimal numbers. The method involves taking the modulo sum of the digit numbers and adding a 9 to this sum. The modulo sum of a series of decimal numbers results in a single decimal digit sum with a discard of all carries. For example, the odd parity digit for 23,456 is generated in the following manner:

$$
\begin{array}{l}
2 \\
3 \\
4 \\
5 \\
\underline{6}
\end{array}
$$

Carry dropped   2 $\overline{0}$ = modulo sum
Modulo sum   + $\underline{9}$ = radix of decimal system − 1
             9 = parity digit

The number would be written as:

1 2 3 4 5 6 P
0. 2 3 4 5 6 9

If a single-digit error occurs, even if it is the parity digit itself, it will be detected. To check the parity, the digits plus radix − 1 are summed and subtracted from the existing parity digit. If the parity is correct, the result of the subtraction will be 0. Table 3·28 illustrates the application of the above method for a correct parity check (Example 1) and for an error-detecting condition (Example 2).

TABLE 3·28 Parity Checking

1. *Correct*	2. *Error Detecting*
Word received = 0.234569	Assume 4 changed to 7 in transmission Word received = 0.237569
$\left.\begin{array}{l}2\\3\\4\\5\\6\end{array}\right\}$ data digits	$\left.\begin{array}{l}2\\3\\7\\5\\6\end{array}\right\}$ data digits
$\underline{9}$ = radix − 1	$\underline{9}$ = radix − 1
2 9 sum (modulo 2)	3 2 sum (modulo 2)
9 = parity digit	9 = parity digit
− $\underline{9}$ sum digit	− $\underline{2}$ = sum
0 = correct transmission	7 = incorrect transmission $\neq$ 0

Error-correcting codes.   It is possible to detect an error in a computer word by using a parity-checking scheme, but a parity-checking scheme in itself will not indicate where the error has occurred. Several methods have been evolved for detecting and correcting errors in computer words by using special error-correcting codes. The following method, devised by R. W. Hamming, is used to detect and correct a single-binary-digit error in a number. The code consists of a mixture of four binary digits (limiting the size of the maximum number to 15_{10}) and three check digits. The number is arranged as shown below, with the number 11_{10} shown in its formatted form.

Bit	1	2	3	4	5	6	7						
	$C1$	$C2$	$D1$	$C3$	$D2$	$D3$	$D4$		$(D1$	$D2$	$D3$	$D4)$	
	0	1	1	0	0	1	1	$= 11_{10} =$	$(1$	0	1	1	$)$

The check digits are determined by taking the modulo 2 sum of the check digit concerned plus the respective number digits shown. The particular check digit will be chosen to yield a modulo 2 sum of 0. The modulo 2 sum results from a binary addition with carries discarded.

$$C1 = \text{modulo 2 sum of } C1 + D1 + D2 + D4 = 0$$
$$C2 = \text{modulo 2 sum of } C2 + D1 + D3 + D4 = 0$$
$$C3 = \text{modulo 2 sum of } C3 + D2 + D3 + D4 = 0$$

Table 3·29 illustrates the development of the check digits in the above word.

It should be noted that in Table 3·29 a modulo sum is developed for the digit positions involved in the formation of each check digit. The check digit itself must then assume a value (0 or 1) which, when added to the modulo sum value (1 or 0), equals a modulo sum of 0.

TABLE 3·29   Check-digit Generation for Error-correcting Code

$C1$		$C2$		$C3$	
$D1 =$	1	$D1 =$	1	$D2 =$	0
$+ D2 =$	0	$+ D3 =$	1	$+ D3 =$	1 1
$+ D4 =$	1	$+ D4 =$	1	$+ D4 =$	1
	1 0 Modulo		1 1 Modulo		1 0 Modulo
	sum		sum		sum
$+ C1 =$	0	$+ C2 =$	1	$+ C3 =$	0
$=$	0	$=$	0	$=$	0

TABLE 3·30 Check-digit Computation

$C1$	$C2$	$C3$
$D1 = 1$	$D1 = \quad 1$	$D2 = 0$
$+ D2 = 0$	$+ D3 = \quad 1$	$+ D3 = 1$
$+ D4 = 0$	$+ D4 = \quad 0$	$+ D4 = 0$
$+ C1 = \underline{0}$	$+ C2 = \quad \underline{1}$	$+ C3 = \underline{0}$
1	$1\ 1$	1

An example of error detection and correction is given below. The coded format for 11_{10} has been established above as 0110011. Assume that bit $D4$ were lost during transfer. The word received would be 0110010. The check at the receiving end would be to compute the check digits on the basis of the word received and compare them with the check digits received. If they are alike, the data received is correct; otherwise, an error has occurred. The computation of the check digits for the data received is shown in Table 3·30.

$C1$	$C2$	$D1$	$C3$	$D2$	$D3$	$D4$
0	1	1	0	0	1	0

If the information received were correct, the newly generated digits (111) should correspond with the check digits received (010). The newly computed digits $111 \neq 010$, the check digits of the received word. The error or data loss which occurred during transmission has been detected.

If the C bits calculated are arranged in the order $C3\ C2\ C1$ with $C1$ as the LSD, the binary number formed will point to the bit in the original word that is in error. In this example $C3\ C3\ C1 = 111_2$; therefore bit 7 is in error. This method holds true even if the error occurred in the check digit. This method will detect and indicate an incorrect bit in any data or check-digit position as long as only one error has occurred.

It is also possible to have the circuitry correct the error condition by simply complementing the bit that is in error. Changing bit 7 from 0 to 1 restores the data received to the form that it held at the time it was transmitted.

SUMMARY

The decimal system, employing 10 digits or symbols (radix 10) is the most commonly used numbering system. Early electronic computers utilized this system; however, the hardware considerations in mechanizing for the use of this numbering system made it extremely costly. Because of the ease of mechanization, the binary system was adopted, and it is used almost exclusively as the language of the computer. The binary system has a radix of 2, and 0 and 1 symbols are used for this representation. Two-way conversions can be made between the two systems. The octal system, with a base of 8, is a convenient way to represent large binary numbers and has found extensive use in the computer industry. Conversion can readily be made among the decimal, octal, and binary systems. A further relationship has been developed between the decimal and binary numbering systems in what is known as the binary coded decimal system. In this system, decimal values are represented by binary digits in either weighted or unweighted codes. The difference in the codes is the ability for direct translation from a weighted BCD code to its decimal equivalent. A base-16 code known as the hexadecimal system also finds fairly widespread use in the computer industry. In addition to the decimal symbols 0 through 9, the letters A, B, C, D, E, and F are used to represent the available code positions.

Arithmetic operations in computers may be performed through the use of the basic ADD or SUBTRACT operation. Addition is the most prevalent method used. The operations of subtract, multiply, and divide are performed through the use of the ADD operation and complement and shift sequences. In performing the arithmetic operations, the computer may treat the numbers as integers or as fractions. A binary point is used to determine the conventions used. If all bits are placed in a register to the right of the binary point, the machine is considered a fractional machine; if the bits are placed in a register to the left of the binary point, the machine is an integer machine. The leftmost bit in the register indicates the sign of the value (0 = positive, 1 = negative). Integer or fractional values may be operated upon in either type machine after they have been scaled. Scaling is merely a manipulation of the numbers which allows "sizing" the numbers for a system but retains the original relationship which exists among the numbers. This function is performed by the programmer in a fixed-point system or automatically by the computer in a floating-point machine.

The numerous transfers which take place within the machine increase the possibility of error. A method devised to check for the presence of errors is called parity checking. In this method the word is formatted in a special way at the transmission point and then checked at the reception point. Simple checks reveal if an error exists. More sophisticated codes have been developed which can not only detect the error but initiate action to correct it.

QUESTIONS: SECTION 4

3·39 What is meant by normalized numbers (fractional machine)?

3·40 What is the advantage of a floating-point machine over a fixed-point?

3·41 Scale and normalize the following numbers for use in a signed 5-bit machine.

Original numerical
relationship

1 2 3 4 5 6 7
1 1 0.3 6
    0.0 0 2 5
    3.5 2

3.42 Before adding or subtracting floating-point numbers, what must be assured?

3.43 If the number 0.360×10^2 is to be added to 0.250×10^4, which number must be rescaled? Show the rescaling and addition.

3.44 What are the rules for exponents for multiply and divide operations?

3.45 What is the most common system of error detection?

3.46 What is the disadvantage of a parity-checking system?

3.47 Using seven bits, show an error-correction code (three-bit) for the binary number 7. (Format $C1$ $C2$ $D1$ $C3$ $D2$ $D3$ $D4$.)

3.48 If the check sum received on a computer word (Question 3.47 format) is 001 (in $C3$, $C2$, $C1$) and the check sum generated by the receiver is 101 ($C3$, $C2$, $C1$), what does this indicate?

chapter four

Boolean Algebra

In the previous chapter the various numbering systems which can be used in computers were presented, with emphasis placed on the binary system. It will be recalled that in the binary system there are only two discrete notations: 0 and 1. In this chapter, this system will be utilized to introduce and demonstrate a simplified method of computer-function analysis called *Boolean algebra*. Sometimes referred to as the "algebra of logic," Boolean algebra lends itself well to electrical applications where there are switches that are closed or open and circuits in which an electric current is flowing or is not flowing. Any device that has two states, or conditions, may be represented by Boolean-algebra notation.

Compare the possibility of describing computer functions by simple equations with the method of analysis and troubleshooting of electronic equipment such as radios, television sets, or radar systems. In the case of the latter group, meters, oscilloscopes, and schematic wiring diagrams are needed to locate troubles in the equipment. Although computers are in a sense more complex, Boolean algebra permits the detailed diagrams to be simplified so that the technician can "see the forest in spite of the trees." Boolean algebra has in recent years developed along with computers and has proved to be a great asset in both design and troubleshooting.

Why study Boolean algebra? A working knowledge of Boolean algebra can be the technician's and engineer's most valuable tool. In fact, logic is becoming widely understood by students in colleges and technical institutes and even by well-informed laymen. This chapter will provide a firm foundation for proper interpretation of the more complex logic diagrams in the following chapters. If a career is planned in the telephone or computer fields, a working knowledge of Boolean algebra is essential.

History of Boolean Algebra

Boolean algebra is named after George Boole, who, about 1847, wrote papers on the mathematical analysis of logic. Boole was a distinguished professor in an English university and made no claim to being a mathematician. He was a philosopher, especially interested in man's intellect and thought processes.

The importance of George Boole's contribution was not recognized for some 90 years; meanwhile, his unused books gathered dust on library shelves. Then in 1937 a Bell Telephone Company engineer, interested in problems arising from telephone expansion, became urgently in need of a method of simplifying multiple switching and dialing networks. C. E. Shannon took Boole's original ideas and developed the logic now called Boolean logic, or Boolean algebra. Since that time this treatment of electric circuits has enormously simplified work in both the telephone and the computer fields.

There are many possible manipulations of Boolean algebra that are beyond the scope of this book, but the basic operations are covered in this chapter.

Basic Principles of Boolean Algebra

Boole's logic is based upon the premise that a statement is either *true* or *false*. True statements have a value of 1, while false statements have a value of 0.

The nature of data processors, which have "all-or-nothing" signal levels, facilitates the use of Boolean algebra in descriptive analysis of the functions of the electronic circuits employed. To say this another way, designers have found the algebra of logic to be a shortcut method useful in describing the operation of a variety of electronic circuits used in digital equipment.

Boolean algebra is an extremely simple form of algebra. While it does not necessarily lead to the best circuit (one with the smallest number of components), it provides a convenient method of representing switching circuits. The remainder of this discussion is devoted to the development of the basic rules of Boolean algebra and to the demonstration of its application in switching circuits.

John Venn, a British mathematician of the nineteenth century, evolved a graphical means of illustrating logical truths. In Venn diagrams, a rectangle is used to represent a class of elements with certain characteristics. Within this rectangle are an infinite number of points representing all elements of the general category which fall into the particularly defined category. A further breakdown can be indicated by a circle which represents a subclass or a more sharply defined group within the overall class.

Venn diagrams will be used in developing the proofs for the Boolean functions to be discussed in this chapter. However, before the Venn diagrams are applied to the Boolean functions, a more generalized example of the use of these diagrams is presented.

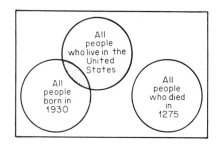

FIG. 4·1   Venn diagram with three subclasses.

A class might include all people or all fish or all cities. There are other significant characteristics of each of these classes which might categorize them into a subclass. For the example, consider the category of all people. Three of the many subclasses of people might be (1) all people who died in A.D. 1275, (2) all people who live in the United States, and (3) all people born in 1930. Figure 4·1 illustrates a Venn diagram which encompasses the category selected and the subclasses within that category.

The rectangle of the figure represents an infinite number of persons including all those who have lived prior to our times, those now living, and those yet to be born. The circles within the rectangle represent the subclasses chosen for the illustration. The subclass "all people who died in 1275" has nothing in common with the other two defined categories and hence stands alone as including some portion of the total class of all people. Persons who died in 1275 could neither have been born in 1930 nor have lived in the United States, since the political entity known as the United States did not exist at that time. The other two subcategories chosen include some portion of the total population of all people. In this instance, however, a certain number of persons in each of the categories fits both the condition of being born in 1930 and living in the United States. This condition is shown by the overlap of the circles, and the degree of the overlap is, of course, a function of the number of persons in each category who fit into both categories. Thus the conditions discussed above have been graphically illustrated in their existing relationships.

In Boolean algebra, each variable is considered a unique subclass and each subclass can be considered either true or false. The true or false condition in a computer is normally represented by a 1 or a 0, or in the actual circuitry by the presence or absence of a specified voltage or current level. For example, a 1 might be represented by plus 5 volts and a 0 by a ground level. The 1 and 0 might also be represented by different magnitudes or directions of currents. Although there is no best way to represent the two possible conditions, the method chosen must allow the 0 and 1 to be easily discernible.

The basic assumptions underlying a system of mathematics, such as ordinary algebra or geometry, are called *postulates*. Postulates are also developed for Boolean algebra. Two fundamental postulates that are extremely important are the AND function and the OR function. The AND function will be discussed first.

POSTULATE 1

$$A \cdot B = C$$

This postulate states that condition C can be represented by the combination (overlap) of quantities A and B. The multiply sign ($\cdot$) used in the Boolean equation is termed and read as the AND function. The AND function is represented in the Venn diagram of Fig. 4·2.

Postulate 1 and Fig. 4·2c illustrate that both variables must be present in an overlap condition to provide the variable C. The shaded area indicates this. The condition existing here is similar to the example of Fig. 4·1 in that two independent subclasses exist, with the combination of part of each resulting in a more refined or unique state. The dot convention is only one of the means available for the representation of the AND function.

The following examples illustrate the AND function:

(1) $0 \cdot 0 = 0$
(2) $0 \cdot 1 = 0$
(3) $1 \cdot 0 = 0$
(4) $1 \cdot 1 = 1$

The symbol 0 represents the absence of the variable (subclass) and the symbol 1 represents the presence of the variable. The symbols can be referred to also as false and true, respectively.

In Example 1, both variables are false; therefore the result is false. Examples 2 and 3 illustrate that if either condition is false, then the result is false. Example 4 illustrates the only condition that can yield a true result. All variables of an AND function must be true to yield a true result.

FIG. 4·2 Venn diagram for $AB = C$. (a) Variable A; (b) variable B; (c) $AB = C$.

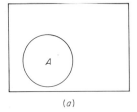
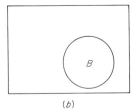
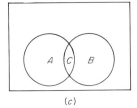

(*a*)   (*b*)   (*c*)

Letter variables may be substituted for one or more of the variables, as shown in the following examples.

(5) $A \cdot 0 = 0$
(6) $A \cdot 1 = A$
(7) $A \cdot A = A$

Example 5 illustrates that if one variable is known to be false, the result will always be false. Examples 6 and 7 illustrate that if no known variable is false, the result is determined by the unknown variable.

Postulate 2 is another important fundamental concept in Boolean notation, the OR function.

POSTULATE 2

$A + B = C$

This postulate states that condition C can be represented by either the quantity A or B or both. The plus sign used in Boolean equations is termed and read as the OR function. The OR function is represented in the Venn diagrams of Fig. 4·3.

Figure 4·3c illustrates a shaded overlap area of A and B which indicates that a combination of subclasses A and B satisfies condition C. However, unlike the conditions existing in Fig. 4·2c where only the overlap area was shaded, the remaining areas of A and B are also shaded. This indicates that either subclass A or subclass B individually is equivalent to subclass C. Although this is true, subclass A and subclass B remain independent and different entities. Therefore variables connected by means of a plus sign will provide a true result if any one of the variables is true (present).

The following examples further illustrate the concept of the OR function:

(8) $0 + 0 = 0$
(9) $0 + 1 = 1$
(10) $1 + 0 = 1$
(11) $1 + 1 = 1$

FIG. 4·3 Venn diagram for $A + B = C$. (a) Variable A; (b) variable B; (c) $A + B = C$.

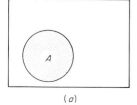
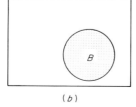
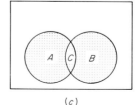

(a)   (b)   (c)

Example 8 shows that if neither variable is true (both false), the result is not true (false). Examples 9 and 10 show that if either variable is true, the result is true. Example 11 illustrates that if both the variables are true, the result is true. The same concepts apply if letters are substituted for one or more of the variables, as in the following examples:

(12) $A + 0 = A$
(13) $A + 1 = 1$
(14) $A + A = A$

In Example 12 if A equals a 0, then $0 + 0 = 0$; if A equals a 1, then $1 + 0 = 1$. The result is dependent upon the condition of variable A. In Example 13, if A equals 0, then $0 + 1 = 1$; if A equals 1, then $1 + 1 = 1$. In this case it does not matter what the state of A is; the result will always be equal to the term that is true. This is an extremely important concept to remember. Example 14 illustrates a result that is dependent upon itself. Both the AND function and the OR function are termed *connectives* because they connect logical elements of an equation.

Commutative law. There are additional important relationships that are extremely important in the manipulation of Boolean equations. The first of these is the *commutative law*, which states that the results of the AND and OR connectives are unaffected by the sequence of the logical elements that they connect:

POSTULATE 3

$A + B = B + A$
$1 + 0 = 0 + 1$

POSTULATE 4

$AB = BA$
$1 \cdot 0 = 0 \cdot 1$

Hence, as long as the same type of logical connective is used between a given group of elements, the positions of the elements on either side of the equal sign may be interchanged.

Associative law. The law of association states that the elements of a proposition may be grouped in any quantity as long as they are connected by the same sign. Figure 4·4 illustrates Postulate 6.

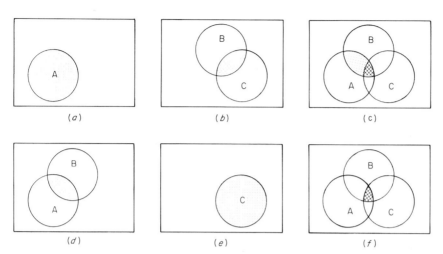

FIG. 4·4 Venn diagram for $A(BC) = (AB)C$. (a) Variable A; (b) variables BC; (c) $A(BC)$; (d) variable AB; (e) variable C; (f) $(AB)C$.

POSTULATE 5

$$A + (B + C) = (A + B) + C$$

POSTULATE 6

$$A(BC) = (AB)C$$

The proof of association is represented by the small shaded areas in Fig. 4·4c and f. As long as the connectives remain the same, the grouping may be different.

Distributive law. The distributive law is contingent upon the characteristics of the logical connectives themselves and can be proved by manipulation of the elements. This manipulation is similar to factoring and expansion in basic algebra. The major difference is that in Boolean algebra the powers of the letter variables are not used. For example,

$$A \cdot A \neq A^2$$

POSTULATE 7

$$A(B + C) = (A \cdot B) + (A \cdot C)$$

POSTULATE 8

$$A + (BC) = (A + B) \cdot (A + C)$$

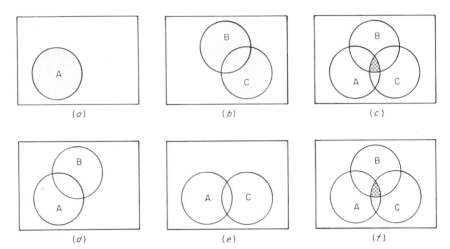

FIG. 4·5 Venn diagram for $A(B+C) = (A·B)+(A·C)$. (a) Variable A; (b) variable $B+C$; (c) $A(B+C)$; (d) variable AB; (e) variable AC; (f) variable $AB+AC$.

Postulate 7 is illustrated in Fig. 4·5.

A more formal proof is applied to Postulate 8 in order to illustrate the use of the previously stated laws in the derivation of more complex equations.

$$A + (BC) = (A + B)·(A + C)$$

If

$$A·A = A$$

then

$$A + BC = A·A + BC$$
$$A·A + BC = (A + B)(A + C)$$

Proof

$(A + B)(A + C) = AA + AC + BA + BC$	Algebraic expansion
$AA + AC + BA + BC = AA + AC + AB + BC$	Postulate 3
$AA + AC + AB + BC = A + AC + AB + BC$	Example 7
$A + AC + AB + BC = A·1 + AC + AB + BC$	Example 6
$A·1 + AC + AB + BC = A(1 + C + B) + BC$	Factoring out A
$A(1 + C + B) + BC = A(1) + BC$	Example 13
$A(1) + BC = A + BC$	Example 6

Therefore

$$A + BC = (A + C)(A + B)$$

Simple algebraic factoring and expansion and the fundamental logical relationships can be effectively applied to the manipulation of Boolean equations.

Complementation and involution (double negation). A unique concept peculiar to Boolean algebra is the NOT function, indicated by a bar ($\overline{\quad}$) over a symbol or a prime sign (′) placed immediately after the symbol. The NOT sign means "the converse of," or the alternate value of, either the symbol or the logical connective. For example, $\overline{1}$ (NOT 1) is equal to 0, for if it is not 1, the only other value it can have is 0. Conversely, $\overline{0}$ (NOT 0) can be equal only to 1. It follows, then, that if a variable A is assigned the value of 1, then $\overline{A}$ (A NOT) is equal to 0, for if A is not 1, the only other value it can have is 0. When the NOT function is applied to a logical connective, the connective assumes the alternate function: for example, $\mp$ (OR NOT) becomes AND, and $\div$ (AND NOT) becomes OR. From the preceding definition, the following rules are obtained:

POSTULATE 9

$A + \overline{A} = 1$ or   Either A or A NOT is equal to 1

POSTULATE 10

$A\overline{A} = 0$ or A AND A NOT can never occur simultaneously

POSTULATE 11

$\overline{\overline{A}} = A$ or   The converse of A NOT is A

The complementation of logical connectives will be illustrated in the proof of De Morgan's theorem.

The Venn diagram in Fig. 4·6 illustrates the NOT function. It can be seen that $\overline{A}$ represents all the variables not included in variable A. Since a variable has only two states, if A is true, then the complement of A ($\overline{A}$) must be false. Postulate 9 states that when A is true the result must be true or 1. If A were false, then $\overline{A}$ must be true. A reference to Example 13 and Postulate 3 supports the contention that Postulate 9 is always true. Postulate 10 can be proved by referring to Example 5. Since A and $\overline{A}$ could never be true at the same time, then the result must always be false. Postulate 11 states that if a complemented number is complemented, the original number will be the result.

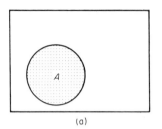 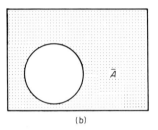

(a)   (b)

FIG. 4·6 Venn diagram NOT function. (a) Variable A; (b) $\bar{A}$.

$$\bar{1} = 0 \quad \text{and} \quad \bar{0} = 1$$

Therefore

$$\bar{\bar{1}} = 1$$

De Morgan's theorems.   The final postulates to be discussed are De Morgan's theorems which apply the principles of the NOT function to an equation containing more than one element.

De Morgan's first theorem will be formally proved to further illustrate the method of evolving more complex equations from simple functions.

POSTULATE 12

$$\overline{A + B} = \bar{A} \cdot \bar{B}$$

The Venn diagram in Fig. 4·7a and b shows that $\overline{A + B}$ is the complement of $A + B$. De Morgan's first theorem can be proved by showing that $A + B$ is also the complement of $\bar{A} \cdot \bar{B}$; therefore $\overline{A + B}$ is equal to $A \cdot B$. The following conditions must first be stated.

CONDITION 1 $(A + B) + (\bar{A} \cdot \bar{B}) = 1$ Postulate 9

CONDITION 2 $(A + B)(\bar{A} \cdot \bar{B}) = 0$ Postulate 10

To prove the first condition:

$$(A + B) + (\bar{A} \cdot \bar{B}) = 1$$
$$A + (\bar{A} \cdot \bar{B}) + B = 1 \qquad \text{Rearrange expression (Postulate 5)}$$
$$(A + \bar{A})(A + \bar{B}) + B = 1 \qquad \text{Postulate 8}$$
$$1(A + \bar{B}) + B = 1 \qquad \text{Postulate 9}$$
$$A + \bar{B} + B = 1 \qquad \text{Example 6}$$
$$A + 1 = 1 \qquad \text{Postulate 9}$$
$$1 = 1 \qquad \text{Example 13}$$

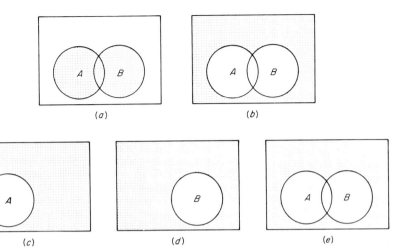

FIG. 4·7 Venn diagram for De Morgan's first theorem. (a) $A + B$; (b) $\overline{A + B}$; (c) $\bar{A}$; (d) $\bar{B}$; (e) $\overline{A \cdot B}$

To prove the second condition:

$$(A + B) \cdot (\bar{A} \cdot \bar{B}) = 0$$
$$A\,\bar{A}\,\bar{B} + B\,\bar{B}\,\bar{A} = 0 \qquad \text{Postulate 7}$$
$$(0 \cdot \bar{B}) + (0 \cdot \bar{A}) = 0 \qquad \text{Postulate 10}$$
$$0 = 0 \qquad \text{Example 5}$$

If

$$(A + B) + (\bar{A} \cdot \bar{B}) = 1 \qquad \text{and} \qquad (A + B) \cdot (\bar{A} \cdot \bar{B}) = 0$$

then $(A + B)$ is the complement of $(\bar{A} \cdot \bar{B})$.

$$1 + 0 = 1 \qquad 1 \cdot 0 = 0$$

It was shown originally that $(A + B)$ was the complement of $(\overline{A + B})$. If $(A + B)$ is both the complement of $(\bar{A} \cdot \bar{B})$ and $(\overline{A + B})$, then $(\overline{A + B}) = (\bar{A} \cdot \bar{B})$. De Morgan's first theorem is illustrated in Fig. 4·7. De Morgan's second theorem states:

POSTULATE 13

$$\overline{AB} = \bar{A} + \bar{B}$$

The proof for De Morgan's second theorem can be evolved in a manner similar to the proof of the first by showing that $A \cdot B$ is the complement of $\overline{A \cdot B}$ and is also the complement of $\bar{A} + \bar{B}$. Since a technique

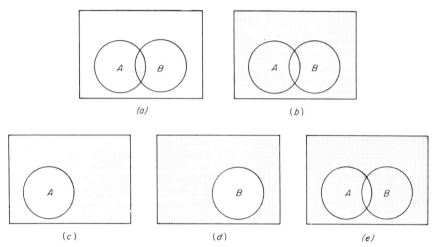

FIG. 4·8 Venn diagram for De Morgan's second theorem. (a) AB; (b) AB; (c) $\bar{A}$; (d)$\bar{B}$; (e) $\bar{A}+\bar{B}$.

similar to that used for the first proof can be derived, the second theorem will be illustrated only by means of the Venn diagram in Fig. 4·8.

De Morgan's theorems will facilitate the simplification of a Boolean expression by enabling alternate methods of implementation of logic circuitry. By using methods such as these, a complex function can be reduced to a form more economically feasible.

Logical representation of Boolean functions. The usefulness of Boolean algebra can best be shown through the use of the basic postulates in equation simplification. Postulate 8 states that $(A + B)(A + C)$ may be reduced to $A + BC$ without alteration of the existing relationships. The original configuration of $(A + B)(A + C)$ is shown in Fig. 4·9a; it requires two OR gates and one AND gate and utilizes six diodes (two for each gate). The simplified version performs the same function but requires only one AND gate and one OR gate, resulting in a saving of two diodes.

In this case only two diodes were eliminated, but in actual computers,

FIG. 4·9 Equivalent logical diagrams $(A + B)(A + C) = A + BC$. (a) $(A + B)(A + C)$; (b) $BC + A$.

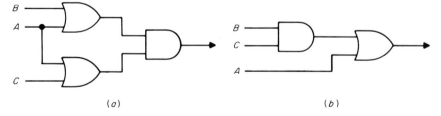

where hundreds of these gates are used, the reduction of components results in a substantial reduction in the cost of the equipment.

The following discussion illustrates a method of developing Boolean equations from logical diagrams. Beginning with first-order logic (single-gate function) and progressing through fourth-order (four-step gating sequence), rules will be evolved for writing the equations.

Equations from Logical Diagrams

In the gating sequences used in digital computers, it will be observed that two important conventions are followed: AND gates are normally connected to OR gates, and OR gates are normally connected to AND gates. Seldom will one AND gate connect to another AND gate; it is equally unusual for an OR gate to provide an input to another OR gate, because the diodes of one gate may simply be connected to the diode load resistor of the gate that it supplies, provided that both gates perform the same function. The limiting factor in this practice is the power requirement of the gate.

First-order logic. Figure 4·10 shows logical diagrams of first-order AND and OR circuits. This, of course, presents nothing new but provides a springboard for accepting new concepts.

The equation for Fig. 4·10a may be written $A \cdot B \cdot C \cdot D = E$. The $\cdot$ between each letter may be eliminated as in regular algebra, allowing the expression to be stated as $ABCD = E$. If this term is translated verbally, it becomes: "If, and only if, inputs A, B, C, and D are true simultaneously, there will be a result E; further, this result will exist only for the duration of the shortest time signal."

For the OR circuit of Fig. 4·10b the equation may be written

$$A + B + C + D = E$$

The sign of addition between each letter may not be omitted to simplify the expression. Again, translated verbally, this becomes: "If any one of the inputs A or B or C or D is true, then there will be a result E; further, this

FIG. 4·10 Logical diagrams for first-order logic AND and OR circuits. (a) $ABCD = E$; (b) $A + B + C + D = E$.

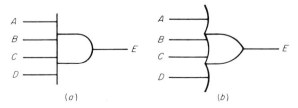

(a) (b)

result will exist for the entire period of time that any one or all of these signals is true."

Second-order logic. Working with logical diagrams, which are compounded by having an AND circuit supply an OR circuit, or vice versa, gives rise to a problem of grouping within the equation. This indicates the requirement for a universal system which will allow the systematic expansion of the functions within an expression. In Fig. 4·11 examples of this type of expression are given.

Figure 4·11a shows an AND circuit supplying an OR circuit. Only four discrete inputs are involved; however, writing the equation for this diagram goes one step further. Designating the output of the AND circuit in Fig. 4·11a as x simplifies the problem. The equation for the OR circuit becomes $x + C + D = E$. However, this does not indicate the structure of x; but x taken by itself may be stated as $AB = x$. Therefore, the complete equation for output E may be described as $AB + C + D = E$. In the OR circuit, three distinct inputs are recognized. One of these inputs is in the form of an AND circuit. Therefore, the final equation should be an expression of three terms which will indicate that the overall diagram consists of an OR circuit being supplied by an AND circuit. This is called an overall OR gate.

Figure 4·11b shows the converse of Fig. 4·11a. It is an OR circuit supplying an AND circuit. Similarly, there are still only four discrete inputs involved. However, the logic arrangement complicates matters somewhat. Again, designating the output of the circuit $(A + B)$ as x simplifies the problem. The equation then will be $xCD = E$, but the contents of x are not apparent. The output x nevertheless describes the OR gate, $A + B = x$. Combining directly the expression $A + B$ with CD would result in $A + BCD$, which would give a false impression of the circuits. Therefore, an additional step must be taken to ensure that circuits of more than first-order logic will not be misconstrued.

The parentheses and other similar marks of grouping used in ordinary algebra form the separation between terms. Thus, the term $A + B$ would be placed in parentheses $(A + B)$ to indicate a complete quantity to be

FIG. 4·11 Logical diagrams for second-order logic AND and OR circuits. (a) $AB + C + D = E$; (b) $(A + B)CD = E$.

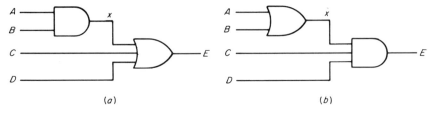

(a)   (b)

combined in an AND circuit with CD to make up the output signal E. The equation is written $(A + B)CD = E$. Use of the other symbols for grouping will be discussed as they are required.

Third-order logic. It is now convenient to analyze more complex forms of the same types of logical diagrams, included in Fig. 4·12. These are treated in the same manner as those of Fig. 4·11.

Figure 4·12a illustrates two AND circuits supplying an OR circuit. While a total of five discrete inputs is involved, the OR circuit receives only three. Therefore, in the same manner as before, the two AND gates may be designated x and y to simplify writing the equations.

The equation for Fig. 4·12a will be $x + C + y = F$. Working with one AND gate at a time gives $AB = x$, $DE = y$; therefore, the entire equation is $AB + C + DE = F$. Again it should be noted that each AND function is treated as a total quantity.

The technique of designating the outputs of a secondary circuit may appear cumbersome at this point; however, this is a useful tool until proficiency is attained. Also, when the equation for a four-level complex logical diagram is written, this "crutch" will eliminate mistakes.

Figure 4·12b illustrates two OR circuits supplying an AND circuit. Again, five discrete inputs are involved, but the AND circuit receives only three. As before, the input OR gates may be designated x and y for simplification.

The equation for Fig. 4·12b will be $xCy = F$. The equation $A + B = x$ is now developed. This case points up the necessity for tools of separation. For example, if $A + B$ were combined with Cy without parentheses, the final equation would be $A + BCy$, which alters the logic. Therefore, the marks of a complete term or expression must be included to form $(A + B)Cy$. The remaining portion y, which equals $D + E$, is now added. This will round out the equation in its correct form:

$$(A + B)C(D + E) = F$$

This is read "quantity A or B, and C, and quantity D or E equals F."

FIG. 4·12 Third-order logical diagrams. (a) $AB + C + DE = F$; (b) $(A + B)C (D + E) = F$.

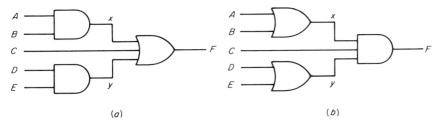

(a)   (b)

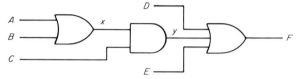

FIG. 4·13 Third-order logical diagram. $(A+B)C+D+E=F$.

Two additional OR circuits will be considered in order to show the treatment of third- and fourth-order logical diagrams.

Figure 4·13 illustrates an overall OR circuit. By using x and y to identify the secondary inputs, the problem of setting up the equation resolves itself to a matter of expanding y and x.

The overall equation could be written $y + D + E = F$. Working backward gives $y = xC$. The next step for writing the equation results in the equation $xC + D + E = F$. Note that xC forms an independent term and may be treated as a single input. However, expanding x requires that $A + B$ be enclosed within parentheses before being combined with C. Now the complete expression is $(A + B)C + D + E = F$. The total number of inputs to the final OR circuit remains at three.

Fourth-order logic. Figure 4·14 represents an overall AND circuit with three inputs. Three letters x, y, and z are employed to indicate the undeveloped secondary inputs. Solving in the same manner as before gives the first equation as $zFG = H$. In a step-by-step process, the stages are completed as follows:

1. $zFG = H$
2. $y + E = z$; therefore, substituting for z,
3. $(y + E)FG = H$
4. $xD = y$; therefore substituting for y,
5. $(xD + E)FG = H$
6. $A + B + C = x$; therefore, substituting for x,
7. $[(A + B + C)D + E]FG = H$

In step 5 an OR circuit was placed in parentheses in order to retain a given quantity, either xD or E. Within this quantity exists another quantity

FIG. 4·14 Fourth-order logical diagram. $[(A+B+C)D+E]FG=H$.

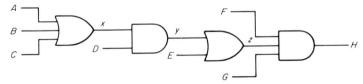

$A + B + C$, which is represented by x. Therefore, to maintain identity and correct separation, the quantity $A + B + C$ must be enclosed in parentheses, and the total expression $(A + B + C)D + E$ must be placed in brackets at step 7.

In addition to the parentheses and brackets, braces, vincula, or other signs of grouping may be employed for these equations. Speed and confidence with the operations required can be gained through practice.

Mechanization of Boolean Equations

Simple equations, such as $ABCD = E$ or $A + B + C + D = E$, pose no particular problem in drawing out the correct logical diagram. The equation $(A + B)(C + D) = E$ will also offer little challenge. This second equation should be recognized as an AND circuit with two inputs, each of which is an OR gate with two inputs. If we follow through in the manner suggested in the previous section, by designating each quantity x and y, respectively, the task evolves to drawing an AND circuit with the inputs x and y. Then both x and y are expanded to show their individual structures.

For the purpose of illustration, one problem will be taken step by step from the equation to the finished logical diagram.

EXAMPLE

The equation: $[(A + B + C)(D + E) + F + G(H + I)]J = K$

Step 1.   Identify the overall circuit type.
   (a)   Two-input AND circuit
   (b) J and quantity within bracket
Step 2.   Perform simplest operations first.
   (a)   Draw logic for AND circuit first
   (b)   Show two inputs J and z (Fig. 4·15)
Step 3.   Write the equations for z.
   (a) $(A + B + C)(D + E) + F + G(H + I) = z$
   (b)   Brackets no longer necessary
   (c)   Identify remaining circuit
       (1)   OR gate with three inputs
       (2) z represents OR output

FIG. 4·15 $Jz = K$.   FIG. 4·16 $(w + x + y)J = K$.

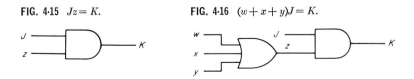

Step 4. Develop inputs to OR output.
 (*a*) Identify the three inputs *w*, *x*, and *y* (Fig. 4·16)
 (*b*) Write the equation for each label
  (1) $(A + B + C)(D + E) = w$
  (2) $F = x$
  (3) $G(H + I) = y$

Step 5. Perform simplest operations.
 (*a*) Substitute *F* for *x*
 (*b*) Show two AND inputs for *w* and *y* (Fig. 4·17)

Step 6. Expand AND gate *y*.
 (*a*) Single input *G*
 (*b*) OR circuit input $H + I$ (Fig. 4·18)

Step 7. Expand AND gate *w*.
 (*a*) Two OR circuit inputs
 (*b*) Identify and expand (Fig. 4·19)
  (1) $A + B + C$
  (2) $D + E$

FIG. 4·17 $(w + y + F)J = K.$

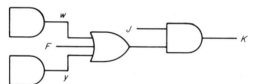

FIG. 4·18 $[w + F + G(H + I)]J = K.$

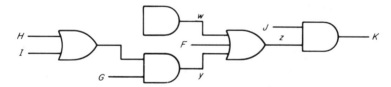

FIG. 4·19 $[(A + B + C)(D + E) + F + G(H + I)]J = K.$

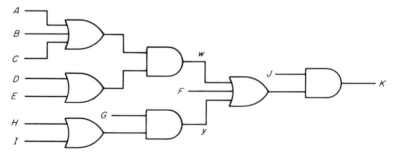

Step 8. Diagram completed.
  (a) Check each portion of equation for agreement
  (b) Write equation from diagram as a check for errors

An example of the use of Boolean equations in defining hardware requirements is presented below. Assume that a device is required to implement the basic rules of addition previously discussed in Chap. 3. Table 4·1 presents a summary of these rules.

An equation must be written to equate four possible combinations of two input variables with four possible combinations of two output variables. The two input variables are the augend bit, which is arbitrarily assigned the symbol A, and the addend, which is assigned the symbol B. The two output variables are the sum bit assigned the symbol S and the carry bit assigned the symbol C. The possible states of the input and output variables are shown in Table 4·2. Note that the outputs of combinations 2 and 3 consist of a sum equal to 1. The first operation is to represent the conditions of combinations 2 and 3 in Table 4·2. The Boolean representation is

$$(15) \quad \bar{A}B + A\bar{B} = S$$

An examination of Example 15 shows that the equation consists of an overall OR gate fed by two AND gates. The inputs to one of the AND gates consist of one of the input variables and the complement of the other input

TABLE 4·1 Summary of Basic Rules of Binary
          Addition

1.	2.	3.	4.
0	0	1	1
0	1	0	1
0	1	1	10

TABLE 4·2 Literal Representation of Rules of
          Binary Addition

1.	2.	3.	4.
$\bar{A}$	$\bar{A}$	A	A
$\bar{B}$	B	$\bar{B}$	B
$\overline{CS}$	$\overline{C}S$	$\overline{C}S$	$C\bar{S}$

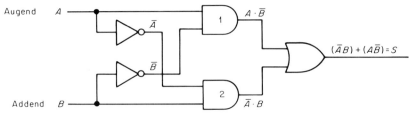

FIG. 4·20 Sum generator.

variable. The second AND gate is identical with the first except the opposite input variable is complemented.

In Fig. 4·20 AND gate 1 generates a 1 output only if the augend A bit is 1 and the addend B bit is a 0. No other combination will produce an output from this gate. A brief reflection on the basic postulates will prove this. If the addend bit B were true, the rules of complementation make $\bar{B}$ false. To have a true output from an AND gate, all inputs must be true; therefore B must be false to get output S from gate 1. The same rules can be applied to gate 2; however, gate 2 generates a 1 output only if the addend B bit is a 1 and the augend A bit is 0. No other combination will produce an output from gate 2. The logic diagram of Fig. 4·20 represents the gating requirements necessary to produce the sum S which could result from the combination of two input variables. Examination of the output variables yields only one combination (4) in which the input variables A and B result in a carry C of 1. The carry function can be implemented by the addition of a two-input AND gate that samples both input variables A and B. Figure 4·21 illustrates the addition of gate 3 to the logic of Fig. 4·20. Figure 4·21 represents the gating requirements to satisfy the conditions for sum-and-carry generation stated in the four basic rules of addition.

The output S will be achieved when one and only one of the inputs is present. If both the inputs are either true (present) or false (absent), the output S will be false. If both inputs are true, the carry-out will be true.

FIG. 4·21 Logic implementation of the laws of binary addition.

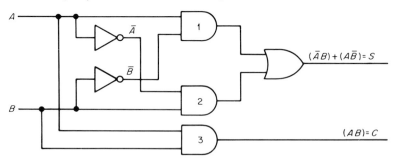

A digital computer contains many complex groupings of the simple logical gates that have been discussed. In the design of the device, every effort is made to minimize the circuitry required to perform a specific function since each additional or extraneous logic gate adds to the cost of fabrication.

An examination will be made of a method of reducing the circuitry necessary to implement the laws of addition. The first step in this reduction is to modify the equation for the summing logic of Fig. 4·21 as follows:

$$S = (\bar{A}B) + (A\bar{B})$$
$$\bar{A}B + A\bar{B} = A\bar{A} + \bar{A}B + A\bar{B} + B\bar{B} \qquad \text{Postulate 10}$$
$$A\bar{A} + \bar{A}B + A\bar{B} + B\bar{B} = (A + B)(\bar{A} + \bar{B}) \qquad \text{Algebraic factoring}$$

Therefore

$$(\bar{A}B) + (A\bar{B}) = S = (A + B)(\bar{A} + \bar{B})$$

Since $C = A \cdot B$, the expression for NOT C can be written as follows:

$$\bar{C} = \overline{A \cdot B}$$

De Morgan's second theorem states:

$$\overline{A \cdot B} = \bar{A} + \bar{B}$$

Therefore

$$S = (A + B) \cdot (\bar{A} + \bar{B})$$
$$= (A + B) \cdot (\overline{A \cdot B}) \qquad \text{Postulate 13}$$
$$= (A + B) \cdot \bar{C}$$

Figure 4·22a illustrates the logic necessary to implement this equation.

FIG. 4·22 Improved half-adder. (a) $(A + B)\bar{C} = S$, $A \cdot B = C$; (b) $(A\bar{B}) + (\bar{A} \cdot B) = S$, $A \cdot B = C$.

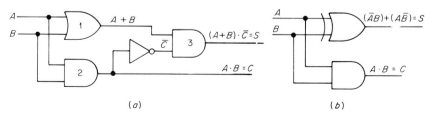

The sum equation consists of an AND gate with inputs from an OR gate and from an inverted AND gate output. Note that the input $\bar{C}$ consists of two different signals ANDed together and then inverted. This practice of signal combination into new signals is common in the complex logic circuitry of digital computers.

It can be proved that the logic of Fig. 4·22a accomplishes the same function as the more involved logic of Fig. 4·21. It should be remembered that the only time a sum output is desired is when only one of the inputs is true. An examination of gate 3 of Fig. 4·22a shows that the $\bar{C}$ input will be true only when there is no true output from gate 2. This will be the case when only one of the inputs is present. To have an output from gate 3, both of the inputs must be true. The sum of 1 and 1 is always 0, and this will be the case because $\bar{C}$ will be false under this condition, yielding a false sum output from gate 3. The carry condition will occur when gate 2 output is true; this should occur because both A and B are true at this time.

The logical exclusive OR gate previously discussed in Chap. 2 could be used in place of the inverters, AND gates, and OR gate of the sum generator in Fig. 4·21 to produce the desired result. Figure 4·22b illustrates the necessary changes in the logic.

The logical circuit that can sum two bits and produce an arithmetic sum with a possible carry is known as a *half-adder*. It is given this name because it does not have the capability of adding a carry-in from a "lower-order" stage in a parallel adder circuit. A circuit called a full-adder will be discussed in a later chapter and will be capable of adding a carry-in, an addend bit, and an augend bit to produce a sum and a possible carry-out.

Review of Basic Principles

Translation of either a Boolean algebra equation into a logical diagram or a logical diagram into a Boolean equation is one of the technician's most useful tools for developing troubleshooting techniques for computers and data processing equipment. The principles applicable to performing a conversion from equation to diagram and vice versa are summarized as follows:

1.   Always perform the simplest operation first.
2.   Recognize the type of overall circuit involved.
3.   Combine like functions of the same logic order.
    (a)   AND circuits should not supply AND circuits.
        (1) $(AB)(CD) = x$
        (2) $ADCB = x$
    (b)   OR circuits should not supply OR circuits.
        (1) $(A + B) + (C + D) = x$
        (2) $A + B + C + D = x$

(c)   Exceptions are sometimes necessitated by driving-power requirements.
4.   Designate secondary inputs where possible to avoid mistakes in expanding.
5.   Use marks of grouping.
   (a)   If an OR function is to be used with one or more signals in an AND function, parentheses, brackets, or vincula must be used for separation.
      (1) $(A + B)(C + D) = x$
      (2) $(A + B + C + D)E = x$
   (b)   If an OR function is to be used with another OR function in an AND function, each term must be enclosed with marks of grouping.
      (1) $(A + C + D)(D + E + F) = x$
      (2) $(A + B + C)(D + E) = x$
   (c)   If an AND function is to be used with another AND function of the same logic level in an AND function, marks of separation are not required.

Signal Designations

Within any large computer or data processor there are hundreds of different signals, each of which has a special importance and some job to perform. Attempting to memorize the origin of all the signals seems impossible. However, the task is not so towering as it may appear. A general organization of signals according to type and function simplifies the problem. While there are exceptions, a key to most of the situations to be encountered is as follows:

1.   To correctly categorize signals, the flip-flop is mentioned again in passing. This is merely a logical element used in computers and processors for storage and counting; it has two outputs, 0 and 1. A capital letter represents a flip-flop output; for example, when a flip-flop is designated A:
   (a)   ONE-side output is written A.
   (b)   ZERO-side output is written as either A' or $\bar{A}$ (A NOT).
2.   A numeral is added to indicate order within a series, as in a serial counter with five flip-flops.
   (a) $A1, A2, A3, A4$, and $A5$ for ONE-side outputs.
   (b) $\overline{A1}, \overline{A2}, \overline{A3}, \overline{A4}$, and $\overline{A5}$ for ZERO-side outputs.
3.   The outputs of inverters are given a letter that is the complement of the input letter.
   (a)   Signal A into an inverter becomes $\bar{A}$ or A' at the output.
   (b)   Input signal $\bar{A}$ becomes $A (\bar{\bar{A}} = A)$.

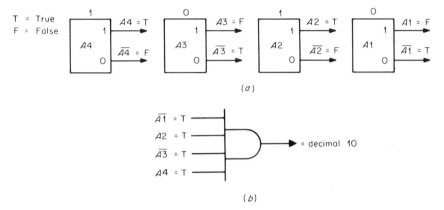

FIG. 4·23   (a) Flip-flops indicating 1010 (decimal 10); (b) detect 1010 (decimal 10) AND circuit.

The NOT function is also used to derive equations to detect specified counts in a register or counter. Consider the problem of detecting the decimal value of 10 in a four-stage serial counter. The binary configuration will be 1010. This means simply that the flip-flops will have the configuration shown in Fig. 4·23a. $A1$, the LSB, will be in the ZERO state, $A2$ in the ONE state, $A3$ in the ZERO state, and, finally, $A4$ in the ONE state. To have an output when this count occurs, an AND circuit could be designed to accept inputs from the flip-flops so that only the combination of 1010 will cause an output. The corresponding AND gate is connected as shown in Fig. 4·23b. This procedure is termed decoding and is covered in Chap. 8.

Essentially the principles of applying the NOT function to an equation have been illustrated in the paragraph above. For clarification, the rule for applying the NOT function to an equation may be stated as follows: When an equation or function is to be given the NOT function, make all terms and signs opposite; that portion of the equation to be given the NOT function will be enclosed with marks of grouping. An example of this is as follows:

$$A + (\overline{BC + DE}) = A + (\bar{B} + \bar{C})(\bar{D} + \bar{E})$$

Inverters. Remember that most computer components utilize two selected voltage levels. Suppose these are +5 volts for the "on," or "true," condition and 0 volt for the "off," or "false," condition. Then terms like the following could be used:

$A = +5$ volts
$B = +5$ volts
$\bar{A} = 0$ volt
$\bar{B} = 0$ volt

Now if an inverter is used, it would change an input of $+5$ volts to an output of 0 volt. Also, if 0 volt is applied to the inverter, the output would be $+5$ volts.

The diagram in Fig. 4·24 indicates that when A is present and B is not present, the gate will be enabled. In this case the circuit must have $+5$ volts applied at its A input and 0 volt at its B input.

Another system involving an inverter is shown in Fig. 4·25. Notice that gate 1 is an AND gate feeding an inverter, so there will be an input to gate 2 if there is no output from gate 1. However, if either A or B is absent, there will be no output from gate 1; so $\overline{AB} = \bar{A} + \bar{B}$. This is an extremely important concept. Then $C + \bar{A} + \bar{B} = L$ could be written for this. Similarly, $\overline{A + B} = \bar{A} \cdot \bar{B}$ is the same as the logical diagram of Fig. 4·26. This is of course an illustration of De Morgan's theorem.

To expand this idea to more complicated equations, the following example is used:

$$\overline{(AB + \bar{C}D)E\bar{F}} = L$$
$$(\bar{A} + \bar{B})(C + \bar{D}) + \bar{E} + F = L$$

The original equation was basically an overall AND circuit of three inputs. This is clearly seen from the diagram in Fig. 4·27 by looking at gate 4. However, the line over the whole function is represented by $I3$; negating, or inverting, the function provides the equivalent circuit shown in Fig. 4·28. Hence, by looking at gate 8 it can be seen that the result is an overall OR circuit with three inputs with $I3$ eliminated.

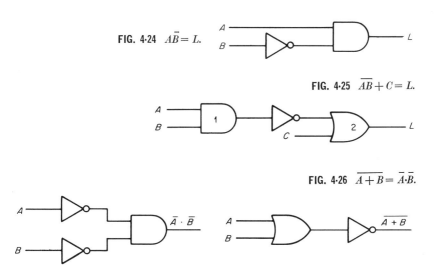

FIG. 4·24 $A\bar{B} = L.$

FIG. 4·25 $\overline{AB} + C = L.$

FIG. 4·26 $\overline{A + B} = \bar{A} \cdot \bar{B}.$

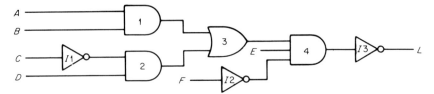

FIG. 4·27 $(AB + \bar{C}D)E\bar{F} = L.$

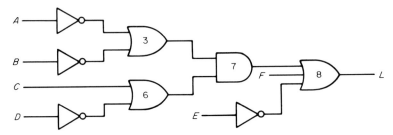

FIG. 4·28 $(\bar{A} + \bar{B})(C + \bar{D}) + \bar{E} + F = L.$

In the first case, three AND gates, an OR gate, and three inverters were needed. In the second case, an equivalent circuit has been constructed out of three OR gates, an AND gate, and four inverters.

SUMMARY OF CONVERSION PRINCIPLES

The following steps summarize the principles of conversion from logic diagrams to Boolean algebra and back again. It will be found later that a complete grasp of this subject matter will be a most useful tool in troubleshooting digital computers.

1. Decide on the type of overall circuit represented by the diagram (last gate) or by the given equation. Is it a three-input AND circuit or a four-input OR circuit, etc.?
2. Perform the simplest operation first, then proceed to the more complicated operations.
3. Combine like functions wherever possible.
4. Use brackets and parentheses as in regular algebra.
5. Use signs of grouping before manipulating NOT functions.
6. The innermost expressions in a complex function are farthest from the output in the diagram.

Considerable proficiency should be developed in manipulation of equations, in changing equations around through the use of Boolean algebra, in drawing equivalent circuits from equations, and in deriving equations from logical circuit diagrams. These equations in actual computers are complex but may be simplified by applying the foregoing principles.

Take the complex equation given below, simplify it, and draw a diagram for the original equation and for its simplified form:

$$\overline{AB + D(C + \bar{A}) + E(F + G)} = L$$

On a sheet of paper, copy this equation. Put down this book and try to simplify the equation and make the two diagrams. After this has been done, check your work against the following solution.

The given equation is a three-part OR circuit assigned the NOT function. So the last gate on the right will be an OR gate and an inverter. The complete diagram is shown in Fig. 4·29.

Another way to express the equation is to carry through the NOT function by applying De Morgan's first theorem:

$$(\overline{A + B}) = (\bar{A} \cdot \bar{B})$$

$$\overline{AB + D(C + \bar{A}) + E(F + G)} = (\overline{AB})[\overline{D(C + \bar{A})}]\,[\overline{E(F + G)}]$$
$$= (\bar{A} + \bar{B})(\bar{D} + \bar{C}A)(\bar{E} + \bar{F}\bar{G})$$

Now the circuit is an overall AND gate with three inputs from three OR gates. The original diagram (Fig. 4·29) is preferred because it used only two inverters, whereas the second drawing (Fig. 4·30) used seven inverters and required the same number of gates.

The reader should work several problems of this type. The practice will promote proficiency and will bring out some point that may not have been fully appreciated.

One final point should be made concerning logical inversion of Boolean equations. Notice that in the examples given up to this point, only one side

FIG. 4·29 $AB + D(C + \bar{A}) + E(F + G) = L.$

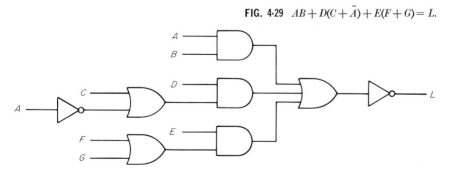

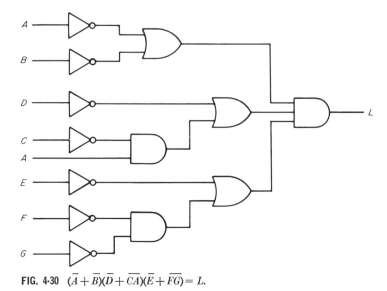

FIG. 4·30 $(\bar{A} + \bar{B})(\bar{D} + \overline{CA})(\bar{E} + \overline{FG}) = L.$

of the equation was logically inverted. The effect was to generate the same end result with complementary gating. If it is desired to produce an *inverted function*, then both sides of the equation must be inverted. For example:

$$L = AB + D(C + \bar{A}) + E(F + G)$$

$$\bar{L} = \overline{AB + D(C + \bar{A}) + E(F + G)} = (\bar{A} + \bar{B})(\bar{D} + \bar{C}A)(\bar{E} + \bar{F}\bar{G})$$

The logical diagram for this equation is the same as Fig. 4·29 with the final inverter eliminated.

Truth Tables

A truth table shows all possibilities of the variables of an equation and their effect on the output or result of the equation. A two-variable table would have four possible states, a three-variable table would have eight, a four-variable table would have sixteen, etc.

Table 4·3 shows an OR truth table. Notice that the output f is true if any one or all the letter variables are true. Table 4·4 shows the AND function. It can be seen that the output is "true" only if all the variables are "true."

TABLE 4·3 OR Truth Table
$A + B + C = f$

A	B	C	f
0	0	0	0
0	0	1	1
0	1	0	1
0	1	1	1
1	0	0	1
1	0	1	1
1	1	0	1
1	1	1	1

TABLE 4·4 AND Truth Table
$A \cdot B \cdot C = f$

A	B	C	f
0	0	0	0
0	0	1	0
0	1	0	0
0	1	1	0
1	0	0	0
1	0	1	0
1	1	0	0
1	1	1	1

TABLE 4·5 Combination AND and OR Truth Table
$A \cdot B + C = f$

A	B	C	f
0	0	0	0
0	0	1	1
0	1	0	0
0	1	1	1
1	0	0	0
1	0	1	1
1	1	0	1
1	1	1	1

TABLE 4·6 Simplification Using Truth Tables
$A \cdot \bar{B} \cdot \bar{C} + A\bar{B}C = f$

A	B	C	f
0	0	0	0
0	0	1	0
0	1	0	0
0	1	1	0
1	0	0	1
1	0	1	1
1	1	0	0
1	1	1	0

Combining AND and OR functions into the second order is shown in Table 4·5. Output f is "true" only when A and B are true, or if C is "true."

An illustration of the use of a truth table in reduction of terms is presented in an examination of equation $A \cdot \bar{B} \cdot \bar{C} + A\bar{B}C = f$. Table 4·6 lists the possible configurations of the input variables and the outputs that result. Note that variable C plays no part in the equation. The output function is "true" whenever $A \cdot \bar{B}$ is "true." It becomes clear through the use of the table that the expression $A\bar{B}\bar{C} + A\bar{B}C$ can be reduced to $A\bar{B}$, and the same overall function is retained. Simplifying Boolean expressions before the hardware implementation phase reduces manufacturing costs.

During the past 20 years, Boolean algebra has become increasingly important to complex telephone dialing systems and computers. It is an extremely simple form of algebra that describes logical switching functions.

Because of its ability to express complicated switching functions in terms of "true" or "false," Boolean algebra is well suited for analysis, trouble-shooting, and design of computer circuitry.

The basic rules of Boolean algebra reduce all functions to either AND or OR. The AND function requires that all factors contributing to this function be "true" before a "true" output may be obtained. In the OR function, any contributing factor that is "true" produces a "true" output.

Application of Boolean algebra to logical switching circuits will help evolve numerous approaches to the solution of problems of logic encountered in computers and data processors; it is directly applicable to the design of diode matrices, adders, subtracters, and other logical functions. Practice and facility in the use of Boolean algebra are necessary for the computer technician and specialist. Table 4-7 presents a summary of identities of Boolean algebra.

TABLE 4-7 Summary of the Basic Boolean Algebra Identities

Fundamental operations

OR	AND	NOT
$0 + 0 = 0$	$0 \cdot 0 = 0$	$\overline{0} = 1$
$0 + 1 = 1$	$0 \cdot 1 = 0$	$\overline{1} = 0$
$1 + 1 = 1$	$1 \cdot 1 = 1$	
$A + 0 = A$	$A \cdot 0 = 0$	$A + \overline{A} = 1$
$A + 1 = 1$	$A \cdot 1 = A$	$A\overline{A} = 0$
$A + A = A$	$A \cdot A = A$	$A = A$
$A + \overline{A} = 1$	$A \cdot \overline{A} = 0$	

Associative laws

$$(A + B) + C = A + (B + C)$$
$$(AB)C = A(BC)$$

Commutative laws

$$A + B = B + A$$
$$AB = BA$$

Distributive laws

$$A(B + C) = AB + AC$$
$$A + BC = (A + B)(A + C)$$

De Morgan's laws

$$\overline{AB} = \overline{A} + \overline{B}$$
$$\overline{A + B} = \overline{A} \cdot \overline{B}$$

QUESTIONS

4-1   Why is Boolean algebra considered such a useful tool for computer design and troubleshooting?

4-2   What types of devices are ideally portrayed by Boolean algebra?

4·3   On what basic premise is Boolean algebra based?

4·4   What is the function of a dot ($\cdot$) connective between two terms of a Boolean equation?

4·5   The following equation is an illustration of what basic law?
$AB(C\bar{D} + E) = (ABC\bar{D}) + (ABE)$

4·6   The logical complementation of the OR connective will generate the AND connective: true or false?

4·7   Using a method similar to the proof of De Morgan's first theorem, prove the second theorem.

4·8   Express the following Boolean equation as a logical diagram:
$[(\bar{A} + B)C + D]E + F = G$

4·9   Draw a logical diagram of the NOT function of G in Question 4·8.

4·10 What are the five general steps to be followed in converting between Boolean equations and logical diagrams?

4·11 If the NOT side output of a flip-flop is "true," what state is it in?

4·12 Rewrite the following equations in the inverted form:
(a) $A(B + C) = Y$
(b) $A + BC = Y$
(c) $ABC + AD = \bar{Y}$
(d) $(\overline{AC})(AB + CD) = Y$

4·13 Draw a logical diagram for the following Boolean equation:
$(A + \bar{B}C)(\bar{A} + B + C) = F$

4·14 Draw a logical diagram for the following Boolean equation:
$A(B + CDE) + F(G + H) = I$

4·15 Why is a truth table so useful for logic analysis?

4·16 How many combinations of variables are possible in an AND truth table describing a Boolean equation with four variables?

4·17 Draw a truth table for the following equation:
$(\bar{A}\bar{C} + B)(A + \bar{B}C) = F$

4·18 Using the truth table from Question 4·17, simplify this equation:
$(\bar{A}\bar{C} + B)(A + \bar{B}C) = G$.

4·19 Write the Boolean equation for the following logical diagram:

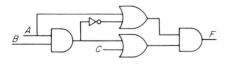

4·20 How many gates and inverters are required to implement the following equation:
$(\bar{A}\bar{C} + B)(A + \bar{B}C) = F$

chapter five

Fundamentals of Magnetic Devices

When a mathematician solves a problem, he may write his computations on paper. He does this to have a step-by-step record of the process used in arriving at the final solution. In like manner, a computer requires a memory or storage device to record its arithmetical operations, both intermediate and final. In some computers the memory system is also used to store the program, which lists the type and sequence of operations to be performed.

Magnetic drums, magnetic coincident-current cores, and thin-film devices are used as memory elements in computers.

An understanding of the fundamentals of magnetism and the properties of magnetic materials is useful in discussing these storage devices.

This chapter is divided into four sections:

1. Basic electromagnetism
2. Magnetization and hysteresis curves
3. Ferromagnetism and information storage
4. Methods of recording on magnetic surfaces

SECTION 1   BASIC ELECTROMAGNETISM

This section covers the artificial creation of magnetic behavior by electric currents. A magnetic field exists concentrically about any current-carrying conductor as shown in Fig. 5·1. This magnetic field is commonly known as *magnetic flux*. The unit is the *maxwell*, and the symbol is the Greek letter phi (ϕ). One flux line corresponds to 1 maxwell. If a paper is placed so that a current-carrying wire runs directly through it, iron filings scattered on the paper align in a manner to describe the magnetic field (flux lines).

The right-hand rule is used to determine the direction of the lines of magnetic flux about the wire. This rule states that if the thumb of the right hand points along the wire in the direction of conventional current flow (opposite to the direction of electron flow), the direction of flux or magnetic force about the conductor is indicated by the direction of the fingers of the closed hand (see Fig. 5·2).

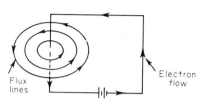

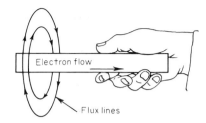

FIG. 5·1 Flux pattern about current-carrying conductor.

FIG. 5·2 Right-hand rule.

In the circuit shown in Fig. 5·1, current flow in the conductor produced three flux lines about the current-carrying conductor. The field strength in this example is 3 maxwells. The total flux in a magnetic field is not as important as the flux concentration in a given area. This flux concentration is termed *flux density* and is measured in maxwells per square centimeter. The unit of measure is the gauss, which is equal to 1 maxwell per square centimeter.

The size and strength of a magnetic field may be increased if the current-carrying conductor is wound into a spiral or helical form. The cross section of such a magnetic field is shown in Fig. 5·3. A dot (·) in the center of the wire designates electrons coming out of the paper, and a plus (+) designates electrons going into the paper. Figure 5·3 shows that, according to the right-hand rule, the magnetic fields of the individual wires combine with the fields of neighboring turns of wire to form a large magnetic field.

As either the number of turns of wire or the amount of current passing through the wire is increased, the magnetic field will become proportionately stronger. The magnetizing force, termed *magnetomotive force* (mmf), is directly proportional to the number of turns of wire and to the amount of current flowing through the wire. The unit of magnetizing force is the ampere-turn, represented by NI, where N is the number of turns and I is the current in amperes. However, in order to keep the units used with magnetic quantities in the same class or system, the term gilbert will be used as the unit of magnetomotive force (mmf). This unit is directly related

FIG. 5·3 Combination effect of single conductor fields (cross section of coil).

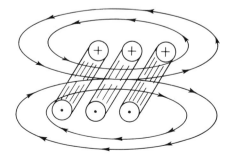

to ampere-turns as shown by the formula F (or mmf) $= 0.4\pi NI$; that is, 1 amp-turn corresponds to 1.26 gilberts (0.4π). When F is used, it is intended to indicate the total mmf of a circuit. The mmf generated in a magnetic circuit is consumed in various parts of the circuit as mmf drops, similar to voltage drops in an electric circuit. These drops can be measured as so many gilberts per centimeter. When stated in this manner, the unit of magnetic intensity is the oersted and the symbol is H. One gilbert/cm corresponds to 1 oersted. In diagrams, graphs, and discussions, the letter H is frequently used to represent the mmf per unit length.

Basic units of measurement.   There are many magnetic measurements that can be made, starting with the definition of a unit magnetic pole. Each magnet has two poles, north and south. One of the fundamental laws of magnetism is that like poles repel one another and unlike poles attract one another. A simple compass needle has a north-seeking pole and a south-seeking pole. One pole never exists without the other; but for the sake of fundamental definition, imagine two identical poles, 1 cm apart, repelling each other with a force of 1 dyne (Fig. 5·4). A dyne is $\frac{1}{980}$ g and represents the force which will accelerate a 1-g mass at the rate of 1 cm/sec each second.

These poles are, by definition, unit poles and have one line of force acting between them. If stronger poles of five units each were used, there would be 25 lines between them since the force between two poles varies directly as the product of the strength of the poles and inversely as the square of the distance between them. If these two 5-unit poles were moved twice as far apart (2 cm), the field would be only $\frac{25}{4}$ lines. Since these lines of force are known as maxwells, the field (flux) between the two poles in the latter case is 6.25 maxwells. This relationship can be written in a general formula, as follows:

$$\phi = \frac{P \times P'}{d^2}$$

where ϕ = flux, maxwells
d = distance between poles
P and P' = strength of magnetic poles in terms of a unit pole

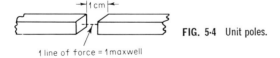

FIG. 5·4   Unit poles.

EXAMPLE

$$\phi = \frac{5 \times 5}{2^2}$$

$$= \frac{25}{4}$$

$$= 6.25 \text{ maxwells}$$

If a piece of glass is inserted between the poles, the strength of the magnetic field might be expected to be reduced; but glass, paper, and many other materials have no effect on the lines of force. A piece of iron or steel, however, does have considerable effect; the lines of force will converge in their attempt to pass through the metal, which offers less resistance than the surrounding air. Brass will have an effect opposite to that of iron, causing the lines of force to diverge around it. Other metals affect the magnetic field to a lesser degree. The ease with which magnetic flux is transmitted by a substance is measured by its reluctance. The unit of reluctance most frequently used is the rel. Reluctance in a magnetic circuit is the equivalent of resistance in an electric circuit. Just as resistance is equal to the electromotive force (voltage) divided by the current, so reluctance is equal to the mmf divided by the magnetic flux (ϕ).

It can be seen that there is, in magnetism, a relationship very similar to Ohm's law in electricity. This is shown in Table 5·1.

It is frequently more useful to use the reciprocal of reluctance. This is termed *permeability*, represented by the Greek letter mu (μ). The permeability of a material is the ratio of the flux in the material to the flux that would exist in the same area if the material were replaced by a vacuum. For all practical purposes, most materials have a permeability value of $\mu = 1$, but there are some exceptions: for iron or steel μ varies from 50 to 2000; for Permalloy (nickel-iron), $\mu = 87,000$. This can be stated as $\mu = B/H$ where

TABLE 5·1 Magnetic-unit Relationship

Magnetic unit	*Formula*	*Electrical equivalent*
F (mmf)	$= \phi \times$ reluctance	$E = IR$
ϕ (flux)	$= F/$reluctance	$I = E/R$
Reluctance	$= F/\phi$	$R = E/I$

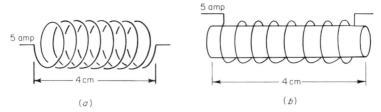

FIG. 5·5 Simple electromagnet. (a) Air core; (b) iron core.

B is the flux density and H is the mmf per unit length. These relationships may also be expressed as $H = B/\mu$ and $B = H\mu$.

Accurate magnetic measurements are much more difficult to make than electrical measurements; these figures will therefore vary widely depending upon the actual composition of the material and conditions under which the test for permeability is performed.

Referring to Fig. 5·5a, assume 5 amp of current are passed through eight turns of wire. This arrangement is a basic electromagnet and will produce an mmf of 50.4 gilberts (40 amp-turns). If the coil is assumed to be 4 cm long, there will be 12.6 gilberts/cm. Since an oersted is the number of gilberts per centimeter of length, this condition is equivalent to 12.6 oersteds. Assuming the coil to be 2 cm² in cross-sectional area, we find that there would then be a flux density B of 6.3 oersteds for each square centimeter. As stated previously, the unit of flux density is the gauss, so the measure of gauss in this circuit is 6.3. The flux density could be increased considerably by inserting a bar made of metal, such as iron, into the coil to replace the air gap. Since iron has a permeability of from 50 to 2000 times that of air, the flux density would be increased by that ratio. This is not intended to indicate that B can be increased to any extreme by using a metal with a very high μ, such as Permalloy ($\mu = 87,000$), because at a certain level, B will reach saturation. Permeability and its relationship to B will be discussed later.

Electromagnets normally have their coils wound on iron or some other material. Figure 5·5b is included to provide some basis for comparison of the field strength which can be achieved by the use of a core of other than air in an electromagnetic device.

SECTION 2   MAGNETIZATION AND HYSTERESIS CURVES

In terms of permeability, there are generally three types of magnetic materials: diamagnetic, paramagnetic, and ferromagnetic. Diamagnetic materials have a permeability of less than 1, paramagnetic substances have a permeability slightly greater than 1, and ferromagnetic materials, much

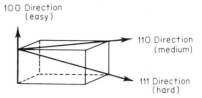

FIG. 5·6 Domain alignment directions in a crystal of iron.

greater than 1. Examples of diamagnetic substances are gold, silver, copper, and hydrogen. Examples of paramagnetic substances are platinum, aluminum, and oxygen. Examples of ferromagnetic substances are iron, nickel, cobalt, and various steels used in electrical materials. The economics of the situation dictate the choice of ferromagnetic materials for use in magnetic applications. Most ferromagnetic substances consist of *domains*, which are small subelements which exhibit individual states of magnetic behavior. When most of these domains are aligned in the same direction, the ferromagnetic substance is said to be magnetized. Domains are filamentlike in form, with volumes of approximately 10^{-9} cm³, and are of lengths varying from less than one up to several centimeters. In the crystal of a substance such as iron, there are many magnetic domains which can be arranged along directions of easy magnetization as shown in Fig. 5·6.

Direction of easy magnetization means that a given field applied along a certain axis provides optimum rearrangement of domains within a crystal. In the case of iron, a smaller field force is required along the 100 direction than along either the 110 or 111 direction. The characteristics of nickel are quite different, with the direction of easy magnetization being along the 110 axis.

Despite the fact that the domain is a small body, its change of state causes significant results. The alignment and reorientation of domains bring about physical stress to the point that the physical dimensions of the material actually change. This change is called *magnetostriction*.

If the magnetization curve (Fig. 5·7) is greatly enlarged, the change in flux density B caused by a change in field intensity H does not follow a smooth curve. Rather, the overall curve is a series of small steps, which are caused by the sudden switching of domains within the crystal. This is

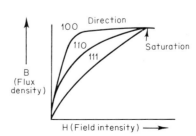

FIG. 5·7 Magnetization curves of an iron crystal.

known as the *Barkhausen effect* and may be detected as audible clicks when a secondary loop is wound on a specimen and its output is amplified and applied to earphones or a loudspeaker.

Upon application of increasingly greater magnetic forces, the domains align in the direction of the applied force more swiftly and in greater numbers. When all domains are aligned in the easy direction of magnetization and this axis coincides with the applied magnetic field, then magnetic saturation has been reached (Fig. 5·7).

Although the equation for permeability is $\mu = B/H$, it can be seen on the magnetization curve that B does not usually follow in direct proportion as field intensity H is increased. Thus, it becomes clear that μ is not a fixed value but depends chiefly on the type of material and the magnitude of the magnetizing force.

The change from the demagnetized state to one of magnetic saturation is shown in Fig. 5·7. If the applied field is removed, magnetization falls to a point below saturation (Fig. 5·8).

Hysteresis loops. When a piece of iron is magnetized, considerable energy is expended in lining up the magnetic domains in a definite direction. When these domains are aligned first in one direction and then in the other many times each second, such as, for example, in an ac circuit, considerable energy is lost in the form of heat. This dissipation of energy is a hysteresis loss and is evidenced by heat given off by the metallic core or laminations in ac motors and transformers. Hysteresis loss occurs because the magnetization of the core does not reverse in polarity at the same time that the magnetizing force does.

In order to plot a hysteresis loop, a magnetizing field is applied to a demagnetized piece of iron residing at point O (Fig. 5·8).

FIG. 5·8 Hysteresis loop for iron.

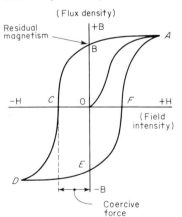

FIG. 5·9 Major and minor hysteresis loops.

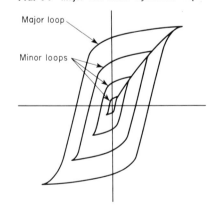

The applied field can be increased in intensity by increasing the current in the conductor surrounding the iron. After a considerable increase in the intensity, all the domains are aligned, the easy axis of magnetization coincides with the applied field, and magnetic saturation (point A) is reached. If the field intensity is returned to zero, the field density or magnetic flux state of the iron does not follow but decreases to point B. OB is the amount of residual magnetism in the substance. Residual magnetism is the magnetic flux exhibited by the specimen after an induction field is removed.

If the current in the conductor surrounding the magnetic material is reversed and the field intensity is increased to OC, the residual magnetism is reduced to zero by the coercive force. If the reverse current is increased still further to take the field intensity beyond OC, the direction of magnetic flux through the ferromagnetic material also reverses until the material reaches a state of saturation D, the opposite of point A. If the magnetizing force is once again removed, there is a return from saturation, point D, to the Y axis at point E. Again the curve does not return to zero flux density. OE indicates the reverse residual flux remaining after a $-H$ magnetizing force is removed. If a substantial $+H$ is once again applied, the residual flux is removed and the $+B$ flux is reinstated with a return to point A.

The cycle of forward and reverse magnetization produces a hysteresis loop. The area within the loop is a measure of power dissipated during the cycle. Reiterating, hysteresis is defined as the lag in changes of magnetization behind the variations in magnetizing force. The greater the lag, the more power is consumed in reducing or reversing the state of magnetization.

Actually, there are several related hysteresis loops upon which a given piece of ferromagnetic material may operate (Fig. 5·9). The outermost loop is known as the *major* loop. The magnetization forces needed to establish it are greater than those used in forming the minor loops contained within it. The ferrite cores used in the main memory of many computers operate on a minor loop.

SECTION 3 FERROMAGNETISM AND INFORMATION STORAGE

The choice of two states of residual flux in a ferromagnetic material readily affords application as a storage medium for intelligence. The binary system, widely used in computers, uses a combination of only 0's and 1's to represent any information, whether numerical or alphabetical. Consequently, for the binary system only a simple bistable device is needed. In Fig. 5·10 point B on the hysteresis loop could represent ONE, and point E could represent ZERO, or vice versa. Thus it is convenient, size and economy permitting, to use a ferromagnetic substance as a computer storage device.

However, the residual flux in either state is relatively small in comparison with the maximum flux experienced when the core is switched by a

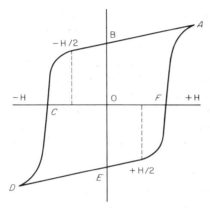

FIG. 5·10 Rectangular hysteresis loop.

full-select pulse. Some material with the property of a much larger residual flux, almost as large as the flux present while a magnetizing force is being applied, is thus required for core storage. The ideal core would literally have a rectangular hysteresis loop. Since this ideal material is not practicable, a satisfactory substitute with a hysteresis loop approaching the qualities of a rectangular loop is used, as shown in Fig. 5·10.

In the hysteresis loop in Fig. 5·10, point B represents the residual flux in a typical ferrite core after the magnetizing force which caused saturation (point A) is removed. This is the ONE state of the core. Point E represents residual flux in the opposite direction when a reverse magnetizing force is applied, causing saturation (point D), and then removed. This is the ZERO state. The ferrite loop has a characteristic much more nearly square than that of the iron hysteresis loop, and it is considered a rectangular hysteresis loop.

Bistable magnetic storage elements. The prime memory systems of the processors in use range in capacity from a few thousand words to tens of thousands of words. The memory systems use as their basic storage device ferrite cores, thin-film spots, and superconductive elements. Each of these elements will be discussed in its basic form as a bit-storing device.

Ferromagnetic cores. The square-hysteresis-loop characteristic and the readily discernible bistable nature of the ferromagnetic core have led to its selection for use in computer devices. Two types of ferromagnetic cores are the *bimag core* and the *ferrite core*. These cores are easily magnetized and can store binary information for long time periods even after the external power source is removed. They are small and extremely reliable.

The bimag core is frequently used in temporary storage and shifting applications. The metallic tape or bimag core is so termed because of its bimagnetic properties. The bimag cores are physically larger than the ferrite cores. To construct the bimag cores, various types of metallic substances are mixed chemically to form an alloy that is usually cast in thin sheets. These sheets are then cut into small strips and wound on a toroidal ceramic bobbin to become the well-known tape-wound core. Typical dimensions of the bimag core vary from $\frac{1}{4}$ to 1 in., depending on the application. Windings that insert and remove binary information are wrapped around the core as shown in Fig. 5-11.

The ferrite core is most commonly used as a storage element in coincident-current memory systems. The ferrite core is a small toroid composed of brittle ceramic-type material. As the name implies, the ferrite core is composed of various iron compounds. The basic ingredient used is the iron ore hematite (Fe_2O_3), which may be blended with (1) FeO to form iron ferrite (Fe_3O_4), (2) NiO to form nickel ferrite ($NiFe_2O_4$), or (3) MnO to form manganese ferrite ($MnFe_2O_4$). Some of the materials used do not exhibit any magnetic properties by themselves; but when they are mixed, bound, heated in a kiln and cooled, the resulting compounds display strong ferromagnetic characteristics. The percentage of mixture and chemical blending is a carefully controlled process, and firing of the oxides at a predetermined temperature produces a material possessing the desired switching characteristics. In production, ferrite cores for computers are tested to meet certain specifications. A typical core may be fabricated to switch states on as little as 330 ma(H) and not switch on 200 ma($H/2$). Switching time is roughly inversely proportional to driving current. For example, at a minimum of 330 ma, switching time is 6.5 μsec. At the nominal drive of 370 ma switching time is reduced to 4 μsec. The switching time of some cores is well under 1 μsec. As stated previously, the ferrite core is extremely small (Fig. 5-12). The outside diameter of a typical core is 0.020 in., while its inside diameter is 0.012 in. Because of the small physical sizes attainable, it is possible to store thousands, or even millions, of words in a few cubic feet of space.

FIG. 5-11 Bimag core and windings.

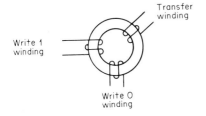

Transfer winding

Write 1 winding

Write 0 winding

FIG. 5-12 Ferrite memory core.

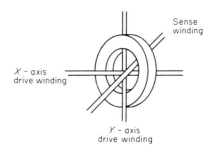

Sense winding

X - axis drive winding

Y - axis drive winding

There are two reasons for the selection of the ferrite core with its rectangular hysteresis loop for use in a memory system. The two residual states of the cores contain much more flux than does iron under equal conditions. When information is stored in the cores and readout, a larger-amplitude output signal and, consequently, a higher signal-to-noise ratio result. In addition, a rectangular-type hysteresis loop is preferred in that it can, by amplitude selection, discriminate against small switching currents through the conductors threading the core. A small current in a conductor through a ferrite core might generate a magnetizing force $-H/2$, which is called a half-select current (Fig. 5·10). If the core is in the ONE state (point B), this half current is not a large enough current to switch the core to the ZERO state. Only the full field force $-H$, caused by the combined time-coincident effects of two such currents in the conductors through the core, could switch the core to the ZERO state. It can be seen from Fig. 5·10 that at a point between $-H/2$ and $-H$, a small additional magnetizing force suddenly switches the core from the ONE state to the ZERO state (B-E). In order to switch the core back into the ONE state, a full select current is applied in the opposite direction ($+H$), and at point F the core suddenly changes state. It should be noted that the change from E to B or from B to E is a 180° flux reversal.

In the ferrite-core memories, there are several methods employed for threading the ferrite cores for reading and writing purposes. A typical example is shown in Fig. 5·12.

In this arrangement, three wires (conductors) are threaded through the core: an x drive line, a y drive line, and a read/sense line. This type memory is referred to as the *coincident-current* type because it requires aiding currents in the x and y lines in time-coincidence in order to obtain the necessary magnetizing force to switch the core. That is, if just one of the lines has current, the resulting H will be a half current and of insufficient magnitude to switch the state of the core. However, if current occurs in x and y simultaneously, full select force H results and the core switches. The x-y aiding currents are in one direction to place the core in the ONE state and in the opposite direction to place the core in its ZERO state. The purpose of the sense winding is to detect the large flux change that occurs when the core is switched from the ONE to the ZERO state. This is known as *reading* the core. When the core is read it is placed in the ZERO state (destructive readout). If an attempt is made to switch a core into a state that it is already in, the resulting flux change (either B to A or E to D of Fig. 5·10) will be so small as to be undetectable. It should be noted that a large flux change is also produced when a core is switched from the ZERO state to the ONE state (writing). This change is likewise sensed by the sense winding, but unlike the READ flux change, is usually ignored by the output circuit connected to the sense line. A description of the organization of cores into a memory system with selection, drive, and sense networks is presented in Chap. 11.

The cores are sensitive to temperature changes, operating normally at room temperature (70 to 80°F). The hysteresis loop changes shape as a function of temperature (Fig. 5·13). The B dimension of the loop decreases as temperature decreases. Because of the curtailed dimension of the loop along the B axis, the voltage generated on the output winding is not sufficiently large in amplitude and tends to approach a 1:1 signal-to-noise ratio. Decreased temperature also widens the dimension of the loop along the H or horizontal axis. This increased loop dimension reduces the possibility of core switching by the full-select current H, since a larger magnetizing force is required. Eventually, the width of the H dimension may be large enough to make it impossible to drive the core to a new state. Temperature increase causes the H dimension at the loop to become narrow, and flux density along axis B increases. As the H dimension becomes shorter, the core may be switched by smaller currents. The core no longer discriminates, and it switches at signals below the value of H. In short, at low temperatures the core switches less readily, and at high temperatures it is inclined to switch on any pulse. The temperature problem can be solved by the use of air conditioning or by a more elaborate system of temperature sensing or full current variations or both.

Thin-film element. Another bistable element used in mass memory systems is the thin-film spot. The thin-film element is a thin-film concentration of a nickel-iron alloy known as Permalloy. This material exhibits the bistable storage characteristics previously discussed for the ferrite core. If the thickness of the Permalloy film is made comparable to the wavelength of ultraviolet light, less than 3000 angstroms (Å; 1 Å = about 1×10^{-8} cm), gross movement of magnetic domains will not occur in the presence of an external magnetic field. Switching will be achieved by the rotation of magnetization, which is inherently a much faster process than the movement of domain walls. The time necessary to accomplish the switch is reduced considerably because the hysteresis loss is no longer a factor. Another contributing factor is a reduction in the amount of switching that will have to be achieved. A

FIG. 5·13 Effects of temperature variation on hysteresis loops. (a) Temperature decrease; (b) normal; (c) temperature increase.

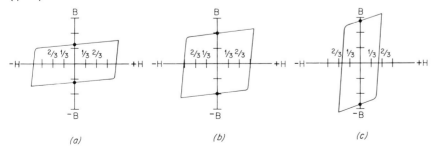

ferrite core must be switched a total of 180° in order to accomplish its basic function of information storage; a thin-film spot performs the same storage function with a switch of only 90°.

Ferrite cores are extremely fragile. The manufacturing techniques required in the manufacture of ferrite-core memories are almost totally manual operations. The operations are delicate and expensive, and mechanization of the process is limited to larger core sizes. Core sizes which lend themselves to the manual operations necessary in memory fabrication are a factor in the space required by a memory with a certain word capacity. Thin-film arrays are manufactured by techniques similar to those used in integrated-circuit manufacture and a thin-film array of a given size is capable of a larger storage capacity than a ferrite core memory of equal physical size.

Manufacturing techniques. Two techniques in use in the manufacture of thin-film storage devices involve either the evaporation of Permalloy in a vacuum through a mask onto a glass or metal substrate, or the chemical electroplating of the substrate. In the first method, the Permalloy is evaporated through a mask to produce small rectangular spots with a thickness of from 1000 to 2000 Å. A strong magnetic field applied parallel to the long dimension of the rectangle causes the magnetic domains to align themselves permanently with the field during the process.

The mask is produced by photographic reduction techniques on a photosensitized copper sheet that is then etched to form the mask holes. There is practically no limitation to the amount of size reduction obtainable from a photographic standpoint, but there is a limitation to the minimum size of a thin-film spot with respect to detectable changes in magnetism. It is possible to produce a spot so small that a change in its magnetic state will be lost because of the magnetic "noise" found in any memory array.

The wires required to switch the thin-film spots and detect data outputs are fabricated by means similar to those used to manufacture the masks. A film of Mylar with etched copper wires is superimposed over the glass substrate to form a sandwich of thin-film spots and control wires.

Magnetic characteristics of thin film. At the completion of the manufacturing process, the magnetic domains are aligned along the long dimension of the rectangular spot. If an external magnetic field is applied perpendicular to this long dimension, the internal field of the spot rotates, aligning itself with the external field. It is interesting to note that the domains themselves do not move to any great extent, indicating that there will be negligible hysteresis losses. A square hysteresis loop cannot be used to represent the effects of an external magnetic field perpendicular to the long dimension of the spot.

Since the domains were not rotated, if the external field is removed, the internal field rotates back to a position parallel to the long dimension. An important point to remember is that the field can switch to either direction from the perpendicular state.

The direction of magnetization perpendicular to the long dimension is termed the "hard" state because it does not have square hysteresis-curve characteristics and therefore cannot remain magnetized in this direction. Since the thin-film spot is easily magnetized in the direction parallel to the long dimension, this direction is called the "easy" state. The "easy" state exhibits a square hysteresis loop because no external field is required to maintain it. Figure 5·14 illustrates the "easy" and "hard" states of the thin-film spots and the hysteresis characteristics of each state.

Figure 5·14a shows that there can be two directions of magnetization associated with the "easy" state and two directions of magnetization associated with the "hard" state. The arrows represent the direction of internal magnetic flux.

An analogy may be applied to illustrate the significance of the "easy" and "hard" states. If a pencil is balanced on its point, it will remain in that position as long as it is held there. When the pencil is released, it will fall in some random direction. In a like manner when the external field is removed from a thin-film spot, the flux field will revert at random to some "easy"-state condition.

Storage on thin-film spot. An examination will be made of how the properties of thin-film spots are utilized for the storage of binary numbers. As in the ferrite core, one state of magnetization is designated to represent the

FIG. 5·14 Thin-film spot. (a) Composite "easy/hard" states; (b) "hard"-state loop; (c) "easy"-state loop.

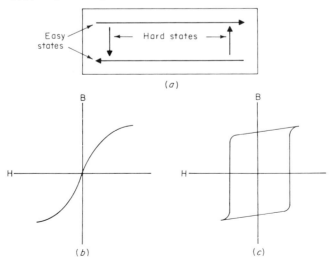

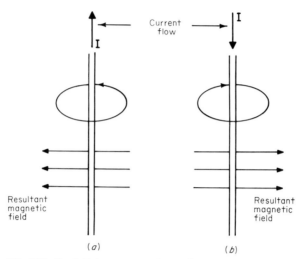

FIG. 5·15 Flux fields in current-carrying conductor. (a) Current flow up;
(b) current flow down.

binary 1 and the opposite state to represent the binary 0. In the thin-film
spot, these points are the opposites of the "easy" magnetization states. In
the thin film, however, a flux rotation of only 90° is required to read out a 1
or a 0 instead of the 180° flux reversal of the ferrite core.

Figure 5·15 illustrates the application of the right-hand rule in establishing the direction of the magnetic fields resulting from opposite
currents in a conductor. The arrows at the top indicate the direction of
conventional current flow. Arrows are also used to indicate the direction of
the resultant magnetic field exerted on the surface beneath the wire.

Figure 5·16 represents a single thin-film spot and the necessary wires
required to read out the binary 1 or 0 that may have been stored previously.

FIG. 5·16 Thin-film memory spot.

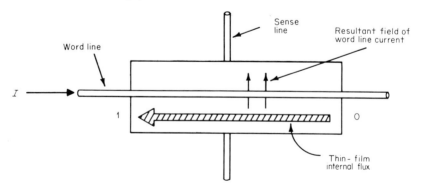

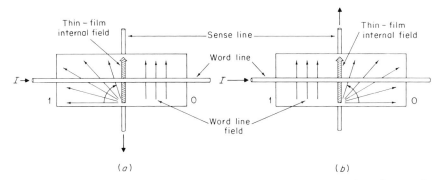

FIG. 5·17 Sensing data stored in thin-film spot. (a) Reading out a 1; (b) reading out a 0.

For purposes of the discussion, when the thin-film spot is in the "easy" state with the internal magnetic field pointing left, a 1 is stored; when the internal magnetic field is pointing right, a 0 is stored.

To determine the contents of the spot, it must be switched to the "hard" state. The process of switching will destroy the contents of the spot, just as the information was destroyed in the switching of a ferrite core.

The word line illustrated in Fig. 5·16 accomplished the switch by generating a strong magnetic field perpendicular to the "easy" direction of the thin-film spot. Figure 5·16 shows the internal field representing a stored binary 1.

Figure 5·17a illustrates how the internal field rotates clockwise from the 1 "easy" state to the "hard" state. The movement of the magnetic field induces a current in the sense line as shown by the direction of the arrow. If a 0 had been previously stored, the internal field would have rotated counterclockwise to align with the word-line field as shown in Fig. 5·17b. For a 0 sensing, the current induced into the sense line would flow in the opposite direction because of the difference in rotation of the internal field. A circuit known as a *differential amplifier* discriminates between the positive and negative currents induced in the sense line and indicates to the external logic whether a 1 or 0 had been read out. With the removal of the word-line switching current, the flux field reverts randomly to some "easy"-state direction and the original stored data is lost.

Return to the analogy of the pencil for a moment. The direction of fall of the pencil can be ensured if instead of releasing it from a vertical position, it is tipped in the desired direction prior to release.

If it were possible to tip the internal field of the thin-film spot prior to the removal of the word-line current, the "easy" state direction to which the internal field would return could be controlled. This controlling action would allow the restoring of old data or the storing of the desired new data to take place.

This tipping action in a thin-film storage device is achieved by adding to or subtracting from the word-line field by the addition of a small field at right angles to the word-line field. It should be remembered that the word-line field is only intense enough to allow alignment of the internal field with it. A small "outside" field acting on this field is controlled by an information line which is positioned perpendicular to the word line. It should be noted that the information line is not the sense line of the earlier discussion. Figure 5·18 illustrates the positioning of the word and information lines in relation to each other and the interaction of the respective fields. Since the wires are perpendicular to each other, an algebraic addition or subtraction of the interacting fields occurs so that the resultant force exerted on the internal field is a trigonometric function of the "summing" of the interacting fields. The wide arrow represents the internal field under the combined influence of both external fields. The amount of tipping is exaggerated in these examples.

In the example of Fig. 5·18a, current flows downward in the information line which results in an external field (dotted arrow) in the "easy" direction of the 0-store direction. The vector representation illustrates the direction of forces, with the shaded arrow indicating the direction of tip. Figure 5·18b illustrates the opposite condition with the information-line field exerting the tip in the 1-store direction. Termination of the word-line current results in the internal field moving in the direction of the information-line tip to store the desired bit (0 or 1).

The storage cycle of the film spot is similar to that of the ferrite core. The cycle is initiated, the storage element is sensed for content, and data is made available for insertion into the location. The data for writing may be

FIG. 5·18 Summing of word-line and information-line fields. (a) Write 0; (b) write 1.

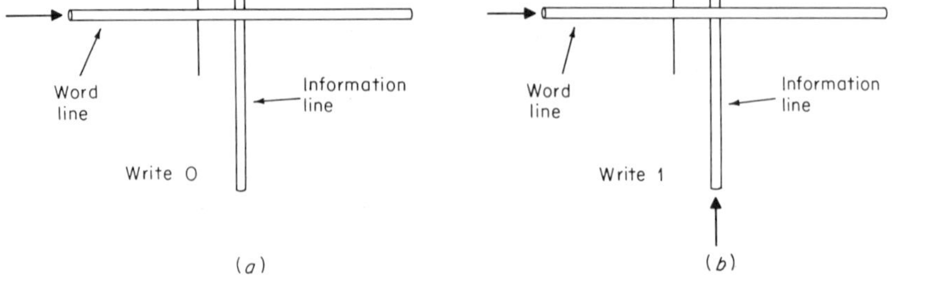

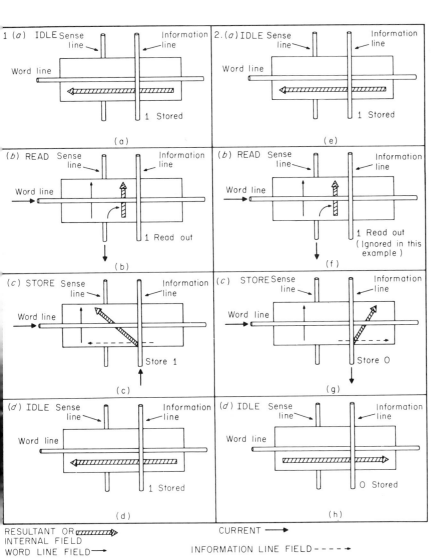

FIG. 5·19 Data manipulation in thin-film spot. (1) Read/rewrite 1; (2) read 1, rewrite 0.

the data just removed or it may be new data. On the sense, the data readout may be used or discarded depending upon the operation called for (read or write).

Figure 5·19 presents a complete film-spot cycle of reading and writing on the film spot. In Example 1 (Fig. 5·19a to d) the spot is read, and the 1 bit which is read out is restored on the film spot. In Example 2 (Fig. 5·19e to h) a 1 is read out, and a 0 is stored. The direction of current and the field force lines are shown.

In Example 1 of Fig. 5·19a, the device is idle or at rest. The application of the read current on the word-sense line (Fig. 5·19b) causes the internal field to rotate to a position perpendicular to the 1 "easy" state in which it resided. The downward flow of current results in the sense line indicating a 1 bit stored. An upward flowing current is initiated in the information line (Fig. 5·19c) resulting in the tipping of the internal field in the direction of the 1 "easy" direction. The removal of word-line current (Fig. 5·19d) results in the restoring of a 1 in film since the internal field is returned to the 1 "easy" state.

A similar action is shown in Fig. 5·19e to h. In the second example, after the read has occurred, the information-line tip of the internal field (Fig. 5·19g) is in the direction of the 0 "easy" direction. The result is a 0 store when the word-line current is removed (Fig. 5·19h).

Superconductive bistable storage devices. The advent and development of the ferrite core and thin-film memory storage devices have provided memories capable of storing millions of bits of data. Physical memory size has been reduced and access times are in the range of fractions of a microsecond. The advancing state of the computer art dictates further size reductions and increased bit capacities. Integrated-circuit techniques appear to be the direction to move in achieving these goals. One approach to the problem has been the implementation of large-scale integrated circuitry as the storage element. A storage "cell" consisting of 12 transistors (in a typical circuit) is required to store a single binary digit. The storage cell is quite small considering its complexity, only 0.015 in. on a side. A major disadvantage of this approach for bulk storage is the loss of data with a loss of power. A more promising approach lies in the realm of superconductivity. A typical superconductive memory has a packing density of 13,000 cells per square inch compared with an average of only three or four thousand per square inch in the integrated memory.

Fundamental concepts. When some metals are placed in a very low temperature, their electrical resistance drops to zero. This phenomenon or state is termed *superconductivity* and was discovered by H. K. Onnes, a Dutch physicist, in 1911, three years after he succeeded in liquefying helium.

The resistivity of many superconductors is relatively high at room temperatures but drops as the materials are cooled. Relatively poor conductors, such as tin and lead, become superconductors at very low temperatures, whereas good conductors such as gold, silver, and copper do not. The resistivity of superconductors is truly zero below their transition temperature, the point at which superconductivity begins to occur. An experiment that demonstrated zero resistance was performed at the Massachusetts Institute of Technology on March 16, 1954. A persistent current of several hundred amperes was induced in a lead ring immersed in liquid helium. The current continued to flow until the experiment was voluntarily terminated on September 11, 1956. During the experiment, there was no observable change in the magnitude of the current.

Some 22 elements have been found to exhibit superconductive properties; the two elements referred to in the discussion are tin and lead. Their transition temperatures are $3.73°K$ and $7.22°K$, respectively. The Kelvin scale references absolute zero ($-273.18°C$); $3.73°K$ is actually $3.73°C$ above absolute zero.

When a superconductor is in its superconductive state, a magnetic field of sufficient intensity can destroy its superconductivity (in the area of the magnetic field) and cause normal resistance to reappear. The transition time between the conductive and superconductive states is on the order of nanoseconds (1 nanosecond $= 1 \times 10^{-9}$ sec), which is an ideal property for a memory device.

The magnetic-field intensity at which the superconductor switches back to the normal resistive state is called the *critical magnetic field*. The value of the critical field varies with both the metal involved and the temperature at which the metal is held. For example, lead at $4.2°K$ is in its superconductive state. If a magnetic field of approximately 550 oersteds is applied, the metal will switch back to its normally conductive state. As the temperature of the lead is lowered, a stronger magnetic field is required to accomplish the switch; if the temperature is raised, the magnitude of the field required to cause the switch is lowered. If the temperature is lowered from 4.2 to $2°K$, a critical field of 750 oersteds is required to switch the conductivity state of the lead.

It was mentioned previously that tin has a transition temperature of $3.73°K$. If the operating temperature is held to a value of $0.2°K$ below the transition temperature (or $3.5°K$), a very small field of 50 to 100 oersteds will be sufficient to cause the switch in the conductivity state of the tin. At this same temperature of $3.5°K$, a magnetic field of 650 oersteds is required to cause the switch in lead. For this reason, tin is usually chosen as the storage loop and lead as the drive line in a cryotron. The name *cryotron* is derived from *kryos*, Greek for "icy cold," and represents a single-bit storage device. Storage loops and drive lines are discussed later.

Fabrication of thin-film cryotron. The fabrication techniques for thin-film cryotrons are similar to methods utilized in the manufacture of integrated circuits and magnetic thin-film memories. The process involves the evaporation of tin through a mask onto a substrate. The tin is evaporated through a mask which deposits a small storage loop and a digit line as a single

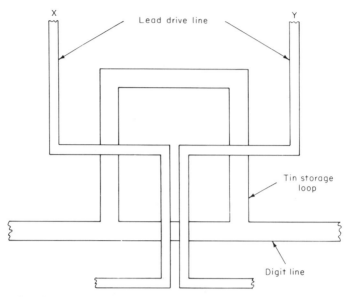

FIG. 5·20 Cryotron storage element.

integrated element. See Fig. 5·20. An insulating layer of silicon monoxide is then applied. The lead drive lines which are used for reading and writing are then deposited to form a single integrated memory plane.

The thin-film cryotron as a storage device. The cryotron switch stores data in the form of a persistent circulating current. The storage and reading of data are accomplished through the completion or the interruption of the storage loop by the application of the critical magnetic field. The x and y drive lines are used to provide the required field for switching. Each of the x and y drive lines carries half the current necessary to produce the critical magnetic field. The currents in the drive line must occur in coincidence to switch the lower leg of the storage loop between the conductive and superconductive states. Figure 5·21a illustrates the loop with a persistent circulating current while Fig. 5·21b indicates the leg of the loop which undergoes the switch during normal operation.

A memory cycle similar to the one used in other magnetic storage devices is required in the cryotron memory system. The process of reading out of the storage loop destroys the information content; hence, data must be restored or rewritten in order to be retained. The convention followed in a cryotron memory is that a binary 1 is represented by a persistent circulating current while a no-current condition indicates a 0 content. The memory system must be held in the temperature range for supercon-

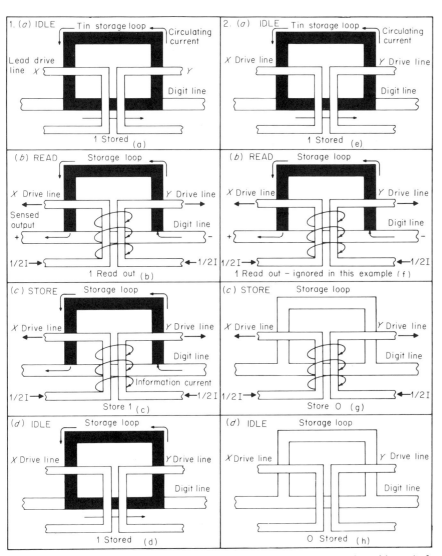

FIG. 5·21 Data manipulation in thin-film cryotron. (1) Read/rewrite 1; (2) read 1, rewrite 0.

ductivity for the metals used in the memory system. The range of 3.5°K is required for the memory being discussed.

Example 1 provides the sequence of operation to read a 1 initially stored in the device and to restore the 1 to storage. Figure 5·21a shows the 1 bit stored by the circulating current in the storage loop. In Fig. 5·21b the coincident currents of the x and y drive lines produced the critical field necessary to switch the lower leg of the storage loop. The current dissipation resulting from the sudden introduction of the "resistive" load to the storage loop generates a voltage which is sensed on the information (digit) line by the appropriate circuitry. The 1 bit is read from storage. It should be noted that if a 0 were stored in the loop, the application of the critical field would result in no current interruption and, hence, no sensed output. The rewrite of a 1 bit is illustrated in Fig. 5·21c and d.

An information current is applied to the digit line and flows as indicated in Fig. 5·21c. The removal of the drive-line currents while the information current is flowing reestablishes the lower leg of the storage loop as superconductive. A persistent circulating current is now present in the storage loop (Fig. 5·21d).

Example 2 illustrates the condition of an initial 1-bit store, a read of the information with a subsequent 0 store in the memory cell. The read action is as described previously. The sensed output, however, is discarded. In Fig. 5·21g no information current is flowing on the digit line through the loop at the time the drive currents are terminated. Although three legs of the storage loop remain in the superconductive state, a 0 has been stored since the circulating current has not been reestablished in the storage loop by the return of the interrupted leg to the superconductive state.

SECTION 4   METHODS OF RECORDING ON MAGNETIC SURFACES

The bulk storage devices used in computer systems have several things in common. They are normally rotating-type devices, and they record information on magnetic surfaces. A typical magnetic surface consists of a coating of iron oxide powder mixed with a binder that is used to make the mixture adhere to the surface to be coated. The coated surface can be magnetized in much the same manner as an iron bar is magnetized when placed in the field of a current-carrying conductor. Storage devices of this type are magnetic tapes, magnetic drums, and magnetic disks. These devices are covered in a later chapter. These devices may differ in operation, speed, and storage capacity; however, they employ one of several recording methods. Some of the recording methods used are the return-to-zero, return-to-bias, and non-return-to-zero methods. Regardless of the method chosen, in order to record (write) information on a magnetic surface, or reproduce (read) that information from the same surface, some type of magnetizing force is necessary. This force is provided by a device known as a read/write head. The head assembly may consist of a single head capable of both write and read operations or separate read and write heads. The read/write head is a basic electromagnet and can be thought of as a conductor wound on a ring core (air gap). This arrangement is shown in Fig. 5·22a. If a current is passed through the coil, a magnetic field (flux) will be produced, whose direction will be determined by the direction of the current

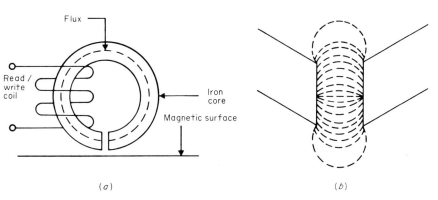

FIG. 5·22   Read/write recording head. (a) Basic assembly; (b) flux pattern at air gap.

flow. The core has a tendency to concentrate the flux within the core material. However, the flux pattern is radiated at the air gap break as shown in Fig. 5·22b. If the magnetic surface is passed under the read/write head during the time the current is flowing, the associated magnetic field will magnetize the surface in a given direction for as long as the current is present. In other words, a 1 could be indicated (written) by magnetizing the surface in one direction, while a 0 could be indicated by the opposite magnetization.

Another way in which 1's may be represented is by flux changes in either direction, with a constant magnetization used to indicate 0's. Regardless of the period of the magnetization, the flux field on the magnetized surface will remain after the magnetizing force (current) has been removed. This assumes, of course, that the information is not destroyed by the action of some external field force. The recorded information can be retrieved (read) by passing the magnetic surface under a read head. This "reading" does not destroy the information stored. When the magnetized surface is passed under the head, the flux field of the surface will induce a voltage into the read coil. The polarity of the voltage is determined by the direction of the magnetic flux. It should be noted that all recording techniques are not the same. Some methods magnetize the magnetic surface in a given direction along its entire length, while others magnetize the surface only for a short duration for each bit of information to be recorded. Several recording methods are explained in the following paragraphs.

Return-to-zero (RZ) method. The return-to-zero method of recording utilizes a pulse for each digit to be recorded. The magnetic surface is magnetized in one direction for a 1 and in the opposite direction for a 0. In this method, the recording head current is normally 0. When a digit is to be recorded, a current sufficient to saturate the magnetic surface is passed through the head for a brief period of time. To record a 1, current is passed through the write head in one direction, and to record a 0, current is passed in the opposite direction. Each recorded bit becomes a tiny permanent magnet on the recording surface. The length of this magnet depends upon the write-pulse duration and the speed of the moving magnetic surface. It should be noted that there exists a no-flux area between bits of information in this type of recording. When the recorded surface is passed under a read head, a flux change in one direction induces a current to indicate a 1 bit, while an opposite flux change induces an opposite current to represent a 0. The write and read waveforms for this method are shown in Fig. 5·23.

The return-to-zero method of recording is complicated by the fact that the magnetic surface must be erased (all flux removed) prior to recording new information. Moreover, some type of phase detection must be employed to discriminate a 1 bit from a 0 bit on readout. A modified version of return-to-zero is sometimes used. This modified RZ method is more correctly termed the return-to-bias method.

Return-to-bias (RB) method. In the return-to-bias method (Fig. 5·24), the recording head is biased with a direct current so that the magnetic surface is saturated in one direction in the absence of write pulses. The recording-pulse (write) current strength is sufficient to saturate the magnetic surface in the opposite direction. The dc bias eliminates the need for a separate

FIG. 5·23   RZ waveforms.

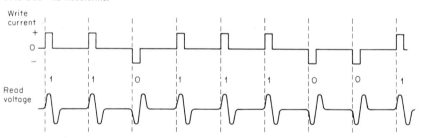

FIG. 5·24   RB waveforms.

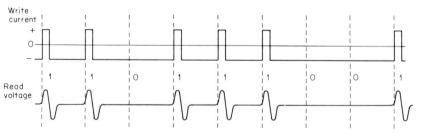

erase head and enables the read-back voltage to be approximately doubled. With this type of recording, only 1's are actually written (produce-flux changes). The absence of a flux change indicates the presence of 0 bit(s). When the magnetized surface is passed under the read head, every flux reversal (1 bit) induces a voltage into the read coil, while the absence of any flux change is indicative of a 0.

Non-return-to-zero (NRZ) method. In the NRZ method, the write-head current is sufficient to saturate the magnetic surface. This should not be confused with the dc bias of the RB method. In the NRZ method, full write current is always flowing in one direction or the other. One form of NRZ recording incorporates the method in which the recording current is reversed each time a 1 is to be written on the magnetic surface. The presence of a flux change (reversal of magnetization) on the surface indicates a 1 and the absence of flux changes signifies a 0. This method is similar to the return-to-bias method except that in the NRZ method a 1 is indicated by a flux change in either direction, whereas in the RB technique, 1's are signified by flux changes in a given direction. The waveforms for the NRZ method are shown in Fig. 5·25.

By changing the read-and-write control circuits, the NRZ method can become a modified NRZ (actually just another form of NRZ recording). For example, referring to Fig. 5·26, the waveforms shown are exactly the

FIG. 5·25 NRZ waveforms.

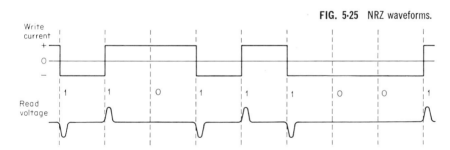

FIG. 5·26 NRZ waveforms (modified version).

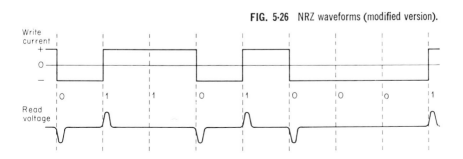

same as shown in Fig. 5·25; however, the information storage produced by these waveforms is not identical. In the previous discussion it was stated that every flux reversal indicated a 1 and no-flux changes represented 0's. In the modified NRZ method (Fig. 5·26), each flux change indicates information bit conditions (1's and 0's) opposite to those of the NRZ method. Assume a negative-going write current indicates a 0 until a positive current occurs, and the positive current indicates a 1 until the current switches again. In this manner, the same write waveform that produced an information pattern of 110111001 would now generate an information pattern of

FIG. 5·27 Block diagram of return-to-zero recording method with associated waveforms.

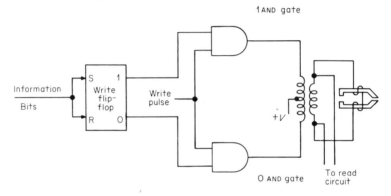

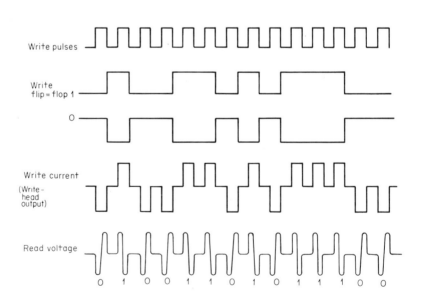

011010001. Two different information patterns can be obtained from the same write waveform because of the operation of the read circuit. In the normal NRZ method, the read circuit is designed to recognize any read pulse (flux reversal), regardless of polarity, as a 1 bit at the proper timing interval and the absence of pulses as 0 bits. In the modified NRZ method, the read circuit is designed to discriminate the negative read pulses from the positive pulses. Assume that the negative pulses are used to reset a flip-flop, and the positive pulses to set the same flip-flop. Again referring to Fig. 5·26, the first information pulse being negative would reset the flip-flop which represents a 0 bit. At the next read/sample interval, a positive pulse is detected which sets the flip-flop and thus stores a 1 in the flip-flop. Since at the next sample time there is no pulse available, the flip-flop remains in the set state indicating another 1. Likewise, a string of 0's would be indicated by the information flip-flop remaining in the reset state indicating 0's when sampled.

Figure 5·27 illustrates a simplified read/write circuit and the associated waveforms. The return-to-zero recording method is used in the example. The state of the write flip-flop is controlled by the information to be recorded on the magnetic surface. If a 1 is to be recorded, the flip-flop goes to the ONE state; if a 0 is to be recorded, the flip-flop goes to the ZERO state. Whichever output of the flip-flop is high will enable one of the AND gates. The AND gate output is clocked by the write pulses and feeds the primary of a center-tapped transformer, inducing currents of the opposite polarity in the secondary and setting up the polarity of the write head itself. This produces the waveform designated write-head output which is identical with the output shown for the return-to-zero recording method. In this basic circuit the read head is the same head used for write; hence the read circuit is inhibited during the write cycle. The read-voltage waveforms obtained when the magnetized surface is passed under the read head are shown in Fig. 5·27.

SUMMARY

In magnetism there is a formula parallel to Ohm's law in electricity:

$$\text{Reluctance} = \frac{\text{magnetomotive force}}{\text{magnetic flux}}$$

Permeability, represented by the Greek symbol μ, is the reciprocal of reluctance. Magnetomotive force F is measured in ampere-turns or in gilberts. The gilbert is equal to $0.4\pi NI$, where NI is in ampere-turns.

Magnetization curves and hysteresis loops are graphs of field density B plotted against field intensity H. The magnetic characteristics of different materials plotted in graphs demonstrate that the permeability μ of all materials varies according to the applied field intensity H.

Many modern computers use small ferromagnetic cores as bistable switching and storage elements which switch their magnetic state at the application of an electric pulse. These cores are composed of metallic alloys and compounds possessing almost square hysteresis loops that produce sudden switching, noise discrimination, and storage of a large amount of residual flux.

Increased storage capacity and reduced physical size have been achieved in thin-film spots and thin-film cryotrons. Both of these devices are fabricated by processes which involve vapor deposition of metals on a substrate element. In thin film the magnetic properties of the metal are used in the storage process. In the cryotron, superconductive characteristics achieved through temperature control are used as the basis of data storage.

Bulk storage devices use the magnetic properties of a metal as the basis of storage. These devices utilize recording procedures termed return-to-zero, return-to-bias, or non-return-to-zero. In all these recording methods either undirectional or bidirectional flux fields or changes are used for 0 and 1 storage and sensing.

QUESTIONS

5·1   State the right-hand rule.

5·2   Define reluctance.

5·3   Define permeability.

5·4   What are the three classifications of magnetic materials?

5·5   What is the term used to describe the strength of a magnet?

5·6   Define: (a) domain alignment; (b) Barkhausen effect; and (c) magnetic saturation.

5·7   What is meant by residual magnetism?

5·8   Define coercive force.

5·9   What is hysteresis?

5·10 Does a ferrite memory core normally operate on a major or a minor loop? Why?

5·11 Give two reasons why a rectangular hysteresis loop is preferred for magnetic information storage devices.

5·12 What is the main application of the ferrite core?

5·13 Describe how information is placed into and removed from ferrite cores.

5·14 How are cores affected by temperature variations?

5·15 What is the major advantage of thin-film memory over a ferrite-core memory?

5·16 Why will a magnetic thin-film spot return to an "easy" state if the external magnetic field is removed?

5·17 How is a binary 1 stored in a magnetic thin-film device?

5·18 Define superconductivity.

5·19 How is a binary 1 sensed from a cryotron?

5·20 Why must a write cycle follow a read cycle to retain the "old" data in a cryotron?

5·21 If a 1 is read from the cryotron loop, how is a 0 stored in its place?

5·22 What effect will a lower temperature have on a cryotron-type memory?

5·23 Name three recording methods commonly used.

5·24 Which recording method requires an erase before recording new information?

5·25 In which method is a 1 recorded with each flux change?

5·26 Which recording method is characterized by a no-flux condition between information bits?

chapter six

Transistor Switching Characteristics

Transistors are used in digital computer circuits as current controlling or switching devices. When transistors are used as switching devices, they are normally operated at the extremes of their operating regions. In other words, they are operating at maximum conduction (saturation) or they are not conducting (cut off). Operation at these two extremes requires consideration of certain undesirable characteristics of transistors that are not of great importance in the use of transistors as amplifiers. The most important of these characteristics are the time considerations involved in transistor turn-on, turn-off, and carrier storage. New manufacturing techniques have accomplished much to improve these characteristics; however, these time considerations still pose a problem in switching-circuit design. Circuit techniques have been developed which are used to compensate for the effects of these characteristics and improve the response time of a transistor to an input pulse.

This chapter will describe the output pulse characteristics of the transistor with respect to an input pulse and show how response may be improved.

Characteristic-curve Analysis

Transistor amplification characteristics are classified in two categories, (1) small-signal operation and (2) large-signal operation. Transistor switching characteristics are classified as large-signal operation.

The regions of transistor operation are graphically depicted in Fig. 6·1, which plots collector current in terms of collector voltage for a given family of base-current values. The three regions of operation are the cutoff region, the active region, and the saturation region. The cutoff region (I) is the shaded region between the collector voltage line and the $I_b = 0$ line. In this region the only collector current is the leakage current (I_{co}) caused by thermal agitation. The active region (II) is the normal operating region. Here the collector current is controlled by the base current. The saturation region (III) is the shaded region beyond the bend of the characteristic curves. The saturation region is generally defined as the region where the collector voltage becomes smaller than the base voltage. When this happens, the collector-base junction is forward-biased and the collector begins to inject its carriers into the base region. In this mode of operation, collector current is no longer controlled or limited by the base current, but instead is limited only by the collector and emitter external resistive load.

The maximum power that the transistor can safely dissipate is indicated by the dashed line (Fig. 6·1). In normal amplifier use, the load line (the straight diagonal line) is kept to the left of the maximum power-dissipation curve. In switching circuits, portions of the load line may be to the right of the power-dissipation curve, since the maximum power-dissipation rating will be exceeded only for a short time, as the transistor goes from the cutoff to the saturation state or vice versa.

Transient Response

In order to analyze the response of a transistor, an ideal current pulse is applied to the base of a common-emitter-amplifier stage, and the resulting changes in output voltage are observed at the collector as shown in Fig. 6·2. A brief explanation of the indicated pulse terminology is also given to ensure that subsequent explanations can be followed more easily by the reader.

Delay time.   Delay time (t_d) is the time from the leading edge (or beginning of change) of the input pulse to the 10 percent point (from minimum value) of the output pulse. This delay is incurred for a number of reasons. One of the major reasons for delay is the distance the current carriers must travel

FIG. 6·1 Regions of transistor operation.

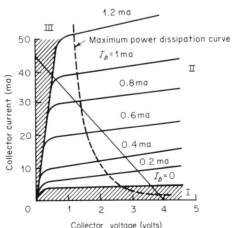

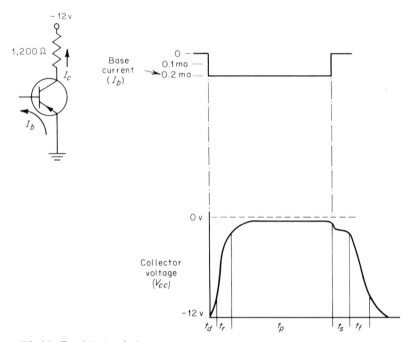

FIG. 6-2 Transistor transient response.

from the emitter contact through the emitter, base, and collector regions to
the collector contact. Thus the thicker the regions of a transistor, the larger
will be the values of t_d. Another factor is the emitter-to-base capacitance.
Since this capacitance is acting in a manner similar to a filter capacitor, it
must be discharged before an effective base current can begin to flow. This
factor further increases the value of t_d.

Rise time.   Rise time (t_r) is the time in which the output pulse rises from the
10 percent point to 90 percent of the maximum value. Rise time is dependent upon the frequency response of the transistor, the circuit capacitance, and the magnitude of the applied base current.

Pulse time.   The pulse time (t_p), or width, is the time between the 90 percent values at the leading and trailing edges of the pulse.

Storage time.   Storage time (t_s) is the time in which the output pulse remains
at or near its maximum value after the input pulse has returned to its zero
value. This time is often referred to as *saturation delay time.* When a
transistor is driven into saturation, the voltage drop across the load resistor

will bring the collector voltage to a value less negative than the base voltage (PNP transistor assumed). In this condition both the emitter-base and collector-base junctions are forward-biased. The forward biasing of the collector-base junction causes the collector to inject minority carriers into the base, where they are stored as an additional base charge in excess of the base charge introduced by the input waveform. At turn-off time the excess minority carriers (charge) must be discharged from the base region before the output pulse begins to change.

Fall time. Fall time (t_f) is the time in which the output pulse falls from 90 to 10 percent of its maximum value. The factors governing rise time also apply to fall time.

Methods of Improving Transient Response

The trend in computers toward faster clock frequencies requires that transistors used in switching circuits turn on or turn off at higher rates. Turn-on time is the sum of the delay time and the rise time. Turn-off time is the sum of the storage time and the fall time.

Some special-type high-frequency transistors having turn-on and turn-off times in the nanosecond range may even be driven into saturation and still produce little storage time. These special types are used in high-frequency switching applications.

There are circuit techniques that will increase the switching speed of ordinary junction transistors to make them useful as switching devices. There are two techniques used to improve turn-on and turn-off time: one is to *overdrive* the transistor during turn-on and turn-off time, and the other is to design a circuit to prevent saturation, thereby preventing storage effects.

Newer manufacturing techniques as well as refinements in some of the older methods have helped to reduce turn-on and turn-off times.

Manufacturing techniques. Reduction of transistor element size has helped to reduce delay time by reducing the travel distance of the current carrier. An added benefit of the smaller element size is the reduced base-to-emitter capacitance values. The surface barrier, the micro-alloy, the micro-alloy diffused base, and the mesa transistors have resulted from improved manufacturing methods. These transistors exhibit such characteristics as faster turn-on times through reduction of delay time, faster rise time, shorter storage time, greater current handling capability, emitter efficiency, and ruggedness.

The development of epitaxial manufacturing processes allows for a choice of semiconductor material types and resistances. This flexibility allows the desired final product characteristics to be manufactured into the

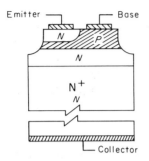

FIG. 6·3 Epitaxial mesa transistor.

device. Figure 6·3 is an example of an epitaxial mesa transistor with the following built-in characteristics:

1. Small emitter area resulting in shorter emitter transient times and small emitter-to-base capacitance.
2. Alloy-diffused or epitaxially grown base, providing a thin base region (less recombination).
3. A thin, high-resistivity epitaxial layer N as the collector side of the base-collector junction. High-resistivity material used here favors a high breakdown voltage for the collector junction and low inherent collector capacitance values.
4. The major portion of the collector block $N+$ is formed of low-resistivity material. This gives a lower ohmic voltage drop across the collector, allowing lower values of collector-to-emitter voltage when the transistor is saturated.

Overdriving to increase switching speed. The turn-on and turn-off times of the transistor may be reduced by overdriving the transistor. Overdriving means to apply more than the required amount of base current to turn the transistor on or off. The effect of overdrive is illustrated in Figs. 6·4 and 6·5.

In Fig. 6·4, the maximum collector current is

$$\frac{V_{cc}}{R_L} = \frac{12}{1200} = 10 \text{ ma}$$

If the transistor has a β of 50, the required amount of base current to keep the collector current at 10 ma is $I_c/\beta = 10/50 = 0.2$ ma.

When 0.2 ma of base current is applied, the collector current will increase toward 10 ma at an exponential rate because of the rise-time factors mentioned previously. Since turn-on is considered to be 90 percent of the maximum collector current, the collector will reach maximum current in approximately three time periods. The time period divisions are arbitrarily

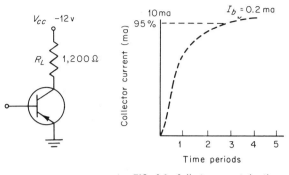

FIG. 6·4 Collector current rise time.

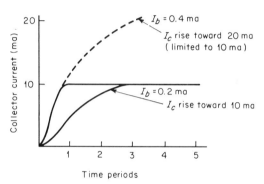

FIG. 6·5 Effect of overdriving on collector current rise time.

chosen as a periodic increment of time for circuit explanation only and should not be confused with a formulated time constant, such as seconds or minutes resulting from circuit component values.

Now suppose that 0.4 ma of base current is applied. The collector current attempts to increase to $\beta \times I_b = 50 \times 0.4 = 20$ ma. However, the collector current is limited to 10 ma by the values of V_{cc} and R_L. The latter current curve, upon attempting to rise toward 20 ma, is more linear than the former curve rising to 10 ma. A comparison of the two curves is shown in Fig. 6·5.

In Fig. 6·5 it can be seen that by overdriving the transistor during turn-on, the collector current reaches 10 ma in less than one time constant instead of three time constants. In a like manner, overdriving the transistor in the opposite direction during turn-off decreases turn-off time.

The decrease of turn-off time is due mainly to the reverse drive helping to discharge the excess carriers from the base region.

Ideal base-current waveform. An ideal current waveform applied to the base of the transistor is one that overdrives the transistor to obtain rapid turn-on, reduces to a value necessary to maintain the desired collector conduction level, and overdrives the transistor in the opposite direction for rapid turn-off. The ideal waveform illustrated in Fig. 6·6 shows that an additional 0.2 ma of overdrive current is applied during turn-on and turn-off time.

The circuit shown in Fig. 6·7 provides a base-current waveform that approximates the ideal waveform of Fig. 6·6.

The additional overdrive current is supplied to the base by the charge and discharge of capacitor $C1$ through the base and emitter of the transistor. The normal base current flows through resistor $R1$.

The circuit operation may be more clearly explained by calculating the theoretical values of $C1$ and $R1$.

If the collector current at saturation is 10 ma and the β of the transistor is 50, then the base current required to saturate the transistor must be 0.2 ma. This value of base current will flow through $R1$. Assume that the turn-on time desired is 0.5 μsec. If 0.4 ma of base current will provide the desired turn-on time, then $C1$ must provide a charging current of 0.2 ma so that the total base current during turn-on will be 0.4 ma.

FIG. 6·6   Ideal base-current waveform.

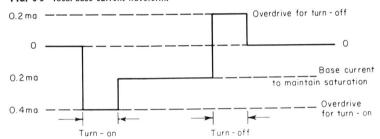

FIG. 6·7   Circuit to provide overdrive.

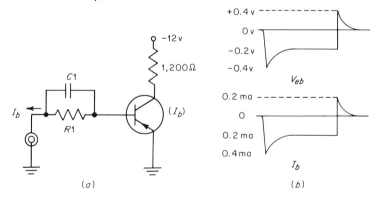

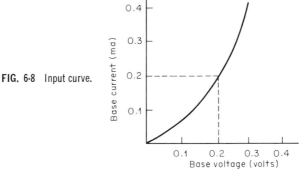

FIG. 6·8 Input curve.

The first step is to determine what value of base voltage produces 0.2 ma of base current. This can be done by referring to the input curve for the transistor.

In Fig. 6·8, 0.2 volt must be applied to the base to allow 0.2 ma to flow through the transistor. If the input voltage varies between 0 and −3 volts, the value of $R1$ is

$$\frac{(3 - 0.2) \text{ volts}}{0.2 \text{ ma}} = \frac{2.8}{0.2} = 14,000 \text{ ohms}$$

The 0.2-ma overdrive current must be supplied by $C1$. The current through a capacitor is found by the following equation:

$$I = \frac{C \, \Delta V}{\Delta t}$$

Therefore

$$C = \frac{I \, \Delta t}{\Delta V}$$

The voltage change ΔV across $C1$ is $3 - 0.2 = 2.8$ volts; the required current is 0.2 ma and the turn-on time Δt is 0.5 μsec. Then

$$C1 = (0.2 \times 10^{-3}) \frac{0.5 \times 10^{-6}}{2.8} = 35 \ \mu\mu\text{f}$$

The capacitor, on charging, inserts additional electrons into the base. At turn-off time the input goes to 0 volt and the capacitor discharges. On discharging, the capacitor attracts electrons from the base region as the transistor is turning off. Electrons flowing out of the base into the base lead tend to turn the transistor off.

Disadvantage of saturation.   A disadvantage of saturation is that driving the transistor into saturation will increase the storage time. When fast turn-on and turn-off are required, special techniques are employed to prevent the circuit from going into saturation. Several of these techniques will now be discussed.

Nonsaturating Techniques

In Fig. 6·1 the saturation region was shown as the region where the collector voltage becomes smaller than the base voltage and the collector junction is forward-biased. Consequently, the collector injects its majority carriers into the base, and turn-off time is increased. The purpose of the nonsaturating techniques discussed here is to prevent the collector voltage from becoming smaller than the base voltage by preventing the transistor from actually conducting at saturation.

Collector clamp.   The simplest method to prevent saturation is the collector clamping method shown in Fig. 6·9. Here the collector voltage is prevented from becoming more positive than the base voltage by diode $CR1$. When the collector voltage attempts to become more positive than -1 volt, $CR1$ conducts and the collector voltage is clamped at a negative level. If the current flow through $CR1$ causes a voltage drop of 0.2 volt across the diode, the collector is clamped at -0.8 volt. Thus, the collector-base junction remains reverse-biased, and the collector does not emit carriers into the base. This method is useful with the intrinsic-barrier transistor, where the majority carrier density in the collector region decreases rapidly as V_c approaches zero.

FIG. 6·9   Collector clamp to prevent saturation.

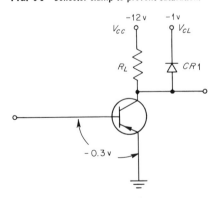

A disadvantage of the collector clamp method is that the recovery time of diode $CR1$ becomes part of the total turn-off time. The transistor still conducts maximum current, and the current divides between the load and $CR1$.

Single-diode collector clamp.   Another nonsaturating technique is to reduce the collector current by controlling the base current. This technique is called *nonlinear feedback*. The circuit is shown in Fig. 6·10.

Assume the collector saturation current is 12 ma. If the current gain is 30, the amount of base current required to saturate the transistor is 0.4 ma. To decrease turn-on time, the 0.4-ma saturation current and the additional overdrive current supplied by $C1$ are applied to the base to produce the desired turn-on time. Assume an input pulse forward-biases the base-emitter junction and drives the transistor toward saturation. If the collector current were allowed to reach saturation, then the collector voltage would be approximately -0.1 volt. However, when the collector voltage attempts to become more positive than the negative voltage at the junction of $R1$ and $R2$ (-1 volt), $CR1$ conducts and a portion of the base current is diverted to the collector; hence the collector current cannot increase beyond its value at this point. The total collector current, then, consists of the amplified base current ($\beta \times I_b$) and the excess base current; the current flowing through the load remains constant since it is only the amplified base current. If the voltage drop across $CR1$ is 0.2 volt, then the falling collector voltage stops at -0.8 volt; hence $CR1$ prevents the collector-base junction from becoming forward-biased by shunting the excess input current into the collector. Since only a fraction of the base current flows through $CR1$, diode recovery time contributes little to the widening of the output pulse.

Back clamping.   Resistor $R2$ in Fig. 6·10 can be replaced with a silicon

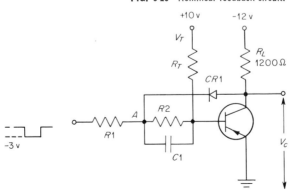

FIG. 6·10   Nonlinear feedback circuit.

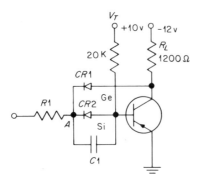

FIG. 6-11   Back-clamping circuit.

diode $CR2$, as shown in Fig. 6-11. The resulting circuit operates reliably and is fairly insensitive to minor changes in supply voltages.

A silicon diode is selected for $CR2$ because of its inherently higher forward voltage drop than that of the germanium diode $CR1$ and its constant forward voltage drop over the relatively wide range of current values normally applied to the base of the switching transistor. The biasing diode $CR2$ is forward-biased throughout the functioning of the circuit and has a forward voltage drop of 0.7 volt. The clamping diode $CR1$ is reverse-biased when the transistor is cut off. Capacitor $C1$ provides the overdrive current the same as in the single-diode clamping circuit (Fig. 6-10). $CR1$ will conduct when the transistor is turned on and the collector voltage attempts to go slightly more positive than the negative voltage established at the junction of the two diodes (point A, -1 volt). When $CR1$ conducts, it exhibits a forward voltage drop of 0.2 volt; the collector is therefore clamped at -0.8 volt when $CR1$ conducts and diverts the excess base current to the collector. The voltage drop of $CR2$ establishes the base voltage at -0.3 volt. Because of their different voltage drops, the two diodes will maintain a fixed voltage relationship between the base and collector, keeping the base-collector junction reverse-biased when the transistor is switched on. There are variations of the double-diode clamp circuit, one of which eliminates resistor R_T. This results in a saving of a power supply since V_T is no longer required. Circuit operation is essentially the same.

Current-mode switching. Another method of preventing saturation is to limit the amount of collector current by using a resistor and a voltage supply in the emitter circuit, as shown in Fig. 6-12. The values shown for R_E, R_L, and the supply voltages are chosen so that the collector voltage does not become smaller than the base voltage.

The current supplied by V_{ee} and R_e is switched in and out of the transistor, depending upon the voltage applied to the base. If the base

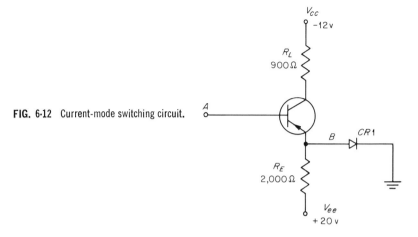

FIG. 6-12 Current-mode switching circuit.

voltage is sufficiently negative, the 10 ma (minus the required base current) flows to the collector circuit.

Assume that the voltage applied to point A is $+0.6$ volt and that the transistor is off. The 10-ma current must flow through $CR1$. If 10 ma of current drops 0.3 volt across $CR1$, the voltage at point B is 0.3 volt. The base is then 0.3 volt positive with respect to the emitter. If the input drops to -0.6 volt, the emitter junction becomes forward-biased and the 10-ma current flows through the transistor. If the gain of the stage is 50, the base current will be 0.2 ma for a 10-ma current. Assume that the base input characteristics show that the base voltage is 0.2 volt at 0.2-ma base current. When the transistor conducts, the voltage at B is -0.4 volt and diode $CR1$ is reverse-biased.

The load resistor R_L may be selected so that the collector voltage is out of the saturation region. The collector voltage V_c may be found by the equation $V_c = V_{cc} - I_E R_L$. Therefore $R_L = (V_{cc} - V_c)/I_E$. If V_c is to be -1 volt and the collector supply voltage is -12 volts,

$$R_L = \frac{12 - 1 \text{ (volts)}}{10 \text{ ma}} = 1100 \text{ ohms}$$

High switching speeds are possible using current-mode switches. The circuit may be operated as far out of saturation as desired. A high current may be switched in and out of the transistor by using a relatively small voltage applied to the base.

Nonsaturation by circuit design. It is possible to design switching circuits that will not saturate merely by the correct choice of components.

The switching speed of a transistor becomes an important characteristic when the transistor is used in computing devices. The turn-on and turn-off times of the transistor are the determinants of transistor switching speeds. Improvements in the manufacturing process have accomplished much in providing high-speed switching transistors. In addition, circuit design techniques may be used to improve transistor switching speeds.

Turn-on and turn-off times depend on the delay, rise, fall, and storage times of the transistor. Turn-on time can be decreased (improved) by overdriving. However, this overdrive technique increases the storage time which results in a worse turn-off time. A speed-up capacitor can be utilized to provide an overdrive current during turn-on time, keep saturation current at the minimum level to maintain saturation until turn-off time, and provide an opposite overdrive current to decrease turn-off time by decreasing storage time.

Storage time can be kept to a minimum by preventing the collector junction from becoming forward-biased. The methods used to implement this are referred to as nonsaturating techniques. These techniques include collector clamp, nonlinear feedback, back clamping, current mode, switching, and circuit design.

QUESTIONS

6·1 What factors should be taken into consideration when selecting a transistor for switching applications?

6·2 Describe saturation and its effect on switching operations.

6·3 Explain how the speedup capacitor improves turn-off time.

6·4 Refer to Fig. 6·8 and determine the value of the base-input resistor for Fig. 6·7 when β is 40 and saturation current is 12 ma.

6·5 How do nonsaturating techniques improve turn-off time?

6·6 In Fig. 6·10 explain how the diode $CR1$ prevents the transistor from becoming saturated.

chapter seven

Computer Circuits

The process of computation and control is performed in the computing system through combinations of various types of basic circuitry. In some cases, each circuit is an independent entity varying in physical size dictated by the manufacturing process employed. In some circuits it is possible to effect repairs through the removal and replacement of a single component. Other manufacturing processes provide a myriad of logic functions in so small a physical area that troubleshooting and repair involve the substitution of entire logic functions by the removal of a chip or element of integrated circuitry. Chapter 9 discusses integrated circuitry.

The purpose of this chapter is to discuss the operation of some of the basic circuits used in computing systems. The circuits to be discussed may not represent the present state of the art but rather have been selected for ease of presentation. Depending upon the system, the technician may come into contact with them as basic units or in some combination.

The circuits have been divided into four classes or categories:

1. Gate logic
2. Amplifiers
3. Oscillators and multivibrators
4. Power supplies — regulation and control

SECTION 1   GATE LOGIC

Gating logic may be implemented through the use of transistors or diodes or a combination of both.

Gating circuits are switching circuits that provide Yes or No information. The transistors may be connected in series, in parallel, or in series-parallel to provide a variety of logical functions such as the AND, OR, NOT, NOR, and other functions peculiar to the logical design of the computer. Transistor gates have an advantage over diode gates: the transistor is capable of amplifying the input signal, so that the amplitude of a signal is not reduced as it passes through several gates.

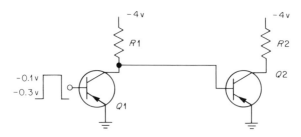

FIG. 7·1 Two-stage DCTL amplifier.

There are several types of transistor logic configurations which can be used to construct logical gates and systems. The common-emitter circuit is the most frequently used because of its low input drive requirement and current and voltage gain. The system of logic employed will depend upon the desired switching speed, power requirements, and relative cost of the components used. The basic transistor logical systems are as follows:

1. Direct-coupled transistor logic (DCTL)
2. Resistor transistor logic (RTL)
3. Resistor-capacitor transistor logic (RCTL)
4. Hybrid logic (diodes and transistors)
5. Current-mode logic (CML)

Direct-coupled Transistor Logic

DCTL indicates that the output of one amplifier stage is coupled directly to the input of a following stage. A two-stage amplifier circuit is shown in Fig. 7·1.

The amplitude of the voltage swing is small, usually about 0.2 volt. No external circuitry is required to establish the lower-level clamp because the emitter-base junction of $Q2$ acts as a diode clamp on the collector of $Q1$. Assume that the input voltage varies between -0.1 and -0.3 volt. The -0.1-volt level is considered positive, and the -0.3-volt level is considered negative. The -0.1-volt level is used to turn the transistor off; the load resistor and collector supply voltages are selected so that the transistors saturate when the -0.3-volt level is applied.

If -0.3 volt is applied to the base of $Q1$, $Q1$ turns on and its collector voltage drops to -0.1 volt. This voltage is applied to the base of $Q2$; hence, $Q2$ turns off. When the input to the base of $Q1$ rises to -0.1 volt, $Q1$ turns off and its collector voltage begins to fall toward -4 volts. However, when

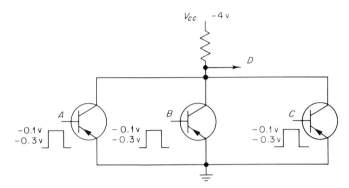

FIG. 7·2 Parallel DCTL circuit.

the collector voltage reaches −0.3 volt, $Q2$ turns on. The base current of $Q2$ flows through $R1$ and the collector voltage supply. This base current keeps the collector of $Q1$ clamped to −0.3 volt when $Q1$ is turned off.

The collector voltage of $Q1$ varies between −0.1 and −0.3 volt. If another stage is coupled to $Q2$, the output of $Q2$ will vary by the same amount.

Parallel logical gate. In Fig. 7·2, three transistors are placed in parallel, with the collectors tied to a common point D. If the input at A, B, or C is −0.3 volt, the output at D will be −0.1 volt. If all inputs are −0.1 volt simultaneously, the output at D will fall to −4 volts provided it is not coupled to another stage.

The phase of the output signal is inverted since a common-emitter configuration is used. When all three inputs are "positive" (−0.1 volt), the output is negative. When either input is negative, the output is positive. The gate is either a positive-input AND gate with polarity reversal or a negative-input OR gate with polarity reversal.

Series gate. The series gate shown in Fig. 7·3 can perform both AND and OR operations. All three transistors must conduct if current is to flow into the load. If −0.3 volt is applied to all three inputs, the collector of $Q1$ supplies the emitter current of $Q2$, and the collector of $Q2$ supplies the emitter current of $Q3$. The circuit is a negative-input AND gate with polarity reversal or a positive-input OR gate with polarity reversal.

Logical gate symbols and notations. Logical schematic diagrams are used as an aid to tracing signals through gates that perform the logical operations of

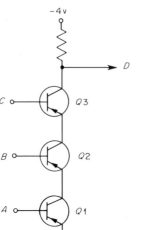

FIG. 7·3 Series DCTL circuit.

a computer. These schematic diagrams indicate whether a gate is a series or parallel gate and whether the gate is performing an AND or an OR function. The logical symbols for the gates are shown in Fig. 7·4.

FIG. 7·4 Gate symbols and electrical circuits. (a) Parallel gates; (b) series gates.

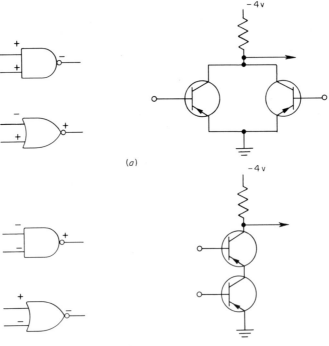

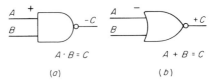

FIG. 7·5 Basic parallel gate used as a building block. (a) AND gate; (b) OR gate.

In each of the gates shown, a polarity reversal exists. The polarity symbols are necessary to maintain a correct polarity throughout a sequence of gates. This problem is eliminated when two basic assumptions are made in the design of a logical network. These assumptions are:

1. It is unnecessary to select one pulse level to represent a 1 or "true" condition and to maintain this notation throughout the system.
2. An inversion of polarity does not necessarily mean an inversion in logic.

With these two basic assumptions made, the task of arranging gates to perform logical operations becomes easier and more flexible. Most systems use one basic gate to perform both AND and OR operations. For example, a two-input parallel DCTL gate may be chosen as the basic building block to perform all logical operations. For AND-gate operations, the "true" inputs are positive and the "true" output is negative. For OR-gate operations, the "true" inputs are negative and the "true" output is positive. The equation for the AND gate shown in Fig. 7·5 is $AB = C$, and the equation for the OR gate is $A + B = C$.

Most logical sequences have AND gates driving OR gates and OR gates driving AND gates. When such an arrangement exists, the "true" output of an AND gate is of the correct polarity to drive an OR gate and vice versa. The circuit arrangement shown in Fig. 7·6 can perform two logical functions: $AB + CD = E$ or $(A + B)(C + D) = E$. These logical functions are shown in the logical schematic diagrams of Fig. 7·6a and b. If the function depicted in Fig. 7·6a is desired, positive input signals must be used; if that depicted in Fig. 7·6b is the desired function, negative input signals must be used.

DCTL circuit characteristics.   Since direct coupling is employed, the characteristics of the circuit are dependent largely upon the transistor itself. The characteristics of the transistors used in this system must be closely controlled. The transistors must have a low saturation voltage from collector to emitter, and they must be driven well into saturation to ensure a stable "on" condition. The surface-barrier type of transistor is the only type that has suitable characteristics for DCTL applications. Diodes are not used with DCTL because of the low voltage levels employed.

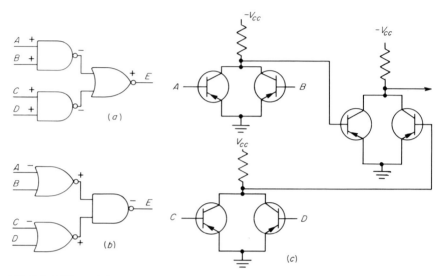

FIG. 7·6 DCTL symbology. (a) $AB + CD = E$; (b) $(A + B + C)(D + E + F) = G$; (c) electrical schematic.

DCTL is relatively expensive because of the large number of transistors required. Each logical input requires a separate transistor. There are practical limits to the number of transistors that may be used in parallel or in series. The leakage current I_{co} determines the number of transistors that may be placed in parallel. The sum of the I_{co} current of each transistor flows through the common load resistor. If the total I_{co} is too large, the collector will not maintain its lower-level voltage (in the example, -0.3 volt) when all transistors are off, but will rise toward -0.1 volt. The large I_{co} current produces a false "on" condition. To ensure correct operation, no more than 10 transistors should be placed in parallel.

When series gates are used, the transistor saturation voltage is the limiting factor. The desired saturation voltage is -0.1 volt. This means that the collector voltage of the top transistor is -0.1 volt with respect to ground. If two transistors are placed in series, the saturation voltage of each transistor is 0.05 volt; if three transistors are used, the saturation voltage of each transistor is 0.03 volt. Usually a DCTL logical gate has three transistors.

The switching speed of DCTL is rapid because of the high cutoff frequency of the transistors. This speed is hampered, however, because the transistor is driven into saturation. The main advantage of DCTL is circuit simplicity. There are other less expensive logical systems that have faster switching speed.

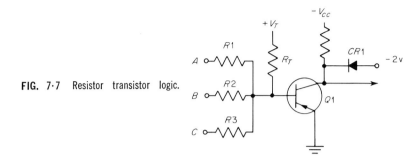

FIG. 7·7 Resistor transistor logic.

The proper nomenclature for the gates described are NAND and NOR gates since there is a signal inversion. AND and OR gates would be depicted if the circuits were changed to an emitter-follower configuration.

Resistor Transistor Logic

RTL offers a circuit design which does not require stringent control of transistor parameters. The gate consists of a resistor current-summing network followed by an inverting amplifier. The circuit is shown in Fig. 7·7.

The inputs are pulses whose magnitudes are usually at least 1 volt. The resistors $R1$, $R2$, and $R3$ are equal in value. Assume that the input varies between -0.1 and -2 volts. If all three inputs are at the upper level (-0.1 volt), transistor $Q1$ will be off. However, the resistor values are chosen so that if one input is at its lower level (-2 volts), $Q1$ is driven into the saturation region. If more than one input is at its lower level, the transistor is driven deeper into saturation. The resistors provide a current-summing network, and the total current is drawn through the base of $Q1$. When the transistor is turned off, the collector voltage is clamped to -2 volts by $CR1$.

The circuit is a positive-input NAND gate or a negative-input NOR gate. For ease of logic design, the same assumptions made in the DCTL logic apply to RTL gates. The gates may be considered as straightforward AND or OR gates with polarity reversal. A complex arrangement of gates to perform a logical operation is shown in Fig. 7·8. This arrangement may perform the functions $ABC + DEF = G$ or $(A + B + C)(D + E + F) = G$.

Component calculations. Without considering worst-case aspects, the method of determining base input resistor values will be shown. If the collector current desired is 5 ma and the transistor has a β of 20, the required base current is 0.25 ma. The input characteristic curve gives the amount of base voltage required to provide a 0.25-ma base current.

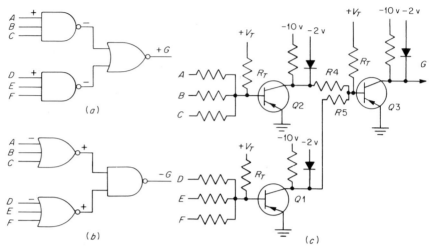

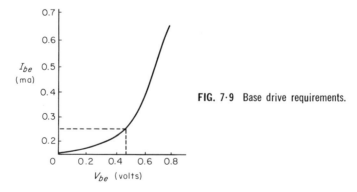

FIG. 7·8 RTL symbology. (a) $ABC + DEF = G$; (b) $(A + B + C)(D + E + C) = F$; (c) electrical schematic.

Figure 7·9 shows that approximately 0.46 volt provides a 0.25-ma base current. Assume that only one input — A, for example — is at its low value. The current through $R1$ is the sum of the V_T/R_T current and the base current (Fig. 7·7). If the V_T current is 0.16 ma, the value of the input resistor $R1$ is

$$\frac{(2 - 0.46) \text{ volts}}{(0.25 + 0.16) \text{ ma}} = 3760 \text{ ohms}$$

Each input gating resistor will have this value.

When a transistor is off, its base voltage should be close to ground potential. The inputs are usually from the collectors of other transistor

FIG. 7·9 Base drive requirements.

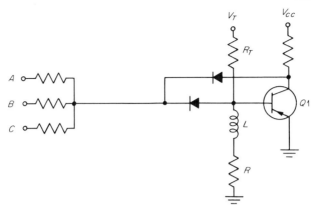

FIG. 7·10 Improving RTL frequency response by back clamping.

stages. For example, the inputs to $Q3$ in Fig. 7·8 are from the collectors of $Q1$ and $Q2$.

To ensure that $Q3$ remains off, the temperature-stabilizing network (V_T and R_T) provides a small current through $R4$ and $R5$ to aid in reverse-biasing the base-emitter junction. The V_T/R_T current is the sum of the expected cutoff current and the current necessary to maintain a base voltage of 0 during turn-off.

Circuit characteristics. RTL is applicable to low-frequency switching circuits. However, at higher frequencies the circuit becomes more complex. To increase speed, higher-frequency transistors and additional circuits to provide base overdrive can be used.

Figure 7·10 shows an RTL stage using diodes to prevent saturation and an RL network to provide base-current overdrive during turn-on and turn-off.

Resistor-capacitor Transistor Logic

The standard method of providing base overdrive is to use speedup capacitors across the gating resistors as shown in Fig. 7·11.

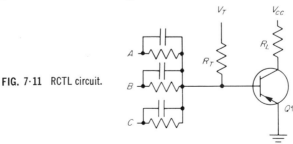

FIG. 7·11 RCTL circuit.

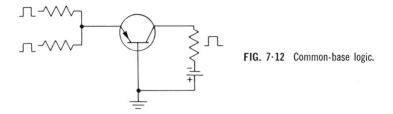

FIG. 7·12 Common-base logic.

The use of speedup capacitors may cause malfunctions in circuit operation. Without the coupling capacitors, the gating resistors serve to isolate the low input impedance of transistor $Q1$, from the outputs of the collectors at A, B, and C. The coupling capacitors reduce this isolation. If A, B, and C are all at their lower level, the transistor is in saturation. Without the capacitors, if two of the inputs were to go to their upper level, the transistor would decrease its conduction slightly but still remain in the saturation region. With the capacitors, the amount of charge current drawn out of the base as the inputs go to their upper level may be sufficient to turn the transistor off. At high frequencies the capacitors increase the amount of interaction between adjacent collectors. These disadvantages limit the number of inputs that may be applied.

Common-base configurations.   A common-base configuration such as the one shown in Fig. 7·12 provides logical functions without phase inversions. The circuit does not provide current gain and thereby creates a heavy drain on the input. Coupling between stages presents a greater problem than does the common-emitter configuration since the common-base configuration has a higher output impedance and a lower input impedance.

Hybrid Logic

Hybrid logic is a combination of diode gates and transistor amplifiers. Since diode gates provide no amplification, amplifier stages must be placed between the gates at various intervals to prevent excessive attenuation of the signals.

It is not a task to determine exactly where in a logical sequence to place the amplifier stages. A good approach is to construct a basic building block composed of diode gates combined with an amplifier output. The basic building block will have a known input drive requirement and a known output drive capability. All required logical operations may be accomplished by combining the basic building blocks.

There are two basic switching techniques used in hybrid logic. These techniques differ in the way the transistor-amplifier stage is switched. One

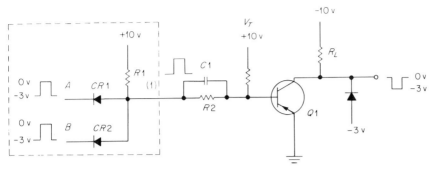

FIG. 7·13 Voltage-switching hybrid gate.

technique is voltage switching, in which a voltage is applied to the base of the transistor. The other technique is current switching, in which a constant current is switched in and out of the base of the transistor. Both techniques are now discussed.

Voltage-switching hybrid logic. A basic diode-gate–amplifier configuration is shown in Fig. 7·13. Diodes $CR1$ and $CR2$ and resistor $R1$ constitute an AND gate for positive logic. The voltage at point 1 follows the lowest inputs applied to the gates. The input voltage levels used are -3 volts and 0 volt. The voltage at point 1 is 0 volt only if A and B are 0 volt simultaneously. If one of the inputs, B for example, falls to -3 volts, $CR2$ conducts harder and the entire voltage, disregarding the drop across the diode, is dropped across $R1$. The voltage at point 1 falls to -3 volts, and $CR1$ is reverse-biased. Resistor $R2$ limits the voltage applied to the base of $Q1$.

The basic block in Fig. 7·13 can be expanded to include more gates. The most widely used sequence is a series of AND gates driving an OR gate. A logical diagram, together with its associated circuit, is shown in Fig. 7·14.

Diode gate $G3$ is an OR gate for positive "true" signals. If, for example, point 1 is 0 volt and point 2 is -3 volts, $CR1$ conducts harder than $CR2$. Point 3 is 0 volt and $CR2$ is reverse-biased. $Q1$ conducts only when point 3 is -3 volts. The two-stage amplifier provides sufficient power to drive several stages. If required, the NOT function is available at the output of $Q1$, and the "true" output is present at $Q2$.

Current-switching hybrid logic. Current-switching techniques may be preferred to voltage-switching techniques because lower-amplitude pulses may be used and faster switching speed is obtained.

The principle of current switching is that a constant current is switched into either a transistor base or a diode. In Fig. 7·15 the 20,000-ohm resistor and the -5-volt supply provide the 0.25 ma of current to be switched.

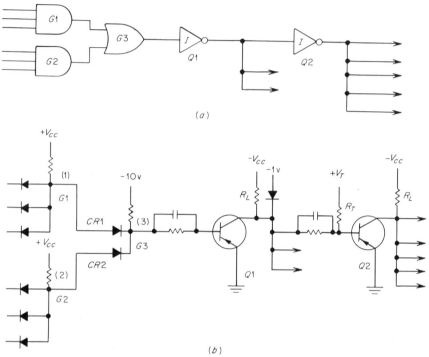

(b)

FIG. 7·14 AND-OR gate with inverters. (a) Logical diagram; (b) schematic.

If the input characteristics of the transistor indicate that a 0.25-ma base current requires a base-to-emitter voltage of -0.4 volt, then the voltage at point 1 is -0.4 volt. If -0.4 volt is applied to the anode of $CR1$, the diode cannot conduct, and the 0.25-ma current will flow into the base of

FIG. 7-15 Current-switching gate.

FIG. 7·16 Current-switching gate with OR logic input.

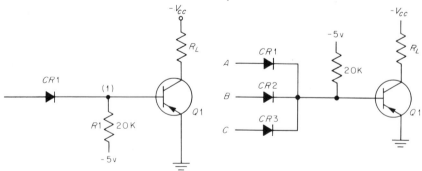

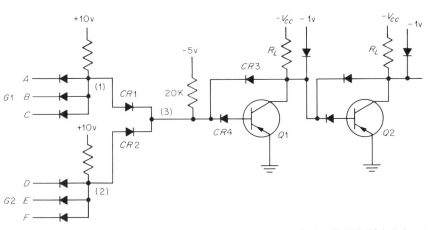

FIG. 7·17   Current-switching circuit with AND-OR logic input

the transistor. However, if the anode of $CR1$ rises to $+0.4$ volt, $CR1$ can conduct, the 0.25-ma current is switched out of the transistor base into the diode, and the transistor turns off. Consider the arrangement shown in Fig. 7·16.

If the inputs to A, B, and C are -0.4 volt, the diodes ($CR1$, $CR2$, and $CR3$) cannot conduct and current flows into the base of $Q1$, turning $Q1$ on. If one of the inputs rises to $+0.4$ volt, the current is diverted away from the base into the conducting diode, and the transistor turns off. The voltage swing required to operate the gate is less than 1 volt as compared with the voltage swing of several volts used in voltage switching. The circuit is an OR gate for positive inputs or an AND gate for negative inputs. An AND-OR gate combination for positive inputs is shown in Fig. 7·17.

Gates $G1$ and $G2$ are positive AND-gate inputs. The diodes $CR1$ and $CR2$ provide the OR function for current steering. If the output of one of the AND gates goes positive, $G1$ for example, $CR1$ conducts, and current is removed from the base of $Q1$. The two-stage inverter output provides both the NOT function, when required, and current to drive several other inputs.

The inputs to the AND gates are from the collector outputs of other logical stages. A level-shift problem must be overcome to ensure that when all inputs are at their upper levels the voltages at the anodes of $CR1$ and $CR2$ are sufficiently positive to allow $CR1$ and $CR2$ to conduct. The problem can be overcome by using silicon diodes in the AND gates and germanium diodes in the OR gates. The silicon diodes have a higher voltage drop than germanium diodes. Assume that the collector potential at input A goes no lower than -0.1 volt. If, for the amount of current drawn, the silicon diode has a voltage drop of 0.7 volt, the voltage at point 1 will be $+0.4$ volt.

This voltage is sufficient to allow $CR1$ to conduct. When the voltage at A rises to -1 volt, the voltage at point 1 is -0.4 volt and the OR-gate diode $CR1$ cannot conduct.

A diode back-clamping circuit may be used to prevent saturation. The back-clamping circuit may also provide a base overdrive current to decrease turn-on time. The constant-current source supplies more than the required amount of base current to saturate the transistor. When the collector potential falls so that $CR3$ can conduct, the additional base current flows through $CR3$ and is not amplified in the base. $CR4$ is a silicon diode used to maintain a constant base voltage.

Circuit characteristics.   If the current-steering technique is used, the collector voltage varies by only a few tenths of a volt. This voltage swing is small compared with the collector supply voltage; hence, very little power is consumed. The system is often referred to as *low-level logic.* The base current comes from a constant-current source; therefore, the number of diode inputs does not affect the base current. Since only a small portion of the collector swing is used, the switching speed is increased.

Current-mode Logic

CML utilizes another form of current switching. The input transistor current is provided by a constant-current source. This current is switched from one transistor to the other, as shown in Fig. 7·18. In this illustration the total current is 10 ma. This current flows through the transistor which has the more negative base potential. Assume that the base of $Q1$ (point A) is -0.4 volt and the base of $Q2$ is grounded. Transistor $Q1$ conducts and the 10 ma, less the base current, flows to the collector of $Q1$. If we assume a

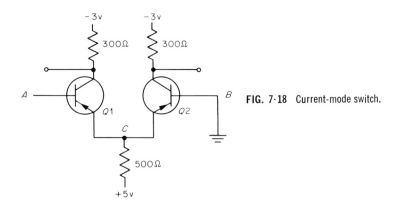

FIG. 7·18 Current-mode switch.

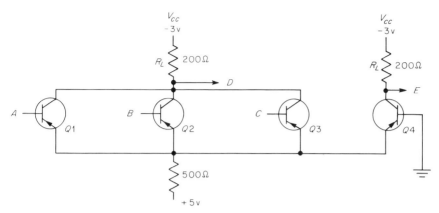

FIG. 7·19   Current-mode logical gate.

0.2-volt drop across the base-emitter junction of $Q1$, point C is -0.2 volt and the base-emitter junction of $Q2$ is reverse-biased.

Assume that the voltage at point A rises to $+0.4$ volt. $Q1$ turns off and $Q2$ conducts. Point C becomes slightly positive because of the base-emitter voltage drop at $Q2$.

Figure 7·19 shows a current-mode logical gate. The three inputs to the gate are A, B, and C. If a negative voltage is applied to any input, the collector rises to its upper level. If all inputs are positive simultaneously, the current is switched into $Q4$, and the collector of $Q4$ rises to its upper level. The circuit is a negative-input OR gate or a positive-input AND gate.

The voltages at outputs D and E are the logical inverse of each other; hence, the circuit can provide both an inverted and a noninverted output. If the noninverted output of $Q4$ is not required, the transistor may be replaced by a diode.

The circuit can be designed so that the transistor may be operated as far out of saturation as desired. The collector voltage V_c is determined by the following equation:

$$V_c = V_{cc} - I_e R_L$$

If the collector voltage at the upper level is to be -1 volt, the load resistor R_L may be found by the following equation:

$$R_L = \frac{V_{cc} - V_c}{I_e}$$

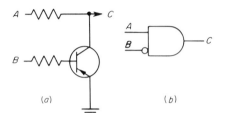

FIG. 7·20 Inhibit gate. (a) Schematic; (b) logic symbol.

If V_{cc} is -3 volts and I_e is 10 ma, R_L is determined by the following equation:

$$\frac{(3-1) \text{ volts}}{10 \text{ ma}} = 200 \text{ ohms}$$

Special Gates

Gates such as inhibit gates and gated pulse amplifiers are often used in computers. Descriptions of both types of gates follow.

Inhibit gates. Inhibit gates are used to provide a BUT-NOT function; that is, an output from the gate is obtained only when one input is present and the another input is absent. For example, the equation $A\bar{B} = C$ (A BUT-NOT B equals C) may be achieved by using an inhibit gate such as that shown in Fig. 7·20.

Assume that the "true" level is -6 volts. If -6 volts is applied to A and B simultaneously, the transistor conducts, and the output at C is close to 0 volt. If -6 volts is applied to A, and B is 0 volt, the transistor does not conduct, and the voltage at C is -6 volts. C can only be at -6 volts when the condition $A\bar{B}$ exists. The dot on the B input line in Fig. 7·20 indicates that B must not be present if an output C is to be obtained.

Exclusive-OR gate. An exclusive-OR gate is shown in Fig. 7·21. Assume a $+3$ volt input on pins 1 and 2. Diodes $CR1$, $CR2$, $CR3$, and $CR4$ will conduct (3 and 4, less, 1 and 2, more) resulting in $+3.3$ volts at the base of transistors $Q1$ and $Q2$. The emitter-follower action of $Q2$ causes the emitter of $Q1$ to be at $+3$ volts, back-biasing $Q1$, and no collector current flows. A voltage division takes place by electron flow from -15 volts to $+15$ volts through $R5$, $R6$, and $R8$, placing approximately -1.5 volts on the base of $Q3$. Transistor $Q3$ conducts, causing current to flow in the collector-emitter diode circuit, and the output at pin 3 will be 0 volt.

If inputs at pins 1 and 2 are 0 volt, diodes $CR3$ and $CR4$ conduct, causing electron flow from pins 1 and 2 through $CR3$ and $CR4$ to $+15$ volts.

This places $+0.3$ volts on the base of $Q1$. Zero volts on pins 1 and 2 cause $CR1$ and $CR2$ to conduct less, and the base of $Q2$ is at a -0.3-volt potential. The emitter-follower action of $Q2$ causes the emitters of $Q2$ and $Q1$ to both be at 0 volt. Transistor $Q1$ is again back-biased, and the action is the same as explained in the previous paragraph.

With $+3$ volts on pin 1 and 0 volt on pin 2, $+3$ volts are applied through $CR1$ to the base of $Q2$. The emitter of $Q2$ tries to follow the base but is clamped to approximately $+1$ volt through $CR5$, the diode action of the base-emitter circuit of $Q1$, and through $CR4$ to the pin-2 input of 0 volt. With the above conditions base current flows in transistor $Q1$, and the transistor turns on. The collector of $Q1$ swings positive, causing the junction of resistors $R5$ and $R6$ to be approximately 0 volt. The voltage developed at the junction of resistors $R6$ and $R8$ goes positive and is clamped at $+3$ volts by diode $CR6$. The emitter-follower action of $Q3$ causes the output at pin 3 to be $+3$ volts. The same circuit action takes place if the voltage levels at pins 1 and 2 are reversed.

SECTION 2 AMPLIFIERS

Computing machines require many types of nonlogical special amplifier circuits to perform numerous tasks. Special-purpose amplifiers are used to

FIG. 7·21 Exclusive-OR gate.

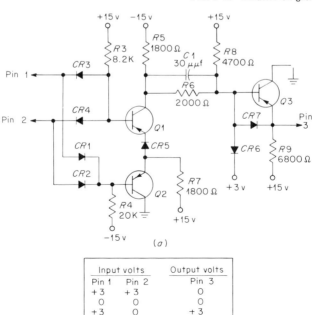

Input volts		Output volts
Pin 1	Pin 2	Pin 3
+3	+3	0
0	0	0
+3	0	+3
0	+3	+3

(b)

increase the signal amplitude or change the shape of a pulse waveform, isolate one stage of a circuit from another, control the lighting of indicators, and control relays which perform a wide variety of operations. These are but a few of the many functions amplifiers perform in modern computing systems.

An understanding of the operating principles of these amplifier circuits is important if computer operations are to be thoroughly understood.

Pulse Amplifier or Current Driver

The pulse-amplifier circuit has a variety of functions in a computing system. It can be used to generate a pulse-output waveform from either a square-wave input or a spiked differentiated input waveform. This pulse output can be used to supply drive to the various shift registers and counters in the system.

Figure 7·22 shows a transistorized current driver with its input and output waveforms.

FIG. 7·22 Transistorized current driver and waveforms. (a) Schematic diagram; (b) waveforms.

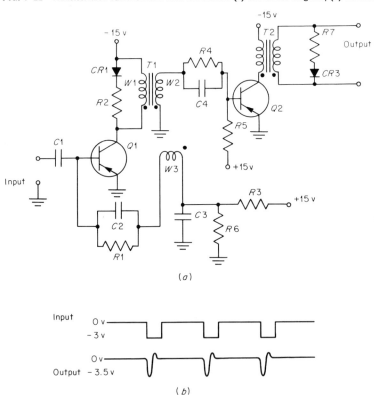

Circuit operation. Transistor $Q1$, a triggered blocking oscillator, is held at cutoff by a positive reverse bias on its base from the voltage divider (consisting of resistors $R6$ and $R3$) between ground and the positive 15-volt supply. Transistor $Q2$, used for isolation and amplification, is held at cutoff by the positive voltage appearing at the junction of resistors $R4$ and $R5$.

When an input pulse is applied, its leading edge will immediately turn transistor $Q1$ on. This causes collector current to flow in winding $W1$ of transformer $T1$, generating a large magnetic field. The field induces a voltage in windings $W2$ and $W3$ of transformer $T1$. The voltage induced in $W3$ is coupled through capacitor $C2$ and resistor $R1$ to the base of transistor $Q1$ and is in phase with the input signal. This causes more collector current to flow through $W1$ of the transformer and generates an even larger magnetic field. This action is cumulative and continues until $W1$ of transformer $T1$ becomes saturated, allowing no further change in magnetic field density to take place.

The voltage induced in $W2$ is determined by the rate of change of magnetic flux generated and also by the turns ratio of the transformer. With the correct turns ratio, enough base current is supplied to transistor $Q2$ through coupling network $R4$ and $C4$ to cause it to saturate. The collector of transistor $Q2$ changes then from -15 volts to nearly 0 volt. This voltage change of almost 15 volts is impressed across the primary winding of $T2$. Transformer $T2$ is a step-down transformer with a turns ratio of approximately 4.3:1. The primary winding contains 60 turns, and the secondary winding contains 14 turns. With a 15-volt change across a 60-turn winding, the figure of four turns for each volt is obtained. Using the ratio of four turns for each volt, we can see how the voltage induced in the 14-turn secondary winding of $T2$ will be 3.5 volts. This is a large decrease in voltage; however, a step-down in voltage causes a step-up in current by the same ratio. Therefore, the output current is quite large, actually 4.3 times greater than that appearing in the primary winding of transformer $T2$.

The output pulse width is determined by the length of time required to saturate transformer $T1$ in the collector circuit of transistor $Q1$. Once this condition is reached, the signal on the base of transistor $Q2$ falls off, and the dc bias voltage appearing at the junction of resistors $R4$ and $R5$ turns transistor $Q2$ off. This transistorized circuit generates a high-current pulse of short duration capable of driving many logic circuits in the computer.

Buffer Amplifier

The buffer amplifier is used throughout the computing system for isolation, power amplification, and impedance matching.

Figure 7·23 illustrates a basic buffer circuit. It should be noted that the circuit is a single-stage emitter follower whose output waveshape will be the

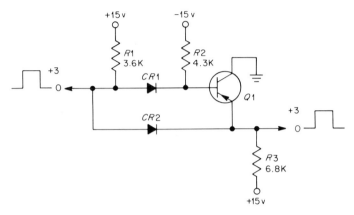

FIG. 7·23 Transistor buffer.

same as the input. Diode $CR1$ is used to compensate for dc voltage level shifting of previous stages, $R1$ provides protection for the transistor when the preceding stage is removed, and $CR2$ compensates for the stray capacitances in the succeeding stages that would tend to round off the leading edge of the output waveshape.

In the quiescent state with no input pulse present, $Q1$ is conducting heavily and the output is at 0 volt (ground). If a positive input pulse is applied to the base of $Q1$, $Q1$ will decrease conduction, and the reduced current through $R3$ will cause the emitter to "follow the base" or swing positive. Since an emitter follower has a gain of almost unity, the output voltage will be slightly less than 3 volts for the duration of the input pulse.

Inverter Buffer

Figure 7·24 shows a transistorized version of another buffer amplifier. This is a one-stage common-emitter amplifier whose output is obtained from the collector of transistor $Q1$. Since the input signal is applied to the base circuit, phase inversion will take place.

Circuit operation. Assume the input logic levels to be 0 volt and -6 volts. Resistor $R1$ supplies a constant current to the base of $Q1$ when its input is -6 volts. Capacitor $C1$ is a speedup capacitor which allows additional base current to flow in $Q1$ during transitions of the input square wave. This additional current decreases the switching time of transistor $Q1$, causing sharp leading and trailing edges to appear in the output waveform. Diodes $CR1$ and $CR3$ provide a back-clamping action to clamp the collector potential so that it cannot fall below the base voltage to forward-bias the collector

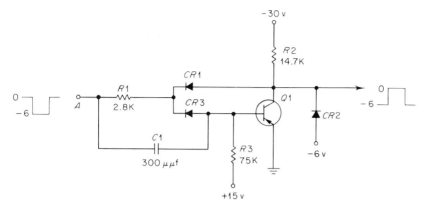

FIG. 7·24 Transistor inverter buffer.

junction. This avoids saturation of transistor $Q1$ when it is on, thereby decreasing its turn-off time. Diode $CR2$ clamps the collector potential of transistor $Q1$ to -6 volts when $Q1$ is not conducting.

With 0 volt as an input to point A, transistor $Q1$ is cut off, and its collector potential is clamped at -6 volts. When the input signal is -6 volts, $Q1$ is conducting heavily, and its collector potential is nearly 0 volt. It can be seen then that the output waveform is $180°$ out of phase with the input. In most cases, however, this is not a disadvantage. Isolation is obtained for the circuit preceding the buffer because now all outputs to other circuits will come from the collector of transistor $Q1$.

Buffer amplifiers are used throughout all computing and data processing systems to provide isolation between stages. They have many desirable characteristics, such as power amplification, impedance matching, and waveshaping. The buffer amplifier is needed to prevent loading of critical circuits and to provide stable and reliable operation of computer systems.

Relay Amplifier

The relay-amplifier circuit is used to control the operation of the relays used in a computing system. Usually each relay will have its own relay-amplifier circuit. One of the uses of relays in a computing or data processing system is to control the starting and stopping of the peripheral equipment associated with the system. Peripheral equipment consists of equipment external to the computer, such as tape readers, card readers, print-out or punch-out systems, and test equipment.

Relays are also used to actuate various indicators on control panels

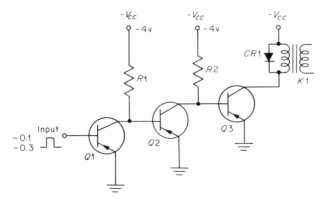

FIG. 7·25 Relay amplifier.

which indicate to the operator when the computer has completed certain operations or when an error or fault has occurred. Figure 7·25 illustrates a typical transistorized relay-amplifier circuit and shows the output relay winding and the input to the amplifier.

The relay-amplifier circuit consists of transistors $Q2$ and $Q3$, resistors $R1$ and $R2$, diode $CR1$, and relay coil $K1$. Transistor $Q1$ supplies the input to the amplifier.

Circuit operation. The signal input will be at one of two logic levels. These levels are assumed to be -0.3 and -0.1 volt. The circuit is designed to actuate the relay when an input of -0.3 volt is applied to the base of transistor $Q1$. The -0.3-volt input turns on transistor $Q1$ and causes its collector voltage to decrease from approximately -0.3 to -0.1 volt because of current flow through collector resistor $R1$. This -0.1-volt level is applied to the base of transistor $Q2$, turning it off. $Q2$ had previously been conducting because of the negative collector potential of $Q1$ on its base. When transistor $Q2$ turns off, its collector potential increases negatively. This increase is coupled to the base of transistor $Q3$, turning it on. Transistor $Q3$ is a high-current driver type of transistor. When $Q3$ saturates, its emitter-to-base current clamps the collector of transistor $Q2$ to -1 volt. The collector current of transistor $Q3$, when it is saturated, is approximately 160 ma. A current of 150 ma flowing through relay coil $K1$ is sufficient to energize the relay.

Assume the input to transistor $Q1$ to be -0.1 volt. This will turn transistor $Q1$ off, causing its collector voltage to rise toward $-V_{cc}$. The negative rise is coupled to the base of transistor $Q2$, turning it on. With transistor $Q2$ saturated, its collector potential will be -0.1 volt, which biases the high-current driver transistor $Q3$ off. The leakage current of transistor $Q3$, when it is off, is considerably more than that of a typical low-current transistor; however, it is not large enough to cause relay $K1$ to energize; therefore, the armature will not be actuated.

Diode $CR1$ connected across the relay coil prevents damage to transistor $Q3$ by shunting the high-inductive transients generated when $Q3$ is turned off. The relay-amplifier circuit, then, is nothing more than a transistorized switch which, when closed, causes a relay to energize and, when opened, causes the relay to deenergize.

Bipolar Sense Amplifier

The bipolar sense amplifier shown in Fig. 7·26 is used to amplify low-level voltage signals which indicate data bits. The difference between a binary 1 and a binary 0 is a 180° phase shift of the signal applied to the base and emitter of $Q1$. The circuit contains three common-emitter amplifiers ($Q1$, $Q3$, and $Q5$), two of which are operating as class A ($Q1$ and $Q3$) amplifiers, and two emitter-followers (transistors $Q2$ and $Q4$).

Circuit operation. When a binary 0 is sensed, assume a positive signal is applied to the base of transistor $Q1$ and a negative signal is applied to the emitter of $Q1$. The forward bias of transistor $Q1$ is reduced, and conduction

FIG. 7·26 Bipolar sense amplifier.

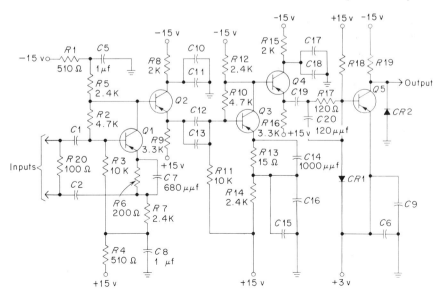

decreases, causing the collector of $Q1$ to swing in a negative direction. This negative-going signal is direct-coupled to the base of the emitter-follower $Q2$ causing heavier conduction in $Q2$, resulting in a negative-going pulse at the junction of $R9$, $C12$, and $C13$. This negative pulse is coupled through capacitors $C12$ and $C13$ to the base of transistor $Q3$ causing increased conduction in $Q3$, and the collector of $Q3$ swings positive. This positive pulse is applied to the base of the emitter-follower $Q4$ causing reduced conduction in $Q4$. This reduced conduction results in a positive pulse being coupled by $C19$ to the base of transistor $Q5$. The positive pulse causes transistor $Q5$ to reduce in conduction resulting in the collector of $Q5$ attempting to go negative. Diode $CR2$ clamps the output at a 0-volt level preventing a negative voltage swing at the collector of $Q5$.

When a binary 1 is sensed at the input of $Q1$, a negative signal is applied to its base and a positive signal is applied to its emitter. Transistor $Q1$ conducts heavier, and its collector swings positive. The positive pulse is coupled through emitter-follower $Q2$ and capacitors $C12$ and $C13$ to the base of transistor $Q3$. $Q3$ amplifies and inverts this signal to a negative-going pulse at the base of $Q4$. The negative pulse is coupled through emitter-follower $Q4$ and capacitors $C19$ and $C20$ to the base of $Q5$. Amplifier $Q5$ conducts heavily causing the output to go positive where it is clamped at $+3$ volts by the emitter potential.

It should be noted that a binary 0 input to the amplifier results in a 0 volt output, whereas a binary 1 input will result in a $+3$ volt output.

Lamp-driver Amplifier

The lamp-driver amplifier circuit is used to control the lighting and extinguishing of incandescent lamps. These lamps are used extensively in computer systems to display information concerning the power status, ON or OFF, malfunction conditions, and data representation in the various counters and registers throughout the computer.

Circuit operation. The amplifier illustrated in Fig. 7-27 provides the switching required to control the state of indicator lamps. The input volt-

FIG. 7-27 Lamp-driver amplifier.

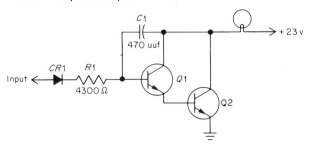

age levels required are 0 volt to turn the lamp off and +3 volts to turn the lamp on. During the time that the input voltage level is 0 volt, transistors $Q1$ and $Q2$ will be back-biased and not conducting. This condition will present an open circuit to the +23-volt level being provided to the other side of the lamp; hence the lamp is extinguished.

With the input voltage level at +3 volts, transistor $Q1$ conducts, and the emitter provides a forward bias for transistor $Q2$. Transistor $Q2$ provides a ground return for the 23-volt level being applied to the lamp and causes the lamp to be illuminated.

SECTION 3   OSCILLATORS AND MULTIVIBRATORS

Oscillators

Oscillators are used in computing systems to provide the pulses required for system timing and as delay devices for timing pulses. The oscillators most commonly used in computing systems may be placed within two basic classifications, namely, timing oscillators and blocking oscillators.

Timing oscillators. Digital computers solve problems by following a detailed system of instructions called a *program*. Each instruction contained in the program must be performed by the computer at the correct time and in the correct sequence. To do this, two components must be incorporated into the computing system: (1) a timing oscillator to divide time into small, equal intervals, and (2) a clock to record the number of timing intervals that have passed since the start of the program. The timing oscillator and clock synchronize all functions performed by the computer and ensure that each function occurs precisely on time.

Program synchronization. The timing oscillator is the heart of the synchronizing system in a computer. It generates the basic timing interval and determines the rate at which the computer processes information. To see how this is done, consider the simplified block diagram in Fig. 7·28. As shown in the diagram, the output of the timing oscillator (signal A) is a continuous sine wave. A period of one cycle of this oscillating waveform establishes the basic timing interval. In a computer, the free-running frequency of the timing oscillator may be 20 MHz; therefore the basic timing interval (duration of one cycle) is 50 nsec. The output of the timing oscillator is delivered to a pulse-forming-and-shaping circuit which produces one output pulse (called a *clock pulse*) for each input cycle (signal B).

The clock shown in Fig. 7·28 is an electronic counter. This clock records the number of timing intervals which have passed since the start of the program by counting the number of clock pulses delivered to its input.

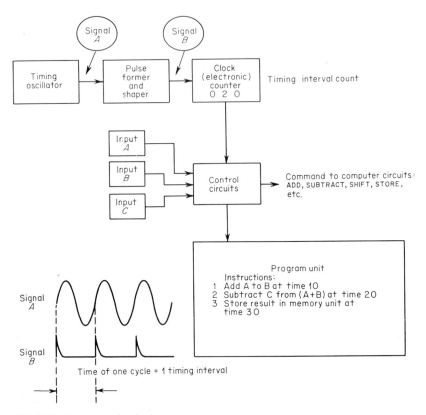

FIG. 7·28 Program synchronization.

At a predetermined count or timing interval, the computer performs a function determined by an instruction contained in the program unit.

The simplified program illustrated in Fig. 7·28 contains three instructions. When the counter or clock contains a count of 10, the computer adds the information present at input A to that present at input B. At time interval 20, input C is subtracted from the sum of A plus B; and at timing interval 30, the computer stores the result of the subtraction in its memory unit.

In modern computers thousands of instructions are contained in the program unit. The time required for the computer to execute each instruction depends, of course, on the nature of the instruction. A SHIFT-TO-STORAGE instruction, for example, cannot be executed as quickly as an ADD instruction. If the execution time for the average instruction is 10 timing intervals, a computer with a 20-MHz timing oscillator can perform 2 million operations a second.

While the above example illustrates the chief use of timing oscillators in computer systems, often more timing oscillators are used in auxiliary equipment at the input or output of the computer. Regardless of specific application, however, the purpose of all timing oscillators is the same: to divide an interval of time into small, equal, and precisely measured time increments.

Since the basic timing interval generated by a timing oscillator will change if its frequency drifts, frequency stability is an important characteristic of such devices. In many cases, oscillators used in these applications are crystal-controlled to provide frequency stability over long periods of time.

The operating principles of sine-wave oscillators are covered in the following pages. Feedback oscillators employing LC resonant circuits are treated first. This treatment is followed by the development of the crystal oscillator from oscillators controlled by conventional LC-type circuits.

Sine-wave oscillators. A sine-wave oscillator is a device capable of converting direct current into an alternating current at a frequency determined by circuit constants. The output waveform of a sine-wave oscillator is shown in Fig. 7·29a.

Sine-wave oscillators may be classified into two broad groups: (1) feedback oscillators and (2) negative-resistance oscillators. Although the term "negative resistance" may be used to account for the cancellation of circuit resistance in any continuously oscillating device, when used to classify oscillator types it has a more specific meaning. Negative-resistance oscillators employ special circuit elements that display negative-resistance characteristics, or characteristics opposite to those of a conventional resistor. For example, when the voltage across a negative-resistance element increases, the current through it decreases and vice versa. The negative-resistance oscillator is rarely used in timing-oscillator applications. For this reason, this discussion will be limited to feedback oscillators.

The block diagram of a feedback oscillator is shown in Fig. 7·29b. As shown in the diagram, the oscillator contains three essential parts: (1) a frequency-determining element, (2) a power amplifier, and (3) a feedback loop with a feedback element. The frequency-determining element, usually a resonant circuit, limits oscillations to a single frequency and supplies a varying signal at this frequency to the power amplifier. The power amplifier increases the power of the signal applied to its input. Part of the output power from the amplifier is supplied to the load, and part is returned as feedback power to the input of the oscillator. The power fed back to the input must be returned in phase with the input power. This is called *regenerative*, or *positive*, feedback. The feedback power is used to overcome resistance losses in the frequency-determining element and for this reason is said to contribute an element of negative resistance to the circuit. The feedback element provides coupling between the output and input of the oscillator and controls the amount of energy fed back to the input. When the feedback power is just sufficient to overcome the resistance losses in the feedback loop, the circuit oscillates continuously at a constant amplitude.

FIG. 7·29 Sine-wave oscillator. (a) Block diagram and output waveform; (b) feedback oscillator; (c) proper amount of feedback; (d) insufficient feedback; (e) excessive feedback.

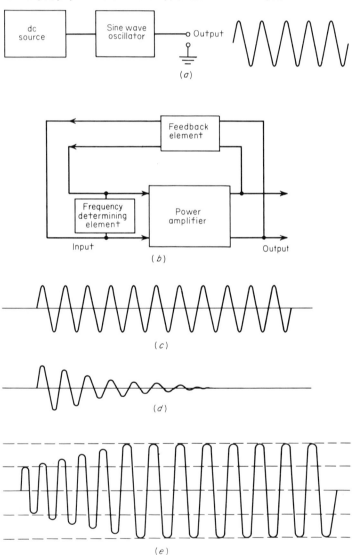

If an excessive amount of feedback energy is returned to the input, the amplitude of the output signal will continuously increase until it is limited by circuit saturation. If insufficient feedback is provided through the coupling element, the circuit will oscillate only momentarily, and oscillations will decay exponentially to zero in a relatively short period of time. The three conditions of feedback are shown in Fig. 7·29. The ratio of the feedback power to the power delivered to the input of the amplifier is termed the *loop gain* of the circuit. To provide continuous oscillations in the output, the loop gain of the circuit must be greater than unity.

The usable output power of any feedback oscillator is reduced by the amount of power fed back to the input to sustain oscillations. For this reason, losses in the feedback loop must be kept at a minimum, and the feedback circuit must be designed to match the input and output impedances of the amplifier. These requirements are particularly important in power oscillators and in oscillators designed to operate at extremely high frequencies.

Sine-wave oscillators employing feedback principles are often classified in accordance with the type of frequency-determining element used in the oscillator. Included in this classification are LC resonant oscillators, crystal-controlled oscillators, and resistance-capacitance-controlled oscillators. Oscillators whose frequency is controlled by RC networks find their widest use as audio-frequency generators and are not covered. LC resonant and crystal-controlled oscillators, however, are frequently employed in timing applications and are discussed in the following paragraphs.

LC resonant oscillators. LC resonant oscillators utilize the resonating properties of an inductor-capacitor combination to control the frequency at which the circuit oscillates. When power is momentarily applied to such a combination of components, the circuit becomes shock-excited and oscillates for a short time. To understand how oscillations originate in an LC network, consider the circuit shown in Fig. 7·30.

FIG. 7·30 LC network. (a) Schematic; (b) output waveform.

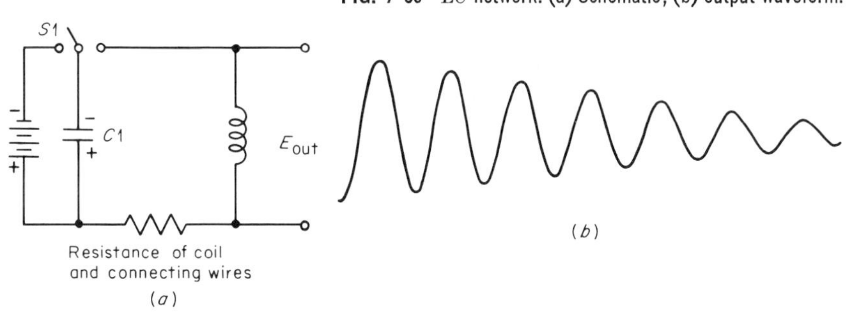

E_{out}

Resistance of coil and connecting wires

(a)

(b)

When switch $S1$ is thrown to the left, capacitor $C1$ charges to the applied voltage with the polarity shown. During the charge, energy is stored in the electric field between the plates of the capacitor. When the battery is removed and switch $S1$ is thrown to the right, the capacitor discharges through the inductor. During the discharge, energy in the electric field of the capacitor is transferred to the magnetic fields that builds up around the inductor because of the flow of current. When the capacitor is completely discharged, all the energy originally contained between the plates of the capacitor is stored in the magnetic field of the inductor. At this point, with no moving charge to support it, the magnetic field collapses. The collapsing magnetic field induces a voltage across the coil, and the capacitor becomes charged in the opposite direction.

The circuit action described above is repetitive. Energy is alternately exchanged between the capacitor and the inductor as $C1$ charges and discharges through L. Oscillation in this manner continues until all the energy received during the initial charge $C1$ is dissipated in the form of heat caused by circuit resistance. As shown in the figure, the output voltage, taken across the inductor, is sinusoidal in shape and decays exponentially to zero as energy in the circuit is dissipated.

The frequency at which the circuit oscillates is a function of the product $L \times C$ and can be determined through the use of the formula

$$F = \frac{1}{2\pi\sqrt{LC}}$$

The circuit shown in Fig. 7·30 would oscillate continuously were it not for the circuit resistance. In feedback oscillators, circuit resistance is overcome through use of a power amplifier and regenerative feedback. A circuit to accomplish this is shown in Fig. 7·31a.

The tuned-collector oscillator uses a tickler coil for inductive feedback. These elements determine circuit operation. Resistors $R1$ and $R2$ establish the base bias for the transistor and determine the operating point on the characteristic curve of the transistor. Resistor $R3$ is an emitter-swamping resistor and minimizes the effects of temperature variations in the emitter-base junction. Capacitors $C2$ and $C3$ are ac bypasses for resistors $R2$ and $R3$, respectively. The tuned circuit is comprised of transformer winding 3–4 and variable capacitor $C1$. Transformer winding 1–2 provides the feedback by coupling the signal developed across winding 3–4 to the input of the transistor power amplifier. The phase of the feedback signal, regenerative or degenerative, is a function of the transistor type (NPN or PNP) and the coupling phase of the feedback winding.

Circuit operation. (Refer to Fig. 7·31a.) With normal biasing of the transistor, oscillations begin when power is first applied. The transistor will

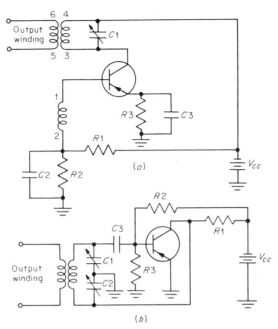

FIG. 7·31 Transistorized oscillators. (a) Tuned collector oscillator;
(b) transistorized Colpitts oscillator.

conduct with the amplitude of current steadily increasing because of the
regenerative feedback coupled from the collector circuit to the emitter
circuit by transformer windings 3–4 and 1–2.

A point of current saturation is reached, and no further change in
collector current can take place. The negative signal being fed back to the
base will increase for a period of time determined previously by the natural
resonant frequency of the tank circuit in the collector. After 180° of the
cycle, the feedback voltage reverses (goes positive) and begins to cut off the
saturated transistor. The circuit is biased in such a manner as to allow the
transistor to conduct only during the positive pulses of the output signal
(measured at terminals 3–4). The amplifier supplies energy to the tank
circuit in phase with the output ac signal of sufficient amplitude to compensate for the energy lost in the tank circuit because of circuit resistance.

The transistor is alternately driven into saturation and to cutoff. The
time required for the change from saturation to cutoff is determined primarily by the tuned circuit (capacitor $C1$ and transformer winding 3–4)
which in turn determines the frequency of oscillation.

Many variations of this basic feedback oscillator are possible. The
frequency-controlling element could be placed in the base circuit, in which
case the circuit configuration would be a tuned-base oscillator, and the out-

put would be taken from across the collector-emitter circuit. Another variation, as shown in Fig. 7·31b, is the transistorized Colpitts oscillator. The circuit operation is essentially the same except that the feedback is developed across capacitor $C1$. Capacitors $C1$ and $C2$ form a voltage divider that enables more accurate adjustment of the tuned circuit and feedback amplitude. Either or both of the capacitors can be adjusted to control the frequency and amount of feedback voltage.

The operating frequencies of the LC oscillators described above change with variations in the supply voltage, variations in the load on the oscillator, and changes in temperature. These factors affect the frequency of the oscillator because all alter the total circuit capacitance that shunts the parallel resonant circuit. Despite the inherent frequency instability of the LC resonant oscillator, frequency drift can be considerably reduced through correct design. Frequency stability sufficient for most applications can be achieved through use of regulated power supplies, buffer amplifiers to isolate the oscillator from its load, and negative temperature-coefficient capacitors to compensate for capacitance changes caused by temperature.

When the frequency of feedback oscillators must be held to close tolerances, crystal control is usually employed. The operating principles of crystal oscillators follow.

Crystal oscillators. The frequency stability of a feedback oscillator may be improved by using a quartz crystal as the frequency-controlling element. The frequency drift in a correctly designed oscillator may be held to less than one hertz each megahertz. This excellent frequency stability is due to the fact that oscillation depends on the mechanical properties of the crystal and is only slightly affected by circuit capacitance.

Crystalline substances like quartz have the same series and parallel resonant properties as electric circuits containing inductance, because of the piezoelectric characteristics of such materials.

When quartz is subjected to mechanical strain, a difference of potential is generated at opposing surfaces of the crystal (Fig. 7·32a). In addition to this effect, the reverse is also true; that is, if an external potential is applied across the surfaces of the crystal, its shape will become altered. For this reason, an alternating voltage applied across the crystal causes the crystal to vibrate mechanically. Maximum vibrations occur when the frequency of the applied voltage is equal to the natural vibrating frequency of the crystal. At this frequency, the crystal behaves electrically like a series resonant circuit.

The resonant properties of a quartz crystal may be demonstrated with the circuit in Fig. 7·32b. The curve in Fig. 7·32c shows how the current in the circuit varies as the frequency applied to the circuit is increased.

When the frequency of the generator is well below mechanical resonance, the crystal vibrates weakly, and the current recorded by the ammeter is relatively small. As the frequency of the generator is increased and the vibrating crystal approaches mechanical resonance ($F1$ in Fig. 7·32c), the current begins to increase and the crystal mass tends to vibrate ahead of the

FIG. 7·32   Resonant properties of quartz crystal. (a) Piezoelectric effect; (b) effect of resonant properties; (c) crystal current characteristics; (d) equivalent circuits.

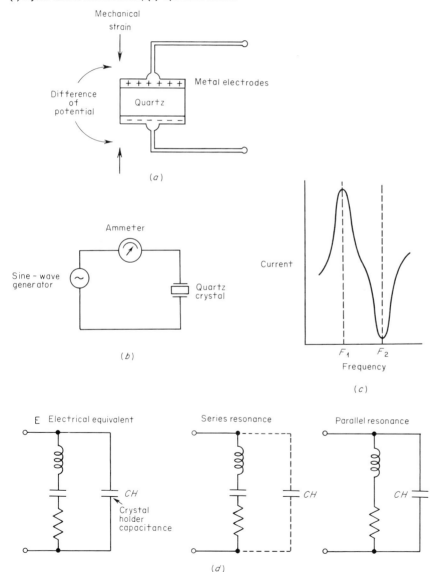

applied voltage. At this point the piezoelectric potential causes the circuit current to lead the applied voltage, producing the effect of capacitance. At $F1$, the current is maximum and in phase with the applied voltage. As the generator frequency is increased above mechanical resonance, vibrations tend to lag behind the applied voltage, and the current decreases rapidly. At this point, the piezoelectric potential developed by the vibrating crystal causes the circuit current to lag behind the applied voltage, producing the effect of an inductance. Notice that up to this point the crystal has displayed electrical characteristics identical with those of a series LC resonant circuit. Unlike its LC counterpart, however, the crystal will also oscillate at a frequency above its natural vibrating frequency ($F2$ on the curve in Fig. 7·32c). At this frequency ($F2$), circuit current drops abruptly, and the crystal displays the characteristics of a parallel resonant circuit.

Because of the behavior of the quartz crystal in electric circuits, a direct analogy may be made between its mechanical properties and their electrical equivalents. The equivalent electric circuit for the quartz crystal is shown in Fig. 7·32d. The inductance L represents the mass of the crystal. The series capacitance C is equivalent to the elasticity, that is, the ability of the crystal mass to return to its original position when the stress is removed.

FIG. 7·33 Transistorized crystal oscillators. (a) Two-stage RC-coupled oscillator; (b) grounded-base RC-coupled oscillator with emitter-follower output.

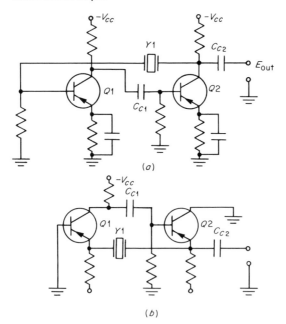

The resistance R represents frictional losses. Capacitor CH represents the capacitance of the crystal holder. The metal electrodes act as the plates of the capacitor, and the quartz material forms the dielectric.

The equivalent circuits to the right in Fig. 7·32d show the active components at both series and parallel resonance. At series resonance, the impedance presented by the vibrating crystal is much lower than the reactance of the crystal-holder capacitance (CH). For this reason the crystal-holder capacitance has no effect on the resonant frequency, and neither has any external circuit capacitance that shunts the crystal.

At the parallel resonant frequency of the crystal, the inductive reactance of L is greater than the capacitive reactance of C. Therefore, the combination of L and C appears as net inductance. This is shown in the equivalent circuit at the extreme right in Fig. 7·32d. This net inductance forms a parallel resonant circuit with the crystal-holder capacitance and any external circuit capacitance shunted across it.

Both the series and the parallel mode of crystal operation can be used in feedback-oscillator circuits. Figure 7·33 illustrates circuits frequently encountered in practical work.

Figure 7·33a depicts a crystal-controlled oscillator utilizing a two-stage RC-coupled amplifier. The two-stage amplifier provides an in-phase output signal at the collector of $Q2$. Crystal $Y1$ provides the regenerative feedback to the base of $Q1$ required to sustain oscillations within the circuit. A variation of the crystal-controlled oscillator is shown in Fig. 7·33b. This circuit consists of an amplifier circuit $Q1$ with an emitter-follower output $Q2$ for driving power and impedance matching. The out-of-phase feedback signal taken from the emitter of $Q2$ is coupled directly to the emitter of the amplifier circuit resulting in regenerative feedback to sustain oscillations.

Blocking oscillators. A blocking oscillator is any oscillator which cuts itself off after one or more cycles of its oscillating frequency. There are two classifications of blocking oscillators, single-swing and self-pulsing. Both types can be triggered or free-running. The output waveforms produced by blocking oscillators are illustrated in Fig. 7·34. The output waveform shown in Fig. 7·34a is generated by a single-swing blocking oscillator. In this type, the amplifier is cut off after one oscillating cycle is complete. In Fig. 7·34b, the output of a self-pulsing blocking oscillator is shown. Cutoff in this type occurs after two or more cycles have been completed.

Blocking oscillators can be arranged in either astable or monostable circuits. In the astable (free-running) circuit, a period of rest occurs between each oscillating interval, and the circuit performs as a relaxation oscillator (Fig. 7·34a and b). The monostable or triggered circuit is held initially at rest by external bias and remains in a stable state until an

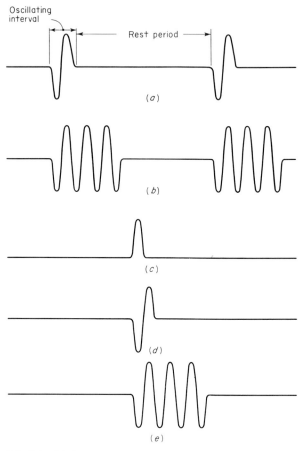

FIG. 7·34 Blocking-oscillator output waveforms. (a) Free-running, single-swing; (b) free-running, self-pulsing; (c) monostable-oscillator trigger input; (d) and (e) triggered monostable output.

external triggering pulse is applied. When this occurs the circuit oscillates briefly, then abruptly cuts off until retriggered. The output waveforms of monostable blocking oscillators are shown in Fig. 7·34d and e.

The type having the widest application in digital computers is the monostable single-swing blocking oscillator. The output waveform of this circuit is shown in Fig. 7·34d. With correct design, the monostable single-swing blocking oscillator can produce output pulses as narrow as 7 nsec. For this reason, the circuit is often used for reshaping broad, rounded input pulses into narrow output pulses with sharp leading and trailing edges. This circuit may also be used in frequency division and counting applications.

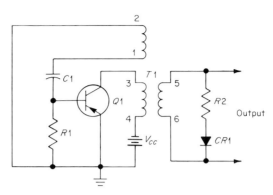

FIG. 7·35 Basic blocking oscillator.

The monostable (triggered) circuit is most frequently used, but the astable type will be presented first to introduce important principles.

Single-swing blocking oscillator (astable type). The basic circuit of the free-running, single-swing blocking oscillator is illustrated in Fig. 7·35. The circuit functions as a relaxation oscillator, and periodically generates a series of narrow pulses. Note the similarity between this circuit and that of the tickler-coil oscillator (Fig. 7·31a).

Circuit operation. When power is applied to the circuit, current rises rapidly in the base circuit because of the forward bias established in the base-emitter circuit. Transistor $Q1$ turns on, causing the current flow in the collector circuit to increase. The increasing collector current induces a negative-going voltage across winding 1–2 of transformer $T1$. This negative voltage charges capacitor $C1$ through the small forward resistance of the base-emitter diode and appears at the base as a large forward bias. Regeneration continues rapidly until the transistor is saturated and the collector current becomes constant.

At saturation there is no longer any induced voltage in winding 1–2, and the charging potential is no longer applied across capacitor $C1$. Capacitor $C1$ begins its discharge through resistor $R1$. The field around winding 1–2 collapses and induces a voltage in the reverse direction in the winding. The base of $Q1$ is driven in a reverse-bias direction, and the base and collector currents fall to zero (cutoff). The transistor is held at cutoff until the capacitor $C1$, discharging through resistor $R1$, reaches the point at which the transistor is again forward-biased and conduction begins. The cycle repeats itself.

The rest period (Fig. 7·34a) is determined by the time constant of

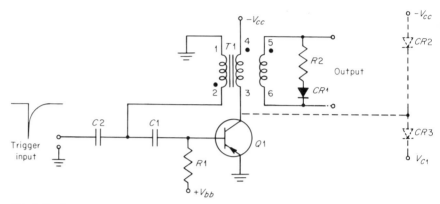

FIG. 7·36 Transistorized monostable blocking oscillator.

capacitor $C1$ and resistor $R1$, whereas the oscillating interval (pulse width) is primarily determined by the natural resonant frequency of the transformer. Resistor $R2$ and diode $CR1$ comprise an anti-ringing circuit that damps out the overshoot normally associated with transformer-coupled circuits. These undesirable oscillations tend to occur because the transformer acts as a shock-excited tank circuit when the transistor cuts off.

Triggered oscillator. The basic astable single-swing oscillator (Fig. 7·35) can be converted into a monostable (triggered) single-swing oscillator by making minor circuit modifications as shown in Fig. 7·36. The base resistor is returned to a potential positive enough to maintain reverse bias until an external trigger is applied to the base. This causes the circuit to remain quiescent until the trigger is applied through capacitor $C2$. Since the circuit operation of the monostable and astable oscillators is similar, only circuit differences will be explained.

Circuit operation. The reverse bias established by $+V_{bb}$ holds transistor $Q1$ cut off, and the circuit is initially at rest in a stable state. A negative pulse of sufficient amplitude to forward-bias the base-emitter junction applied through capacitor $C2$ will cause transistor $Q1$ to conduct. When this occurs, an abrupt switching action, due to regenerative feedback, drives the transistor toward saturation and capacitor $C1$ charges. When saturation is reached, capacitor $C1$ discharges, reverse-biasing the base-emitter junction, and initiates a second transistor switching action that cuts off the transistor. As $C1$ discharges, the base-to-ground potential increases negatively toward the forward-bias potential of the transistor. The conduction level is never reached, however, because of the $+V_{bb}$ level of the base resistor, and the circuit remains in a quiescent state until the next trigger pulse is applied to capacitor $C2$; therefore the frequency of this type oscillator is determined by the frequency of the input trigger.

In some circuits, the diodes shown by dashed lines are added to the circuit shown in Fig. 7·36 to limit collector voltage excursions on both positive and negative swings. Diode $CR2$ prevents the collector voltage from swinging more negative than supply voltage V_{cc}. (This ordinarily occurs during the inductive overshoot period.) Limiting negative excursion in this manner ensures that the maximum permissible reverse voltage is not exceeded and prevents collector breakdown.

Diode $CR3$ reduces the effect of minority-carrier storage by preventing the collector from becoming forward-biased during conduction.

Blocking oscillators are also widely used as timing-delay circuits. A variation of this type circuit utilized in computer systems is the gated pulse generator (GPG) illustrated in Fig. 7·38.

Gated pulse generator (GPG). The gated pulse generator is a timing circuit which produces an output pulse which is delayed by a given time interval from the input trigger. The GPG is used as a delay multivibrator. The use of the GPG, however, provides greater stability, lower cost, and faster recovery time than other delay devices. The amount of delay is determined by an RC time constant in the GPG. Manipulation of the values of the components can provide delays of as little as 48 μsec or as much as 100 msec, depending on timing requirements. The GPG also differs from other delay devices in that when enabled, it produces pulses continuously at a rate determined by its RC network.

The operation of the GPG depends upon the use of a unijunction transistor (UJT). A brief description of the unijunction transistor is presented as an aid to understanding the GPG. Figure 7·37 shows the symbol, base-wiring configuration, current/voltage characteristics, and equivalent circuit of the unijunction transistor.

FIG. 7·37 Unijunction transistor. (a) Equivalent; (b) characteristics; (c) base; (d) symbol.

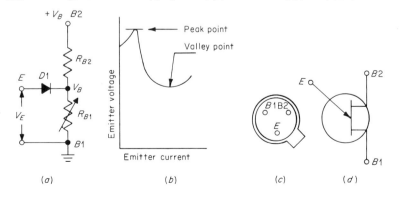

The UJT consists of an N-type silicon bar with terminals on each end called base 1 ($B1$) and base 2 ($B2$). A P-type emitter (E) junction is formed by a 3-mil aluminum wire on the side of the bar. The emitter junction is usually located closer to $B2$, making the device nonsymmetrical.

The UJT is operated with a positive voltage applied to $B2$ with respect to $B1$, as shown in Fig. 7·37a. R_{B2} is the resistance between $B2$ and E, and similarly, R_{B1} is the resistance between $B1$ and E.

To cause emitter current to flow in the UJT, diode $D1$, formed by the emitter connection, must be forward-biased. The amount of positive voltage V_B applied on the cathode of $D1$ is determined by the applied voltage between $B2$ and $B1$, divided by the ratio of R_{B1} to the total resistance of the silicon bar. This ratio R is called the *intrinsic standoff ratio* and is mathematically stated as follows:

$$R = \frac{R_{B1}}{R_{B1} + R_{B2}}$$

Therefore

$$V_B = (+V)R$$

When the emitter potential applied to the UJT becomes greater than V_B, a small emitter current begins to flow because of the forward-biasing of $D1$ (see Fig. 7·37a). As the voltage on the emitter is further increased above the peak point shown in Fig. 7·37b, R_{B1} decreases sharply and current increases accordingly.

In the gated pulse generator, the UJT is used as the controlling device in a relaxation oscillator. An RC charge network is allowed to charge until the emitter potential exceeds a potential established by the applied voltage and the intrinsic standoff ratio. When this occurs, the UJT conducts and discharges the RC network until the UJT again cuts off. The GPG continues to recycle and generate output pulses until disabled by a disabling input level.

Circuit operation. (See Fig. 7·38.) Transistor $Q1$ is an inverter which disables or enables the circuit, depending upon the input level. $Q2$, the UJT, operates with the RC network $C2$, $R5$, and $R6$ to form the relaxation oscillator. $Q3$ is a pulse standardizer.

In the disabled (or quiescent) state, the input to the base of $Q1$ is a 0-volt level causing $Q1$ to be cut off. The resulting negative voltage from the collector of $Q1$ causes $CR1$ to be forward-biased. The voltage divider consisting of $R4$, $CR1$, $R5$, and $R6$ establishes approximately -15 volts on the emitter of $Q2$, the UJT. This causes the emitter junction of the UJT

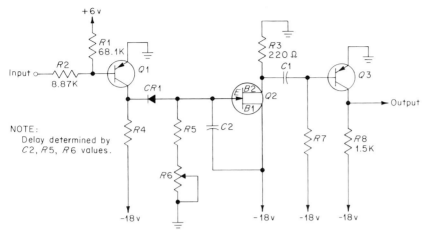

FIG. 7·38 Gated pulse generator.

to be reverse-biased, and no emitter current flows. Pulse standardizer Q3 is in conduction since no signal is coupled to its base by C1, and R7 returns the base to -18 volts. The output, therefore, is close to 0 volt.

The GPG is enabled when the input level goes low (-12 volts). When this occurs, Q1 conducts, and CR1 becomes reverse-biased. With the clamping level from CR1 removed, C2 begins charging from -18 volts through C2, R5, and R6. The voltage at the emitter of Q2 goes positive at an exponential rate as C2 charges. After a delay interval, determined by the size of C2, R5, and R6, the emitter potential of Q2 becomes sufficiently positive in respect to B1, causing emitter current to flow. When the emitter diode becomes forward-biased, current flow increases sharply between B1 and B2 because of the decreased resistance between B1 and the emitter, resulting in a negative pulse at B2. With the B1 emitter junction forward-biased, a quick-discharge path is provided for C2. Discharging C2 causes the emitter of Q2 to swing negative, cutting Q2 off.

The negative pulse developed at B2 is differentiated by the RC combination of C1 and R7. The trailing edge of this pulse results in a positive pulse which cuts off Q3. The output is a negative pulse whose width will be determined by the values of capacitor C1 and resistor R7.

If the input to Q1 remains negative, C2 will begin to charge, and the entire cycle will repeat itself continuously. Q3 will develop a negative-going pulse at a rate determined by the RC network consisting of C2, R5, and R6.

In the logical use of the GPG, the input can go negative to trigger the GPG, and the first output pulse can be returned via additional circuitry to the input to disable the GPG. Input level control is a function of the polarity of the triggering signal and output pulse requirements.

Multivibrators

A workhorse since the early development of radar, the multivibrator in its various configurations has become the backbone of digital computers. A modification of the multivibrator, known by such names as *flip-flop*, *toggle*, *binary*, or *switch*, is found throughout modern automatic high-speed digital computers. Multivibrators have many applications, from storing binary information to generating, shaping, and delaying pulses. While the subject of multivibrators encompasses a wide range of circuitry, this chapter treats only the most frequently encountered stable and mono-stable types.

The multivibrator is a two-stage regenerative amplifier characterized by a large excess of positive feedback. Conduction in one amplifier causes rapid cutoff in the other. Such an amplifier may exist in either of two *end stages* or *states of conduction*. One state exists when one transistor, con-ducting heavily, holds the other at cutoff. The alternative state exists when the opposite is true.

The states of a multivibrator may be either stable or quasi-stable. A circuit in the stable state remains in one of its end states indefinitely or until externally disturbed. A circuit in the quasi-stable state remains in that state only momentarily and then, after a period determined by circuit time constants, makes an abrupt transition to the opposite state. Multivibrators are classified as *astable*, *monostable*, or *bistable*, according to the number of stable end states.

Astable (free-running). The astable multivibrator, as its name implies, has no stable state. Rather, it oscillates between two states that are semistable (quasi-stable). The circuit is often classified as a free-running relaxation oscillator. The output waveform is rectangular and may be symmetrical (square) or nonsymmetrical, depending on the choice of circuit components. The output waveform is the same regardless of the shape or amplitude of the triggering pulse.

Because of its rectangular waveform, the astable multivibrator is often used as a pulse generator for testing digital circuitry. It may also be used as a means of frequency division. The circuit most commonly used in these applications is called the *collector-coupled astable multivibrator* and is illus-trated in Fig. 7·39.

The transistor circuit shown in Fig. 7·39a functions as a relaxation oscillator. The state of conduction in each transistor alternately changes from cutoff to saturation. Conduction of one transistor causes cutoff of the other so that when one is on, the other is off. Oscillations are self-starting when power is applied and continue until power is removed.

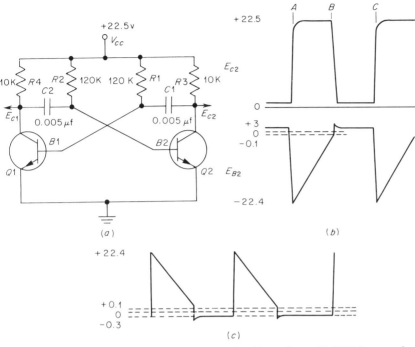

FIG. 7·39 Transistor astable multivibrator. (a) Schematic; (b) waveforms; (c) PNP-base waveform.

The details of circuit action are most easily understood if the explanation is divided into three parts as follows:

1. The transition to the initial end state
2. The circuit action during the semistable state or rest period
3. The transition to the opposite state

Transition to initial end state. (Point A of Fig. 7·39b.) When power is applied to the circuit shown in Fig. 7·39a, because of variation in tolerances of the components, one transistor will conduct more heavily than the other. Assuming transistor $Q1$ conducts more heavily than $Q2$, more current will flow in the base circuit of $Q1$ than in the base circuit of $Q2$. The collector current in transistor $Q1$ increases rapidly causing the collector voltage at the junction of $R4$ and $C2$ to decrease to approximately 0 volt. This decreasing voltage (negative waveshape) is applied through capacitor $C2$ to the base of transistor $Q2$ decreasing the forward bias of $Q2$ which results in decreased collector current in $Q2$. The decreased $Q2$ collector current results in a positive-going signal being applied as an increasing forward bias to the base of $Q1$ through capacitor $C1$. This action continues, causing transistor $Q2$ to be cut off. The circuit rests in its quasi-stable state. The potentials at E_b2 and E_c2 are as shown in Fig. 7·38b.

Circuit operation during rest period. (Interval between points A and B of Fig. 7·39b.) During the time interval between points A and B, the collector potentials of $Q1$ and $Q2$ remain constant. The negative potential developed across $C2$ and applied to the base of $Q2$ was far in excess of that required to stop the conduction of $Q2$ (approximately -0.1 volt). Capacitor $C2$ begins its discharge at an exponential rate, which results in a positive-going voltage applied to the base of $Q2$ decreasing the reverse bias of $Q2$. This action continues until at point B a forward bias is reestablished across the emitter-base diode of $Q2$ and $Q2$ begins conduction.

Transition to opposite state. (See point B of Fig. 7·39b.) As transistor $Q2$ becomes forward-biased, it begins conducting and the collector current increases causing the voltage at the collector to decrease to approximately 0 volt. This negative swing is coupled to the base of transistor $Q1$ causing a decrease in current flow through transistor $Q1$ and a rise in the collector potential of $Q1$. This positive-going signal is coupled to the base of $Q2$ by capacitor $C2$ causing a greater increase in collector current. This action continues until transistor $Q1$ is cut off and transistor $Q2$ is saturated. The circuit assumes its other set of quasi-stable conditions with the voltage at $EC2$ being reversed as indicated in Fig. 7·39b. This potential will remain at the level indicated between points B and C until capacitor $C1$ discharges to approximately -0.1 volt and removes the reverse bias at the base of transistor $Q1$. The cycle will then repeat itself. A point to notice is that the bases of $Q1$ and $Q2$ are returned to V_{cc} instead of ground. Because of this, the $C1$-$C2$ discharge is toward V_{cc} allowing the most linear portion of the discharge curve to control switching, thereby providing better frequency stability.

The oscillating frequency and the output waveshapes of the free running multivibrator are controlled by the $R1$-$C1$ and $R2$-$C2$ coupling elements.

If the polarity of the supply voltage is reversed in the circuit shown in Fig. 7·39a, a *PNP* transistor may be substituted for the *NPN* transistor shown, with no significant change in circuit action. The base waveform associated with the circuit shown in Fig. 7·39a when *PNP* transistors are used is illustrated in Fig. 7·39c.

Monostable multivibrator (one-shot). The monostable multivibrator has one stable state and one quasi-stable state. Unlike the astable type, it does not oscillate. Instead, the circuit rests in a permanently stable condition (one transistor on, the other off) until an external trigger is applied. At that time an abrupt transition from the stable to the quasi-stable state occurs. After a period of rest determined by circuit time constants, the multivibrator returns abruptly to the initial permanent state. Each applied trigger produces one complete rectangular pulse. For this reason the circuit is often referred to as the *one-shot multivibrator*. Figure 7·40c compares the output pulse of the one-shot circuit with that of the free-running type.

In computer equipment, the monostable multivibrator is used for the following purposes:

1. To develop accurately timed gating signals
2. To increase or decrease the width of a pulse
3. To introduce a time delay between two circuits

In the circuit of Fig. 7·40a, $Q2$ is biased positively by the collector supply voltage V_{cc} through $R2$, and $Q1$ is biased negatively by its base-bias supply V_{bb}. Initially, therefore, the circuit rests in a stable state with $Q2$ conducting saturation current and $Q1$ cut off (time 1, Fig. 7·40b). A positive trigger pulse of sufficient amplitude to overcome the negative bias at $B1$ will forward-bias $Q1$ and cause it to conduct. Conduction of $Q1$ due to the positive trigger pulse initiates an abrupt transition to the opposite state and is caused by the regenerative feedback of $C2$, as previously described in the free-running multivibrator circuit.

With $Q2$ cut off and $Q1$ conducting saturation current, the circuit rests in its quasi-stable state (time 2, Fig. 7·40b).

During the rest period, $C2$ discharges toward the low collector potential of $Q1$. The discharge current flowing through $R2$ biases $Q2$ negatively, well below the cutoff level of the transistor. $Q2$ remains cut off until the negative potential at $B2$ decreases to the conduction level of the transistor (approximately 0.2 volt positive).

When $Q2$ conducts, an abrupt switching action again occurs, and the initial stable state is reestablished. C_c is a small overdrive capacitor (approximately 50 $\mu\mu f$) and serves to increase the response time of the circuit as previously described.

The transistor monostable multivibrator may be triggered by a positive pulse at $B1$ or by a negative pulse at $B2$. The same considerations concerning loading by the trigger source apply when the transistor circuit is triggered. The most reliable triggering is accomplished through the use of a separate trigger stage as shown by the dashed lines in Fig. 7·40a. $Q3$ provides the voltage amplification of the trigger pulse and prevents loading of the multivibrator circuit by the trigger source.

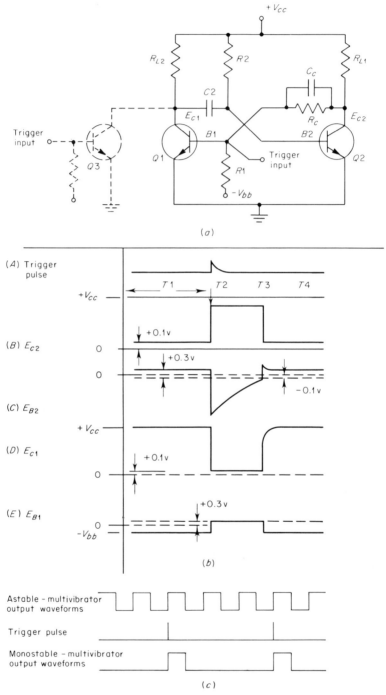

FIG. 7·40 *NPN* monostable multivibrator. (a) Schematic; (b) waveforms; (c) comparison of monostable and free-running multivibrator waveforms.

A practical example of a monostable multivibrator using a PNP transistor is shown in Fig. 7·41. The circuit is used to stretch the duration of an input pulse from 0.4 to 2 μsec. This is a modification of the basic circuit shown in Fig. 7·40.

In comparing Figs. 7·40 and 7·41, note that a direct connection is made between the collector of $Q2$ and the base of $Q1$. There are no coupling re-

FIG. 7·41 PNP monostable multivibrator. (a) Schematic; (b) waveforms.

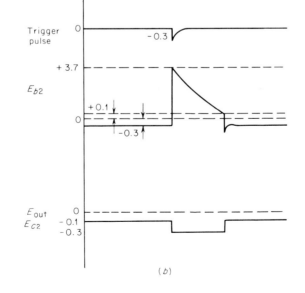

sistors or capacitors, and the cutoff bias supply for $Q1$ has been eliminated. Despite these changes, the action in the circuit in Fig. 7·41 is nearly identical with that of the basic circuit in Fig. 7·40. The only difference between the two concerns the limits of conduction in $Q1$ during operation. $Q1$ is never cut off. Consider the base potential of $Q1$ during cutoff and saturation of $Q2$. When $Q2$ is cut off, its collector-to-ground potential, and therefore the base potential of $Q1$, is approximately -0.3 volt since most of the supply voltage V_{cc} is dropped across $R3$ because of the low base-to-emitter resistance of the conducting transistor $Q1$.

The negative 0.3 volt at the base of $Q1$ forward-biases the PNP transistor and causes a saturation current of approximately 3 ma. When $Q2$ conducts, however, its collector-to-ground potential drops to -0.1 volt. Since a positive voltage of approximately 0.2 volt is required to produce cutoff, $Q1$ still conducts. The amount of conduction, however, is extremely small, approximately $85\mu a$. Hence, $Q1$ is assumed to be cut off for all practical purposes. Action in the circuit in Fig. 7·41 is briefly described in the following paragraphs.

Resistor $R2$ is chosen so that when power is applied, the base current of $Q2$ is sufficient to hold $Q2$ on. When $Q2$ conducts saturation current, the collector-to-ground potential of $Q2$ equals -0.1 volt and effectively holds $Q1$ off. During this interval, $C1$ charges toward the supply voltage of $Q1$ through $R1$ and the conducting transistor $Q2$. Electron flow during the charge of $C1$ is shown by solid arrows in Fig. 7·41. With $Q1$ cut off and $Q2$ conducting saturation current, the circuit rests in a stable state until an external trigger pulse is applied to the base of $Q3$.

The base of $Q3$ has no significant potential and can be assumed to be 0 volt; hence, $Q3$ is initially cut off. A negative pulse at the base of $Q3$ causes it to conduct saturation current. The current of $Q3$ flowing through $R1$ increases the collector-to-ground potential of $Q1$ to -0.1 volt. $C1$ then discharges positively toward this potential through $R2$. The discharge current of $C1$ biases the base of $Q2$ positive with respect to ground and cuts it off. The discharge path of $C1$ is shown in dashed lines in Fig. 7·41.

The circuit rests in this semistable state until the potential at the base of $Q2$ decays to 0 volt. At this time $Q2$ begins to conduct, and the circuit returns abruptly to its initial stable state with $Q2$ conducting saturation current and $Q1$ effectively cut off.

Since PNP transistors are used, rather than NPN transistors, the waveforms associated with Fig. 7·41 are inverted images of those of the basic circuit.

Bistable multivibrator (flip-flop). The bistable type of multivibrator circuit is the one most frequently used in the computer field. As its name implies, the circuit has two stable states of conduction. It can rest in either of its stable states and can be switched from one state to the other by applying a trigger pulse to the input. In computer work, the bistable circuit is referred to as the *logical flip-flop*. One trigger pulse "flips" the state of the circuit, and the second "flops" the circuit back to its initial condition.

Since the bistable multivibrator remains in one of its stable states until triggered, it can be thought of as having a storage ability. Because it has two stable states, it can be used effectively to store the 1 and 0 digits used in the binary system of counting.

Functioning as binary storage devices, flip-flops in various arrangements are used in digital equipment to perform such logical operations as addition, subtraction, multiplication, and division of binary numbers.

Like the monostable multivibrator, the bistable circuit can also be used to generate a rectangular pulse. In this case, however, two trigger pulses are required. Figure 7·42 compares the trigger requirements and output waveforms of the flip-flop with those of the monostable circuit.

The basic circuit from which all bistable multivibrators are developed is termed the *Eccles-Jordan trigger circuit*. In the following paragraphs, the operating principles of this circuit are explained. This is followed by a discussion of the circuit modifications necessary to convert the basic circuit to the logical flip-flop.

Basic NPN flip-flop. The basic circuit of a flip-flop using *NPN* transistors is shown in Fig. 7·43.

FIG. 7·42 Comparison of waveforms of bistable and monostable multivibrators.

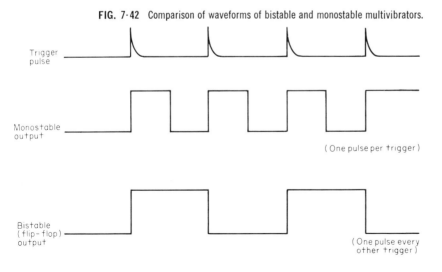

Trigger pulse

Monostable output

(One pulse per trigger)

Bistable (flip-flop) output

(One pulse every other trigger)

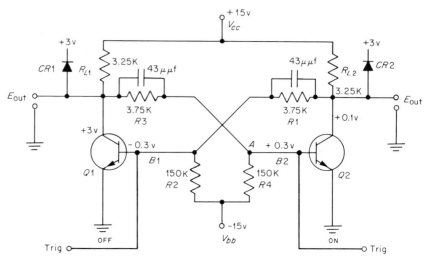

FIG. 7·43 Basic flip-flop using NPN transistors (Eccles-Jordan type).

When power is applied to the circuit shown in Fig. 7·43, a rapid switching action occurs because of regenerative feedback common to all multivibrators. One transistor moves rapidly toward saturation while the other moves toward cutoff. Once the end states are reached, the circuit will rest in this stable condition until an external trigger pulse is applied.

In this stable state, one transistor is held at saturation while the other is held beyond cutoff. These stable conditions are maintained because of the voltages developed at $B1$ and $B2$ through the voltage-dividing action of the coupling resistors.

In Fig. 7·43, the approximate collector and base potentials developed in the stable state are shown. $Q1$ is assumed to be cut off and $Q2$ in the conducting state. With $Q2$ conducting saturation current, its collector-to-ground potential is approximately 0.1 volt positive. This value is typical for the transistor types normally used in this application. A portion of this voltage is coupled to the base of $Q1$ because of the action of the voltage divider, $R1$ and $R2$. Also contributing to the base-to-ground potential at $B1$ is a portion of the negative-bias supply (V_{bb}). Calculation by superposition will show that the net potential contributed by these two sources is approximately 0.3 volt negative. Since the cutoff potential of this NPN transistor is approximately 0.1 volt negative, $Q1$ is definitely cut off. The base-to-ground potential at $B2$ is calculated in a similar manner by determining the net potential contributed by the positive 3-volt collector potential of the cutoff transistor $Q1$ and the negative-bias source V_{bb}. The sources are applied across the voltage divider, $R3$ and $R4$. If the effect of the conducting transistor is disregarded, calculation will show that the net potential at $B2$ is approximately 2.5 volts positive. This forward bias causes saturation current in $Q2$. Since the low base-to-emitter resistance shunts point A, this positive voltage does not actually appear at $B2$ but becomes a driving force that clamps the base to approximately 0.3 volt positive.

$Q2$ holds $Q1$ in the cutoff state, and $Q1$ holds $Q2$ at saturation.

Diodes $CR1$ and $CR2$ in Fig. 7·43 limit the positive excursion of the output signal, provide amplitude stability, and improve the recovery time of the circuit.

To accomplish switching in this circuit the transistor in the OFF condition must be raised to the conduction level. Once conduction begins, regeneration action completes the switching process. Switching can also be initiated by decreasing the forward bias of the transistor in the ON condition until it is reverse-biased. Once cut off, the regenerative action will complete the switching process.

Logical flip-flop. A bistable multivibrator used for the purpose of storing binary information in logical machines is called a *logical flip-flop.* The logical flip-flops shown in Figs. 7·47 and 7·48 are identical with the basic flip-flop shown in Fig. 7·43 but include several input and output circuits that make them more effective in counting and storage applications. These circuit additions are shown enclosed by dashed lines in Fig. 7·47. Before the additional circuitry shown in the figure is discussed, some conventions regarding terminology will be covered.

Logical flip-flop terminology. It has been previously shown that the flip-flop has two stable states of conduction. In one state, $Q1$ is conducting, and $Q2$ is cut off. In the second state, $Q2$ is conducting, and $Q1$ is cut off. The two states of conduction are shown diagrammatically in Fig. 7·44a and b. Since the flip-flop remains in one of its stable states until triggered, it can be thought of as having a storage ability. When at rest in one stable state, the circuit is considered to be storing a binary 1, or, simply, to be in the ONE state. If the circuit is triggered to the opposite state of conduction, it is considered to be storing a binary 0, or, simply, to be in the ZERO state.

An indication of the state in which the flip-flop rests is provided by the voltage levels at its output terminals. It will be shown in a succeeding paragraph that the output of only one transistor could be used to indicate the state of the flip-flop. In the logical flip-flop, however, both outputs are used for this purpose. The output voltage from one of the transistors is used to indicate that a binary 1 is stored in the flip-flop, while the output of the other transistor indicates the storage of a binary 0. This is shown diagrammatically in Fig. 7·44. Although the output of $Q1$ has been chosen in the diagram to represent the 1, the choice is purely arbitrary. $Q2$ could be used for the 1 indication, and $Q1$ for the 0 indication. Once the choice is made, however, the components associated with the transistor selected are designated the ONE-side components of the flip-flops and the output from this side is designated the ONE-side output. Conversely, the other side of

FIG. 7·44 Conduction states of flip-flop.

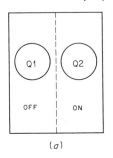

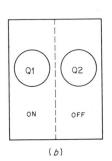

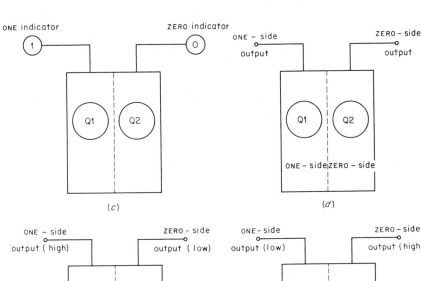

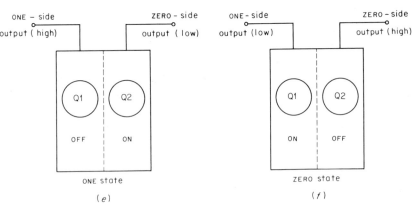

the flip-flop is designated the ZERO side and its output is designated the ZERO-side output. This is shown in Fig. 7·44d.

Consider for the moment a computer system in which the presence of a signal is indicated by a high (most positive) voltage level. A low-output voltage level would then indicate that a signal is not present. This logic will be applied to a flip-flop designated as shown in Fig. 7·44d. Both conduction states shown in Fig. 7·44a and b will be considered to show how the ONE-side and ZERO-side outputs determine whether a binary 1 or a binary 0 is being stored.

Consider first the stable state shown in Fig. 7·44a. This state of conduction is redrawn in Fig. 7·44c and e with the outputs appropriately marked. Since $Q1$ is cut off, its output voltage is more positive than that of $Q2$; that is, the ONE-side output is high, and the ZERO-side output is low. If this type of logic is assumed, the flip-flop is obviously in the ONE state since a 1 is present in the output and a 0 is not present.

Similar reasoning will show that when the flip-flop is switched to the opposite state, it will indicate the storage of a binary 0. Consider the drawing in Fig. 7·44b. This figure shows a state of conduction opposite to that in Fig. 7·44a. The flip-flop is redrawn in Fig. 7·44d and f with the outputs appropriately marked. Since $Q2$ is off, its ZERO-side output is high; therefore, a 0 is present in the output. Conversely, since $Q1$ is conducting, its output is low; therefore, a 1 is not present. Obviously, the circuit is in the ZERO state.

Since the terminology used above to describe the states of the logical flip-flop will be frequently employed in future discussions of logical circuits, a summary of this terminology is given in the table of Fig. 7·45a. It is suggested that this table be used in conjunction with Fig. 7·44e and f so that the logical terms used become familiar. It is important, however, to remember that this terminology applies only to systems employing the most positive voltage level to indicate a 1, or presence of a signal.

A question is often raised concerning the reason for providing two outputs, rather than one, to indicate the state of the logical flip-flop. An explanation for this practice is given in the following paragraph.

When two outputs are employed, both the ONE state and the ZERO state are indicated by a high voltage level. In the ONE state, the high level is available from the ONE-side output; in the ZERO state, the high level is available from the ZERO-side output. The two high levels are used to an advantage when the logical function of AND or OR is to be performed. For example, assume that outputs of two flip-flops are to be given the AND function. Assume, further, that a high level is to be produced in the output of the AND circuit when a binary 1 appears in flip-flop A and a binary 0 appears in flip-flop B. Since high outputs are available from both flip-flops, this logical function can be conveniently performed. A system employing

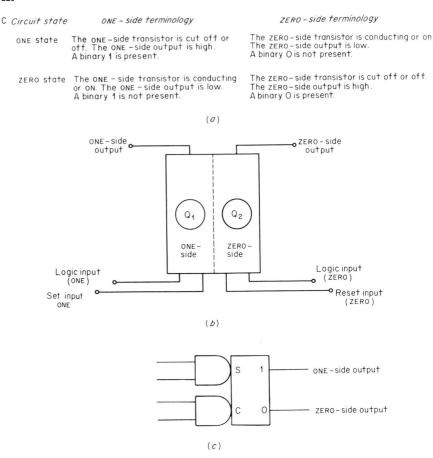

C *Circuit state*   *ONE – side terminology*   *ZERO – side terminology*

ONE state   The ONE–side transistor is cut off or   The ZERO-side transistor is conducting or on.
             off. The ONE –side output is high.   The ZERO-side output is low.
             A binary 1 is present.   A binary O is not present.

ZERO state   The ONE – side transistor is conducting   The ZERO-side transistor is cut off or off.
             or ON. The ONE – side output is low.   The ZERO-side output is high.
             A binary 1 is not present.   A binary O is present.

(a)

ONE – side output

ZERO – side output

Q_1 Q_2

ONE–side   ZERO–side

Logic input (ONE)

Logic input (ZERO)

Set input ONE

Reset input (ZERO)

(b)

S   1   ONE – side output

C   O   ZERO – side output

(c)

FIG. 7·45 Flip-flop terminology and symbols. (a) Terminology associated with logical flip-flop in a positive logic system; (b) simplified logical symbol; (c) complemented flip-flop symbol.

flip-flops with only one output, however, would be at a distinct disadvantage. To see that this is true, consider a flip-flop whose states are described by Fig. 7·44e and f, and assume that the flip-flop has only one output, the output of $Q1$. As shown in Fig. 7·44e and f, the ONE state would be indicated by a high output from $Q1$; but the ZERO state would necessarily be indicated by a low output. Then to perform the logical AND function described above, the output of the flip-flop storing the binary 0 must first be inverted before being applied to the AND-gate input. Since thousands of similar operations are performed in a complex computer, the added expense of providing inverter circuits would be prohibitive.

While a logical flip-flop has only two outputs, it ordinarily has four inputs, two to each side. These inputs are shown in Fig. 7·45b. There is no electrical difference between the LOGIC inputs on the ONE side and the SET input. Trigger pulses applied to either input will switch the flip-flop to the ONE state. The LOGIC inputs on the ZERO side and the RESET input are also identical electrically. Trigger pulses applied to either of these inputs switch the flip-flop to the ZERO state. The outputs of logical switching circuits, such as AND or OR gates, are applied to the LOGIC inputs of the flip-flop, causing the storage of a 1 or a 0 to be conditional on the performance of certain logical operations. The SET and RESET inputs are used to initially preset the flip-flop to some predetermined state prior to the performance of these logical operations. In effect, the SET and RESET inputs clear the flip-flop of information previously stored and set up what could be called *start* conditions.

In order to make the flip-flop usable in a system employing square waves, the ONE-side and ZERO-side inputs are usually composed of a diode and a differentiating network similar to that shown in Fig. 7·46. These

FIG. 7·46 Differentiator and diode to generate negative spike. (a) Schematic; (b) associated waveforms.

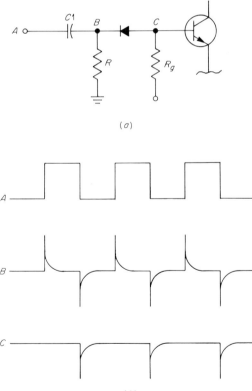

components convert the square-wave input to the negative spike required for efficient triggering of the binary circuit. A square-wave input at A is differentiated by the short-time-constant RC network so that at point B the leading edge appears as a positive spike and the trailing edge as a negative spike. The positive portion of the differentiated waveform reverse-biases the diode and is effectively prevented from appearing at point C. The negative spike, however, forward-biases the diode and is passed on to the base of the conducting transistor of the flip-flop to initiate the switching process.

Logical flip-flop operation. As was stated earlier, the basic flip-flop shown in Fig. 7·43 is converted to a logical flip-flop by the addition of input and output circuits. These are shown enclosed in dashed lines in Fig. 7·47a.

If we again assume the most positive voltage level to represent 1, when $Q1$ is cut off, the flip-flop is in the ONE state. This is true because the ONE-side output is high (3 volts positive), indicating that a binary 1 is present. Also, since $Q2$ is conducting at this time, the ZERO-side output is low (0.1 volt), indicating that a binary 0 is not present.

The ONE-side and ZERO-side outputs (blocks A and $\bar{A}$) provide information on the state of the flip-flop for use by other circuits in the computer. The other output terminal at the ONE side is connected as the return of a lamp-driver circuit for indicating purposes. It should be noted that only the one side output need be connected to an indicator since if the indicator is not lit, it shows the flip-flop is in the ZERO state.

Block B in Fig. 7·47a comprises a differentiating network and a diode clipper. These components produce the negative pulses required for triggering when rectangular pulses of long duration are applied to the input. $C1$ and $R2$ differentiate signals applied to the LOGIC inputs, and $C2$ and $R2$ perform the same function at the SET input. $CR2$ removes the positive spike after differentiation of the input pulse.

A two-input AND gate is provided in this particular flip-flop at the LOGIC inputs (block C). The single-ended SET input (block D) permits presetting of the flip-flop to the ONE state to set up start conditions. The RESET input (block $\bar{D}$) permits presetting of the flip-flop to the ZERO state when desired. A block diagram of the circuit in Fig. 7·47a is shown in Fig. 7·47b. This diagram shows the function of the input and output terminals.

When several flip-flops are connected to form counters and registers, each flip-flop is usually identified by a capital letter. The flip-flop shown in Fig. 7·47c could accordingly be designated flip-flop A.

As previously stated, the logical flip-flop may be used for storage applications or for performing counting functions. The input circuits of the logical flip-flop are arranged so that either function can be performed conveniently and effectively. As an example, consider the circuit in Fig. 7·47

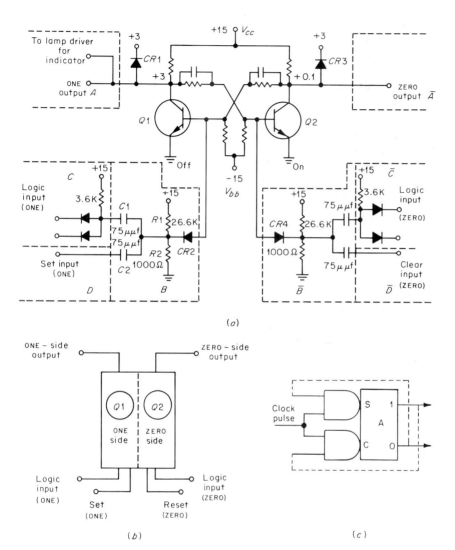

FIG. 7·47 Logical flip-flop using NPN transistors. (a) Schematic; (b) block diagram of logical flip-flop; (c) logical symbol of complemented transistor flip-flop.

to be used to perform a counting function. In this application, repeated switching of the flip-flop is accomplished by applying a continuous train of trigger pulses simultaneously to both the ONE-side and the ZERO-side input. Since the input pulses are applied to both sides simultaneously, some means must be provided to direct the input pulse to the correct side. This is accomplished conveniently through a method of connection called *comple-*

menting. Complementing serves a pulse-steering function and proves reliable when trigger pulses at high repetition rates are used. Complementing is accomplished by applying the ONE-side output of the flip-flop to the AND gate associated with the ZERO side. Also, the ZERO-side output is returned to the AND gate at the ONE-side input. Trigger pulses, called *clock pulses*, are then applied simultaneously to both AND-gate inputs. This method of connection is usually internal to the flip-flop and is shown by the dashed lines in the logical diagram in Fig. 7·47*c*. To see how complementing ensures that each successive trigger pulse is directed to the correct side, assume the flip-flop is in the ZERO state when a clock pulse appears at both the ONE-side and ZERO-side AND gates. Since the flip-flop is in the ZERO state, the high output from the ZERO side renders the ONE-side AND gate permissive, and the clock pulse is allowed to pass. The ZERO-side AND gate is nonpermissive at this time because the low output from the ONE side acts as an inhibiting force upon the gate. In this way, the clock pulse is directed to the ONE-side input and switches the flip-flop to the ONE state.

A logical flip-flop employing *PNP* transistors, rather than *NPN* transistors, is shown in Fig. 7·48*a*. The circuit is identical with the *NPN* flip-flop in Fig. 7·47*a* except for the following changes:

1. All source potentials have opposite polarity.
2. The positions of the cathodes and anodes of *CR*1, *CR*2, *CR*3, and *CR*4 are reversed.
3. Input designation is reversed. For example, the inputs associated with the ONE-side output are now applied to the ZERO side.

All the above changes are necessary because of the opposite bias requirements of the *PNP* transistor when compared with the *NPN* transistor. Changes 2 and 3, however, require elaboration and are explained in the following paragraph.

Diodes *CR*1 and *CR*3 reduce the charge time of the overdrive capacitors by bypassing the load resistors. This occurs when the transistors are switched off. Since the potential toward which the capacitors charge is now negative (V_{cc}), both the polarity of the clipping level and the position of the diodes must be reversed.

The positions of diodes *CR*2 and *CR*4 are also reversed because of the opposite characteristics of the *PNP* transistor.

Since the positive potential is now required to accomplish cutoff, *CR*2 and *CR*4 must be arranged to clip the negative portion of the differentiated input signal and pass the positive spike.

To see why the input designations must be reversed, assume that *Q*2 is cut off and *Q*1 is conducting. With *Q*1 conducting, its collector potential is at its most positive excursion (-0.1 volt). The ONE-side output is there-

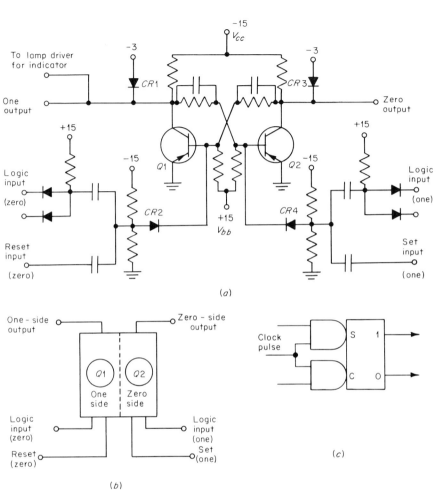

FIG. 7·48 Logical flip-flop using PNP transistors. (a) Schematic; (b) inputs and outputs; (c) logical symbol.

fore high and, assuming logic where a 1 is represented by the most positive voltages, the circuit is in the ONE state. If it is now desired to switch the circuit to the ZERO state with positive trigger pulses, the trigger must be applied to the base of the conducting transistor $Q1$. In other words, to switch the circuit to the ZERO state, the trigger pulse must be applied to the ONE side. This latter requirement is emphasized in the block diagram for the PNP transistor flip-flop shown in Fig. 7·48b. Compare this diagram with that in Fig. 7·47b.

The PNP transistor flip-flop is complemented in the same way as the

NPN transistor; that is, the ONE-side and ZERO-side outputs are applied to
AND gates at the LOGIC inputs.

Input circuit variations.   The flip-flop shown in Fig. 7·49a is a modification
of that shown in Fig. 7·48a.   This circuit features transistor triggering at the

FIG. 7·49   Modified PNP logical flip-flop. (a) Schematic; (b) permissive and nonpermissive modes.

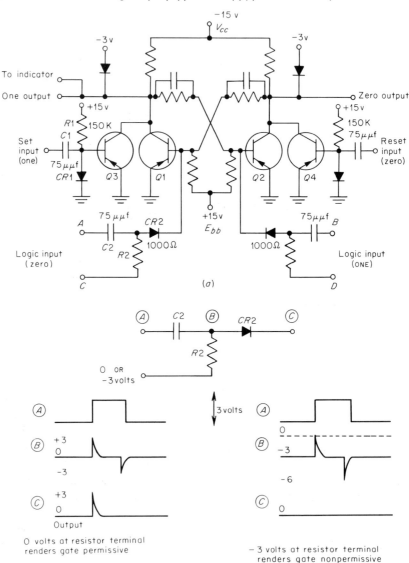

SET and RESET inputs and includes a simplified logic input that eliminates the need for a separate AND-gate input.

Consider first the function of the trigger transistors $Q3$ and $Q4$. The circuit is initially preset to the desired state by the application of a negative pulse to the SET or the RESET input. Trigger transistors $Q3$ and $Q4$ are affected by a negative pulse in a similar way; hence, only the action of the SET input need be explained.

Assume the circuit is in the ZERO state and it is desired to preset the flip-flop to the ONE state. In the ZERO state, $Q2$ is conducting and $Q1$ is cut off. A negative pulse at the SET input will switch the circuit to the ONE state as described in the following paragraphs.

Trigger transistor $Q3$ is cut off during the interval between trigger pulses because $CR1$ is conducting at this time and biases the base of $Q3$ slightly positive. Since both $Q3$ and $Q1$ are cut off, the collector potential of $Q1$ is 3 volts negative. A negative pulse at the SET input reverse-biases $CR1$ and removes the cutoff bias at $Q3$. The negative pulse appearing at the base of $Q3$ provides forward bias, and $Q3$ conducts saturation current. When $Q3$ conducts, the collector of $Q1$ swings positive from -3 volts toward ground potential. This positive pulse is coupled through the over-drive capacitor and appears at the conducting transistor $Q2$. Conduction in $Q2$ decreases, and regenerative action switches the circuit to the ONE state.

The LOGIC inputs on both the ONE and ZERO sides consist of an RC net-work and a series diode. These components perform a dual function. The first function is to convert rectangular input pulses into positive pulses required for triggering the flip-flop. This function is identical with that performed by corresponding components at the LOGIC inputs of all flip-flops previously explained. Under appropriate input conditions, however, these components also function as a two-input AND gate. The capacitor terminal is considered one input to the gate, and the resistor terminal, the other input. The gate is rendered permissive or nonpermissive by the application of the appropriate voltage to the resistor terminal. If the resistor terminal is returned to ground (0 volt), the gate becomes permissive, and a trigger pulse is passed. When returned to a negative potential, the gate is rendered nonpermissive, and no trigger pulse is delivered to the flip-flop. Circuit action during the permissive and nonpermissive modes is illustrated in Fig. 7·49b. Consider first the conditions shown on the left. When ground, or 0, voltage is applied to the resistor terminal, the input pulse is differen-tiated by $C2$ and $R2$ and appears at point B as a positive and a negative spike. The positive spike forward-biases $CR2$ and is passed on to the base of the transistor to accomplish switching. The negative spike reverse-biases $CR2$ and is effectively removed. This action is identical with that described previously. It is important to note, however, that the differentiated signal B swings above ground potential only because point B is at ground potential at the time the input pulse appears. In this case, the differentiated waveform swings above and below a 0-volt reference level. During the nonpermissive mode, the resistor terminal is returned to -3 volts, and point B is biased at this potential when the input signal is applied. For this reason, the differentiated input now rides above and below a reference level of -3 volts. As shown by waveforms B and C on the right in Fig. 7·49b, neither the positive nor the negative spike swings above 0 volt; hence, $CR2$ does not conduct and no trigger pulse is passed.

To complement the circuit shown in Fig. 7·49a, clock pulses are applied

FIG. 7·50 Nonsaturating flip-flops. (a) Schematic; (b) diode-limiting action.

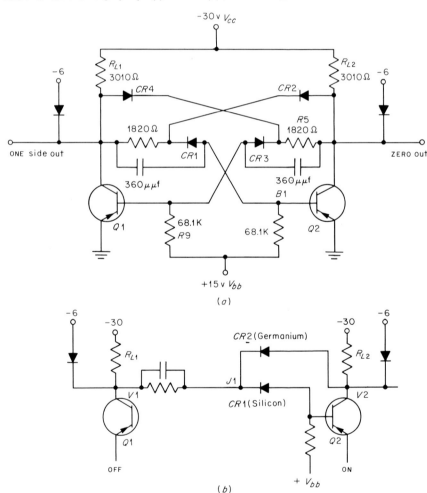

simultaneously to the capacitor terminals (points A and B), and the ONE-side and ZERO-side outputs of the flip-flop are applied to the resistor terminals (points C and D).

Nonsaturated flip-flop. In all previous examples of the logical flip-flop, no provision was made to prevent transistor saturation during the stable state. Consequently, minority-carrier storage effects introduce a delay in the switching process and result in a reduction in the maximum repetition rate at which the circuit may be triggered. In the circuit shown in Fig. 7·50, the transistors are prevented from entering the saturation region in the stable state through the use of diodes $CR1$ through $CR4$. $CR1$ and $CR2$ prevent saturation current in $Q2$, and $CR3$ and $CR4$ perform the same function for $Q1$. To understand how these diodes prevent saturation current, consider the circuit action during the stable state when $Q1$ is cut off and $Q2$ is conducting. These conditions are shown in Fig. 7·50b.

$CR1$ conducts continuously during both the switching interval and the stable state since the base of $Q2$ and, therefore, the anode of $CR1$ are near ground potential. $CR2$, however, is reverse-biased during most of the switching interval and does not conduct until the load current through R_L2 causes the collector potential to swing more positive than the potential at $J1$. When this occurs, $CR2$ conducts and bypasses a portion of the base current to the collector. Limited to this extent, the base current is never sufficiently great to cause saturation current in $Q2$. For correct operations, component values must be chosen so that the collector of $Q2$ is prevented from becoming forward-biased during the stable state. This is usually accomplished by selecting a silicon diode for $CR1$ and a germanium diode for $CR2$. In a typical case, the forward voltage drop across the silicon diode $CR1$ is 1.2 volts, and that across the germanium diode $CR2$ is 1 volt. During the stable state when both diodes conduct, the difference in the voltage drops across the two diodes causes the collector voltage of $Q2$ to be 0.2 volt negative with respect to base, and reverse bias is maintained.

Direct-coupled transistor flip-flop. While most bistable circuits employ resistor coupling between states, direct coupling is possible and, when used, results in a considerable reduction in the number of components required. An example of a direct-coupled bistable circuit is shown in Fig. 7·51. This circuit has two stable states in which one transistor is in saturation and the other is nearly at cutoff. Operation of the circuit will now be explained.

When power is first applied, both transistors conduct since the negative source potential provides forward bias. Because of variations in the tolerances of components, one transistor conducts more heavily than the other. The instant this occurs, positive feedback between collectors and bases of the transistors results in a rapid switching action; one transistor is

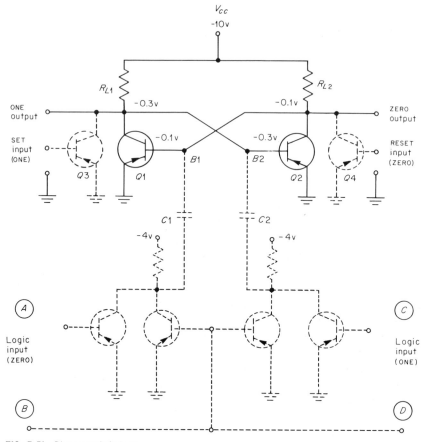

FIG. 7·51 Direct-coupled flip-flop.

driven toward saturation and the other toward cutoff. The circuit reaches a stable state when saturation current flows in one transistor. Assume $Q2$ becomes saturated. The approximate collector and base potentials developed under these conditions are shown in Fig. 7·51.

Saturation current through $R_{L}2$ reduces the collector-to-ground potential of $Q2$ from -0.3 to approximately -0.1 volt. Since this potential is negative with respect to ground, $Q1$ is forward-biased and cannot be in the cutoff state. However, this value of forward bias is low enough to reduce the collector current of $Q1$ to less than 100 μa, and $Q1$ is assumed to be cut off.

With $Q1$ cut off, its collector potential rises toward V_{cc} and provides a forward bias which is more than sufficient to enable $Q2$ to remain saturated.

The collector voltage of $Q1$ never reaches -10 volts, however, but is clamped at -0.3 volt because of the low emitter-to-base resistance of $Q2$.

Although the output-voltage swing of this circuit is only 0.2 volt peak-to-peak, this value is sufficient to turn transistor switches on and off.

The components shown in dashed lines in Fig. 7·51 convert the basic circuit to a logical flip-flop. The circuit is preset to the ONE or the ZERO state by a negative pulse at the SET or the RESET input. The parallel transistors at the LOGIC inputs function as two-input NAND gates. These gates deliver a positive trigger pulse to the base of the flip-flop transistors when the inputs to the gates are satisfied. Consider the ZERO LOGIC input gate on the left of the diagram. The gate is rendered permissive if both input terminals (A and B) are at 0 volt. If a negative trigger pulse is now applied to input B, the output of the gate will go positive. If input terminal A is at -3 volts when the trigger appears, it will have no effect on the output of the gate.

To understand the action of this gate, assume that the flip-flop is in the ONE state. When this is true, $Q1$ is conducting and $Q2$ is cut off. To switch the circuit to the ZERO state with positive pulses, the pulse must be applied to $B1$. This may be accomplished by applying a negative trigger pulse at the ZERO LOGIC inputs when the gate is permissive.

If both terminals A and B are at 0 volt before the trigger appears, both gate transistors are off and the collector potential is -4 volts. A negative trigger of -3 volts applied to terminal B drives the right transistor into saturation. Its collector potential swings positively toward 0 volt, and a positive pulse is coupled through $C1$ to the base of $Q1$. The flip-flop switches to the ZERO state.

If input terminal A is at -3 volts before the trigger appears, the gate will be nonpermissive. This is true because the left transistor will be conducting at this time, and the negative trigger pulse will have no effect.

The flip-flop in Fig. 7·51 is complemented in the conventional manner. The ONE-side output is applied to terminal A, and the ZERO-side output to terminal C. Negative clock pulses are applied simultaneously to terminals B and D. When the circuit is in the ONE state, the ZERO-side output will render the ONE LOGIC inputs nonpermissive because terminal C will be at -3 volts when the trigger appears.

SECTION 4   POWER SUPPLIES — REGULATION AND CONTROL

Power Circuitry

The high degree of reliability realized in the operation of modern data processing systems is achieved, in part, by the power systems used. The "plug in the wall" power concept has been replaced by power systems, internal to the computer, which attempt to provide the near-desired voltage levels supplied for circuit operation. Circuit design considerations usually provide for proper or expected operation over some small range of power fluctuations.

Power regulation and control in computing systems is accomplished through a combination of power-sequencing, power-regulation, and fault-control circuits. The power-sequencing circuits provide the order and control for the application and removal of power to the system. This sequencing ensures that certain operational characteristics are achieved in the required order. For example, the application of negative voltage levels before the positive voltage levels may ensure proper biasing before drive signals are applied. The sequencing may be required to incorporate circuit safety features or information protection, or both.

Power-supply-regulation circuits maintain power-output levels within certain specified tolerance ranges. These circuits are usually capable of providing corrective action in holding the required levels, barring a catastrophic failure within the supply.

Power-fault-control circuits monitor power-circuit operation. Should power deviations occur which the regulation circuits cannot correct or should an ac power failure occur, the fault-correction circuits initiate and control an orderly power shutdown. For example, even on an ac failure,

FIG. 7·52 Power control unit.

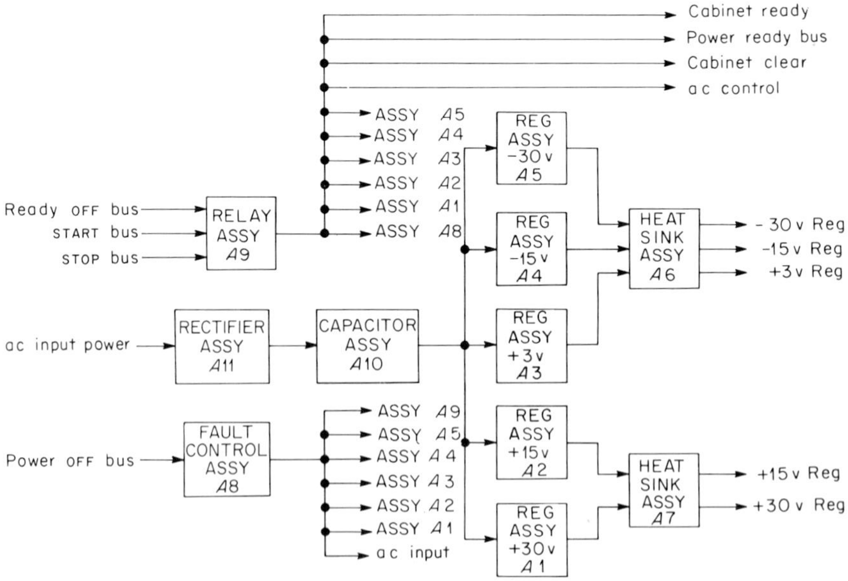

the power supplies will maintain the output voltage level for some minimal time period. This period may allow an operation to be completed or data to be stored before all power is lost. Power-fault control allows "priority users" access to this "reserve" while all others are immediately removed from access to the supplies.

Figure 7·52 illustrates a typical power-regulator unit. It consists of a relay assembly, a rectifier assembly, a capacitor assembly, a fault-control assembly, regulator assemblies, and heat-sink assemblies. As can be seen, this unit is capable of supplying voltages at different levels to meet the operational voltage needs of the computing system in which it is used.

Input power, through transformer action, is applied as 37-, 23-, and 9-volt alternating current to the rectifier assembly. The ac conversion to pulsating dc is effected in the rectifier assembly, and filtering is accomplished in the capacitor assembly. The regulator assemblies sense for output voltage variations and provide control signals to the heat sink assemblies which regulate the output voltage over normal variations in operating current. Note that this sequence of input alternating current, rectify, filter, and regulate exists as a separate path for each of the output voltage levels. The assemblies are modular and allow for removal and replacement maintenance actions. Assembly numbers designate the location within the overall power system.

The fault-control assembly controls power shutdown in the event of power failure. The relay assembly is used to sequence system power application and removal. Figure 7·53 illustrates a simplified +30-volt power supply regulator circuit.

The static conditions are established as a result of the biasing conditions of the differential amplifier $Q2$ and $Q3$. The bias on $Q2$ is established by zener diodes $CR2$, $CR3$, and $CR4$. Each diode causes a constant 7-volt drop resulting in +21 volts on the base of $Q2$. The bias on transistor $Q3$ is maintained by zener diode $CR5$ (constant 7-volt drop from +30 volts) and the sliding arm of $R6$. Assuming that the characteristics of $Q2$ and $Q3$ are nearly identical, the base of $Q3$ will also be +21 volts. These biasing conditions result in conduction of transistors $Q1$, $Q4$, and $Q5$ at levels which cause the unregulated +37-volt output of the capacitor assembly to be dropped to and maintained at a constant +30-volt output.

With an increased load on the power supply, the output voltage decreases. This decrease is coupled to the base of $Q3$, reducing conduction in $Q3$. The common-emitter resistor $R5$ drops less voltage, which increases the forward bias of transistor $Q2$. $Q2$ increases conduction causing a less positive potential on the base of $Q1$, increasing conduction of $Q1$. This increased $Q1$ conduction causes transistors $Q4$ and $Q5$ to increase in conduction resulting in an increase in the output voltage toward the +30-volt level. Any tendency for the output to rise above the +30-volt level is

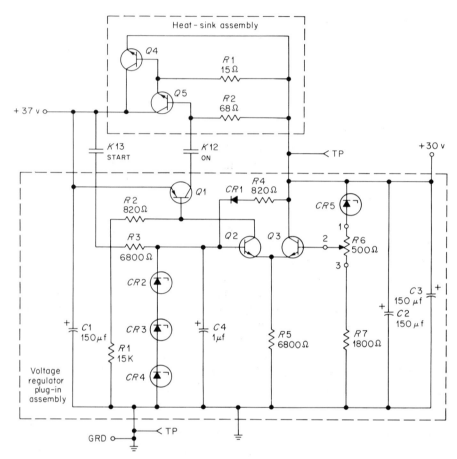

FIG. 7·53 +30-volt power supply regulator.

compensated for by the action which takes place should the loading cause an increase in output voltage.

A decrease in load results in the output voltage of the regulator increasing. This increase is coupled through $CR5$ and $R6$ to the base of $Q3$. This increased positive potential on the base of $Q3$ causes increased conduction of $Q3$ through the common-emitter resistor, resulting in a reduced forward bias on $Q2$. Decreased conduction in $Q2$ results in a more positive potential being applied to the base of $Q1$. Decreased conduction in $Q1$ causes decreased conduction in $Q4$ and $Q5$ with the regulator output moving toward the +30-volt level.

Fault-control circuits. The fault-control assembly is used to detect overvoltage and undervoltage conditions in the regulated power supplies.

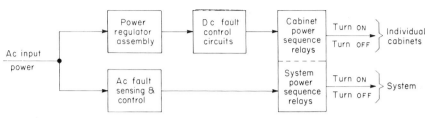

FIG. 7·54   Fault-sensing and control.

Separate fault-sensing and fault-control circuits are used to monitor the ac power circuitry (Fig. 7·54).

Dc fault-control circuits monitor each of the regulated dc supplies in the power-regulator assembly. The sensing of overvoltage or under-voltage conditions results in the initiation of an orderly power shutdown. Note that the shutdown is localized and affects only the unit being supplied by the faulty dc supply.

SUMMARY

The process of computation and control is performed in the computing system through the combinations of various types of basic circuits. The most commonly used circuits fall into the general classes of gates, amplifiers, oscillators, and power.

There are numerous types of logical gating systems used in present-day computers. The choice of a logical system depends upon the switching speeds desired, the relative cost, the power requirements, and the environment in which the system is used (amount of noise voltage present, etc.).

Current models of data processing systems require many types of nonlogical special-purpose amplifiers. These special-purpose amplifiers are used to increase signal amplitude, change the shape of a pulse waveform, provide isolation between pulses, control the lighting of indicators, and control the activation of relays.

Oscillators and multivibrators are used in computing systems to provide the timing characteristics and temporary gating requirements of high-speed systems. The timing characteristics are provided by timing and blocking oscillators, whereas multivibrators are used to provide the temporary gating requirements. Because of the bistable nature of the multivibrator, it is commonly used in circuits to perform logical and storage operations. When used in this fashion, the multivibrator is referred to as a *logical* flip-flop.

Power regulation and control circuitry is a primary factor in ensuring high reliability and accuracy in computing systems. Power regulation is used to provide specified voltage levels to allow circuit operation within the design parameters. Power control circuits are used to provide an orderly unit or system turn-on and turn-off. The orderly sequences provide equipment safety features as well as data protection.

QUESTIONS

7-1   List the five basic transistor gate configurations and give a brief description of each.

7-2   Which types of transistor gates are suitable for high switching speeds? Why?

7-3   Why is the common-emitter configuration most commonly used?

7-4   In the DCTL system, what limits the collector voltage of an OFF transistor to less than -1 volt?

7-5   What is the physical difference between a positive-input AND gate and a negative-input OR gate? Explain.

7-6   Why are nonlogical gates and amplifiers necessary in digital computing systems?

7-7   Why is circuit "loading" undesirable?

7-8   What are the input-output impedance characteristics of buffer amplifiers?

7-9   Why are timing oscillators so vital to the operation of digital computers and data processors?

7-10 What device is generally used in conjunction with the timing oscillator for program synchronization?

7-11 List the three essential sections of the feedback oscillator and describe the function of each.

7-12 What are the two classifications of blocking oscillators? Describe each.

7-13 What factors affect the operating frequency of an LC oscillator?

7-14 What problem is eliminated in the single-swing blocking oscillator by the inclusion of diode $CR1$ (Fig. 7-34a)?

7-15 If the transformer and $B+$ in a free-running blocking-oscillator circuit are fixed, how can the frequency of the blocking oscillator be varied without changing the width of the output pulses?

7-16 What determines the width of the output pulses of a blocking oscillator?

7-17 What determines the output frequency of a triggered blocking oscillator?

7-18 List some uses of the blocking oscillator.

7-19 List the three classifications of multivibrators and the uses of each.

7-20 What factors determine the operating frequency of a free-running multivibrator?

7·21   What accounts for the frequency stability on the free-running multi-vibrator shown on Fig. 7·39?

7·22   What components determine the output pulse width of a monostable multivibrator?

7·23   Is it possible to obtain an inverted and a noninverted output from a monostable multivibrator? Explain how this may be done.

7·24   What is the operational difference between the free-running multi-vibrator and the basic bistable flip-flop?

7·25   Why are the coupling resistors bypassed with capacitors in the bistable flip-flop?

7·26   Show the output waveforms for the monostable and bistable flip-flops for the following input: ⎍⎍⎍⎍

7·27   What are four practical uses of flip-flops?

7·28   How can the output levels of flip-flops be controlled?

7·29   What is complementing and how is it accomplished?

7·30   What is the purpose of $Q3$ in Fig. 7·40?

7·31   Name the major areas of a power regulation and control system and briefly describe the function of each.

chapter eight

Computer Elements

The previous chapter has described various electronic circuits which form the fundamental building blocks of a digital computer. These basic blocks are combined to perform various logical functions such as counting, decoding, storage and shift, and adding and subtracting. Examples of these elements are discussed below.

Counters

The operation of digital computers and data processors depends greatly on counting and comparing functions. Counters are employed in digital computer control circuits to regulate the sequence in which operations are performed and in data processors to facilitate the recording and modification of information.

The term "binary counter" refers to a device, composed of appropriately connected flip-flops and gates, which performs the function of counting in the binary number system. Either *up-counting* (0, 1, 2, 3, etc.) or *down-counting* (3, 2, 1, 0, etc.) can be accomplished, depending on the logical arrangement employed. The counter output can be used in various ways to perform required functions; for example, it may form a gating signal which allows information to be transferred from one register to another at the appropriate count.

The two basic counter configurations are the up-counter and the down-counter. Where the counts begin and end depends upon the logical requirements of the computer. There are variations of the basic counters, such as the combination up-down counter, which can count in either direction according to the needs of the computer.

This chapter describes the basic counter configurations. Analogies will be drawn between serial and parallel counters, and the advantages and disadvantages of each will be pointed out. The counters are shown in logical circuitry with external AND-gate inputs to the flip-flops wherever necessary. This is done to allow the substitution of a simple flip-flop logical symbol in the counter circuitry.

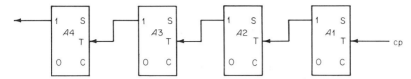

FIG. 8·1   Four-stage serial up-counter.

Serial up-counter.   A serial up-counter is composed of a group of complementing flip-flops with the ONE-side output of each flip-flop connected to the trigger input of the next flip-flop in the chain, that is, the flip-flop which contains the equivalent of the next higher binary digit.   Figure 8·1 shows a serial up-counter which is capable of counting in binary from 0 (0000) through 15 (1111).

The flip-flops are designed to respond to negative pulses (refer to Chap. 7 for the explanation of flip-flops).   The source of negative pulses is normally the trailing edge (designated as *downclock*) of a clock pulse (designated as *cp*) or the downclock from either the ONE side or the ZERO side of another flip-flop.

Flip-flop $A1$ (Fig. 8·1) changes state every time clock pulse cp is applied; that is, the flip-flop switches the high-output voltage from one side to the other.   Two pulses are required to cause a flip-flop output to go through a complete cycle, that is, from the ONE state to the ZERO state and back again to the ONE state.

Since a flip-flop changes state only upon the application of a negative pulse, $A2$ does not change state until $A1$ has switched from the ONE state to the ZERO state.   Flip-flop $A2$ then cannot change state until $A1$ downclocks, that is, until the trailing edge of the pulse from $A1$ triggers it.   Two input pulses are required to cause $A1$ to go through a complete cycle; thus, two complete cycles from $A1$ cause $A2$ to go through a complete cycle.

In order to produce a complete cycle at the output of $A4$, 16 cp's are required.   At the downclock of the sixteenth pulse, $A1$ will have changed state 16 times; $A2$, eight times; $A3$, four times; and $A4$, twice.   The binary relationship of the cycles can be seen.   This configuration of flip-flops is termed a 16:1 up-counter.

The following discussion can be more easily followed if Figs. 8·1 and 8·2 are used as references.   In the timing diagram (Fig. 8·2), the dashed vertical lines are inserted to aid in aligning pulses.

Before the first clock pulse occurs, all four flip-flops ($A1$ through $A4$) are in the ZERO state; hence, their ONE-side outputs are low ("false") and their ZERO-side outputs are high ("true").   At the downclock of $cp1$, $A1$ is triggered from the ZERO state to the ONE state and the ONE-side output becomes high.   The binary value in the counter, which should be read

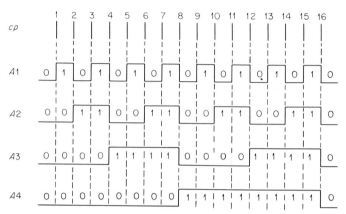

FIG. 8·2 Timing for serial up-counter.

vertically from the bottom (most significant digit) to the top (least significant digit) of the timing diagram, is 0001. On the downclock of $cp2$, flip-flop $A1$ again changes state and the ZERO-side output becomes high. The downclock from $A1$ causes $A2$ to change from the ZERO to the ONE state. As the result of the changes of state of flip-flops $A1$ and $A2$, the binary count is now 0010. Timing pulse $cp3$ changes $A1$ to the ONE state; but since a downclock does not come from the ONE side of $A1$, flip-flop $A2$ does not change state; it remains in the ONE state. The binary configuration is 0011. On the receipt of $cp4$, downclocks are applied simultaneously to $A1$, $A2$, and $A3$, causing $A1$ and $A2$ to go to the ZERO state and $A3$ to go to the ONE state. The resulting binary configuration is 0100.

The states of individual flip-flops thus continue to change with successive cp's until the maximum count of 1111 is attained on the receipt of $cp15$. A count of 1111 (decimal 15) is the highest of which a four-stage counter is capable.

When $cp16$ is received, all flip-flops ($A1$ through $A4$) change to the ZERO state. The downclock of $cp16$ causes $A1$ to go to the ZERO state; and since all flip-flops in the chain are in the ONE state, each generates a downclock to the flip-flop next in line. The downclocks result in a change of count from 1111 to 0000, which was the count present at the beginning of the operation. Each clock pulse following $cp16$ will cause the count to increase by 1 so that $cp17$ causes the count to be 0001, $cp18$ causes the count to be 0010, and so on.

The serial counter has one inherent characteristic which is a drawback to its operation at high speeds: The time required for the counter to change states increases proportionately with the number of flip-flops in the counter. This time is equal to the sum of the switching times of the flip-flops changing states, since each higher-order flip-flop is dependent upon the changing state of the lower-order flip-flop. In multistage counters this time can be significant and is termed *carry propagation time*. The advantage of the serial counter is simplicity.

Serial down-counter.   A down-counter is a counter which successively reduces by unit steps any count which is present in it. Except for one difference, a down-counter is similar in operation to an up-counter in that each successive downclock of a *cp* causes the least significant flip-flop to change state, and each successive flip-flop is triggered by the downclock of the flip-flop preceding it. The difference between the up-counter and the down-counter is that in the down-counter, the ZERO-side outputs of the flip-flops are used to cause the next flip-flop to change state. The clock pulses applied result in the counter's continually reducing its count as follows: 1111, 1110, 1101, 1100, ... , 0011, 0010, 0001, 0000, 1111, 1110, etc.

Parallel down-counter.   A parallel down-counter is composed of a chain of flip-flops whose individual ZERO-side outputs are applied to every flip-flop of higher order. Also, the input pulse (*cp*) is applied directly to every flip-flop in the chain. As has been shown, the flip-flops in a serial down-counter are caused to change state by a downclock from the flip-flop of the next lower order or, in the case of the least significant flip-flop, by the downclock of a *cp*. The parallel down-counter, however, changes state only when it receives the combined outputs of all flip-flops of a lower significance and the *cp*. The flip-flop of the lowest significance, of course, changes state on receipt of the *cp* alone (see Fig. 8·3). It should be noted that the application of the *cp* pulse to each flip-flop in the chain eliminates the carry propagation time present in the serial counter.

The application of pulses in the parallel down-counter is as follows:

1.   The *cp* is applied to flip-flops *D*1, *D*2, *D*3, and *D*4.
2.   The output of $\overline{D1}$ is applied to *D*2, *D*3, and *D*4.
3.   The output of $\overline{D2}$ is applied to *D*3 and *D*4.
4.   The output of $\overline{D3}$ is applied to *D*4.

FIG. 8·3   Four-stage parallel down-counter.

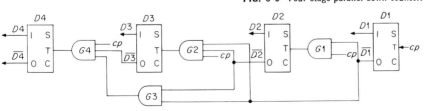

The Boolean equations for changing the states of the flip-flops in the parallel down-counter are as follows:

$$D1 = cp$$
$$D2 = cp \cdot \overline{D1}$$
$$D3 = cp \cdot \overline{D1} \cdot \overline{D2}$$
$$D4 = cp \cdot \overline{D1} \cdot \overline{D2} \cdot \overline{D3}$$

Note that the opposite side input of the flip-flop is not shown in the Boolean equation since it has been indicated that complementing flip-flops are used in the counter.

Each flip-flop in a parallel down-counter changes state only if all flip-flops of lower significance are in the ZERO state. Assume all flip-flops in the counter shown in Fig. 8·3 are set to the ONE state and contain an initial count of 1111. At $cp1$ (see Fig. 8·4) flip-flop $D1$ is reset to the ZERO state and the counter contains 1110. The output $\overline{D1}$ is applied to the trigger gate $G1$ of $D2$, to $G2$ of $D3$, and also to $G3$. The outputs of $G2$ and $G3$ are still false because $\overline{D2}$ is false; therefore $D3$ has no true inputs and will not change state with the next cp.

When $cp2$ is received, it becomes the second input to $G1$ providing true

FIG. 8·4 Timing for parallel down-counter.

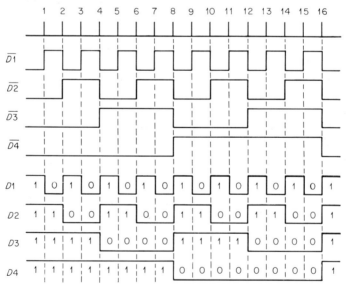

signals to the trigger input of $D2$. Since $D2$ is in the ONE state, it will be reset to the ZERO state. $D1$, which is in the ZERO state, sets to the ONE state. The count in the counter is now 1101. $G2$ and $G3$ are now inhibited by $\overline{D1}$ being false.

Pulse $cp3$ will change only $D1$ since all gates are inhibited by signals $\overline{D1}$ and $\overline{D3}$ being false. The count in the counter is now 1100.

When $cp4$ arrives, it will satisfy the Boolean equation requirements for $G1$, $G2$, and $G3$ to have true outputs; $G4$ output will remain false because $\overline{D3}$ is false. $G2$ output being true provides a true signal to the $D3$ trigger input, which causes $D3$ to reset to the ZERO state. $\overline{D3}$ is now true but $D2$ has been set to the ONE state by the true output from $G1$. $Cp4$ also set $D1$ to the ONE state. The count now contained in the counter is 1011.

The count continues to decrease in the fashion described above; the requirements of the Boolean equations must be met for the flip-flops to change state. At $cp7$, the contents of the counter are 1000. When $cp8$ arrives, all gate equations are satisfied and all flip-flops change state. $D4$ resets to the ZERO state, while $D3$, $D2$, and $D1$ set to the ONE state.

At $cp15$ the counter contains 0000, which is the minimum count for a four-stage counter. When $cp16$ is applied, the equations to change the states of all four flip-flops are satisfied, and each changes from the ZERO state to the ONE state. The count resulting from the application of $cp16$ is thus 1111. This count is the same configuration present before the downclock of $cp1$. The counter has therefore been reset to its initial condition and is ready for recycling.

Parallel up-counter. The parallel up-counter, like a serial up-counter, is composed of complementing flip-flops which represent an increased count with each application of a clock pulse. The advantage gained in the use of the parallel up-counter is the elimination of the carry propagation time present in the serial counter. This allows higher counting speeds. A disadvantage of the parallel counter is that it requires a more complex gating arrangement. The mechanization for the parallel up-counter is similar to that of the parallel down-counter. The difference lies in the use of the ONE-side outputs of the lower-order flip-flops as inputs to the higher-order flip-flops. The counter operates through the count range of 0000 to 1111 and then recycles. The maximum count capacity is determined by the number of flip-flops in the counter.

Counter variations. The maximum count of which a counter is capable is $2^n - 1$, where n equals the number of flip-flops in the circuit. Hence, a five-stage counter can have a maximum content of $2^5 - 1$, or 31 (11111). In certain computer operations it may be desired to count to a number less

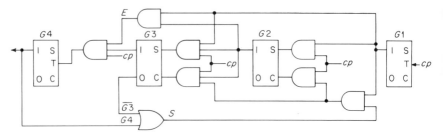

FIG. 8·5 Modulus 10 counter.

than the maximum capacity of the counter and then to recycle after this count. For instance, in order to count to 10, four flip-flops (having a maximum capacity of 15) are required. Consequently, the counter has to be modified through the use of feedback and logical switching circuits to produce only one output pulse at the most significant flip-flop for every 10 pulses received at the least significant flip-flop. Such a counter is called a *modulus 10 counter*, or a *mod 10 counter*. Mod 10 and mod 14 counters are described in the following paragraphs.

Mod 10 counter. Figure 8·5 shows a mod 10 counter. It is a modified parallel up-counter using feedback from $\overline{G3} + G4$ to inhibit the normal reset of flip-flops $G2$ and $G3$ during a portion of the counting cycle. The timing diagram of Fig. 8·6 indicates that a complete output pulse occurs on the tenth, twentieth, thirtieth, etc., input pulse. The logic of the counter is such that the flip-flops may switch to the ONE state at any time when all preceding flip-flops are in the ONE state. Two of the flip-flops ($G2$ and $G3$), however, are inhibited. Flip-flops $G2$ and $G3$ can go to the ZERO state only

FIG. 8·6 Modulus 10 counter timing diagram.

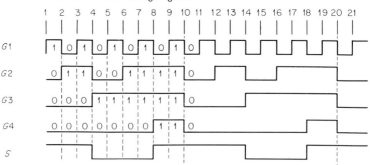

when $G3$ is in the ZERO state or $G4$ is in the ONE state. The count progresses in the manner shown below:

cp	Count
1	0001
2	0010
3	0011
4	0100
5	0101
6	0110
7	0111
8	1110
9	1111
10	0000

The Boolean equations for the mod 10 counter are as follows:

$$G1 + \overline{G1} = cp$$

$$G2 = cp \cdot G1$$

$$\overline{G2} = cp \cdot G1 \cdot G4 + cp \cdot G1 \cdot \overline{G3}$$

$$G3 = cp \cdot G1 \cdot G2$$

$$\overline{G3} = cp \cdot G1 \cdot G2 \cdot G4$$

$$G4 + \overline{G4} = cp \cdot G1 \cdot G2 \cdot G3$$

Mod 14 counter. A minor change in logic can convert the mod 10 counter into a mod 14 counter. Instead of the ZERO-side output of the $G3$ flip-flop and the ONE-side output of the $G4$ flip-flop, the ONE-side output of the $G3$ flip-flop and the ZERO-side output of the $G4$ flip-flop are used. The reader is encouraged to make the changes to Fig. 8·5 and develop a timing diagram for the counter. Modulo counters can be constructed to cycle within any desired range of counts.

Decoders

The four-stage binary counters previously discussed are capable of representing 16 distinct time phases of operation in relation to the clock pulses. The operations and information transfers take place within the computer at

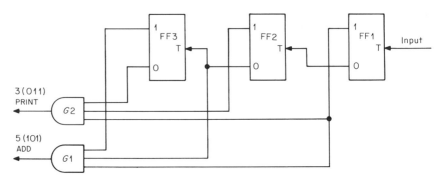

FIG. 8·7 Computer operation decoder.

different times, and perhaps at different rates. The variations in the binary configurations could, upon proper recognition, provide control signals to initiate action in other parts of the computer. Decoders are utilized to generate these control signals during various phases of the count.

A decoder is a circuit consisting of one or more AND gates used to detect certain counts in a counter or register. These decoder outputs can be used to initiate specific actions in the computer or to indicate when certain operations have been completed. For example, assume that a down-counter is used to control two computer operations; that is, the computer is to add on the count of 5 and is to print out the results on the count of 3. Two decoder gates, $G1$ and $G2$, would be connected to the down-counter as shown in Fig. 8·7.

When the count is reduced to 5, only $G1$ will have an output to instruct the computer to add. On the count of 3, only $G2$ will have an output to instruct the computer to print out the results.

The inputs to $G1$ are from the ONE side of $FF1$, the ZERO side of $FF2$, and the ONE side of $FF3$. Hence, $G1$ will produce a high output only on the count of 5 (101). The inputs of $G2$ are from the ONE side of $FF1$, the ONE side of $FF2$, and the ZERO side of $FF3$. $G2$ will produce a high output only on the count of 3 (011).

Regardless of the count to be decoded, there will always be a decoder input from each flip-flop in the counter or register. This is because an undecoded flip-flop may be in the ONE or the ZERO state, and thus the counter or register could have a count other than that to be decoded.

Storage and Shift Registers

As the computer performs its scheduled operations, there is an almost continual data flow within and between its major subdivisions. It is necessary to provide temporary storage locations for data as well as the means whereby transfers of the information can be made. This requirement is met through the use of storage and shift registers.

Storage registers and shift registers must be able to perform the following three functions:

1. Receive information from another source.
2. Preserve this information without alteration or loss of signal strength until it is needed.
3. Deliver this information to another circuit of the computer when it is required by the program.

Schematically, storage registers and shift registers are similar to the binary counter. They are composed of storage cells, such as flip-flops, ferrite cores, thin-film spots, or other bistable devices, each of which is an elementary location capable of storing a single binary digit (bit). These elementary locations, also termed memory cells, are grouped to hold words. A word is, in a fixed-word-length binary computer, of finite length, depending upon the design criteria and the programming requirements. The number of bits in a word determines the size of the register.

Usually, a word which is to be stored has a predetermined function in the computer operation, and thus it will be always transferred to a specific storage register. This transfer may occur either in a serial or a parallel fashion.

A register requires a means by which it is possible to read in, or record, the information without alteration and in proper bit locations. It must also be possible, whenever the program calls for it, to sample either certain bits or an entire word in a register without destroying or removing the contents of this register.

Finally, there must be a means of reading out this information when it is needed and inserting it in another register or in the memory. After this information is removed, the register must be capable of having the previously stored information erased in anticipation of receiving new information. This process of erasing is called *clearing*, and it resets the register states to their normal state, usually ZERO.

Flip-flop storage register. Figure 8·8 shows a three flip-flop, parallel-loaded, storage register, $M1$ through $M3$. This register is loaded by the simultaneous transfer of the information content of register $A1$ through $A3$. The M register in this example is referred to as a non-force-loaded register; that is, the register must be reset before new data is inserted into it. The reset pulse (RM) to the ZERO side of the M register is used to reset or clear the register prior to the transfer of data into the register. This reset pulse

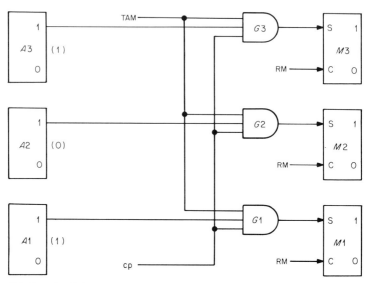

FIG. 8·8 Parallel input storage register.

occurs in time slightly before the transfer level (TAM). The clock pulse cp causes the flip-flops of the storage register to be set to the ONE state to indicate the appropriate data bits.

Assume that flip-flops $M1$ through $M3$ have been cleared by the reset pulse RM, and that flip-flops $A1$ through $A3$ contain the binary configuration 101. The transfer signal TAM is generated. TAM "true" and flip-flops $A1$ and $A3$ in the ONE state require only a clock pulse to satisfy $G1$ and $G3$. The presence of these levels allows the next clock pulse to set flip-flops $M1$ and $M3$ to the ONE state. Flip-flop $A2$ in the ZERO state inhibits $G2$; therefore, the clock pulse has no effect on $M2$ and this flip-flop remains in the ZERO state. Thus the original information content of the A register (101) has been reproduced in the M storage register through a simultaneous transfer of all bits. It should be noted that a separate transfer path exists for each information bit being transferred. The Boolean equations for the transfer action are shown below.

1. $M1 = A1 \cdot \text{TAM} \cdot cp$
2. $M2 = A2 \cdot \text{TAM} \cdot cp$
3. $M3 = A3 \cdot \text{TAM} \cdot cp$

Another method of loading information into a storage register is by force load. This method does not require a clear signal prior to the loading

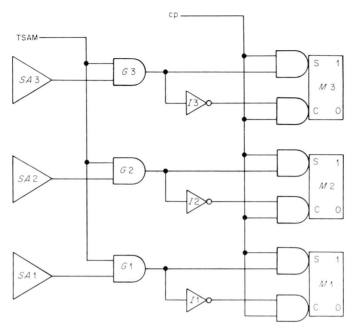

FIG. 8·9   Parallel input force load storage register.

of new data. Figure 8·9 illustrates this loading action. The information to be transferred is applied to gates $G1$, $G2$, and $G3$ through gates $SA1$, $SA2$, and $SA3$, respectively. The transfer level SA to M (TSAM) is applied as the second input to $G1$, $G2$, and $G3$. Note the arrangement at the output of these gates.

The output of each gate is applied as a true input to the internal gating of the set input of the flip-flop. A cp pulse is required to place the flip-flop in the ONE state. The output of $G1$, $G2$, and $G3$ is applied through inverters to the respective clear inputs of each of the storage register flip-flops. A true level at the clear input and cp will reset the flip-flops to the ZERO state. It should be recalled that the presence of a signal at the input to a logical inverter results in the absence of the signal at the output of the inverter and vice versa. The effect of this action is that an output from $G1$, $G2$, and $G3$ will allow cp to set the flip-flops to the ONE state. The absence of an output from these gates will allow cp to reset the flip-flops to the ZERO state. The state of the storage register at the time of transfer has no effect on the transfer itself. The reader is encouraged to follow the gating actions of force loading the M register with data bits 101. Assume that the storage register contains data bits 110 at the time of transfer.

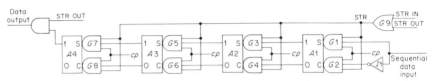

FIG. 8·10 Serial input storage/shift register.

Parallel data transfers are common within the processor system and allow for high-speed transfer of information during the computation cycle. It is not uncommon for data to be transmitted from distant points to the processor for use in computations. This data is transferred via communication lines. If parallel transfer of a data word, of 48 bits for example, were to be made, one data line for each bit or 48 data communication lines would be required. This is not economically feasible since a serial data transfer could take place much more economically, although some additional time is required. The time involved is not a critical consideration. The data transfer of the 48-bit data word could take place in serial fashion with the use of a single data communication line.

Serial input storage/shift register.   Figure 8·10 illustrates a serial input storage register, $A1$ through $A4$. The inputs required for set or clear of the higher-order flip-flops consist of a clock pulse cp, the ONE or ZERO side of the next lower-order flip-flop, and the strobe pulse STR. The strobe pulse is a level which controls the period during which the loading is to take place. The least significant flip-flop, in addition to cp and STR, requires individual input data bits to control its set and clear. The inverter action at the input to $A1$ is as previously discussed. Assume that the register is cleared to zeros by a reset pulse (not shown). This condition is shown on the timing diagram of Fig. 8·11. With the occurrence of $cp1$ and $cp2$, there is no effect on $A1$ since the strobe pulse STR is not preset to indicate a load condition for the register. Note that data is available but is not accepted into the register. The $cp3$ pulse combines with the STR level and the data bit of ONE to set $A1$ to the ONE state. The register content is now 0001. Cp 4 satisfies $G2$ to clear $A1$ (STR·cp·$\overline{\text{data}}$), and $G3$ to set $A2$ to the ONE state (STR·cp· $A1$). Register content is now 0010. Note on the timing diagram that the first two data bits (1 and 0) are now contained in $A1$ and $A2$. The occurrence of the $cp5$ pulse satisfies $G1$ (STR·data), $G4$ (STR·$\overline{A1}$), and $G5$ (STR·$A2$) to set $A1$, clear $A2$, and set $A3$. The register now contains 0101. The initial input bit loaded (1) has progressed to position $A3$ in the register. The advent of $cp6$ causes an output from $G1$, $G3$, $G6$, and $G7$, with results in

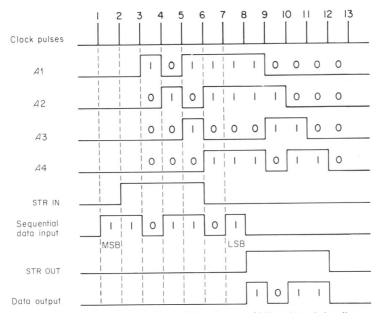

FIG. 8·11 Serial input storage/shift register timing diagram.

a register content of 1011. At this time the STR pulse is removed so that no additional data bits are accepted by the register. The example presented could represent a data input from the communication line. The register will store the data until it is transferred. The transfer of data internally could be implemented as a parallel transfer in the manner previously discussed.

The logical configuration shown in Fig. 8·10 also represents a serial shift register. The action of serial loading is an actual shift operation. The data could be fed serially to the communication link by an inhibit of the data input and the reinitiation of the strobe level. Successive clock pulses would shift the data bits in the manner previously described so that the $A4$ output would place the bits 1011 on the communication link.

The timing of Fig. 8·11 ($cp9 \ldots$) illustrates the shift of data after reinitiation of strobe (STR). Note that at $cp12$ time, the last bit has been shifted from $A4$ to the phone line, and the transfer is complete.

The serial shift register may be a combined element in that its interface with the communication link will be a serial-type operation, whereas its communication with the processor system may be a parallel operation. Many variations of operating modes may be found in storage and shift registers.

Parallel shift registers. Data manipulation within the processor during operations such as scaling and other arithmetic operations requires that the position of bits within a register be changed so that they are displaced either to the left or to the right of their original position. Shift registers are used to perform this function and since speed is a prime consideration in internal processor operations, parallel information transfer is used. The parallel shift register is usually found in some combination of functions. For example, the parallel shift register of Fig. 8·12 is capable of a direct transfer of bits from register to register or of a one-position-to-the-right shift.

The operation of the parallel shift register is similar in operation to the parallel input storage registers discussed earlier. The force-load method of information transfer has been selected for use in the example; hence, no clear pulses are used.

TAB and SHRC are considered to be pulses at a clock-rate frequency to ensure synchronization with other processor operations. Note that the TAB (Transfer A to B) pulse combines with the 1 or 0 output of each of the flip-flops $A1$, $A2$, and $A3$ to allow a direct bit-for-bit transfer of data from the A to the B register. This action is as discussed for Fig. 8·9.

The SHRC pulse is defined as shift right circular. In this operation the data bits of the A register are shifted right circular into the B register. On a one-position shift in this operation, the MSB ($A3$) is shifted into the next lower-order position ($B2$), the next bit ($A2$) is shifted into the $B1$ position, and the LSB ($A1$) is shifted into the highest order position in the B register ($B3$). Examine the transfer path of a 1 bit from $A3$ on the SHRC pulse. $G12$ is enabled, resulting in the set input of $B2$ being pulsed through $G15$. Recall that on force-loading a flip-flop, only one side is triggered. If the triggered side is already in that state, no change occurs; if the flip-flop is in the opposite state, it will assume the state of the input side triggered. Examine now the circular shift path from $A1$ to $B3$. Assume a 1 bit in $A1$. At SHRC time $G4$ and $G13$ are enabled, allowing $B3$ to be set.

Many shift variations exist either left or right, circular or straight (bits "shifted off" end of register discarded), single or multiple.

The concept of multiple shifting results from the continued development of methods to increase processor speeds. In multiple shifting the data is displaced several positions on the transfer instead of a single one. For example, in a 12-bit register, a multiple shift-right of 6 would transfer data from the $A12$ position in one register to the $B6$ position of the other register. This transfer takes place in the same time period that is required for a single-position shift of information from $A12$ to $B11$. The gating circuitry required to implement this capability would provide transfer paths for a one-place shift or for a six-place shift. The optimum shift capability is provided by a logical element capable of allowing any number of shifts up to the maximum register capacity (in number of positions). One approach to providing this capability exists in a logical element termed the Burroughs Barrel Switch.

Barrel switch. The concept of the barrel switch is, through selective gating, to provide a single or multiple shift capability in a single timing period. The example to be presented is that of a 12-position shift-left-circular capability

FIG. 8·12 Parallel shift register.

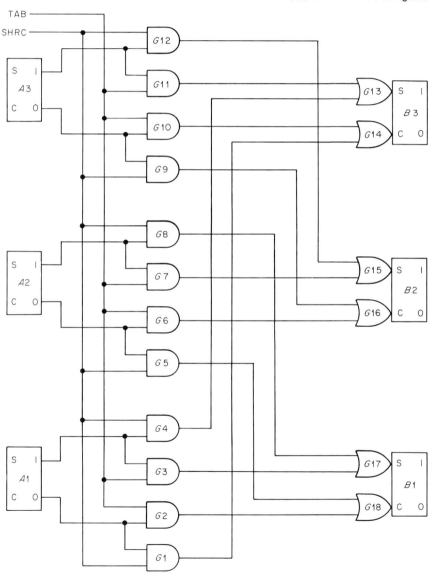

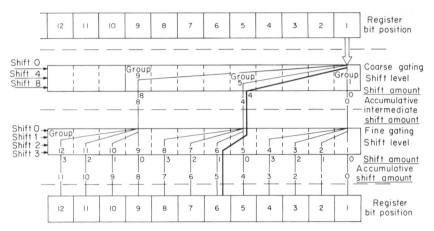

FIG. 8·13 Barrel switch, simplified.

in any amount, 0 through 12 shifts. Two levels of gating are used to effect the shifting action. The first level of gating accepts inputs and directs them on a gross level of zero, four, or eight shifts. The second gating level accepts these outputs and provides for an additive shift of 0, 1, 2, or 3 to the above amounts. For example, the gross-level output of 0 shift may be gated through the fine-gating levels of 0, 1, 2, or 3 to effect the desired shifts in those amounts. The gross-level output from the 4 gating combines with the fine-level gating to effect shifts of 4 (4 + 0), 5 (4 + 1), 6 (4 + 2), and 7 (4 + 3). The 8-level output combines similarly in the fine gating to result in shifts of 8, 9, 10, and 11.

Figure 8·13 illustrates a simplified flow of this shifting action. The register shown at the top and the bottom is the same register and receives the shifted outputs and provides the input data for shifting.

In the example, a bit from position 1 in the register is passed to the coarse-level gating. Depending upon the shift control level, the bit will be displaced either zero, four, or eight positions. Assume a desired shift of five positions. This results in a control-level shift 4 to the coarse-level gates and a control level of shift 1 to the fine-level gates. A shift control level of 4 to the coarse gates results in a group-5 output — representing a four-position shift of the data. This input to the fine-control gates and a shift-1 level to the fine-control gates results in an additional shift of one position or a cumulative shift total of five positions. This output is presented as an input to register position six, a five-position shift.

In a like manner, a 10-place shift requirement provides shift levels of 8 and 2 to the coarse and fine gates, respectively, resulting in gating action which places the original bit 1 in the bit 11 position.

TABLE 8·1   Gating levels

Shift		Coarse		Fine
0	=	SHZC	·	SHZF
1	=	SHZC	·	SH1
2	=	SHZC	·	SH2
3	=	SHZC	·	SH3
4	=	SH4	·	SHZF
5	=	SH4	·	SH1
6	=	SH4	·	SH2
7	=	SH4	·	SH3
8	=	SH8	·	SHZF
9	=	SH8	·	SH1
10	=	SH8	·	SH2
11	=	SH8	·	SH3

NOTE: SHZF = (SHZC + SH4 + SH8)
$\cdot(\overline{\text{SH1}\cdot\text{SH2}\cdot\text{SH3}})$

This gating arrangement is repeated for each of the positions of the register.

A more detailed analysis of the action is presented with the use of Fig. 8·14.

The gating levels provided are the result of a decode resulting from the original shift request. The levels provided to the coarse- and fine-decode gates for the shift range are given in Table 8·1.

In the coarse-level gating (Fig. 8·14), each of the 12 groups allows for the 0, 4, and 8 level of shift inputs; that is, if the output of these gates were to meet the total shift requirements, inputs for 0, 4, and 8 shift possibilities would come from specific bit positions. Examine the group-1 coarse-level gates. A 0 shift would have the bit-1 output position of the register as the controlling bit. If a four-bit shift were called for, the controlling bit must come from bit-9 output of the register since a four-position left shift of bit 9 would reside in bit 1. In a like manner the bit-5 position would reside in register bit 1 after an eight-place left shift. Note that on a shift of 0, 4, or 8, the fine-level gating would allow the direct transfer of data bits 1, 9, or 5, respectively, into the 1-bit position since the shift 0 level is present at the fine-gating level.

It should be noted that shifts other than those discussed above result in other gating action at the fine-level gating.

For example, an additive shift of 1, 2, or 3 is provided for the 0, 4, and 8 output at the fine-level gating.

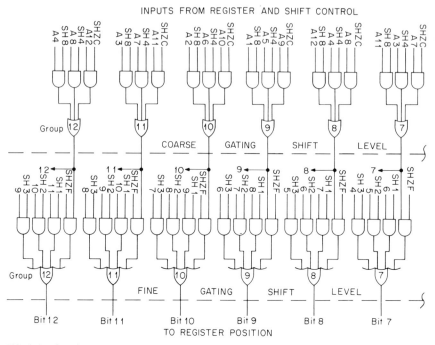

FIG. 8·14 Barrel-switch logic.

The output of the fine-level gating is the shifted data and is transferred directly into the original register. In the group-1 fine-gating level, bit-1 position of the register may be activated by a 1 from original bit position 9 (in a shift 4), bit position 5 (in a shift 8), or from bit positions 12, 11, or 10 in a shift 1, 2, or 3, respectively.

Note also that the output of the group-1 coarse-level gating is provided to fine-level gating groups 2, 3, and 4 to provide for accumulative shifts of 5, 6, 7, or 9, 10, 11, depending upon the activating level present at the group-1 coarse-gating level.

This gating action is repeated for each of the bit positions of the register. Follow the action for a six-position shift of a bit from position 11. The request for a six-shift operation results in an initial decode of shift level 4 to the coarse-level gates and shift level 2 to the fine-level gates. Data bit 11 appears as an input to the group-3 coarse-decoding gates. The presence of the sh4 level provides an output (3) to the fine-decoding gates. At this point an intermediate displacement of four register positions has occurred. This output becomes an input with the sh2 level to the group-5 fine-level gates. The result is an output to bit position 5 of the storage register. A six-position shift in the register results in the original data bit in position 11 residing in bit position 5 at the completion of the shift. Each of

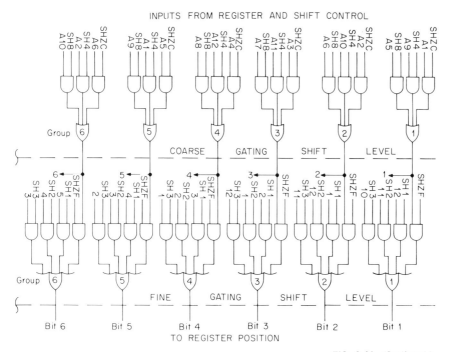

INPUTS FROM REGISTER AND SHIFT CONTROL

FIG. 8·14 (Continued.)

the other bit positions in the register is gated in a similar manner so that the simultaneous transfer of all bits occurs. Thus the transfer of data displaced by the desired number of positions is effected without the need for separate transfer paths for each of the positional transfer possibilities which exist in the device.

Matrices

The control function necessary in data processing and arithmetic operations is implemented largely through the use of switching networks of various sizes. These switching networks, or *matrices*, are composed of circuits producing a discrete output signal for each combination of input signals. The term matrix is used to describe these large switching arrangements because of their similarity to mathematical matrices, being neatly arranged in rows and columns. Matrices are used in both decoding and encoding operations. Some of these applications are discussed in this section.

Diode matrix. Figure 8·15 is a logical diagram of a system composed of a counter, a detect net, and a NOT detect net. Corresponding Boolean equations are also shown for this figure. The diodes (two for each AND and OR

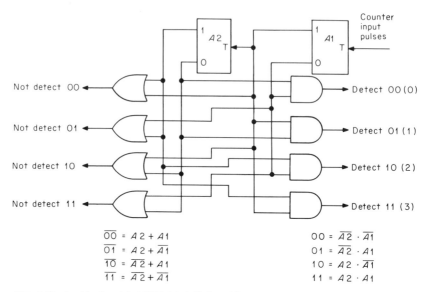

FIG. 8·15 Combination detect-NOT detect diode matrix.

gate) are not shown. This diagram would be complicated further if the counter contained three, five, or more flip-flops, because the gate inputs would be increased proportionately.

The detect net shown in Fig. 8·16 performs the same functions as that shown in Fig. 8·15; however, it is drawn schematically as the grid or matrix type of detect net. In this form there is a simple means for showing the flip-flop outputs and the diode voltage potentials ($B+$ for the AND gates, $B-$ for the OR gates).

Diodes $CR1$ and $CR2$ constitute the AND gate for detecting binary 01. When this number occurs in the counter, the $B1$ and $\overline{B2}$ lines go positive, ("true"), causing diodes $CR1$ and $CR2$ to cut off, producing a high output ("true") on line 01. When the counter configuration changes from 01 to 10, diode $CR1$ conducts; a substantial voltage is dropped across $R1$, and the output at X goes low ("false"), thus terminating the detected signal. The detected signal will not occur again until $B1$ and $\overline{B2}$ outputs are again true; there is no other count configuration in the entire counting range where this can happen.

Diodes $CR5$ and $CR6$ constitute the OR gate for NOT detecting binary 10. When any configuration other than binary 10 is present in the counter, either diode $CR5$ or diode $CR6$ is conducting. While either diode $CR5$ or diode $CR6$ is conducting, there is substantial voltage drop across load resistor $R2$, causing the output at point Y to remain high ("true," positive in respect to the $B-$ voltage). However, when the $B1$ and $\overline{B2}$ lines are "false" (binary 10), diodes $CR5$ and $CR6$ are not conducting heavily. As a result, the output at Y drops from its previous "true" level to the "false" logic level. This "false" output remains until either diode $CR5$ or diode $CR6$ conducts. Thus, the Y output is true for all configurations except binary 10 (decimal 2).

The other AND and OR gates (two diodes connected to each horizontal line) function in the same manner but at different times.

Figure 8·17 illustrates a matrix which will detect the eight possible configurations of a three-flip-flop counter. Note the absence of NOT detect gates and associated circuitry. Flip-flops $C1$, $C2$, and $C3$ will produce count configurations of 2^3, or 8. Each of the eight counts requires three diodes for proper detection. Thus, a total of 8×3, or 24, diodes are required. It follows then that a counter containing four flip-flops requires $2^4 \times 4$, or 64, diodes; a counter composed of five flip-flops requires $2^5 \times 5$, or 160, diodes.

FIG. 8·16 Single-stage AND-OR diode matrix.

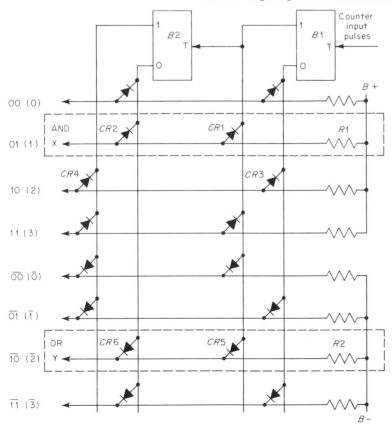

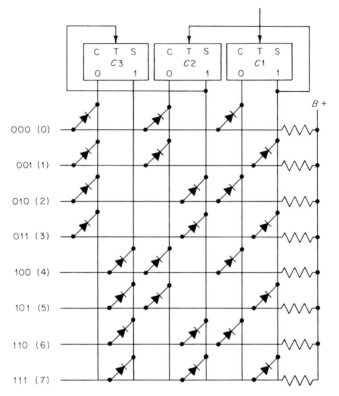

FIG. 8·17 Single-stage diode matrix utilizing a three-stage counter.

The general formula for the one-stage matrix is $n2^n$, with n representing the number of input variables.

It is apparent that the number of diodes required as the number of flip-flops increases becomes prohibitive if diode economy is a factor. There is a method of matrix arrangement, however, that reduces the number of diodes required to detect the larger binary configurations. This arrangement is called a *tree* or *pyramid* because of its branching appearance.

An example of treeing is shown in the two-stage matrix of Fig. 8·18 (each dot represents one diode in an AND gate). The economy of diodes is achieved by (1) dividing the counter into pairs of flip-flops, (2) ANDing each possible output combination from each pair, and (3) ANDing the output of the two ANDed pairs to yield the decoded binary number. Note that in Fig. 8·17 each diode is used only once. In Fig. 8·18, however, the diode pair 1 and 2 is used four different times; this pair is used in the detection of counts 0, 4, 8, and 12. Diode pair 3 and 4 is used in the detection of counts

1, 5, 9, and 13. Each pair of diodes is used in the detection of four numbers. This eliminates the need for 16 of the 64 diodes required if a one-stage matrix were used to detect all possible configurations of Fig. 8·18; hence, only 48 diodes are necessary. The diode AND gate arrangement can be seen in Fig. 8·19 which shows the detect = 7 portion of the two-stage matrix.

FIG. 8·18 Two-stage detect matrix.

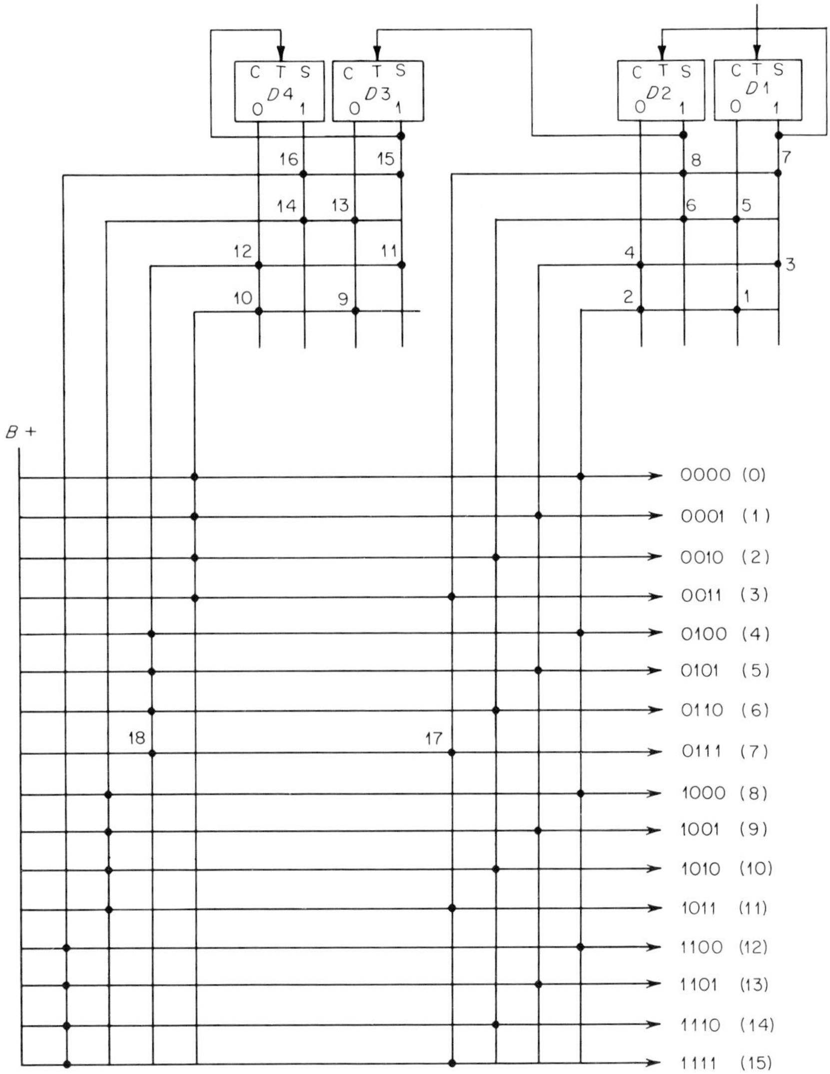

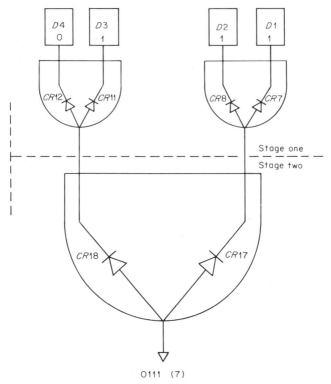

FIG. 8·19   Detect =7 portion of matrix of Fig. 8·18.

Encoder.   Just as a decoder consists of a group of AND gates used to decode a binary number configuration to select one of several ouputs, an encoder may be considered as a group of OR gates used to translate a given input into its equivalent binary configuration. Both encoders and decoders accomplish translation.

Figure 8·20 is an example of a decimal to binary-coded-decimal diode matrix encoder.

The theory of operation of the encoder is the opposite of the decoder. Assume, for example, that it is desired to encode the decimal number 9. In Fig. 8·20, the vertical line for number 9 would be made "true" (high). This places a forward bias on diodes $CR1$, $CR2$, $CR3$, and $CR4$ causing them to conduct heavily. $CR1$ in conduction causes a voltage drop across $R1$ providing a high ("true") signal to the 1 line of the 2^0 binary order. In a like manner the conduction of diodes $CR2$, $CR3$, and $CR4$ causes a voltage drop across $R4$, $R6$, and $R7$. This action results in "true" levels on the 2^1 order 0 line, 2^2 order 0 line, and 2^3 order 1 line. The result is a binary encode

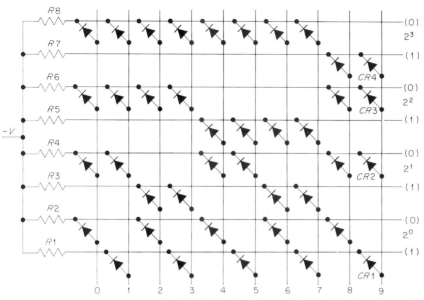

FIG. 8·20 Decimal to binary-coded-decimal diode matrix encoder.

of 1001 or 9_{10}. In a like manner, the other decimal digits may be encoded by the activation of the respective vertical (decimal) lines of the matrix.

As in other computer elements, many variations of the matrix are used to meet specific large-scale encoding and decoding applications.

Arithmetic Elements

The processing unit in a computing system usually performs its arithmetic operations by addition. The other arithmetic operations are performed through variations of the basic addition function. Although some processors use the subtracter as the arithmetic element, most computing systems use the adder.

Variations of the adder may be found elsewhere in the processing system to provide, for example, the comparison function as in the exclusive OR circuit.

Adder. The logical requirements of an adder can be determined by constructing a truth table for addition (Table 8·2).

TABLE 8·2   Truth Table for Half-adder

Augend	X	0	1	0	1
Addend	Y	0	0	1	1
Sum	S	0	1	1	0
Carry	C	0	0	0	1

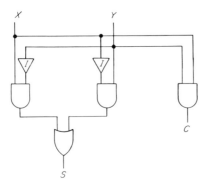

FIG. 8·21 Half-adder, logical diagram.

The truth table considers a single order, and only two binary digits are added at one time. The truth table indicates which of the four possible combinations of X and Y will produce a sum and a carry. From the truth table it can be seen that a sum is produced when the augend X is 1 and the addend Y is 0, and vice versa. A carry is produced when both X and Y are 1. Logical equations may be written for the sum and the carry in terms of X and Y, as follows:

$$S = X\bar{Y} + \bar{X}Y$$
$$C = XY$$

The equation for the sum describes the exclusive-OR function. The exclusive-OR function provides a "true" output when one, but not both, of the inputs is present. A logical diagram can be drawn from these equations (Fig. 8·21).

The truth table considered only two inputs. In practice, an adder must be able to accept a carry from a previous order and add it to the augend and addend bits in the order under consideration. Since the equation and diagram do not consider the possible carry from a previous order, the adder as developed to this point (Fig. 8·21) is termed a *half-adder*.

Full adder. A full adder handles the possible carry from a previous order. A full adder consists of two half-adders. One half-adder adds the augend and addend in a particular order. The other half-adder adds the resulting sum to a carry from a previous order. As a result of these two additions, a single sum and a single carry output are produced for that particular order. A block diagram of the full adder is given in Fig. 8·22.

Half-adders are represented by the blocks labeled *H.A.* Half-adder 1 adds the X and Y inputs for that order. Half-adder 2 adds the sum output of half-adder 1 to the carry input developed in a lower order. As a result,

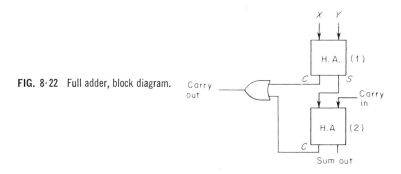

FIG. 8-22 Full adder, block diagram.

a sum output for the order is developed. A carry may develop from either half-adder and hence is applied to the OR gate. It is seen from inspection that a carry output cannot exist at both outputs simultaneously.

A truth table for the full adder (Table 8-3) indicates all possible combinations when three inputs are used.

The truth table shows that there are four combinations that produce a sum and four combinations that produce a carry. They are as follows:

$$S = X\bar{Y}\bar{C}_{in} + \bar{X}Y\bar{C}_{in} + \bar{X}\bar{Y}C_{in} + XYC_{in}$$
$$C_{out} = XY\bar{C}_{in} + X\bar{Y}C_{in} + \bar{X}YC_{in} + XYC_{in}$$

Terms may be collected so that the operation of the full adder as previously discussed becomes more apparent:

$$S = C_{in}(\bar{X}\bar{Y} + XY) + \bar{C}_{in}(X\bar{Y} + \bar{X}Y)$$
$$C_{out} = C_{in}(X\bar{Y} + \bar{X}Y + XY) + \bar{C}_{in}XY$$

Parallel and Serial Adder Units

Half-adders and full adders using only the components necessary to execute the operations of a single order have been developed. It will now be shown how the adders are used to add binary numbers of several orders. Addition

TABLE 8-3 Full-adder Truth Table

Augend	X	0	1	0	1	0	1	0	1
Addend	Y	0	0	1	1	0	0	1	1
Carry	C_{in}	0	0	0	0	1	1	1	1
Sum	S	0	1	1	0	1	0	0	1
Carry	C_{out}	0	0	0	1	0	1	1	1

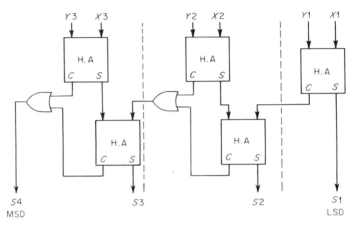

FIG. 8·23 Three-stage parallel adder.

can be performed in parallel (each order added simultaneously) or in series (each order added sequentially). Both parallel and serial units are discussed.

Parallel operation. A computer operating in parallel requires an adder for each order; hence, a three-bit word requires three adders. The diagram in Fig. 8·23 illustrates an adder unit capable of adding two three-bit numbers.

The least significant order requires a half-adder since no carry input is involved. Each subsequent order uses a full adder. A complete full adder consists of two half-adders and an external OR circuit. A carry output from the most significant order becomes the most significant digit (MSD) of the sum.

A numerical example describes the operation of the adder unit more clearly. The following numbers are applied to the adders:

$$
\begin{array}{r}
X = 111 \\
Y = 110 \\
\hline
1101
\end{array}
$$

The first order is applied to the half-adder. A sum output, but no carry, is developed. In the second order both X_2 and Y_2 are 1's. The sum from the upper half-adder portion is 0, and a carry is generated. No carry from the least significant digit (LSD) order was generated; hence, the sum from the lower half-adder of the second order is 0.

In the third order both X_3 and Y_3 are 1's. The sum from the upper half-adder portion is 0, and a carry is generated. The 0 sum output from the upper half-adder portion of the third order is added to the carry from the second order. The sum output of the third order is 1.

The carry developed from the third order becomes the MSD of the sum.

In the high-speed processors with word lengths approaching 48 bits or more, speed considerations dictate the use of parallel adders. Since all semiconductor devices require a finite time to switch from one state of operation to the other, every gate through which a signal passes adds some time to the total operation. Thus if a carry must propagate through multiple adder stages, the total accumulated times of all the devices are summed to define the propagation time of the carry. Worst-case conditions consider the time involved in the propagation of a carry from the LSD to the MSD. This time in a multi-bit register could approach or be greater than the time period allowed for the addition operation. This condition is not acceptable to any processor.

In most high-speed processors, the adder logic has sensors within its add stages which allow it to examine the conditions of the next lower-order stages (2 or 3) from which a carry could be generated into the stage.

Carry logic that incorporates this sensing is termed as having anticipated carry or look-ahead-for-carry. An arithmetic unit in which the adder logic has the anticipated carry capability provides a worst-case carry-propagation time of two or three times less than the same adder without the look-ahead feature.

Serial adder. To perform serial addition, only one full adder is necessary. The orders are shifted into the adder sequentially with the LSD applied first. Any carry is delayed one bit time so that it may be added to the following order. Figure 8·24 shows a serial adder and the inputs that are contained in shift registers.

The serial-adder unit is composed of two half-adders, an OR circuit, and a delay device. The inputs to the first half-adder provide a sum and a possible carry. The sum output from the first half-adder is applied to the second half-adder. The delay time of the delay device is equal to the pulse repetition time (PRT) of the shift pulse so that the second half-adder adds the sum output of the order applied to the (serial-adder) unit to a carry

FIG. 8·24 Serial adder.

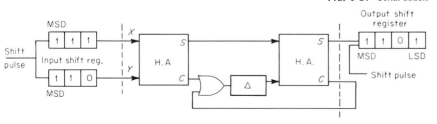

TABLE 8·4 Half-subtracter Truth Table

Minuend	X	0	1	0	1
Subtrahend	Y	0	0	1	1
Difference	D	0	1	1	0
Borrow	B	0	0	1	0

from the previous order. The final sum output is generated one PRT after the final shift has occurred. Any carry that was propagated from the most significant order of the augend and addend travels through the delay line during this time and becomes a sum output.

Subtracter. A logical subtracter can also be developed by using truth tables. Table 8·4 is a half-subtracter truth table, from which it is seen that the equations for the difference and the borrow are

$$D = X\bar{Y} + \bar{X}Y$$
$$B = \bar{X}Y$$

The equation for the difference is the same as the sum equation of the half-adder. The borrow output occurs when the minuend is 0 and the subtrahend is 1. The borrow output indicates that a 1 must be borrowed from a higher order.

The output of a 1 from the borrow is subtracted from the minuend of the next higher order just as in the decimal system.

It is now possible to draw a logical diagram from the equation. The only differences between the half-subtracter and the half-adder are the carry and borrow equations.

The truth table (Table 8·4) describes the function of a half-subtracter because no provision is made for a borrow from a previous order. A full subtracter provides for this borrow.

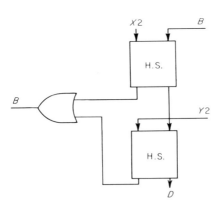

FIG. 8·25 Single-stage full subtracter.

TABLE 8·5 Full-subtracter Truth Table

Minuend	X	0	1	0	1	0	1	0	1
Subtrahend	Y	0	0	1	1	0	0	1	1
Borrow	B_{in}	0	0	0	0	1	1	1	1
Difference	D	0	1	1	0	1	0	0	1
Borrow	B_{out}	0	0	1	0	1	0	1	1

Full subtracter. Figure 8·25 shows a full subtracter, which consists of two half-subtracters and an external OR gate. Two subtractions are performed. First a borrow indication from a previous order is subtracted from the minuend X, and the subtrahend Y is subtracted from the difference. If necessity for a borrow arises from either half-subtracter, it is applied through the OR gate to the next higher order.

A truth table for the full subtracter (Table 8·5) shows that the equations for the difference and the borrow are as follows:

$$D = X\overline{Y}\overline{B}_{in} + \overline{X}Y\overline{B}_{in} + \overline{X}\overline{Y}B_{in} + XYB_{in}$$
$$B_{out} = \overline{X}Y\overline{B}_{in} + \overline{X}\overline{Y}B_{in} + \overline{X}YB_{in} + XYB_{in}$$

Subtracters can be arranged to operate in parallel or in series. Both arrangements are illustrated.

Parallel operation. The parallel-subtracter unit (Fig. 8·26) has three orders. The first order is a half-subtracter, and the next two higher orders are full subtracters. The borrow output from a lower order is applied to the next higher order and subtracted from the minuend in the first half-subtracter. The subtrahend is subtracted from the difference in the second half-

FIG. 8·26 Three-stage parallel subtracter.

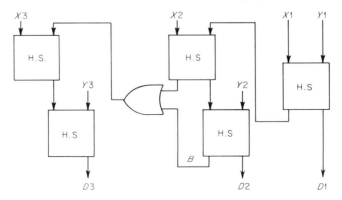

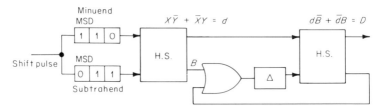

FIG. 8·27 Serial subtracter.

subtracter, and the correct difference for the particular order is obtained. The subtracter subtracts only when the minuend is larger than the subtrahend.

Serial subtracter. A serial subtracter and a serial adder are similar in logical operation. The only difference is the generation of the borrow. A serial subtracter is shown in Fig. 8·27.

Subtraction can also be accomplished if the subtrahend Y is first subtracted from the minuend and the borrow is subtracted from the difference. The delay time is one shift PRT, allowing any borrow to be subtracted from the next higher order.

Basic computer circuits are combined in various ways to provide required functions in the processor.

The flip-flop is interconnected to provide the capability for counting, storage, and shift operations. These interconnections may result in a configuration which allows for either serial or parallel transfer of information as well as for data left or right shift, as in scaling. Counting may be in ascending or descending order of count.

AND and OR gates are interconnected to provide the ability of signal sensing or decoding of register counts for control functions. Large-scale decoding operations are achieved through the use of matrices. Matrix organization allows for this multiple decoding, in many cases at a considerable saving in hardware.

The basic arithmetic element in the processor may perform its function through either addition or subtraction, which is performed by logical elements termed adders or subtracters.

There are many combinations or variations in the implementation of these devices. A single operation may result from the use of an element, or it may be mechanized to perform a desired operation through a combination of functions.

QUESTIONS

8·1   What is a binary counter?

8·2   What is the difference between an up-counter and a down-counter?

8·3   What are a serial counter and a parallel counter?

8·4   State the advantages and disadvantages of serial and parallel counters.

8·5   Draw a logical diagram and develop the waveforms for a four-stage serial down-counter.

8·6   What is the maximum count of a 12-stage counter?

8·7   Draw a mod 3 counter with timing diagram.

8·8   Define a decoder.

8·9   What variations exist for storage registers?

8·10   Discuss the difference between force load and non-force load of a flip-flop register.

8·11   What advantage does the parallel shift register have over the serial shift register?

8·12   What is the difference in the action of a serial storage register and a serial shift register?

8·13   What advantage does the barrel switch offer over the conventional shift register?

8·14   Name two functions which a matrix can perform.

8·15   Name the devices used to perform arithmetic operations in the processor.

8·16   What method can be employed in adders in order to speed up the operation?

8·17   What is the difference between a half-adder and a full adder?

chapter nine

Integrated Circuits

The advancing technologies in all fields are directed toward the production of the bigger and the better in everything. This trend is apparent in the data processing industry in the movement toward more powerful equipment. This increase in system capability has been achieved, historically, through an increase in physical size directly proportional to the increase in processing capability. Developments in electronics components have reversed this trend and "bigness" is being achieved through decreased component size or increased packing densities.

The transistor was developed and introduced into the electronics field in about 1947 when the computer industry was in its infancy. The first electronic computer, called ENIAC, was only two years old. It consisted of 19,000 vacuum tubes and hundreds of thousands of electromechanical relays in housings of room-size dimensions. ENIAC had a modest work capacity. However, the problem of handling many discrete electronic devices was apparent, and this condition later became known as "the tyranny of numbers." The solution to the problems of mounting complexity in devices was sought within the electronics industry.

In 1950 at the request of the Navy, the National Bureau of Standards initiated project "Tinkertoy" to study the problem and recommend a solution. This study resulted in the design of standard device combinations packaged in compact circuit modules. The combination of modules could provide most desired circuit functions. Although the study provided for better packing densities (eight devices per cubic inch), it did nothing to reduce the number of devices and interconnections required per function.

Similar studies followed with the emphasis on increased packing densities through improved manufacturing techniques. "Swiss cheese," "Cord wood," "2D," and "3D" were some of these studies, but produced no significant reduction in the number of devices and connections required to implement a circuit function. Since electronic circuit reliability is roughly inversely proportional to the number of circuit components, the packaging techniques developed as a result of the studies resulted in no improvement in reliability. Although not contributing directly to an improvement in reliability, these early attempts set the wheels in motion for future developments which would have a significant impact on the computer industry.

The advent of the transistor and transistor technology hurdled some of the economic barriers to large systems that vacuum tubes presented. Performance characteristics, cost, and reliability improved dramatically during these years. The efforts of the electronics industry to increase reliability and performance have led to results that were undreamed of 20 years ago. From the eight electronic devices per cubic inch of 1950, present-day large-scale integration (LSI) modules contain over 200,000 active elements per cubic inch. This is the age of microcircuitry.

Microcircuitry is referred to as micrologic, microelectronics, and integrated circuits (IC), with the latter most commonly used. While no precise definition of IC has been accepted throughout the industry, the Electronic Industries Association (EIA) proposes the following definition: "Integrated circuits are the physical realization of a number of circuit elements inseparably associated on or within a continuous body to perform the function of a circuit."

Integrated circuits are not a revolution in the state of the art, but rather an evolution of transistor manufacturing techniques. Present microelectronic techniques evolved from two independent lines of study. One involves the semiconductor technology developed for making discrete transistors and diodes; the other is the thin-film technology developed to produce high-quality resistors and capacitors.

The study of the properties of thin films is older than the transistor and is the study of very thin layers or films of insulating and conducting materials. These layers range in thickness from a fraction of a micron to several microns (a micron is a millionth of a meter).

Thin film. In thin-film technology the base or foundation upon which the circuitry is to be built, called a *substrate*, is usually of ceramic, glass plate, or some nonconducting material which is required to supply structural strength. A typical thin-film resistor consists of a narrow line of semiconducting material only a few thousandths of an inch wide and only long enough to supply the required value of resistance. If a high value of resistance is desired the line may be run in a zig-zag fashion. Capacitors are formed to a great degree of accuracy by deposition of a thin film of metal, a film of insulating material, and another film of metal. The value of capacitance is determined by the thickness of the insulating film and the area of the metal plates.

Thin films are commonly deposited by evaporation, or if the thin-film material does not readily vaporize, a method known as *cathode sputtering* is used. Cathode sputtering is a process in which positive ions of gas are used to bombard a negatively charged target constructed of the desired film ma-

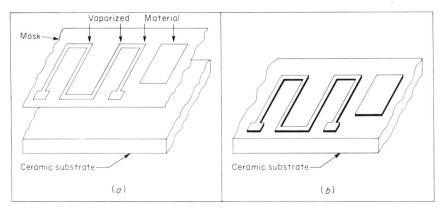

FIG. 9·1 Formation of thin-film elements. (a) Mask registration; (b) deposited elements.

terial. The gas ions act as high-speed projectiles that will vaporize the material by bombardment rather than by heat. The substrate is coated with the atoms driven from the cathode.

Evaporation is achieved by heating the metal above its boiling point inside a vacuum chamber containing the substrate. The evaporation material then condenses uniformly on the substrate until the desired thickness of material is achieved. If the substrate is masked prior to insertion into the vacuum chamber, the deposition of vaporized material through the cutouts of the mask will provide the desired component outline as shown in Fig. 9·1.

Etching. An alternate method of component shaping is the etching method illustrated in Fig. 9·2. As shown in Fig. 9·2a, no mask is used in this method during the deposition phase. The result is an even layer of material covering the entire surface of the substrate. The surface is then coated with a photosensitive organic compound that will polymerize when struck by ultraviolet rays. A photographic mask, opaque to ultraviolet radiation in the areas not defining the component shapes, is placed over the substrate and the whole is

FIG. 9·2 Thin-film-element formation by etching technique. (a) Initial material deposition; (b) exposure; (c) formed elements.

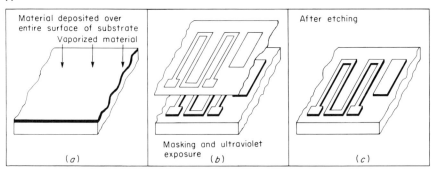

exposed to ultraviolet radiation (Fig. 9·2b). After exposure, the organic compound shielded from the ultraviolet radiation is washed off by immersing the entire wafer in an etching acid. Only the deposited material protected by the polymerized organic compound remains, as shown by Fig. 9·2c.

In the examples illustrated, only a small portion of the substrate is shown with two components. Of the two components shown, only the resistor is complete. The capacitor requires its dielectric material and the other plate to be formed before it is considered complete. A vaporization and deposition phase are required for the formation of each of these elements. After all components on a wafer are complete, the substrate is coated with an insulating protective coating, and windows are etched through the protective coating to the component terminals to allow connection of package terminal leads to the components.

The masking technique used is determined by component size, circuit complexity, and density of component layout. The cost of masking with cutouts increases rapidly as component density and complexity increase and as component size decreases.

The use of photolithographic techniques allows extreme precision in component layout and positioning. Patterns for photolithographic use are made large, approximately 500 times the size of the finished circuit, and then photoreduced to minimize drafting irregularities. In manufacturing, a large number of circuits are built simultaneously on a single substrate wafer. The wafer can then be sawed apart into individual chips, each containing a complete circuit.

The second line of development in the microelectronic evolution has its origin in semiconductor technology. The manufacture of an integrated circuit begins with the growth of a silicon crystal in the manner similar to that for an epitaxial transistor. Fig. 9·3 illustrates a slice sawed from the

FIG. 9·3 Substrate cut from mother crystal.

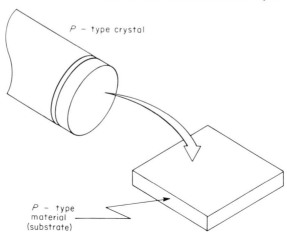

P – type crystal

P – type
material
(substrate)

crystal growth. A single representative block of material is shown extracted for ease of depiction and process explanation. In the manufacturing process all circuits to be built on a single wafer are processed simultaneously before being divided into individual blocks. This block of P-type material forms the substrate which is mainly for circuit support and strength. After sawing, the wafers are placed in an induction-type furnace, and an epitaxial layer of the opposite semiconductor electrical properties is grown on the substrate. This epitaxial layer grows with the same crystalline structure or atomic arrangement as the substrate. Subsequent manufacturing operations on the material, such as diffusion, oxidation, and etching, will not affect the crystalline structure. The completed integrated circuit will thus have the same crystalline structure throughout its substrate, active, and passive components. Because of the uniformity of crystalline structure this type of integrated circuitry is often referred to as monolithic integrated circuits.

After growth of the epitaxial layer on the substrate, the wafer is placed in an oxidizing atmosphere at a high temperature, where a protective, insulating layer of silicon dioxide is formed. Figure 9·4a illustrates the com-

FIG. 9·4 Formation of monolithic integrated circuit. (a) Deposition of insulating layer; (b) completion of initial masking and etching; (c) isolation of components by diffusion; (d) masking and etching completed for final diffusion.

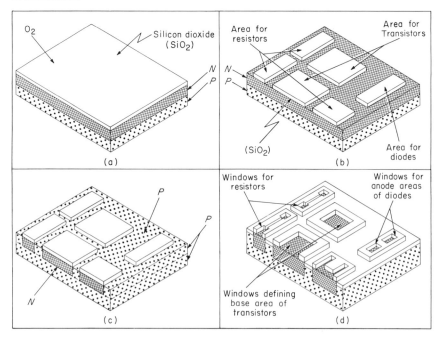

pletion of this step. The epitaxial (N) layer and the silicon dioxide coating are not shown in the proper proportion in relation to the thickness of the substrate. After formation of the protective coating of silicon dioxide, a photosensitive material that will polymerize when struck by ultraviolet radiation is spread over the silicon dioxide. A mask defining the areas in which the circuit components are to be formed is prepared. The areas of the mask corresponding to the areas of the surface of the silicon dioxide that are to be removed are made opaque to ultraviolet light. During exposure to ultraviolet light, the areas protected by the mask will not polymerize. The photosensitive material that has not been changed is removed by immersion in an acid bath. Figure 9·4b illustrates the results of the first masking and etching process. After the first masking and etching process, the surface areas of the epitaxial layer that define the physical shape and layout of all active and passive components is left with a protective coating of silicon dioxide (SiO_2). The N-type epitaxial layer of silicon is exposed in the areas where there are to be no components. The substrate is subjected to a diffusion operation, and the N-propertied expitaxial layer is changed to have the same electrical properties as the substrate, as indicated by Fig. 9·4c. The component areas are isolated from each other. After diffusion, the exposed silicon is again exposed to an oxidizing atmosphere to form the protective SiO_2 layer. A second photolithographic masking and etching process, as indicated by Fig. 9·4d, is used to open "windows" for access to the N-type component areas under the SiO_2.

A second diffusion process using P material produces an area of P electrical characteristics within the N epitaxial isolated areas. For the passive and nonamplifying components such as resistors and diodes, this step represents the last diffusion process. Transistors require an additional diffusion process to form the third element of the transistor. Resistor values are varied by changing the cross-sectional area of the component, length, and resistivity profile of the material. Forming a diode gate is accomplished by having the isolated area for the gate of sufficient size to encompass all the anode areas and an area for a common cathode connection. A single diffusion process forms the required PN junctions. A cross-sectional view of the diode area appears as illustrated in Fig. 9·5.

FIG. 9·5   Cross-sectional view of IC multi-element diode.

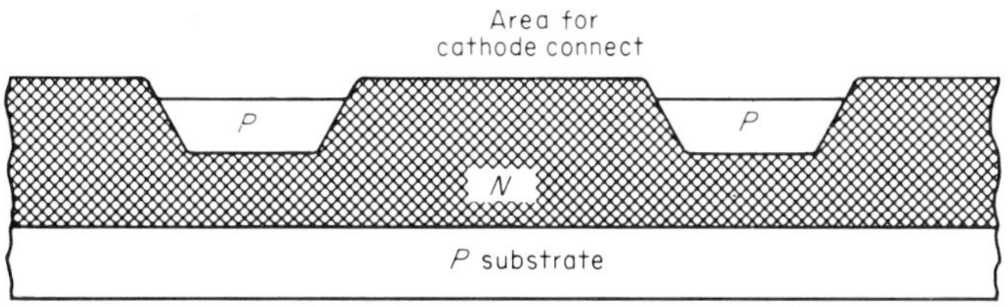

Following the second diffusion process, the exposed areas of silicon are given a protective oxide layer.

Masking and etching is again performed to expose the areas designated to be the emitters of the transistors. If the substrate is of P material, the epitaxial layer is N material. This area is the collector of the transistors after the first masking, etching, and diffusion process. The base area is defined and formed during the second mask, etch, and diffusion process of P material. The next mask, etch, and diffusion of N material forms the emitter of an NPN transistor.

An oxidation process provides a protective oxide layer over the last-formed area of silicon. Figure 9·6 shows the completed monolithic block after the final mask and etch to open the windows for connections to the individual components.

Metallization, by vaporization or sputtering, is performed in the same manner as previously explained for the thin-film technique. This metal film is masked and etched to remove the unwanted metal, leaving only narrow strips forming the connection linkage. These interconnections combine the components into the desired circuit configuration with strips and pads brought out to the edge of the circuit chip for external connections.

FIG. 9·6 Completed monolithic block.

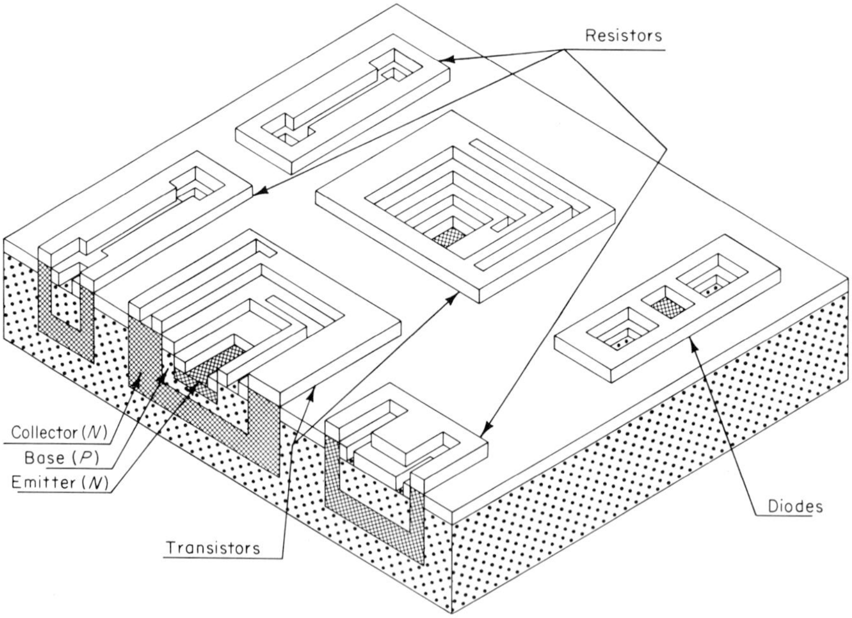

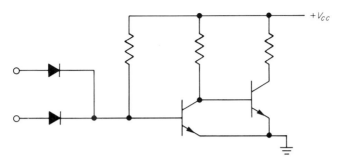

FIG. 9·7 Possible circuit configuration of completed monolithic block.

The two transistors, two diodes, and three resistors (Fig. 9·6) can be connected to form the two-input buffered AND gate circuit of Fig. 9·7.

Capacitors in the monolithic technique are formed in the same manner as diodes. A diode used as a capacitor in the monolithic integrated circuitry requires that reverse bias be present under all circuit-operating conditions.

Hybrids. Hybrid integrated circuitry is a highly flexible technique, which achieves many of the advantages of both monolithic and thin-film integrated circuitry. Hybrid integrated circuitry can take the form of hybrid silicon chips (interconnected discrete silicon chips contain the various elements of the circuit), hybrid thin-film circuits (discrete silicon chips attached to a passive thin-film substrate), or hybrid integrated circuits (passive thin-film elements placed on the surface of a monolithic silicon chip containing active and some passive components).

Monolithic silicon integrated circuits offer the lowest cost per circuit function; however, diffused resistors have a large temperature coefficient. Diffused capacitors can be subjected only to low voltages, are voltage-sensitive, and are polar. A diffused capacitor, unless of rather small value, is relatively large in physical size and consequently expensive.

These difficulties can be overcome by use of the hybrid thin-film circuitry techniques at a higher cost per circuit function. Thin-film resistors do not have the temperature coefficient difficulties of the diffused resistor and can be regulated over a wider range of resistance. The thin-film techniques allow capacitors to be built on the surface of an insulating layer on the top of the substrate without loss of active component area.

From a cost standpoint, the choice between monolithic silicon and thin-film circuits often depends on the ratio between active and passive components that constitute the circuits. If the circuit requires a passive component that would occupy all the area of the chip with relatively few active components, then the thin-film technique for passive components with active elements attached would be the best approach. However, if the passive component area is relatively small when compared with the active component area, the passive elements can be obtained at a minimum additional cost by placement directly on the monolithic silicon substrate, if the interconnection is not complicated.

One method of combining the best features of monolithic technology with those of thin film for complex circuits begins its buildup by bonding aluminum islands on an insulating substrate by a plating and photolithographic process. The thin-film components and interconnections are then plated on the substrate. The monolithic silicon circuits are "flipped" over onto and bonded to the aluminum bonding islands, to form the completed complex circuits.

The result of early attempts to fabricate integrated circuits following existing discrete component circuit formats is the availability of integrated circuits in different logic forms. The example shown earlier in this chapter is of the diode transistor-logic (DTL). Because of the difficulties involved in producing satisfactory passive components in monolithic form, early designs avoided the use of resistors and capacitors where possible.

One of the most significant of the early design approaches was direct-coupled transistor logic (DCTL). The basic circuit elements are transistors, using resistors for loads. This is an economical arrangement for integrated circuits, since resistors occupy a much larger chip area than transistors. Since there are no coupling resistors there is less parasitic capacitance to cause reductions in circuit speed. One of the major problems associated with DCTL is the difficulty in achieving sufficient and reliable fan out. Fan out is the number of inputs or circuits driven by a single current source. In DCTL circuits the bases of all fan-out transistors (the transistors being driven) are connected in parallel, with no current-limiting components in any individual leg. The fan-out problem arises because the emitter-base diode characteristics of transistors are subject to the typical variations accompanying large-volume production. Thus, there is an uneven distribution of base current, because of current-hogging by some devices while other transistors may be starved for base drive and would not remain in the ON state.

Resistor-transistor logic (RTL). RTL is a modification of DCTL by the addition of a series-base resistor. The series-base resistor prevents current-hogging for fan outs greater than 1, but also increases propagation delay. To keep propagation delays to a minimum, small resistance values are used but this increases power consumption. The simple configuration and small resistance values make RTL economical and well-suited to the monolithic process. RTL requires a larger chip area than the DCTL circuit. The noise immunity of RTL is rather low and depends on fan out. The fan out of RTL is limited to help increase the noise immunity, as well as to allow for greater resistor tolerances. RTL is affected more by temperature variations than other logic configurations.

Resistor-capacitor-transistor logic (RCTL). RCTL is similar to RTL but includes speed-up capacitors and higher resistance values. The larger resistance and capacitance values make this configuration less suitable for the monolithic process, because of the increased chip area required. The speed-up capacitor greatly reduces the ac noise immunity. The RCTL logic is more costly to integrate than RTL because the capacitors require a large chip area. For these reasons, RCTL has not received much attention, and its availability in monolithic form is limited.

Diode-transistor logic (DTL). The major improvement of diode-transistor logic over RTL is the requirement for a lower base-drive current. This permits considerably improved noise immunity. Because of the variations in monolithic processing, the lower base current that is required eliminates the requirement for the series-base resistor and permits higher fan out.

Transistor-transistor logic (TTL). TTL is similar to DTL, with the diodes replaced with a multi-emitter transistor. The multi-emitter transistor (refer to Fig. 9·8) is smaller than the diodes, which reduces parasitic capacitance. This feature, combined with the active turn-off characteristics of the input transistor, makes TTL a high-frequency form of saturated logic. TTL is well-suited to monolithic fabrication as the transistors allow for higher component tolerances.

Current-mode logic (CML) or emitter-coupled transistor logic (ECTL). CML is basically a current switch rather than a voltage switch. The bias is set to prevent the transistors from being driven into saturation, thereby eliminating the saturation storage time. Since CML is nonsaturating, power dissipation is generally high but it is among the fastest logic forms available. CML

FIG. 9·8 TTL multi-emitter transistor.

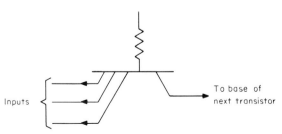

Inputs

To base of next transistor

has rather small signal swings and therefore low noise immunity. It does not, however, tend to generate noise, nor is it as susceptible to noise because of impedance levels. This type of logic has high speed, high fan-out and high capacitive-load-driving capabilities, but low output-voltage swings and higher power dissipation.

Metal-oxide–semiconductor–transistor logic (MOSTL). MOSTL is derived from the application of insulated-gate, metal-oxide semiconductor field-effect transistor technology (MOSFET) to integrated circuitry. This is perhaps the most rapidly expanding area of development in the present state of the art. The MOS integrated circuit operates on a principle similar to the field-effect principle described by W. Schockley in "A Unipolar Field-effect Transistor" (*Proceedings of the Institute of Radio Engineers*, vol. 40). The dc fan-out capability of the MOS is high because of the high input impedance of each gate. The limiting factor concerning fan out is the capacitive load presented by the gate to channel capacitance of the fan-out device. MOS devices are readily made in integrated form. Chip areas are small even for complex circuits, since direct coupling is used and no passive elements are required.

Cost reductions in data processing equipment which uses integrated circuits have been possible because of cost reductions for device fabrication labor. The packaging cost for an IC is approximately the same as that for an individual transistor. The IC may contain a multiple transistor/resistor/

FIG. 9·9 Circuitry evolution. Vacuum tube, transistorized logic, early integrated circuit chip.

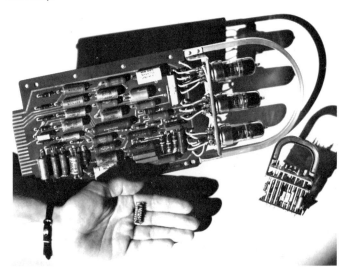

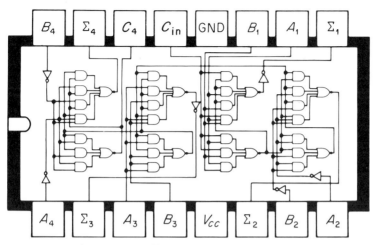

FIG. 9·10   Logic diagram of 4-bit adder in a 16-pin flat pack. (Texas Instruments, Inc.)

capacitor combination already interconnected with only a single packaging cost involved.

Figure 9·9 shows a comparison of the sizes of the vacuum tube logic circuitry of the early 1950s, the transistorized logic circuitry of the late 1950s
to early 1960s, and the integrated circuitry of the mid 1960s. The IC
package held in the hand is a 16-pin flat pack. Figure 9·10 illustrates the
logic capability of the 16-pin flat pack. This device is capable of the addition of two 4-bit binary numbers.

IC technology has developed to the point where reference is now being
made to the integration of circuit functions as medium-scale integration
(MSI) or as large-scale integration (LSI). This continued development in

FIG. 9·11   Integrated circuit evolution. 14–16-pin flat pack. 50-pin flat pack, LS1
module. (Texas Instruments, Inc.)

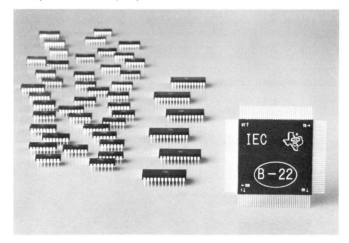

integrated circuitry is illustrated in Fig. 9·11. The modules pictured on the left are representative of the 14–16-pin integrated-circuit packages. The center modules represent MSI circuitry characterized by two levels of interconnection and contain up to 240 gates with up to 50 module connection pins. The LSI package on the right contains a proportional increase in the number of elements, more than two levels of interconnection and up to 100 module connections. With these advances the individual elements have lost their identity and the chips are considered in terms of function rather than individual element use.

Costs of LSI and MSI chips are dependent upon the way the functions are implemented and the complexity of the interface connections. The three basic approaches to LSI fabrication are discretionary wiring, fixed interconnection pattern, and specific functional. All three methods are directed toward lowered cost and require multiple layers of metallization because of circuit complexity. The fabrication methods are not completely perfected at this time. Interim measures are being used in LSI fabrication. One interim measure is a modification of the hybrid approach. In this method thin-film techniques are used to interconnect ICs mounted on a ceramic or glass substrate. The entire assembly is packaged with several IC chips within the package prewired to perform a specific function.

In the discretionary wiring technique the metallization interconnect is performed using only those circuit cells which have been shown to be good through testing. In the fabrication process, pads are provided to allow testing of the individual circuit cells. After the entire wafer has been probed and the good circuits identified, a computer generates a mask to allow the desired interconnections to be made using known good circuit elements. Second- and third-layer metallization yields must be 100 percent or the entire wafer must be scrapped. However, yield is high since circuits are known to be good prior to interconnect, and a high degree of confidence has been established that the functions represented will meet test specifications.

The fixed interconnection pattern (FIP) is sometimes referred to as the 100-percent yield approach since the designer assumes that all basic cells are functional. The interconnect metallization is performed prior to any testing. When the chip is tested, it either satisfies all functional test requirements, or the entire wafer is scrapped. Failure may be due to crystal structure imperfections or to failures in the insulation or thin-film conduction layers. Identical circuit interconnection patterns result from this fabrication process.

In the specific functional approach, the entire process is directed toward the production of a chip to meet one specified design requirement. This process is the most efficient in terms of silicon area use but, as in the FIP approach, requires a 100-percent yield of all cells on the wafer for acceptance.

The two circuit approaches to LSI mechanization being followed are the bipolar and MOS. The bipolar approach, which utilizes low-impedance devices (such as PNP and NPN transistors), requires many more fabrication steps to produce the same logic functions as the approach using MOS devices. The bipolar devices, being current-operated, require isolation between the individual active elements to prevent logical interaction. MOS devices, on the other hand, are high-impedance devices and therefore can be packed with greater density.

There is one major disadvantage of the MOS device with respect to the bipolar that could be compensated for with careful design. Intra-element data transfers between MOS devices are frequency-limited and therefore speed-limited. This effect is caused by the large RC time constants created by the high internal impedance of the devices and the output circuit parasitic capacitance. Careful control of device geometries or the use of complementary MOS devices for interface may be used to overcome this condition.

Large-scale Integrated-circuit Memories

With the advent of large-scale integration, it has become economically feasible to devise logical memory elements for internal local storage which are competitive with core and thin-film memories. This is due to the high packing densities possible with LSI. Large-scale integration is particularly well-suited to complex functions that are repetitive in nature, such as memory arrays. With the present state of the art, it is possible to pack over 1 million bits of data into only 1 sq in. of area; this is by no means the theoretical limit. An added advantage of LSI memory devices is that they operate at the internal speed of the computing device. LSI memories have a disadvantage in that they are dependent upon the continuous application of power and are therefore considered volatile. This disadvantage may be overcome to some degree by the use of a standby permanent storage device to store critical locations in the advent of power failure. This storage medium may take the form of a specially designed high-speed disk memory that would be utilized only for this special function. As discussed in Chap. 7, power failures, when they occur, are never instantaneous in nature. There is usually a period of several milliseconds between the detection of a serious power fluctuation and the point at which the power level from the regulated supply drops below some critical value. For example, an LSI memory may have an average access time of 100 nsec. During an approximate 2-msec power decay period, 20,000 LSI memory locations could be transferred to high-speed disk storage.

LSI memories can be logically grouped into two basic types, read-only and read/write. The logical organization of both types is generally the same with the difference centered in the complexity of the basic bit storage cell. Because of the dynamic nature of the data stored, the storage elements of the read/write memory consist of MOS transistors connected as flip-flops. Read-only memory storage cells consist of single MOS transistors acting as simple switches since the data stored is permanent. Addressing circuitry, consisting of MOS NOR gates, is located on the same chip with the storage cells for both type memories.

A typical chip might contain 1024 bit positions organized into 128 eight-bit words. This includes all circuitry necessary to select any desired word on the chip. Physical size of the chip is in the order of 0.008 in. on a side.

Read-only memories. Read-only memories may be utilized to store micro-operations that are used to perform complex functions. It can be shown that all complex arithmetic and logical functions are defined by algorithms that are further defined by a series of "primitive" or "micro" operations. Primitive operations are simple operations such as a single-position left or right shift, a complementation of a number, or a transfer of a number from one register to another. A series of these primitive operations stored sequentially in a read-only memory can perform almost any desired function.

To effectively utilize LSI circuitry in modern computers, the percentage of unique control circuitry used in the system is minimized. The concept is to divide a computer into functional blocks interconnected by a data bus. In keeping with the modular concept, the control circuitry necessary to perform a desired function is located within the block responsible for accomplishing that function. For example, an arithmetic unit could be constructed from one or possibly several LSI chips mounted on a small, printed circuit card. Associated with this circuitry is a read-only memory that contains the micro-sequences that control the arithmetic or logical operations.

The arithmetic unit functions are initiated by the transference of a control word from the central control unit via the data bus. Part of the control word is interpreted by the arithmetic unit as a start address of a micro-sequence routine in the read-only memory that defines the operation to be performed. The control word also defines the locations of operands or control information, depending on the desired operation. Once arithmetic unit functions are initiated, the sequences are executed independently of further control until the desired operation terminates.

Another practical application for read-only memories is code conversion. It may be desired to translate a unique internal machine code used for computation into a form that would be universally recognized by all computers, such as the ASCII code (American Standard Code for Information Interchange). Many business applications require data interface over phone lines, in some cases between different types of computer systems.

The read-only memory could utilize an address-by-contents addressing scheme where each number to be converted would represent the address of a unique location in the memory. The actual contents of the memory location would be the ASCII character to be transmitted. Reconversion of received ASCII characters to internal code would utilize similar techniques. This scheme would allow the extremely rapid data throughput required for modern business applications.

As mentioned previously, the basic storage cell circuitry of a read-only memory depends on the application of an MOS transistor as a switch. An individual storage cell stores a binary 1 whenever a channel can be established between the source and the drain of the MOS transistor; the oxide layer in the gate region is made thin enough to open the channel when an electric signal is applied to the gate. Where a binary 0 is to be stored, the oxide insulating material is left sufficiently thick in the gate region so that the channel cannot be opened.

The mask that is used to expose the gate areas for etching the oxide during manufacture would allow all the bit positions, if left unaltered, to store binary 1's. Prior to the etching operation, the mask positions corresponding to binary 0's are covered with tape to prevent etching. Once final metalization occurs it is no longer possible to alter data stored.

Readout of stored data is accomplished by application of select voltages from the addressing circuitry to the gates of all the addressed MOS transistors. Only the transistors with thin oxide coatings in their gate regions produce a binary-1 output.

Read/write memories. In most complex programs, intermediate results are usually computed that are required at some future time for final problem solution. Arithmetic units do not usually contain sufficient hardware registers to be used for temporary storage; therefore, these operands must be returned to intermediate-result locations in main memory until needed. Storage and retrieval of these operands is time-consuming and tends to limit the speed and therefore the throughput of the entire computer system.

A solution to this problem is the utilization of small LSI read/write "scratch-pad" memories in close proximity to the arithmetic logic.

The logical organization of a read/write memory is more complex than a read-only memory because of the additional circuitry necessary to store new data. The actual storage element or cell is more complex because a flip-flop function is necessary instead of the simple switch found in the read-only memory.

Two addressing schemes may be used, the linear and the address-by-contents. The linear addressing technique dictates that each location in the read/write memory be assigned a unique address usually starting with 0. As operands are stored, they are placed in consecutive locations until the highest-order location has been loaded. "Wrap around" will occur if more operands are stored. This technique destroys previously loaded low-order locations. The control circuitry keeps track of locations that contain "valid" data that has not been used and decides which locations may be loaded with new data.

The address-by-contents scheme is the more versatile of the two. Each time it is desired to return an operand to an intermediate-result location in main memory, the intermediate result is stored along with its absolute main memory address into a location of the local read/write memory. When it is desired to fetch an operand from main memory, the absolute address that will be used to fetch the operand is simultaneously compared with all the absolute addresses stored in the local read/write memory. If the desired data is located in local storage, the operand stored in association with the address will be transferred to the arithmetic logic for subsequent use. If the data is not local, a fetch of the operand from main memory occurs.

When storing an operand into the read/write memory, a check is made to determine if the absolute address to be stored already exists somewhere within the read/write memory. The "old" operand, if it exists, must first be invalidated before the "new" operand can be stored. The "new" operand will not necessarily be stored in the same location that contained the "old" operand.

An advantage of the address-by-contents scheme is the rapidity of stored-operand extraction due to simultaneous address comparison techniques. The main disadvantage is the requirement for more complex addressing circuitry that must contain address storage elements and comparator logic. As the state of the art advances, it will become practical to locate this complex addressing circuitry on the same LSI chip as the storage cells.

Additional applications for LSI memories are in look-ahead storage of program instructions and as temporary storage of control words for use in indexing operations and conditional jumping.

SUMMARY

Integrated circuits are being used in increasing numbers in small-, medium- and large-scale computing systems. They are providing systems of increased reliability and greater processing capabilities without the heretofore required physical-size increases attached to system capacity increases.

Integrated circuits are an integral part of the data processing industry! This chapter has dealt mainly with the fabrication of these devices to provide an understanding of the how and why of integrated circuits. Discussion of individual circuits has been neglected. There is no need to examine the IC from the standpoint of circuit maintenance. Repair is not possible. A failure of the IC will be detected as a function failure rather than an individual circuit or component failure. An understanding of the fabrication concepts should aid in the acceptance of an attitude toward the IC which will be useful in troubleshooting. The orientation should be toward an understanding of the functional interaction among the ICs, what each contributes to the whole of the operation. If an IC is not providing the intended function, be it composed of 20 or 1000 elements, it is replaced in its entirety to effect the corrective action. *System* rather than *circuit* is the proper IC attitude.

QUESTIONS

9·1   Give a general definition of integrated circuits.

9·2   What is a monolithic integrated circuit?

9·3   What is the major improvement of diode transistor logic over resistor transistor logic?

9·4   Why are MOS devices preferable to bipolar devices for large-scale integration?

9·5   What is the main disadvantage of LSI memories?

II
COMPUTER AND
PERIPHERALS

chapter ten

The Basic Computer

This chapter is intended to introduce the basic blocks of the computer and to illustrate their functional interrelationships. The computer accepts data and instructions, performs the required operations, and delivers as outputs the results of the computation (Fig. 10·1a). The computer has been introduced previously as consisting of the basic blocks of input, memory, control, arithmetic, output, and program (Fig. 10·1b). Program, which is essential to the operation of the computer, is not part of the hardware organization of the computer. It will be treated with relation to its use in the respective areas of the computer. Program execution and the resulting action of the other computer blocks will be considered in this chapter rather than the possible alternatives in the programming solution to a problem or task. Chaps. 15 and 16 consider programming and the program.

The mechanization of the basic computer is shown in Fig. 10·1c. Note that only five blocks are shown, with the program residing in the memory where it must be located to be executed.

Input and output information movement is to memory via the arithmetic unit (in the computer selected for discussion). This allows the utilization of an arithmetic register as a buffer register.

Information into the computer will be either instructions or data for program execution. The input block under the direction of the control logic interfaces with the peripheral device. The input peripheral device may be, for example, a punched-card reader, a magnetic-tape transport, or a typewriter keyboard. Information is transferred to the arithmetic register at the transfer rate of the peripheral device. Information is transferred more rapidly from a tape transport than from a card reader. The arithmetic register functions as a buffer between the peripheral device and the memory. Data transfers from arithmetic register to memory are made at the transfer rate within the computer. The transfer rate within the computer is significantly faster than the input rate of information flow into the arithmetic register from the peripheral devices. The control logic establishes the locations in memory into which the information is placed.

Memory is the focal point of the computer with respect to the execution

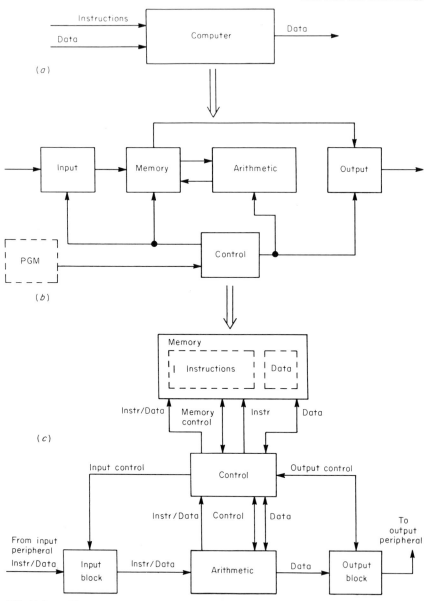

FIG. 10·1 (a) The conceptual computer; (b) basic computer functional organization; (c) basic computer mechanization.

of the program. It stores the original program, provides storage for the results, and stores or fetches information as directed by the control logic. It may be any type of storage device ranging from magnetic drums in early computers to planar memories in current processors. Although the other basic blocks are covered in more detail in this chapter, the memory will not be, since Chap. 11 is devoted to a complete coverage of memory operations.

The arithmetic unit contains all the logic required to perform the operational instructions and the testing for the decision instructions. The most obvious operational instructions are those of arithmetic: ADD, SUBTRACT, MULTIPLY, DIVIDE. However, the arithmetic unit is also capable of performing operations such as logical AND, OR, exclusive OR, and complement. It is usually capable of shifting operands in various manners such as left, right, circular, end-off. It is usually capable of testing for relationships between the operands such as greater than, equal, less than. The arithmetic unit is mechanized to perform a multitude of operations which are not strictly arithmetic. The arithmetic unit is also referred to as the logical section.

The control area unites the various logical blocks into the functioning processor. It provides the logic for instruction execution. It provides the gating necessary for data movement, error-condition monitoring, and all other timing required for proper interface among the other major areas of the processor.

The output block provides the buffering necessary for data transfer from the computer to the peripheral devices. It performs the function of level and timing conversions.

Each of the basic computer blocks will be analyzed on a functional level. Mechanization within each of the blocks will be shown not to indicate how the block must be built, but how it might be constructed to perform the function expected of it.

The program. The program is divided into instructions and data. Programs may be written in various source-language forms such as COBOL, FORTRAN, ALGOL, etc. However, a program to be executed by the computer must be in the language of the machine, that is, in machine code. The programmer need not be concerned with this, however, since other programs, known as *compilers*, are used to make the necessary translation to the required machine code.

Machine code instructions are the systematic method in which the computer is told each operation to perform. The computer is nothing more than a high-speed instruction executor. It must be told in complete detail every move, option, and operation which it is to perform by the instruction portion of the machine-coded program. Instructions may be conveniently grouped as follows:

1. Operational instructions
2. Movement instructions
3. Decision instructions

Operational instructions are those which perform a specific operation such as ADD, MULTIPLY, AND, XOR. An ADD instruction causes the computer to add operands. A MULTIPLY instruction causes the computer to multiply operands. An AND instruction causes the computer to perform a logical AND between the operands. An XOR instruction causes the computer to perform a logical exclusive OR between the operands. Each of these instructions causes a specific operation to be performed.

Movement instructions are those which cause necessary movement of data or those which cause unconditional changes in the execution sequence of instructions.

Data movement is a necessary function which normally precedes and follows operational instructions. In the performance of an ADD, the data (operands) must be moved to the arithmetic unit before the ADD instruction may be executed. FETCH MEMORY TO ARITHMETIC UNIT (FMA) is an example of an instruction which moves an operand into the arithmetic unit. Some operational instructions are mechanized to fetch an operand to the arithmetic unit. A CLEAR-THEN-ADD (CLA) instruction will clear the accumulator and add the operand fetched to 0 in the arithmetic unit. The result of the instruction execution is that the operand fetched is in the accumulator of the arithmetic unit. Since the arithmetic unit is involved in the execution of all operational instructions, the results of individual operations must be moved to memory or they will be destroyed by the continuous execution of instructions. A STORE instruction may be used to move the results from the accumulator of the arithmetic unit to the memory.

Some instructions are used to direct the computer to perform specific operations unconditionally. An UNCONDITIONAL JUMP instruction may be used to direct the computer to the instruction defined by the JUMP instruction. Instructions which cause changes in sequential execution of instructions are referred to as program control instructions.

Decision instructions are program control instructions which are made conditional upon the results of operational instructions. A BRANCH-ON-MINUS (BRM) instruction executes a jump to the instruction defined within the BRM only if the value within the accumulator is negative. If the value within the accumulator is positive, the computer will not jump, but it will continue sequential execution of the instructions. It should be noted that in this example, the decision was based on the sign of the value within the accumulator of the arithmetic unit.

Data may be defined as anything which is not an instruction and is used within the instruction execution. An ADD instruction requires numbers. The numbers used are referred to as *data*. When the data is referenced with respect to the arithmetic unit, it is usually referred to as *operands*. The term data is a general term, and its exact meaning is always relative to an instruction. An ADD instruction may be actually an algebraic summation.

The data required must have a defined sign position. The absolute value of the number may be fractional or integer. The capability of the instruction defines the required data format. Data or field type instructions might be divided into alphameric characters. Data for code conversions might be expressed as six- or four-bit binary coded decimal.

Input block. All instructions and data into the computer pass through the input block. The computer accepts data from devices such as card equipment, magnetic tape, and magnetic drums. In order to properly accept data from these devices, the input area must be capable of synchronizing with each of these peripheral devices and providing buffering of data for memory transfers.

Synchronizing with the peripheral device is necessary for proper data transfers. For example, a 400-card-per-minute card reader transfers its data characters approximately every 1.8 msec. A magnetic drum may transfer its data characters every 1.8 μsec. The magnetic drum is 1000 times faster than the card reader. The receiver (input block) must be capable of synchronizing with the speed of either of the devices.

Buffering of data from the peripheral device is provided to make the inputing of information compatible with the operational speed of the memory. The speed of the memory operations is related to instruction execution. Normally the memory will be designed to fetch or store information as fast as possible to reduce instruction run time. A word-organized memory may be capable of complete fetch or store operation every 2 μsec. Inputing directly from a card reader, for example, is not feasible to a memory of this type. Instead the data characters are accumulated in a register (buffer) until a word is formed. A typical word length may be 48 bits, or 8 six-bit data characters. After a word is accumulated, it will be transferred to the memory at the normal internal transfer rate of the computer. Inputs from a higher-speed peripheral device (a drum) also use the same buffer to allow accumulation of characters into words. The transfer rate within the computer will normally be much faster than the transfer rate of the fastest peripheral device. The transfer rate of the peripheral device should not exceed the transfer rate within the computer. In some cases this could be tolerated by additional buffering within the input area. The additional buffering effectively reduces the transfer rate of the peripheral device, allowing the transfers to memory to be made without loss of information. Buffering is usually provided to mask the slow input speeds of the peripheral devices.

Figure 10·2 illustrates a typical input area. It consists of (1) input interface controls, (2) a character buffer, and (3) a word buffer. The interface controls develop all the required control signals for operating with the peripheral device.

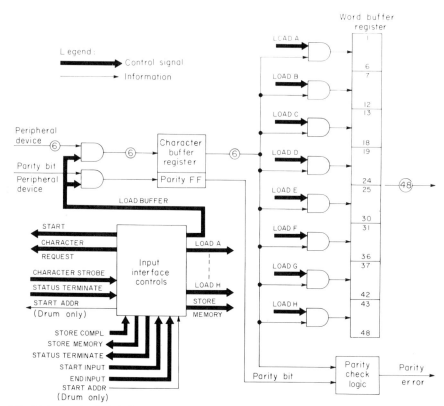

FIG. 10·2 Functional block diagram of input unit.

A START signal is provided to initiate the operation of the peripheral device (PD). It should be noted that the START signal not only initiates the operation but remains "true" during the entire operation. When the START signal goes "false," this indicates to the PD that the operation has been completed. Before the START command is given, the PD must be on and ready for use. A CHARACTER REQUEST is generated to request each character from the peripheral device. It is used by the control area of the PD to allow character transmission. A character will not be transferred from the PD to the computer input area unless it is requested. A CHARACTER STROBE is generated to synchronize the input interface controls and to indicate when the data character is being transferred. The character strobe is developed relative to PD timing and indicates when a character is ready for transfer. The CHARACTER REQUEST and CHARACTER STROBE represent the control communication between the PD and the input area. The interface controls make a request, the PD controls reply with a strobe when the data character is available for transfer. The interface controls will wait for the strobe indefinitely. This allows the PD to determine the transfer rate. However, the PD controls will not wait indefinitely for the request. If the request is "false," this means the input area is not ready for the data character. A card reader or drum cannot tolerate a delay when information is ready for transfer; therefore the operation must be terminated because the data transfer will not be correct. (The PD continues to operate at its normal speed.) A STATUS TERMINATE signal enables the PD to request that the operation be terminated. The TERMINATE signal enables the PD to handle the no-character-request situation. It also allows it to request termination for malfunction detection within the PD. For example, a card reader might detect a feed-check error which means the next card was not sent through the read station.

A START INPUT signal is provided to initiate the operation of the interface controls. The START INPUT signal comes from the control area of the computer. The START and CHARACTER REQUEST signals cannot be sent to the PD unless the START INPUT signal is "true." The END INPUT signal is generated to allow the control area of the computer to terminate the operation when the required number of words has been transferred. The LOAD BUFFER signal is provided to allow loading of the character buffer. The LOAD BUFFER signal will not go "true" unless the CHARACTER STROBE from the PD has occurred. The character buffer provides a single-character storage capability in case the word within the word buffer has not been transferred to memory. It has been included here to illustrate the point related to the use of additional buffering to reduce transfer rates. This allows the memory transfer time to be longer than the time between successive character transfers, which is possible in some computers. The LOAD (A–H) signals are used to direct the characters from the character buffer into their proper positions within the word buffer register. The signals will cycle A through H. Each time a CHARACTER STROBE occurs, a load signal will go "true." For example, the first character of the transmission will be loaded in WB 1–6 by LOAD A, the next character into WB 7–12 by LOAD B, and so on. The STORE MEMORY signal goes "true" when the eighth character is loaded into the word buffer register. It is used to request a memory store operation of the memory control area. The STORE COMPL signal indicates to the input interfacing controls that the memory transfer has been completed and the word buffer is available for loading. The character buffer allows requesting of one character when the word buffer is loaded. However, the character request for the second character will not be made unless the memory transfer has been completed. The START ADDR signals have been included to make the input area compatible with a drum. The drum would have to be told the starting location of the data. The START ADDR signals carry the start address to the local controls of the drum.

The parity check logic allows checking of the character transfer. The parity check logic receives the character from the character buffer. It also receives the parity bit which is transferred from the parity FF with the data character. The parity bit is inserted by the PD, and it will make the seven bits transferred an odd number of binary 1's (for odd parity checking). For example, if the data character is an even number of binary 1's, the parity bit inserted will be a binary 1. The parity error signal will go "true" only if the seven bits are an even number of binary 1's. This signal is used by the control area of the computer as a condition for termination of the operation. The control area of the computer will terminate the operation with the signal END INPUT.

Figure 10·2 shows the basic controls required for interfacing with only one peripheral device. An input area which is mechanized to communicate with more than one PD would have the interface signals (START, CHARACTER REQUEST, etc.) unique to the selected device as shown in Fig. 10·3. The SELECT . . . command from the control area indicates to the input interface controls which PD is involved in the transfer. The data transfer paths are the same, since communication can take place with only one PD at a time. The functional use of the controls previously explained remains unchanged. The only difference is that the interface controls are unique to a PD, one set for a card reader, one for a drum, and so on.

A typical input operation would proceed in the following manner. An instruction indicates to the control area of the computer that an input

FIG. 10·3 Input unit (multiple PD communications).

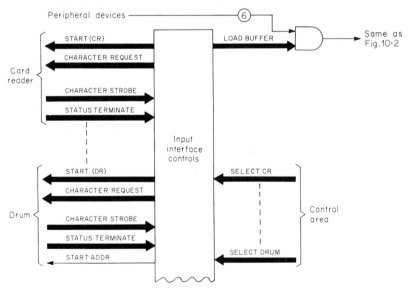

operation is required. The instruction defines the number of words required and which PD is to be used. If the operation were a drum, the instruction would also supply the starting address of the information. The control area of the computer would enable the proper group of interface controls through the SELECT signals (refer to Fig. 10·3). The START line to the selected PD goes "true" (refer to Fig. 10·2). The CHARACTER REQUEST also goes "true" to the selected PD and requests the first character. The interface control area awaits the transmission of the first character. The interface control area always synchronizes with the selected PD. The PD places the first character and parity bit on the lines to the input area and then causes the CHARACTER STROBE signal to go true. The input interface controls load the character into the character buffer. The character is then loaded into bits 1–6 of the word buffer by the LOAD A signal. The character request goes "false," which allows the PD controls to cause the character strobe to go "false." The seven-bit transfer will be monitored by the parity check logic. The parity error signal remains "false" unless an error is detected. The interface controls then cause a new request to be made through the CHARACTER REQUEST signal. This is the request for the second character. The interface controls then await the transfer of the second character. The PD places the second character and parity bit on the lines to the input area and causes the CHARACTER STROBE signal to go "true." The input interface controls load the second character into the character buffer. The second character is then loaded into bits 7–12 of the word buffer by LOAD B. Note that the load word buffer signals have been adjusted to allow the loading of the proper character position of the word buffer. This is easily mechanized through the use of a counter and decode gating. The counter need only be stepped when each character is loaded into the word buffer to select the next position to load. The CHARACTER REQUEST again goes "false," which allows the PD controls to cause the CHARACTER STROBE to go "false." The seven-bit transfer will again be monitored by the parity check logic. The interface controls request the third character by causing the CHARACTER REQUEST signal to again go "true." The interface controls await the transfer of the third character. The movement of the third through seventh characters is the same as for the first two. The first change in the pattern of the operation of the interface controls occurs when the eighth character is received. The reception of the eighth character means a word has been loaded into the word buffer. The interface controls then request a memory store through the STORE MEMORY control signal. The controls will then cycle as before with a request for the next character made. The next character is transmitted when the PD is ready and loaded into the character buffer. However, it will be loaded into the word buffer (1–6) only if the memory transfer of the word has been made. The STORE COMPL signal indicates to the interface controls that the word buffer is available for loading since the word has been stored in memory. The CHARACTER REQUEST signal is also conditional on the memory transfer. When the character buffer has been loaded with the first character of the next word, the interface area has no storage space for another character. Since it cannot store another character, it will not request it. However, when operating properly (no errors), the word transfer to memory would have been completed so that the CHARACTER REQUEST could be made. The STATUS TERMINATE signal handles the situation where the word was not transferred. It causes the control area of the computer to terminate the operation with the END INPUT signal.

The character movement continues as described until the required number of words has been transferred to the memory. The control area of the computer detects completion of the operation and transmits the signal END INPUT to the interface controls to cause termination of the operation. The interface controls cause the START signal to the selected PD to go "false," signifying the end of the operation. The basic pattern of character movement is the same for any peripheral device. Some additional controls may be required as in the case of the drum; however, the basic area remains functionally adequate for the movement of information. Any hardware mechanization is feasible as the input block, as long as it provides for synchronization and buffering with the peripheral device.

Arithmetic unit. The arithmetic unit performs all the operations required by the instructions. If an instruction requires two operands to be added, it is performed within the arithmetic unit. If an instruction requires operands to be compared, the comparison is accomplished within the arithmetic unit. The arithmetic unit functions as the work area for the instructions. Any operation related to operands is performed within the arithmetic unit. Specific functions of the arithmetic unit are defined by the individual instructions; however, all arithmetic units are capable of performing arithmetic operations, logical operations, comparison testing, and shifting.

A general-purpose computer usually contains an arithmetic unit which is capable of performing all the arithmetic operations: addition, subtraction, multiplication, division. The arithmetic unit may be mechanized to work with algebraic numbers, absolute values (no sign), or both. The basic differences in arithmetic units are not apparent at the functional block level. The arithmetic units are organized basically in the same manner. Figure 10·4 illustrates an arithmetic unit which is capable of performing all arithmetic operations.

The arithmetic unit illustrated is assumed to be a fractional fixed-point machine which is formatted as shown in Fig. 10·5. The binary point is defined to exist to the left of the most significant bit (bit 2). The number is

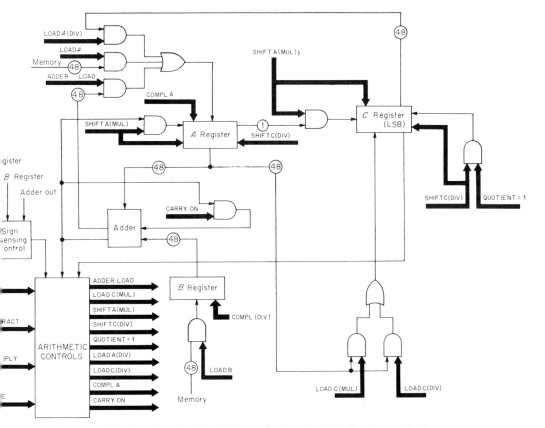

FIG. 10·4 Functional block diagram of arithmetic unit (arithmetic operations).

fractional and can never equal 1. The bit-1 position is used to indicate whether the number is positive (0) or negative (1).

The arithmetic unit (Fig. 10·4) consists of three registers, adders, and controls. The A register has two functions: it stores one of the operands transferred from the memory for the arithmetic operation, and it serves as the accumulator of the result of the arithmetic operation. The B register always stores the second operand for any of the arithmetic operations. It is

FIG. 10·5 Computer operand format.

1	2		48
SIGN	MSB	— — — — — — — — — —	LSB
	•		

never used to accumulate the result of the arithmetic operation. The C register is used in multiplication or division operations. It serves as an extension of the A register for accumulating the product during multiplication or as the temporary accumulator of the quotient during division. The adder elements perform the arithmetic, while the controls provide the necessary command timing for instruction execution.

Adding of two numbers within the arithmetic unit is performed in the following manner. The two numbers are loaded into the A and B registers, respectively, through the execution of instructions. When the FETCH instruction to load the A register is performed, the control area of the computer develops the LOAD A signal. The LOAD A signal strobes the operand from memory into the A register. The B register is loaded by the LOAD B signal in similar fashion. When the ADD instruction is recognized by the control area, it gives the ADD command to the arithmetic controls. The arithmetic controls give the ADDER LOAD command which loads the sum from the adder into the A register. The adder is capable of summing two 48-bit operands. A sum resulting from the combination of the contents of the A and B registers is always present at the output of the adder; however, the ADDER LOAD allows accumulation of the sum only when the A and B registers are to be added.

The sum of the two numbers has been accumulated within the A register. It should be noted that the contents of the B register remain unchanged. If the sum is not to be used in the next instruction, it must be stored in memory. The result has to be moved out of the accumulator since this register is used in all operations performed within the arithmetic unit. The sign sensing and control area is used to initiate the proper form for the number in the A register. The requirements of the number form depend upon the operation being performed and whether the number is positive or negative. The mechanics of this conversion are covered in Chap. 3 in the section on machine arithmetic. The reader is invited to refer to Chap. 3 for examples of the process and to relate those examples to the logic flow being discussed in the respective operations.

Subtraction of two numbers within the arithmetic unit is performed in the following manner. The two operands will be loaded into the A and B registers as previously described. The operands are classified as minuend in the B register and subtrahend in the A register. The sign sensing and control area initiates the complement of the subtrahend, sign and magnitude, as required. The data inputs from the A and B registers are presented to the adders, and the summing takes place. Note the end-around carry path available in the adders. Sign sensing is used to check for overflow as well as to establish the sign of the result. Since the accumulator contains signed magnitude numbers, sign sensing is also used to establish the need for a complement of the accumulator content. The arithmetic unit logic shown

in Fig. 10·4 is representative of the logic organization required to allow subtraction to be accomplished in a computer which employs full adders as the
arithmetic elements.

Multiplication of two numbers within the arithmetic unit is performed
in the following manner. The two operands are loaded into the A and B
registers prior to the execution of the MULTIPLY instruction. When the
control area of the computer executes the MULTIPLY instruction, it gives the
MULTIPLY command to the arithmetic unit. The arithmetic controls transfer
the multiplier from the A register to the C register with the LOAD C(MUL)
command. The C register contains the multiplier for arithmetic control
sensing. The A register is cleared after the multiplier is moved to the C
register. The register conditions before the multiplication operation begins
are accumulator (A register) is cleared, the B register contains the multiplicand, and the C register contains the multiplier. The arithmetic controls
examine the LSB of the multiplier in the C register. If the bit is a 1, the sum
of the A and B register content from the adder is loaded into the accumulator by the command ADDER LOAD. The sum at this time would be B register
$+ 0$, which is the equivalent of multiplying by 1. If the bit is a 0, the adder
sum is not loaded in the accumulator. The accumulator is equal to 0, which
is the equivalent of multiplying by 0. After the summation, the A and C
registers are shifted right one place by SHIFT A (MUL); overflow is inserted
into the MSB of the C register. The LSB of the multiplier is shifted out of
the C register. This bit has already been used and is of no further value.
The A register contains the most significant portion of the product defined
by the first digit of the multiplier. The C register contains the LSB of the
product in its most significant bit position. The C register also contains the
second digit of the multiplier in its LSB position after the shift. The same
sequence is repeated. The arithmetic controls examine the LSB of the C
register which now contains the second digit of the multiplier. If the bit is a
1, the sum of the A and B registers from the adder is loaded into the accumulator by the command ADDER LOAD. The sum of $A + B$ is equivalent to
multiplying by 1. If the bit is a 0, the adder sum is not loaded into the
accumulator. The accumulator sum is added to 0, which is the equivalent
of multiplying by 0. After the summation, the A and C registers are shifted
right one place. Overflow is inserted into the MSB position of the C register.
The second digit of the multiplier is shifted out of the C register. The A
register contains the most significant digits of the product defined by the
first two digits of the multiplier. The C register contains the least significant
two digits of the product defined by the first two digits of the multiplier.
The C register contains the least significant two digits of the product in its
most significant bit positions, as well as the third digit of the multiplier in its
LSB position. The basic sequence of sum and shift right 1 will continue
until all digits of the multiplier have been sensed. The arithmetic controls

are mechanized to detect this condition. This sensing is normally performed by counting the number of sequences. For example, if the multiplier is 48 bits, then there will be 48 sequences. After the final sequence, the A register contains the most significant bits of the product, and the C register contains the least significant bits of the product. The A register contains the product which will be stored in memory as a result of the multiplication. Some computers also allow the storing of the contents of the C register in memory. If the 96 bits are stored as the product of the multiplication, it is identified as a double-precision product. Sign sensing compares the signs of the multiplier and multiplicand to establish the product sign. Refer to Chap. 3 for examples of machine multiplication by the above method.

Division of two numbers is performed in the following manner. The two operands are loaded into the A and B registers prior to the execution of the DIVIDE instruction. For explanation purposes, the dividend will be loaded into the A register and the divisor into the B register. The dividend and divisor must be defined because the arithmetic unit requires that the divisor be greater than the dividend to produce a correct quotient. A correct quotient must be a fractional binary fixed-point number to be consistent with the defined word format. A division performed where the divisor is smaller than the dividend cannot be expressed as a fractional binary fixed-point number. When the control area of the computer executes the DIVIDE instruction, it gives the DIVIDE command to the arithmetic controls. The A register will contain the dividend, the B register will contain the divisor. The content of the C register is unknown at this time. The arithmetic controls cause a transfer of the 1's complement of the B register with the COMPL (DIV) command. Adder overflow is examined to see if the divisor is greater than the dividend. If the overflow bit is a 1, then the divisor is smaller than the dividend, and the operation is terminated. If the overflow bit is a 0, the divisor is greater than the dividend, and the operation will continue to produce the quotient. A sign comparison of the newly generated partial remainder and the divisor results in the generation of a quotient bit which will be loaded into the LSB position of the C register under the control of QUOTIENT = 1 when the SHIFT C (DIV) command is given. Both A and C registers will be shifted left one place by SHIFT C (DIV) command.

After the determination of the first digit of the quotient, the register content is as follows: The A register contains the partial remainder of the dividend required to determine the next digit of the quotient, the B register contains the divisor, and the C register contains the first digit of the quotient in its LSB position. The arithmetic controls determine the next quotient digit in the following manner: If the divisor is greater than the current dividend (partial remainder from first operation), the quotient digit will be a 0. If the divisor is not greater than the dividend, the quotient digit will be a 1. The newly generated partial remainder (adder output) is loaded into the A register by the ADDER LOAD command. Note that the adder output represents the numerical result of the specified combination (addition or subtraction) of the dividend (A register) and divisor (B register).

Again the quotient digit determined is loaded into the LSB position of the C register. The A register is shifted left one position, and the remainder (A register) becomes the new dividend. The registers contain the following after the second quotient digit has been determined: The A register contains the new dividend, the B register contains the divisor, and the C register contains the two most significant digits of quotient in its least significant position. The determination of the remaining quotient digits continues until the arithmetic controls determine that the required number of quotient digits has been calculated. Division of two 48-bit numbers, for example, produces a 48-bit quotient. When the last quotient bit is determined, the register content will be as follows: The A register contains the remainder, the C register contains the calculated quotient, and the B register contains the divisor. It should be noted that when the arithmetic controls shift the final digit of the quotient into the C register, the A register remains unaltered. The controls necessary to accomplish this have not been shown on Fig. 10·4 in order to simplify. Note that the quotient is not in the accumulator but in the C register. Since subtraction was the operation involved, it may be necessary to return the value in the A register to its true form with the command COMPL A. The arithmetic controls will then exchange the A and C register contents. Command LOAD C(DIV) moves the remainder to the C register, while command LOAD A(DIV) moves the quotient to the A register. The result of the operation stored in memory is normally only the quotient. However, if a computer has been mechanized to allow transfers of C register to memory, the remainder may be moved to memory by the execution of the appropriate store instruction. Some programs may divide the remainder again by the divisor and produce another quotient bit. The total quotient length is usually referred to as a double-precision quotient. Again the reader is invited to the Chap. 3 coverage for examples of the DIVIDE operation.

The logical operations which may be performed by a general-purpose computer consist of AND, OR, XOR (exclusive OR), and complement.

Figure 10·6 illustrates the logic which might be used to perform these functions.

The AND, OR, and XOR require two operands. These operands are contained in the A and B registers and are loaded from memory.

When the control area of the computer executes an AND instruction, corresponding bit positions of the A and B registers are ANDed to generate corresponding outputs. Only a single gate is shown on the diagram; however, a three-input gate exists for each of the 48-bit positions of the register.

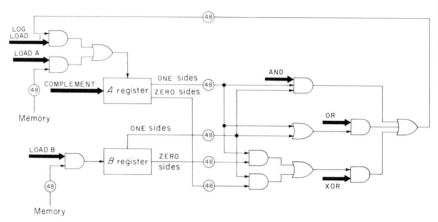

FIG. 10·6 Functional block diagram of arithmetic unit (logical operations).

Normal AND gate action is involved; i.e., all inputs must be present for an output to be generated. The LOG LOAD command is used to gate the result of the logical operation into the accumulator. This signal is also used to gate the result of the OR and XOR logical operations into the accumulator.

On a logical OR operation, a 1 in the corresponding bit positions of either (or both) the *A* and *B* register(s) results in an output to that bit of the accumulator. As in the AND operation, a separate gate exists for each bit position of the register.

The exclusive OR logical operation requires that one or the other of the registers contain a ONE data bit in corresponding bit positions. Note that a 1 contained in any bit position of both the *A* and *B* registers inhibits the output of the XOR gate. LOG LOAD gates the resultant data into the accumulator.

The COMPLEMENT instruction is also performed within the arithmetic unit. A single operand, contained in the *A* register, is involved in this operation. The COMPLEMENT signal is applied to the *A* register. Internal gating contained in the register flip-flops allows the flip-flops to change to the opposite state.

The general-purpose computer is usually capable of performing various types of shift operations. These shifts may be considered single or double, left or right, circular or end-off, arithmetic or logical. Each shift will be defined by one of the characteristics in each of the groupings given above.

A single shift involves the data contained in the *A* register, while a double shift involves the combined data contents of the *A* and *C* registers. The left or right indicates the direction of the shift. It should be noted that a shift left has the same effect on the value of the number as multiplying by the base of the number system in use. A shift to the right has the same effect on the value of the number as dividing by the base of the number system in use. A circular shift causes the bits shifted off the end of the register(s) to be entered into the opposite end of the register(s) so that no data bits are lost. An end-off shift results in the loss of the data bits shifted beyond the limits of the register(s). The arithmetic shift results in the movement of all data bits except the most significant bit of the A register which is assumed to contain the sign of the number. A logical shift would not consider a sign position, and all bits would be subject to the type of shift specified. Figure 10·7 illustrates some of the shift variations possible and the transfer paths involved.

Figure 10·8 illustrates the logic used to control the shifting sequences. The execution command for a SHIFT instruction will be given after the data to be shifted is already contained in the register(s) involved in the shift.

Single circular shifting is controlled by the RT(CIR) SINGLE and LT(CIR) SINGLE control signals Note that RT(CIR) SINGLE provides a shifting path from the bit-48 position to the bit-1 position of the A register. LT(CIR) SINGLE provides the shift path from bit 1 to bit 48 of the A register. The C register is undisturbed by the single-shift sequences.

End-off single shifts are controlled by SHIFT (A)RT and SHIFT (A)LT. Note that on either of these shifts, the shift action takes place within the A register only. The shift of any bits beyond the bounds of the A register results in discarded bits since no transfer paths exist to accept these bits. The number of shifts to be performed on any of these shift variations is controlled by the period for which the command shift signal is present. Note that the C register is undisturbed by the single end-off shifts. Note also that single-shift capability does not exist in the C register.

Double end-off shifting is controlled by the signals RT DOUBLE, SHIFT (A)RT, and SHIFT (C)RT. The RT DOUBLE signal provides the transfer path from the LSB of A into the MSB of the C register. The SHIFT A and (C)RT signals perform the shift within the respective registers. The bits

FIG. 10·7 Arithmetic unit shift variations. (a) Single left circular; (b) single right end-off; (c) double left circular; (d) double right end-off.

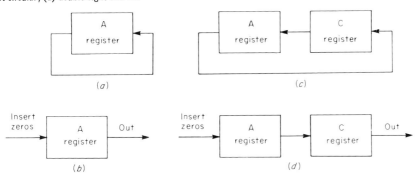

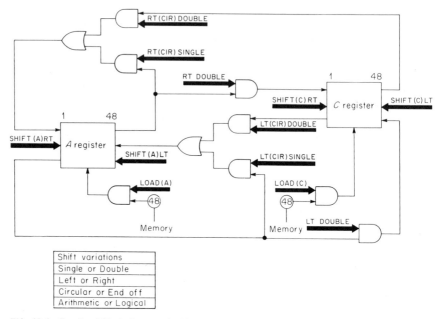

FIG. 10·8 Functional block diagram of arithmetic unit (shift operations).

shifted off the LSB of C are lost because the only transfer path to the MSB of the A register is inhibited since RT(CIR) DOUBLE is false.

On a double circular shift right, SHIFT (A)RT and SHIFT (C)RT control data movement within the respective registers. RT DOUBLE provides the transfer path between the LSB of the A register and the MSB of the C register. RT(CIR) DOUBLE provides a data transfer path from LSB of C to MSB of A.

In a like manner, LT DOUBLE, LT(CIR) DOUBLE, SHIFT (C)LT, and SHIFT (A)LT control circular shifting to the left.

Double end-off shifting to the left and right is controlled by the appropriate command signals.

Certain decision type instructions depend upon a comparison of operands and the relationships which exist between them as the basis for selection of a program path. This comparison between the operands takes place within the arithmetic unit. The operands to be compared are held in the A and B registers. The numbers are compared, and output signals are generated to indicate the existing relationships. See Fig. 10·9. The comparator may be mechanized to handle either absolute values, algebraic quantities, or both. The control area of the computer selects the proper outputs of the comparator when both types are available. The comparator allows the following relationships to be determined by the control area of the computer.

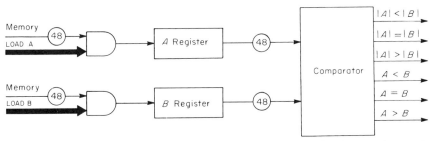

FIG. 10·9 Functional block diagram of arithmetic unit (comparison tests).

	Algebraic	*Absolute*
(1)	$A < B$	$|A| < |B|$
(2)	$A \leqq B$	$|A| \leqq |B|$
(3)	$A = B$	$|A| = |B|$
(4)	$A > B$	$|A| > |B|$
(5)	$A \geqq B$	$|A| \geqq |B|$
(6)	$A \neq B$	$|A| \neq |B|$

The control area could use the comparisons $A < B$ and $A = B$ to determine a condition of A is equal to or less than B. In a like manner the control area could determine that the absolute value of A did not equal B by using the comparator outputs $|A| > |B|$, $|A| < |B|$. It should be noted that any combination tabulated above may be determined by the control area of the computer through the proper selection of comparator outputs. The comparator itself is nothing other than combinations of decoders. The earlier chapters of the text have already provided the background on decoders.

The control unit. The control unit of the computer provides the necessary timing and interface for the integrated operation of the various organizational blocks of a computing system. The control unit must be capable of instruction fetch and execution, program jumps or branches, data fetch and storing, inputting and outputting of information, error recognition and responding. In examining control unit requirements, it may seem that there is an overlap in function between the control unit and other of the organizational blocks. This is true insofar as the control unit provides the master timing and sequencing for all operations performed within the processing system.

A typical instruction-processing area is shown in Fig. 10·10. This organization is capable of instruction fetch and execution and of executing program jumps. A single-address type instruction is assumed with the format shown in Fig. 10·11.

The operation code (OP code) is used to identify the instruction. The

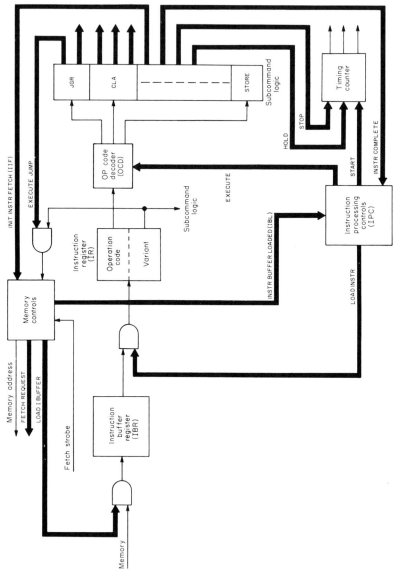

FIG. 10-10 Functional block diagram of control unit (instruction processing).

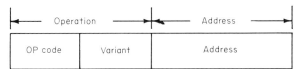

FIG. 10·11   Instruction word format.

CLEAR AND ADD (CLA) instruction could be defined by an 05_8 operation code while an ADD instruction might be defined as 25_8. The variant provides for variations of the basic operation specified by the op code. The variant may also be used to indicate address modification by the use of indexing or indirect addressing routines (discussed later in this chapter). The address portion of the instruction format usually defines an operand (or instruction) address but could define an operation or have no significance for certain instructions. For example, in CLA, STORE, and FETCH instructions, the address is used to specify the memory address for the data operation; in CLA and FETCH, it identifies the memory location from which the information is to be read; for the STORE operation, it specifies the location into which data is to be written.

Jump type instructions use the address to specify the location in memory of the next instruction to be fetched.

Shift instructions might use the address field to specify the type of shift (circular, etc.) and the amount of the shift. In the ADD instruction explained on a previous page, the address has no meaning since the instruction function is to cause the summing of the present contents of the A and B registers. The true meaning of the address portion of the instruction is dependent upon the particular operation to be executed.

The instruction register is used to store the instruction which is being executed by the computer. The OP code decoder interprets the operation code of the instruction and selects the proper subcommand logic associated with the decoded instruction. The subcommand logic is organized relative to the instruction; i.e., the logic related to JUMP ON GREATER (JGR) is so identified, that related to CLA is so identified, that related to STORE is so identified, etc., for each instruction which the computer can execute. The subcommand logic generates all commands and controls the timing required for instruction execution.

The instruction buffer register (IBR) is used to provide temporary storage for instructions from memory. Program run time can be reduced if the next instruction to be executed is fetched from memory while another instruction is in the execution phase. This advance instruction fetch is possible depending upon the instruction in process. For example, while a shift is being executed, the memory is not involved, and a fetch of the next instruction may be made.

The memory controls develop all the signals necessary for information (instruction or data) fetch from memory. Only the master signals for the operation are shown in order to simplify the discussion; other controls will be introduced later. The memory address outputs from memory controls are used to specify memory location. The FETCH REQ signal is used to request a memory fetch operation on the location defined by memory address. FETCH REQ must be true for the fetch to occur. Instruction readout of memory is loaded into the instruction buffer by LOAD I BUF. This command is initiated after the FETCH STROBE is received from memory. The FETCH STROBE indicates the presence of information from the memory. The INSTR BUF LOADED signal indicates to the instruction processing controls (IPC) that the IBR contains an instruction. If the current instruction has been completed before the next instruction is fetched, then the instruction processing controls must hold, awaiting the transfer of the instruction from memory. The INITIATE INSTRUCTION FETCH (IIF) command will be given to the memory controls from the subcommand logic. It will be developed at the proper time depending upon the particular instruction being executed.

The EXECUTE JUMP command will be developed for any conditional test jump instruction if the test is successful. It is referenced only to the JGR area of the subcommand matrix for simplicity. Recall that if the test is successful, a jump must be made to a new instruction. The address in the instruction register defines the location in memory of the new instruction. The EXECUTE JUMP command will load the address into the instruction address register within the memory controls.

The instruction processing controls are used to control the execution of the instructions. The EXECUTE command enables the OP code decoder logic. The decoder logic cannot recognize an instruction until the EXECUTE command is given. The EXECUTE command will be "true" only when the next instruction to execute has been loaded into the instruction register. The START signal is used to initiate the counting cycle of the timing counter. The timing counter is cycled only when an instruction is within the instruction register.

The timing counter provides the timing counts for various commands developed within the subcommand logic. The HOLD and STOP commands allow the subcommand logic to control the operation of the timing counter. The HOLD, when "true," stops the counting, allowing the count to be held. STOP allows reset of the counter to its starting configuration. The HOLD may be given at any time within the instruction execution. The STOP will always be given when the execution of the instruction has been completed. The INSTR COMPLETE command is generated by the subcommand logic when the execution of the instruction is completed. It is used to inform the processing controls that the instruction register is available for loading. The load of the instruction register is made by the LOAD INSTR command. This command will be given only when the buffer has the next instruction (IBL).

The overall flow sequence for instruction execution is as follows. The LOAD INSTR command causes the instruction to be loaded into the IR. The EXECUTE command enables the OCD, and the appropriate sub-command logic is selected for instruction execution. The START signal initiates the cycling of the timing counter, and instruction execution begins. The IIF command given by the subcommand logic requests a fetch of the next instruction by memory controls. An instruction address register, which points to the address of the next instruction, is contained in memory controls. When the instruction which is currently being executed was loaded into the IBR, the address register was incremented by 1. This incrementing of the address register occurs after every instruction fetch. The MEMORY ADDRESS and FETCH REQ signals initiate the fetch operation, and the FETCH STROBE signal indicates data availability from memory. LOAD I BUF places the instruction in IBR, and IBL indicates this condition to the IPC. The completion of the instruction results in the signals, generated by subcommand logic, of INSTR COMPLETE to IPC and STOP to the timing counter. EXECUTE goes "false" until the next instruction is loaded into the IR. If the buffer has been loaded, the command INSTR BUFFER LOADED allows the processing controls to load the IR, and the execution of the next instruction begins. If the buffer has not been loaded, the processing controls hold awaiting the instruction load. It should be noted that every wait increases the time required to run the program (execute all instructions). This is nonproductive time since no instruction is being executed. When the next instruction is loaded into the IR, the preceding sequence (execute cycle) is repeated.

The execute cycle is slightly different when any JUMP instruction is performed. The INIT INSTR FETCH and EXECUTE JUMP commands are given simultaneously if the jump is to be made. The EXECUTE JUMP command enables the loading of the instruction address into the instruction address register. The loading of this address allows the instruction fetch of the instruction defined by the JUMP instruction instead of the next instruction in sequence. The INIT INSTR FETCH command initiates the memory controls on the fetch. The processing controls hold awaiting the fetch of this instruction. When this instruction is loaded into the buffer, the instruction address register within the memory controls will be incremented. This allows sequential execution of instructions to continue from this new point in the program. The execute cycle is the same from this point for the instruction fetched by the JUMP instruction.

Several instructions will be examined to illustrate the functioning of this logic. The first instruction considered is CLEAR AND ADD (CLA). On

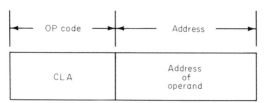

FIG. 10·12   CLA instruction word format.

this instruction the accumulator (A reg) is cleared and loaded with the data operand contained in the memory location defined by the address. This instruction format is shown in Fig. 10·12. For this and the other simplified example instructions, the variant is ignored in order to keep the instruction basic. A more detailed explanation of the variant is given in Chap. 16.

The commands and timing relationships developed by the subcommand logic are shown on Fig. 10·13. The controls required to execute this instruction are initiated by the signal ENABLE CLA. The ENABLE CLA signal is true whenever the OP code decoder is enabled and the CLA instruction is within the instruction register. The ENABLE CLA signal is of the same duration as the EXECUTE command because the EXECUTE command is the ENABLE for the OP code decoder. (Reference should be also made to Fig. 10·10 as required.) The START signal is a one T-time signal which is coincident with the lead edge of the EXECUTE command. A T time is defined as the time interval between two consecutive clocks. The first clock which occurs with the START signal "true" steps the timing counter to 1. The counter had been initially stopped at a count of 0. The counter will continue to count each time a clock occurs unless a HOLD or STOP command is given. The counter furnishes the timing counts which are used by the CLA subcommand logic. The first command given by the CLA subcommand logic is RESET A. RESET A is a one T-time signal which is used to reset the accumulator (A reg). The reset is performed by the clock at the end of $T1$. The FETCH B command requests the memory controls to make a fetch for the B register. The fetch will be made from the location defined by the address in the instruction register. A HOLD command is given to stop the timing counter until the memory fetch has been completed. The timing counter is held at $T2$. The FETCH COMPL signal from the memory controls indicates that the operand has been loaded into the memory communications register (MCR). The MCR serves as buffer register in this operation for the data word (operand) from memory. The INIT INSTR FETCH command is given at the same time the FETCH COMPL command is given. Since this operation does not require any further memory operations, the memory controls are available for fetching of the next instruction. (Data transfers by the memory controls are considered later within this chapter.) The LOAD B command loads the B register from the MCR. At $T4$, the A register contains 0, the B register contains the operand fetched. $T4$ is the last time required in the execution of the instruction. INSTR COMPLETE, ADDER LOAD, and STOP commands all go "true" during $T4$. When the clock occurs at the end of $T4$, the

FIG. 10·13 CLA instruction execution. (a) Functional controls; (b) timing.

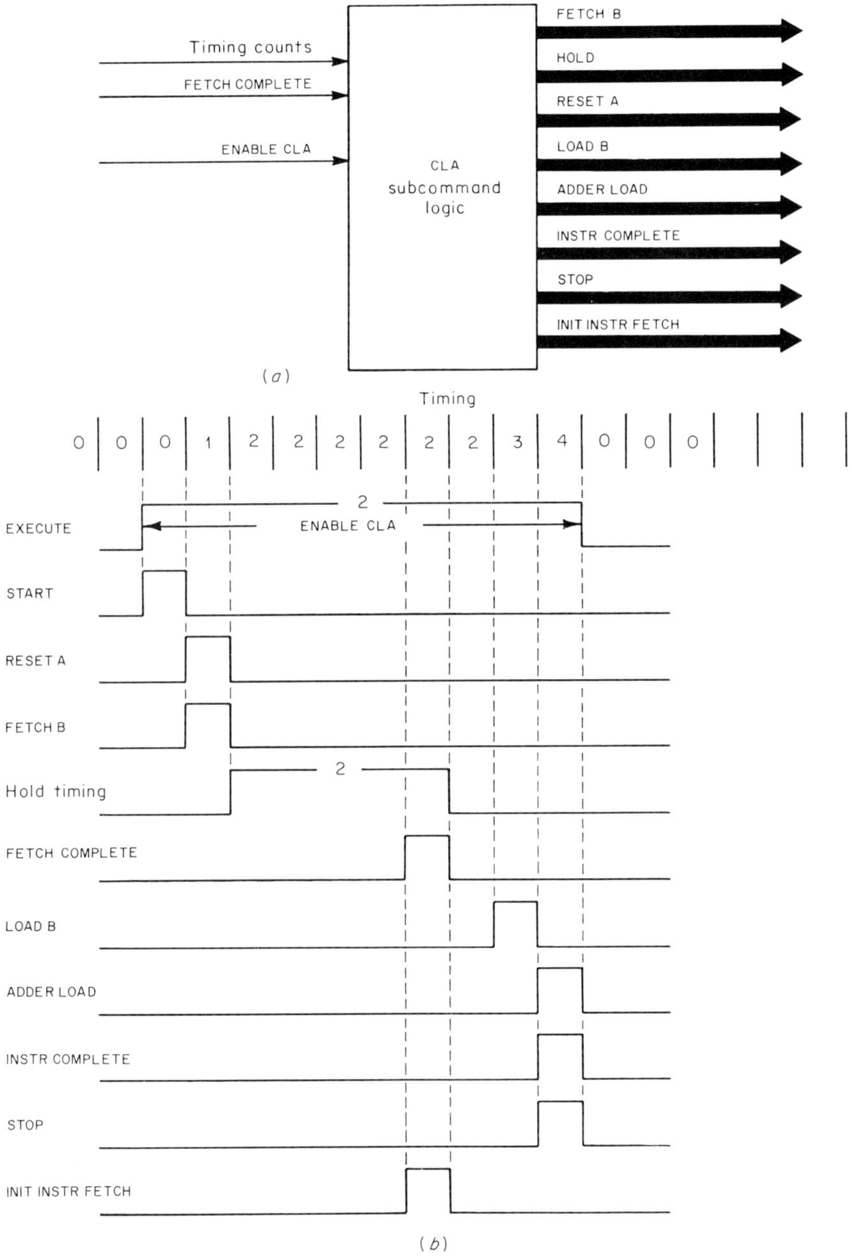

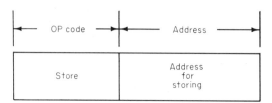

FIG. 10·14 STORE instruction word format.

counter will be reset to 0, the accumulator contains the operand fetched (B reg $+$ 0), and the EXECUTE command will have gone "false." The instruction execution resulted in the clearing of the A register ($T1$) and loading of the A register with the specified operand ($T4$).

On a STORE instruction, the contents of the accumulator are written into the memory location defined by the address of the instruction. The instruction format is shown in Fig. 10·14.

The commands and timing relationships developed by the subcommand logic are shown in Fig. 10·15. The controls required to execute this instruction are initiated by the signal ENABLE STORE. The ENABLE STORE signal is "true" whenever the OP code decoder is enabled and the store instruction is within the instruction register. The ENABLE STORE signal is of the same duration as the EXECUTE command because the EXECUTE command is the enable for the OP code decoder. The START signal occurs coincident with the leading edge of the EXECUTE command. The first clock which occurs with the START signal "true" steps the timing counter to 1. The first command developed by the store subcommand logic is STORE A. This signal requests the memory controls to store the contents of the A register in the location defined by the address. The HOLD command is used to stop the timing cycle until the store has been performed. The STORE COMPL command from the memory controls indicates that the store has been completed. The INSTR COMPLETE, STOP, and INIT INSTR FETCH commands are developed when the STORE COMPL command occurs. After the clock occurs at the end of the STORE COMPL command, the counter will have been stopped at 0, the fetch of the next instruction will have been initiated, and the EXECUTE command will have gone "false." The instruction was completed when the STORE COMPL command was generated by the memory controls. This signal indicated that the contents of the A register had been stored in memory.

The JUMP ON GREATER (JGR) instruction results in a modification in the sequence of instruction execution. Assume that the instruction deals with absolute values, and the test to be made for a jump condition is that $|A| > |B|$. If the contents of the A register are greater than the contents of the B register, the next instruction to be executed is contained in the memory

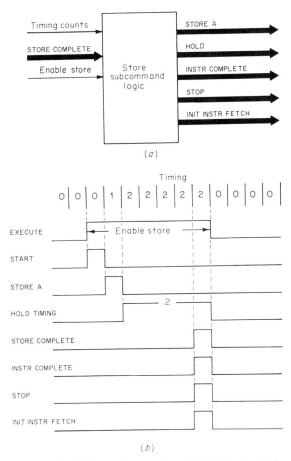

FIG. 10·15 STORE instruction execution. (a) Functional controls; (b) timing.

location specified by the address. This instruction format is shown in Fig. 10·16.

The commands and timing relationships developed by the subcommand

FIG. 10·16 JGR instruction word format.

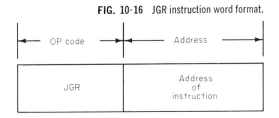

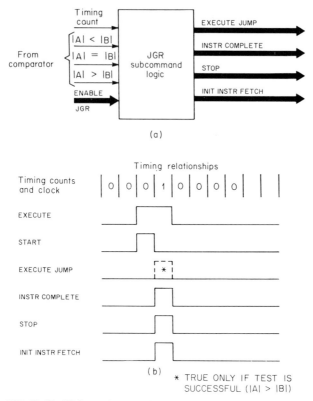

FIG. 10·17   JGR instruction execution. (a) Functional controls; (b) timing.

logic for instruction execution are shown in Fig. 10·17. The controls required to execute this instruction are initiated by the signal ENABLE JGR.
The ENABLE JGR signal is true whenever the OP code decoder is enabled
and the JGR instruction is within the instruction register. The ENABLE
JGR signal is of the same duration as the EXECUTE command. The START
signal occurs coincident with the leading edge of the EXECUTE command
level. The timing counter is stepped to 1 by the first clock after START goes
"true." This instruction requires only one T time to execute. The operands
must be loaded into the A and B registers prior to the test instruction
execution. This instruction evaluates the proper comparator output. If A
is greater than B, the command EXECUTE JUMP is given. EXECUTE JUMP
loads the address into the instruction address register of the memory controls. The instruction fetch will be of the location defined by the address.
If A is not greater than B, the command EXECUTE JUMP remains "false."
The next instruction in the normal sequence will be fetched and executed.

The STOP command resets the timing counter to 0. The INIT INSTR FETCH command initiates the fetch operation for the instruction required as a result of execution of the TEST JUMP instruction. The execute gate will go "false" inhibiting the OP code decoder output. The function of the instruction is accomplished at $T1$ when the EXECUTE JUMP command determined whether or not the jump was to be executed.

The subcommand logic is organized in a similar manner for each instruction which is executed by the computer. It is composed of logic elements, flip-flops, gates, etc., which are organized to generate all the commands required to execute any of the instructions.

The memory controls must generate the required signals for the movement of data between the memory and the computer. (Instruction movement has already been covered.) Memory controls are responsible for all communications with memory. A typical memory control area is illustrated in Fig. 10·18. This control area is capable of fetch and storage of data words, and address modification through indexing or indirect addressing. Indexing and indirect addressing are commonly used for address modification in most computers. This area consists of controls, the memory communications register (MCR), and parity generation/check logic.

The MCR acts as a buffer register for all operations with memory. It is a 49-bit register capable of holding 48 data bits and one parity bit. The data contained in the MCR consists of the content of a memory location on a fetch operation or the data to be written into the memory on a store operation. Note that the LOAD (STORE) and LOAD (FETCH) signals gate data into the MCR from the A register or the memory, respectively.

On a LOAD (STORE) command, the MCR content is used by memory and the parity generation logic. Parity generation ensures odd parity or an odd number of bits in the 49 bits transferred to memory. This allows the memory to check for errors in transmission. The memory communications always involve the data word parity bit combination.

The LOAD (FETCH) command is generated for the fetch operation and allows 49 bits read from the memory to be gated into the MCR. This data is made available to the parity checker for error sensing. An even number of binary 1's in the 49-bit word constitutes an error condition. The fetch operations discussed at this time constitute a data fetch as distinguished from an instruction fetch. Different paths to the computer are available for information (data) transfer from those previously discussed for instruction fetch. Data and instruction fetch commands and gating are never generated simultaneously. The data word from the MCR is loaded into the proper register under the direction of the subcommand logic. The memory at this time ignores the inputs from the MCR because the operation is a fetch. The address and indirect bit outputs are considered later under indirect addressing.

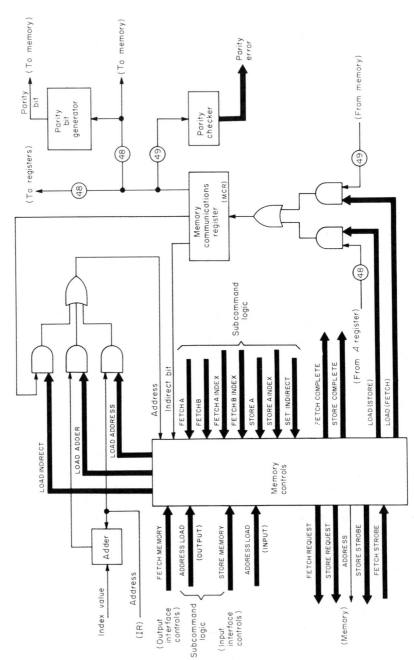

FIG. 10·18 Functional block diagram of control unit (data movement).

For explanation purposes, memory controls are organized as follows: memory interface controls, initiate operation commands, address selection commands, and operation complete commands. The term "memory interface controls" refers to all controls required for memory communications. The store or fetch requests tell the memory the type of operation required, and the address tells the memory what location is involved in the operation. The strobes are used to indicate when data is on the information lines. The initiate operation commands are used to identify the operation required and the address variation (if any) in effect. These commands originate at either the subcommand logic or the input/output interface control areas. Detailed memory operation is covered in Chap. 11.

The input/output interface control area commands are considered first. The STORE MEMORY command is generated by the input interface controls (refer to Fig. 10·2 as required). It is "true" whenever the word buffer register has been loaded with eight characters from the peripheral device. It should be noted that since the MCR may be loaded only from the *A* register, the *A* register functions as the word buffer within this computer. This is common practice in earlier computers. The memory controls initiate a store operation. The STORE REQUEST would go "true" requesting the operation. The LOAD (STORE) command moves the content of the *A* register (word buffer) to the MCR. The address configuration indicates the location for the store and must change each time a store operation is performed. This location change is accomplished through the use of an address register within the memory controls which is incremented each time a store is performed. Each time the STORE MEMORY command is given, the address register points to the next location in memory in which data is to be stored. The initial loading of the address register (starting address) is performed as part of the execution of the input instruction. The ADDR LOAD (INPUT) command requests the loading of the address register from the address within the instruction register. The address is loaded when the LOAD ADDR command is generated by the memory controls. The subcommand logic, controlling the execution of the input instruction, will be informed each time a word is stored in memory by the STORE COMPL command. The subcommand logic, not the memory controls, terminates the operation when the required number of words has been transferred to memory. Recall that the STORE COMPL command indicates to the input interface controls that the word buffer is again available for loading of characters (refer to Fig. 10·2 as required).

Memory communications for output operations with peripheral devices are performed in a similar fashion (the output interface controls are covered later). The FETCH MEMORY signal indicates that another word is required for the output operation. This signal causes the memory controls to initiate a fetch operation. The FETCH REQ command goes "true," requesting the fetch operation of memory. The address configuration indicates the location of the word involved in the operation. The FETCH STROBE from memory indicates when the data word is on the information lines from memory. The LOAD (FETCH) command is used to load the MCR with the data word from memory.

After each instruction fetch, the address register within the memory controls is incremented so that it always points to the next instruction to be executed. Initial loading of the address register is performed by the subcommand logic in its execution of the output instruction. The subcommand logic gives the LOAD ADDR (OUTPUT) command which requests the initial load. The LOAD ADDR command will perform the loading of the starting address into the address register. The subcommand logic and the output interface controls terminate the operation. (Termination of an output operation is considered fully under the section on output interface controls.)

The memory operations initiated by the subcommand logic are basically the same as those initiated by the input/output interface control areas. There are no significant differences in the operation of memory controls for the fetching or storing of data. The differences which exist occur in the address formulation. The subcommand logic is able to request an operation of memory (store or fetch) on a location specified by the address, the address plus an index value (indexing), or by the address field of a data word (indirect addressing).

Memory operations in which the address alone is the source of the address are performed in the following manner. The subcommand logic executing a fetch type instruction generates the command FETCH A or FETCH B. This command identifies the register to be loaded with the content of the MCR. The register to be loaded from the MCR is under the control of the subcommand logic. The memory controls generate the LOAD ADDR command which enables the loading of the address register with the address portion of the instruction. The operation proceeds as a typical fetch with the fetch request made for the location defined by the address configuration. FETCH STROBE allows the loading of the data word and parity bit into the MCR by the LOAD (FETCH) command. The FETCH COMPL command then informs the subcommand logic that the fetch has been completed and the subcommand logic loads the specified A or B registers.

The store operation is performed by the memory controls in a similar fashion. The subcommand logic executing the STORE instruction generates the command STORE A, and memory controls generate the LOAD ADDR command. This command causes the address to be loaded into the address register within the memory controls, and the operation proceeds as a typical store. The MCR is loaded from the A register by the command LOAD (STORE), the store request is made of memory, and the data word is transferred. The STORE STROBE identifies the interval of time that the data word and parity bit are on the information lines to memory. The STORE COMPL command is generated to inform the subcommand logic that the store has been performed and instruction processing may be resumed.

A scheme useful for address modification is referred to as *indexing*. A considerable saving in program steps is achieved by the use of indexing in writing iterative programs, for example. Index modification of the address may be performed by the memory control area. Certain instructions within the instruction set allow the address to be modified by the contents of an index register (address plus index value). The contents of the index register (index value) must be loaded through instruction execution prior to its use. Fetches for either A or B registers (FETCH A INDEX, FETCH B INDEX) have been assumed for explanation purposes. Either fetch would be performed in the same manner, so only the FETCH A INDEX operation is considered.

The generation of the FETCH A INDEX command indicates a fetch operation from an address defined by the value of the address plus an index value. Memory controls generate the necessary control signals to sum the address and the A index value prior to the loading of the address register. The normal fetch operation would then take place. It should be noted that the fetch is no longer defined only by the address, but by the address plus index register (index value). This modification allows the instruction address to remain a fixed value, and the changes in address are the result of the index value.

Indexing could be very useful in fetching a table of numbers from memory. The instruction address could be made equal to the starting location of the table. The index value could be used to step through the table. The only thing required would be to interleave the fetch operations with instruction which would increment the index register. The instructions could be arranged as follows for fetching a table of numbers.

Assumed: address = 0; index register = 0; operation on operand — not considered.

1. FETCH A INDEX. Location fetched is 0.
2. INCREMENT INDEX REGISTER BY 1. Index register is 1.
3. FETCH A INDEX. Location fetched is 1.
4. INCREMENT INDEX REGISTER BY 1. Index register is 2.
5. FETCH A INDEX. Location fetched is 2.
6. Further steps are similar.

Operations (fetch or store) may also be performed through indirect addressing. In indirect addressing, an indirect address (IA) data word is

FIG. 10·19 Indirect address (IA) data word format.

used to define the location required for fetching or storing. The IA data word is formatted as shown in Fig. 10·19.

The IA data word is always composed of an address and a control bit (indirect bit). The address always identifies the next word to be fetched, and the meaning of the address is identified by the indirect bit. If the indirect bit is a binary 0, the address within the current data word defines the address involved in the operation (for the fetch or store). If the indirect bit is a binary 1, the address within the current IA data word specifies the address of another indirect address word. Operations involving more than one indirect address data word are usually referred to as multilevel indirect addressing. Multilevel indirect addressing is performed in the following manner. (Refer to Fig. 10·20.) A fetch would be made of the IA data word defined by the address within the instruction register. After the MCR had been loaded, the memory controls would check the indirect bit. Since the IA bit is a 1, it indicates to the controls that another fetch of an IA

FIG. 10·20 Example of multilevel indirect addressing.

Memory

Address

1 | Address (*A*)

0 | Address (*B*)

Data location
(for fetching or storing)

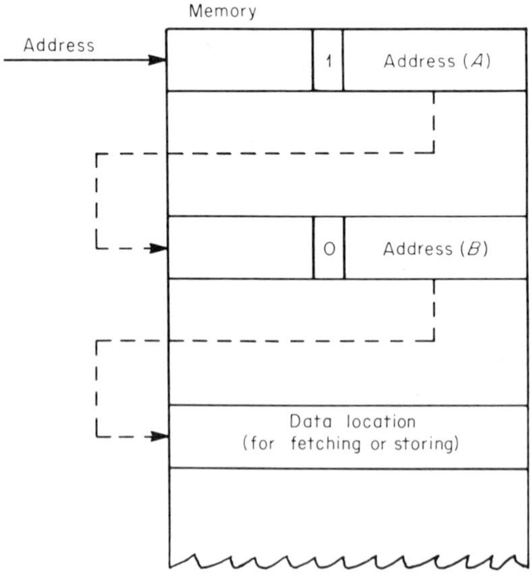

data word is required. The location of the IA data word is defined by
address A. A second fetch is initiated for the contents of the location defined by address A. After the fetch is performed and the MCR is loaded,
the memory controls again check the indirect bit. Since the indirect bit is a
binary 0, this indicates to controls that the final level of indirect addressing
has been reached. Address B specifies the address required for the operation
(fetch or store). The required operation is then performed on the location
defined by address B. The important point to note is that the instruction
address did not define the address for the operation (fetch or store). The
address for the operation is defined by the first IA data word whose indirect
bit is a binary 0. The number of IA data words involved is a function of the
program.

A fetch operation for the A register using indirect addressing is considered. The format for the instruction is as shown in Fig. 10·21. [In this
format, indirect addressing is indicated by the most significant bit (MSB)
of the address field.] The operation proceeds as follows. (See Fig. 10·20.)

The OP code identifies the instruction while the indirect bit within the
address specifies whether indirect addressing is in effect. The address defines the location of the first IA data word to be fetched if indirect addressing
is in effect. The subcommand logic executing the instruction simultaneously
generates the FETCH A and SET INDIRECT commands. The FETCH A command informs the memory controls that a fetch operation is required. The
SET INDIRECT command informs the controls that indirect addressing is in
effect. A fetch is made of the location defined by the address. (The LOAD
ADDR command loaded the address register.) The FETCH STROBE allows the
loading of the MCR through the LOAD (FETCH) command and indicates to
the memory controls when the IA data word may be checked. The indirect
bit is monitored from the contents of the MCR. Since the IA bit is a binary
1, the memory controls must initiate another fetch. The memory controls
load the address from the contents of the MCR into the address register.
The load is enabled by the command LOAD INDIR. A second fetch operation
is initiated by the memory controls on the location defined by the address
register which contains address A. The FETCH STROBE again indicates when

FIG. 10·21 FETCH (A) indirect address instruction format.

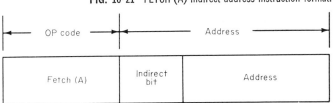

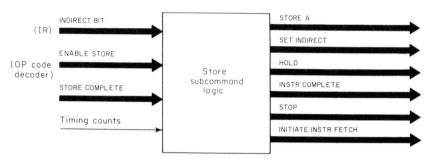

FIG. 10·22 Subcommand logic. STORE instruction indirect addressing.

the second IA data word may be loaded into the MCR. The indirect bit is now a binary 0 which indicates to memory controls that the address in the MCR is the address of the data word to be loaded into the A register. The third and final fetch (in this example) is initiated by the memory controls after the address from the MCR has been loaded into the address register by the LOAD INDIR command. When the fetch of the location defined by the address register, address B, is completed, the command FETCH COMPL is given to the subcommand logic. The subcommand logic then loads the A register with the contents of the MCR.

Store operations may also be made using indirect addressing. The instruction format is similar to the format defined for the FETCH A instruction. The address would contain the indirect bit. The meaning of the indirect bit within the address stays unchanged. The address within the address field is the address of the IA data word whenever the indirect bit is a binary 1. The address, it should be noted, does not define the store location when indirect addressing is in effect. A store operation using the condition shown in Fig. 10·20 proceeds as follows. The subcommand logic executing the STORE instruction would simultaneously give the commands STORE A and SET INDIRECT. (It should be noted that the controls required for indirect addressing were not shown on Fig. 10·15. The subcommand logic for the STORE instruction is added in Fig. 10·22.) Note the addition of the IR and SET INDIRECT levels.

The SET INDIRECT command is given whenever the indirect bit from the IR is a binary 1. The memory controls would initiate a fetch operation. The fetch of the indirect address words is accomplished by the regular memory fetch sequence. The difference in operation occurs when the final level of indirect addressing is reached. When the IA data word which contains address B is within the MCR, the memory controls again check the indirect bit. The binary 0 informs the controls that the address within the MCR is the address for the store operation. The memory controls load address B from the MCR into the address register with the LOAD INDIR command, and the LOAD (STORE) command is given to load the contents of the A register into the MCR. A store cycle is initiated on the location defined by the address register which contains address B. After the store has been completed, the STORE COMPL command is given to the subcommand logic so that instruction processing may be resumed.

The interrupt control area of the computer normally checks for various error conditions such as arithmetic overflow, illegal operation codes, and parity errors. This capability is illustrated in Fig. 10·23. Each of these conditions is considered as a reason for the stopping of instruction execution. Even processors with elaborate interrupt systems respond to specific types of errors with a stop. It should be noted that there are errors which indicate further execution of the program as useless, since the results are invalid. The three error conditions mentioned are normally responded to by any computer. Arithmetic overflow indicates that the number to be stored in the accumulator is too large. Recall that the accumulator holds the results of computations and was assumed to be 48 bits within this chapter. Arithmetic overflow means that the result of the arithmetic operation is greater than can be indicated by 48 bits. Arithmetic overflow is not necessarily the same thing as adder overflow. For example, adder overflow in the execution of a SUBTRACT instruction may be required to accumulate the correct difference. Overflow in this case is not an error condition. However, adder overflow in the execution of an ADD instruction means arithmetic overflow because the accumulator capacity is inadequate to store the sum. Arithmetic overflow is considered a reason for terminating computer operations. The programmer has the responsibility of scaling the numbers involved so that arithmetic overflow will not occur. The overflow indication could also result from a malfunction within the computer. Additional information would be required to determine the exact cause of arithmetic overflow.

Parity errors indicate that an error has been detected in a data transfer. The error may have occurred in a character transfer from a peripheral device

FIG. 10·23 Functional block diagram of control unit (interrupts).

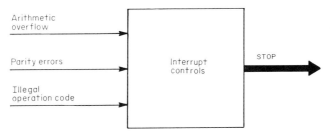

or in a word transfer with memory. In either case this type of error is sufficient reason to interrupt program execution, since this condition indicates
that information movement is no longer reliable.

Illegal operation codes refer to those configurations which are not used
to represent instructions. For example, if a six-bit operation code is used,
there are 64 unique configurations which can be used to identify instructions.
If the instruction set consists of 57 instructions, the seven configurations not
used are detected as illegal operation codes if they appear in the OP code of
the instruction word. Detection of an illegal operation code results in
termination, since it has not been defined as an instruction, and control
signals are not available for its execution. If any of these error conditions
were detected by the interrupt controls, the STOP command would be given
to the instruction processing controls (Fig. 10·10). STOP would cause the
timing counter to reset to its starting count (0). The computer stops with
the current instruction in the instruction register. Under certain conditions, a computer may not stop but initiate execution of specific interrupt
programs. These programs may be termed error recovery programs, and
the ability to respond to these error conditions is different for each computer.

The output block.   The output area provides the buffering and data transfer
paths to move information from memory to the peripheral devices. As in
the input operations, the output communications may be with any number
of peripheral devices which operate at different speeds. A computer which
requires data movement between itself and various output peripheral devices requires an output area which is capable of synchronizing its transfer
rate to that of the peripheral device and providing buffering for data transfer
from memory. The direction of data movement distinguishes the output
from the input area.

The output area must be capable of transferring characters to the
peripheral device at the required transfer rate of the peripheral. For example, disks will accept data at a faster rate than tapes; tapes will accept
data at a faster rate than line printers. A line printer cannot accept data at
the faster transfer rate of the disk, nor could the disk accept data at the
slower transfer rate of the line printer. Therefore the output area, like the
input area, must be capable of synchronizing to the transfer rates of the respective peripheral devices. The output area must be capable of buffering
information from memory since information will be fetched from the
memory in the form of words. Information will be outputted to the peripheral device as characters. Memory transfers are always made at internal
computer speeds while the characters are made available for outputting to
the PD at its required transfer rate. This is the same technique which was
implemented within the input area. The transfer rate of the peripheral device should not exceed the transfer rate from memory. This could be

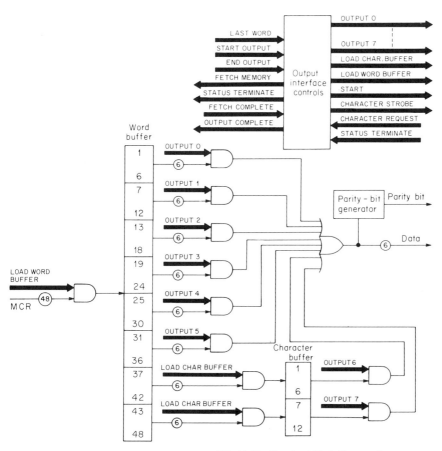

FIG. 10·24 Functional block diagram of output unit.

tolerated in some cases by additional buffering within the output area which effectively increases the transfer rate from memory so that there are always characters available for transfer to the peripheral device.

Figure 10·24 illustrates a typical output area. It consists of a word buffer, a character buffer, and output interface controls. The word buffer provides storage for data words received from memory via the memory communications register (MCR). The contents of the MCR are loaded into the word buffer by the command LOAD WORD BUF. The word buffer acts as source of characters for outputting to the peripheral device. The six-bit data character transmitted to the peripheral device is determined by the output controls (output 0–7). The first six characters (0–5) are taken directly from the word buffer. Characters 7 and 8 are taken from the character buffer (char buffer). The character buffer has been shown to illustrate how additional buffering can be used to increase the memory transfer rate for operation with higher-speed peripheral devices. The character buffer is utilized in the following manner. When character 6 is being outputted, the character buffer is loaded with characters 7 and 8. The word buffer is made available for loading from memory while the last two characters are being outputted. The output interface controls request a fetch operation of the memory controls. The output area has provided a two-character buffer time for the memory to complete the word transfer. In this case, the memory transfer rate could be only one-half as fast as the transfer rate of the peripheral device, and the memory would still provide information fast enough to allow the output operation at the speed of the PD.

The data character transferred to the peripheral device is always accompanied by a parity bit. The parity bit makes the seven-bit transfer an odd number of binary 1's. The parity generator develops the required parity bit to be transferred with the data character.

The output interface controls develop all the required commands for operation with the peripheral device. It is the source of the START and CHARACTER STROBE commands to the PD. The START signal initiates the operation with the PD. START is generated as a result of the command START OUTPUT. The subcommand logic executing the output instruction generates this command to initiate the operation. The START signal will not only initiate the operation but allow it to continue for as long as it is "true." The START signal going "false" informs the peripheral device that the required operation has been completed. A CHARACTER REQUEST from the PD indicates when it requires a character to be transferred. A CHARACTER STROBE from the output interface controls indicates when the character and parity bit are available on the output lines to the peripheral device.

The interaction of these commands is as follows. The PD requests a character, the strobe indicates when the character is available for the PD. This sequence is continued until the operation is completed or until the output area has no characters to transfer. If the memory transfer of the next word to the word buffer has not been made, the CHARACTER STROBE is not developed to allow a request of a character from this word. (The data character is not available for transfer.) In this event the PD could initiate its STATUS TERMINATE signal to request termination of the operation because the strobe was not developed (it remained "false"). The STATUS TERMINATE signal also allows the PD to request termination for various malfunctions which are detected local to the PD.

The OUTPUT (0–7) commands are used to select the characters for transmission to the PD. After each character transmission the OUTPUT command is changed for the next character transmission. The commands cycle 0–7 continuously. The LOAD CHAR BUF command allows the loading of the character buffer with characters 7 and 8. The LOAD WORD BUF command allows the loading of the word buffer with the word from memory (via the MCR). The LAST WORD command allows the output interface controls to terminate the operation after the last character has been sent to the PD. This command is developed by the subcommand logic which is executing the output instruction. However, the output interface controls perform the termination after the last character of the last word has been transmitted to the PD from the output area. The output interface controls, in turn, inform the subcommand logic that the final character has been transferred by the generation of the OUTPUT COMPL command. This interface is necessary in order to resume instruction processing within the computer. The END OUTPUT command from the subcommand logic is used to cause the START line to go "false" for a termination requested by the PD. The FETCH COMPL command from the memory controls allows the output interface controls to load the word buffer with the next word from memory.

A typical output operation proceeds as follows. The subcommand logic executing the output instruction generates the START OUTPUT command and the output interface controls generate the START command to the peripheral device. The interface controls request a fetch of the first data word from memory with the command FETCH MEMORY. The memory controls initiate a fetch operation on the location defined within the address register.

The peripheral device generates the CHARACTER REQUEST for the first character when it is ready. However, the first character cannot be transferred until the word buffer is loaded with the first word. The PD waits until the first character is available for transfer. The start of an output operation is the only time that the peripheral device will wait for the character. When the MCR is loaded, the memory controls send the FETCH COMPL command to the output interface controls. The interface controls load the first word into the word buffer with the LOAD WORD BUF command and the OUTPUT 0 command enables character 1 on the data lines to the PD. (This is the first character to be transferred.) The OUTPUT 0 command has been "true" since the START OUTPUT command was given to the controls. The first character and parity bit are available on the data lines to the PD when the CHARACTER STROBE command is generated. The PD causes the CHARACTER REQUEST signal to go "false" after the first character and parity bit have been transferred. The output interface controls then cause the CHARACTER STROBE to go "false" and the output commands to step to OUTPUT 1. The output area then awaits the CHARACTER REQUEST from the PD for the second character. OUTPUT 1 "true" enables character 2 on the data lines. The data lines, however, will not be monitored by the PD until the CHARACTER STROBE is "true." Since the output area synchronizes to the PD, nothing will occur until the second CHARACTER REQUEST is made.

When the PD generates the second CHARACTER REQUEST, the output interface controls reply with the CHARACTER STROBE. The second character and parity bit are on the data lines. The PD causes the CHARACTER REQUEST to go "false" after the second character and parity bit have been transferred. The CHARACTER STROBE goes "false," and the output commands step to OUTPUT 2. Character 3 will be the third character to be transferred. Again the output area goes idle until the character request is made.

This sequence remains unchanged until the sixth character (output 5) is to be transmitted. When the character request is made, the CHARACTER STROBE is generated to transfer the sixth character and parity bit. The LOAD CHAR BUF command is generated, and the seventh and eighth characters are loaded into the character buffer. A fetch request is made of the memory controls by the FETCH MEMORY command since the word buffer is available for loading with the next word (the second at this time). When the PD causes the CHARACTER REQUEST to go "false," the CHARACTER STROBE (as before) will go "false," and the output commands step to OUTPUT 6. The source for the final two characters for transmission is now the character buffer.

The sequence remains unchanged for the transmission of the final two characters from the character buffer. After the eighth character has been transferred, the OUTPUT 0 signal will be "true," which indicates that the word buffer must be loaded for the next character transfer to be made. If the word buffer has not been loaded, the CHARACTER STROBE remains "false" when the next CHARACTER REQUEST is made. If the word buffer has been loaded, the operation proceeds as before. The CHARACTER REQUEST will be responded to with a CHARACTER STROBE because the first character of the next word and the parity bit are on the data lines.

The character transfers for every word follow the same sequence. The first change in the pattern occurs when the last word of the operation is detected by the subcommand logic. The LAST WORD command informs the output interface controls that this is the last word to be outputted to the PD. The character transfers will be made as previously explained. When character 6 is being requested by the PD, the interface controls load the character buffer, but a fetch request of the memory controls is not made. The FETCH MEMORY command will remain "false" because the output area does not require any more words from memory to perform the operation. After the transmission of the last character (CHARACTER REQUEST goes "false"), the START line will go "false" to the peripheral device. This terminates the operation with the peripheral device. The OUTPUT COMPL command will be given to the subcommand logic to inform it that the output operation has been completed. This will allow instruction processing to be resumed.

The peripheral device checks each seven-bit transfer for parity errors (even number of binary 1's). If a parity error is detected, the PD generates the command STATUS TERMINATE. The subcommand logic replies to this

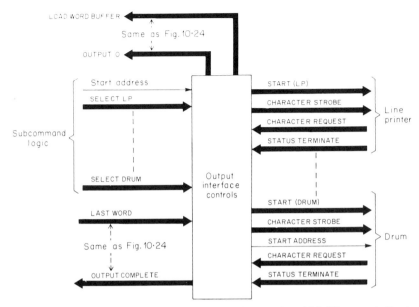

FIG. 10·25 Output unit (multiple PD communications).

request with the END OUTPUT command which terminates the operation (the START line will go "false").

The basic output area depicted in Fig. 10·24 would have to be slightly modified as in Fig. 10·25 to communicate with a number of peripheral devices. The data movement, however, would be unchanged. The output interface controls would be organized so that each peripheral device would have its own START line and CHARACTER STROBE. The subcommand logic would have to indicate with command signals which peripheral device was to be used (SELECT LP, SELECT DRUM, etc.). The output interface controls use only the CHARACTER REQUEST and STATUS TERMINATE signals from the PD being used. Since the drum is a possible output device, start address lines must be provided as part of the interface controls with the drum. Recall that a drum must be told the starting address of the operation.

The subcommand logic would supply the starting address to be outputted to the drum. The sequencing and use of the respective controls remains unchanged, and that operation takes place as previously explained.

SUMMARY

The basic computer may be divided into six functional areas: program, input, memory, arithmetic, controls, and output. These functional areas may be designated by other names, but they exist in all computing systems.

The program is not a hardware element but resides in the memory from where it is executed. The program is a sequence of instructions which tells the computer the type and order of the various operations which it must perform.

The input area provides for buffering and interface between the computer and the input peripheral devices. Its function is to bridge the timing differences which exist internally in the computer with the various timing sequences associated with the input devices.

The memory provides storage for program and data. It is a high-speed device which allows for rapid data and instruction movement within the computer.

The arithmetic section provides the work area within which the computations take place and, generally speaking, where the program is executed.

The control area provides all the timing and interface to coordinate the operations among the various elements of the computer.

The output area provides interface and buffering between the computer and its output peripheral devices. Like the input area, it bridges the timing differences between the internal computer and its external peripheral devices.

QUESTIONS

10·1   Draw a block diagram of a basic computer.

10·2   What is a program? How may it be divided?

10·3   What form must the program take in order to be executed by the computer?

10·4   Define operational instructions, movement instructions, and decision instructions.

10·5   What is data? An operand?

10·6   What functions are performed by the input area?

10·7   Is it possible for the computer to communicate with a device that is faster than the computer? Explain.

10·8   List the major areas which exist in the input unit and briefly describe their function.

10·9   What signal initiates and terminates the operation with the peripheral device?

10·10   What functions are provided by the CHARACTER STROBE and CHARACTER REQUEST signals?

10·11   When does the STORE MEMORY signal go "true"?

10·12   What does the signal STORE COMPL indicate?

10·13   List the major subdivisions of the arithmetic unit and briefly describe their function.

10·14   Can integer operations be performed by a fixed-point fractional machine? Explain.

10·15   For a MULTIPLY operation, what indicates that an addition should be performed?

10·16   Define the term "double-precision product."

10·17   How is subtraction performed in a machine that is mechanized with adders?

10·18   What are the two basic memory operations?

10·19   Name two methods of address modification.

10·20   When indirect addressing, what indicates that the final-level address has been reached?

10·21   Name the various types of shifts.

10·22   Name three computer interrupt conditions.

10·23   What type of instruction can cause an instruction execution sequence change?

10·24   What functions must the control area be capable of performing?

10·25   What type of information is specified in an instruction word?

10·26   What purpose does the variant portion of the instruction word serve?

10·27   What is the advantage of an advance instruction fetch while the previous instruction is in its execution phase?

10·28   When will the signal EXECUTE (in control area) be generated?

10·29   What indicates that the instruction register (control area) is available for loading?

10·30   When is the next instruction in sequence not executed?

10·31   What is the purpose of the two-character buffer in the output area? When is it loaded?

10·32   In what phase of an output operation will a peripheral device (PD) wait for a character without sending STATUS TERMINATE?

10·33   How does the drum output interface differ from other devices?

chapter eleven

Computer Memory Systems

The purpose of the memory system in a digital computer is twofold: (1) to provide adequate storage for all data and instructions necessary for the solution of a given problem and (2) to make this information available when needed by the data processing units. To accomplish this, the memory system must include at least two basic elements: a storage unit, or memory, to hold the data to be processed and a selection mechanism to gain access to each memory location within the storage unit. Memory systems differ chiefly in the number and type of basic elements used.

The most important characteristics of any memory system are access speed and storage capacity. These characteristics are governed primarily by the type of storage unit employed in the system. The ideal storage unit would have a large storage capacity, adequate, for example, to store the complete accounting records of a large business organization. In addition, the unit would permit access to any one of its storage locations within a time interval measured in nanoseconds. A high access speed is necessary if maximum advantage is to be taken of the high-speed components located in other parts of the computer. Unfortunately, no single memory unit available today offers optimum characteristics with regard to both storage capacity and access speed. In general, a storage unit with a large capacity has an inherently long access time. For this reason, memory systems in most modern computers include several different types of storage units arranged in a system to facilitate maximum computing speed. Generally, a low-speed, high-capacity external memory is combined with a medium-speed, medium-capacity buffer memory and a high-speed, low-capacity main memory.

Optimum Memory System

One possible arrangement that could be used to achieve maximum computing speed when large quantities of data must be handled is shown in Fig. 11·1. In the system shown, a magnetic-tape unit is used for bulk storage of reference data. While this unit has a large storage capacity, it is difficult

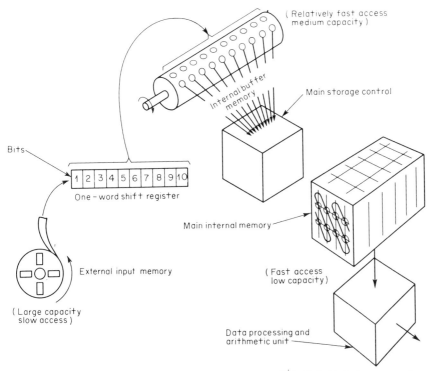

FIG. 11·1 Typical memory system.

to design tape transport mechanisms to provide rapid access to specific memory locations; for this reason, such units are seldom used as the main internal memory of the computer. In the system shown in Fig. 11·1, the main memory is a magnetic-core storage device characterized by its relatively high access speed. The memory unit allows the arithmetic unit in the computer to gain rapid access to any desired word in its storage locations, whenever the data is needed for computation. The magnetic-core memory, however, has a relatively low storage capacity and must be supplemented or "backed up" by a medium-speed, medium-capacity buffer memory. The buffer memory shown in the illustration is a rotating magnetic drum. The system operates as described in the following paragraphs.

All data and instructions necessary for the solution of a given problem are prerecorded on the tape as a series of coded words 10 digits in length. The information is stored on the tape in digit-serial, word-serial form (Fig. 11·2a). For illustration purposes, assume that 1 million 10-digit words are stored on the tape. (This is well within the storage capacity of a 2400-ft reel.) Assume further that the storage capacity of the main core memory is 100 words and the capacity of the magnetic drum is 1000 words.

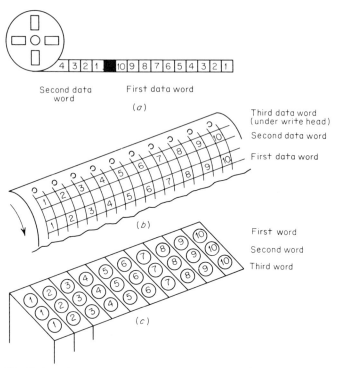

Second data   First data word
word
(a)

Third data word
(under write head)
Second data word
First data word

(b)

First word
Second word
Third word

(c)

FIG. 11·2 Modes of storage. (a) Tape storage: digit-serial, word-serial; (b) drum storage: digit-parallel, word-serial; (c) magnetic-core storage: digit-parallel, word-serial.

Before computation can begin, the main memory must contain 100 words. These words are delivered from the tape to the main memory by way of the one-word shift register and the rotating drum of buffer memory.

The digits of each data word are shifted into the shift register from the tape unit in serial form (one digit at a time). When one complete word is contained in the shift register, it is transferred in parallel to the first memory location on the rotating drum (Fig. 11·2b). Words are continually transferred in this manner until all the data on the tape has been processed. Although the drum rotates at a faster speed than the tape, timing pulses from the computer's control circuits ensure that words from the tape are transferred to sequential locations on the drum.

When the one hundred and first word is transferred to the drum, the first word previously transferred to the drum is delivered from the drum to the main memory. In the system shown, the words are delivered to the main memory in blocks of 100 words. The transfer in this case is at a much faster rate than the transfer from the tape to the drum, and the information is transferred in digit-parallel, word-serial form (Fig. 11·2c).

When the first 100 words have been delivered to the main memory, inhibiting circuits in the storage control unit prevent further transfers until after the arithmetic unit has processed the first 100 words. At that time a second block of 100 words is transferred from the drum to the main memory cores for processing.

A system employing a buffer memory greatly increases the speed of processing when large quantities of data are involved. The buffer acts as a reservoir and ensures that words flow from the tape continuously, even during the processing of data by the arithmetic unit.

Most modern memory systems employ some combination of magnetic-tape, magnetic-drum, and magnetic-core storage units. Before discussing specific storage units, some important properties of storage units in general are discussed.

Important Characteristics of Storage Units

The capacity of a storage unit can be expressed in terms of the maximum number of bits, characters, or words that may be stored within the medium.

Storage units of small capacity, such as flip-flop storage registers, are usually rated according to their bit capacity. For example, a storage register with 36 flip-flops is capable of storing 36 single binary digits and is, therefore, said to have a capacity of 36 bits.

When the storage capacity of larger memory devices such as magnetic tapes and drums is described, the character or word capacity, rather than the bit capacity, is given. In such cases the number of bits in a character or the number of bits in a word must be stated if a comparison is to be made between storage media of different types.

Typical storage characteristics of commonly used storage units are listed in Table 11·1. The storage capacity of each unit is stated in characters. To determine the bit capacity, multiply the figures given by 6.

Modes of access. The bits of information stored in a memory unit are combined to form words of a specific bit length. Each word contains the same number of bits and is assigned a location number within the storage unit which is known as its address. The mode of access refers to the method used in the memory system to gain access to these storage locations, or addresses. The mode of access of the memory system is determined by the address-selection mechanism employed with the memory unit. The mode of access may be either random or sequential.

Random access refers to the ability of the memory system to provide immediate access to any memory location without regard to its physical position relative to other locations in the storage unit. In the random-access mode of operation, any memory location can be addressed in the same amount of time as any other location. Magnetic-core and thin-film memories are usually operated in the random-access mode.

Sequential access indicates a one-after-the-other process. Memory locations on magnetic-tape units are usually addressed in this manner. Operation is as follows. Each memory location passes the read and write heads in turn, but information is read out only when the proper address has been reached in the progression. This can be a relatively short period of time if the information required is near the previous address, but can be extremely long if the next location addressed is at the other end of a 3600-ft reel of magnetic tape.

Sequential-access systems can be further classified into two groups, cyclic and progressive.

The cyclic mode of access is a sequential mode in which each memory location is available for selection at periodic intervals. Examples of this type of access include magnetic drums, tape loops, and delay lines.

The progressive mode of access, like the cyclic mode, is sequential in nature. But, where the cyclic system implies constant movement in one direction to get the periodic return of a piece of information, the progressive system is usually associated with stops and starts and is thus a bidirectional device. Examples of progressive access are magnetic tape (in reels), punched cards, and punched tape.

Table 11·1 shows the differences among the various memory media.

Access time. A discussion of the modes of access naturally leads to the determination of access time. Access time is defined as the time interval between the instant information is requested and the instant it becomes available. It is this time interval which scientists are constantly trying to decrease to speed up the memory systems.

In memory systems using the random-access method, the time interval will be the same for the addressing of any location of the memory medium.

Sequential-access systems, however, will have a different access time for each piece of information from any given starting point. It is in this system that access time is given in maximum, minimum, and average times. The maximum access time is the longest amount of time required to obtain an item of information. As an example, in the magnetic drum the maximum access time is associated with that memory location which has just passed by the read heads and must make a complete revolution before again coming under the read heads. Minimum access time would be the shortest possible time needed to obtain the information. This can be seen in the magnetic drum as the next piece of information to pass under the read head. The average access time is the mean between the minimum and the maximum.

TABLE 11·1 Characteristics of Typical Memory Media

Storage device	Typical capacity, characters*	Access time*	Modes of access	Volatile	Permanence	Use
Thin-film spots	500,000	50-100 nsec	Random	No	Erasable	High-speed internal storage
Magnetic cores	10–100,000	1–10 μsec	Random	No	Erasable	High-speed internal storage
Magnetic drums	20–5,000,000	10–40 msec	Sequential and cyclic	No	Erasable	Medium-speed internal/external storage
Magnetic-tape reels	2–50,000,000†	1–300 sec	Sequential and progressive	No	Erasable	Slow-speed external storage
Integrated memory	1,000,000 bits/in.^{2}	100–500 nsec	Random	Yes	Erasable	High-speed internal storage
Magnetic disks	1–20,000,000	10–70 msec	Sequential and cyclic	No	Erasable	Medium-speed internal/external storage

*Times and storage are typical and are not intended to be minimum or maximum.

†Per reel.

Permanence. This characteristic specifies whether or not information in storage may be erased. A magnetic memory is erasable since any word can be changed or deleted without altering the memory medium. In a nonerasable memory the information cannot be altered without replacing the component used as a memory medium. Examples of nonerasable memories are punched cards and punched tape.

Volatility. If information in the memory system is lost when power is removed, the memory system is said to be volatile. A delay line is a volatile medium, and in order to retain the information it must be periodically rewritten. If a power loss should occur, the information would be lost. Any magnetized memory system is a nonvolatile memory in that it does not lose its information except by being demagnetized.

Cost. A very important factor to any consumer is the cost of a computer. The memory system and its associated circuitry is an expensive part of a computer. When costs of memory systems are being compared, the point of reference is the cost per character of information.

Physical considerations. Many physical characteristics are involved in choosing a memory system. Depending on the point of view, some may be very important while others will make no particular difference in the final selection. The physical considerations include bulk, air-conditioning requirements, and power consumption.

Main Memory

The discussion in this chapter is limited to those devices which are used as the internal or system main memory and will be referred to as memory. These include magnetic core and thin-film memories. Such other storage devices as magnetic tape, magnetic disk, and magnetic drum which provide auxiliary storage are discussed in Chap. 13.

The memory is used to store programs and to provide "scratch pad" storage for the data upon which the program performs its manipulations. The access time is a prime consideration since the memory speeds, to a

FIG. 11-3 Functional block of memory usage.

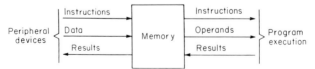

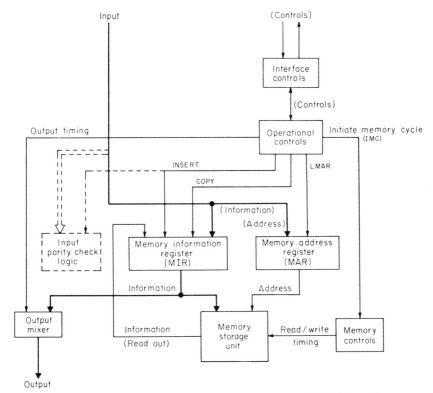

FIG. 11·4 Simplified block diagram of a memory.

degree, limit the overall speed with which the processing element can execute the program.

All programs and data moved into the computer from the peripheral devices are stored in the memory. The memory holds all programs to be executed, the data which is to be operated upon, and the intermediate results of computations. Data which is to be outputted to the peripheral devices is stored in the memory prior to output. The functional use of the memory is shown in Fig. 11·3.

The discussions of the memory systems assume that the reader has mastered the storage concepts of the magnetic cores and thin-film spots presented in Chap. 5.

Memory organization.   Figure 11·4 illustrates the basic organization which exists in a memory system. This organization is present in all memory systems although the terminology used in identifying the functions may be different from system to system. The reader is encouraged to refer to this

FIG. 11·5 Memory operations.

diagram and make comparisons between it and the mechanization shown for the magnetic core and thin-film memories which are to be discussed. The organization shown in Fig. 11·4 is capable of allowing the desired memory operations shown in Fig. 11·5 to take place. The memory must respond to requester STORE or WRITE commands. It must also respond to requester FETCH or READ commands. The sequence of memory operations is the same regardless of whether the information involved is data or program.

The memory contains a control area which performs all control interfacing between the requester and the memory. The requester may be, for example, the control area of the basic computer (Chap. 10), the I/O, or the processor modules of the modular processor (Chap. 12). Figure 11·6 represents a typical control interface which could be used with this memory.

The interface lines interpret the request as either a fetch request (FETCH REQ) or a store request (STORE REQ) which results in one or the other of the control signals being "true." In addition a STORE STROBE signal is used to indicate the time period during which the information to be stored is available on the input lines to memory. In a like manner, if the operation is a READ, a FETCH STROBE signal indicates to the requester the time interval during which the information is available on the output lines from memory. Interfacing controls may vary but the levels generated will always be provided to ensure proper information flow in memory communications.

The memory will use at least two storage registers. In the organization of Fig. 11·4 these registers are designated as the memory address register (MAR) and the memory information register (MIR). The MAR contains the address of the locations involved in the operation, fetch, or store and is supplied by the requester. The address is loaded into the MAR only upon the command of the operational controls to load the MAR (LMAR). The memory information register provides intermediate or temporary storage for information which is either fetched from or to be stored in the memory. Note that when information is to be stored, the MIR is loaded with input

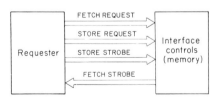

FIG. 11·6 Memory control interface.

information under the operational controls command of insert. If a fetch operation is to be performed, the operational controls, through the copy command, allow the MIR to be loaded with the information read out of memory.

The COPY and INSERT commands determine the information source for MIR loading. Only one of these signals will be generated for each memory operation. During a fetch operation, the MIR serves two functions: It provides the fetched data for transfer to the requester via the output mixer and it provides the information for rewrite into the just-read address so that the information is retained in storage. This rewrite is necessary since the read from core or thin film is a destructive readout.

The operational controls respond to the interface controls' interpretation of requester requirements. In turn, the operational controls initiate and coordinate the timing and gating signals necessary for memory operation. The control signals for MIR and MAR loading are generated and utilized as discussed above. The timing for output gating of information to the requester and the initiation of the memory cycle (IMC) are also generated.

The memory storage unit is the memory. It will consist of either core or thin-film elements. For the present discussion it will be considered a unit which information may be placed into or extracted from. (The operation of reading or writing into core or thin-film spots is discussed in Chap. 5.)

The memory controls generate the timing necessary for the actual read/write operation within the storage unit. The thin-film and core memories both use a full cycle which consists of a read operation followed by a write operation, as shown in Fig. 11·7.

The read cycle refers to the time interval and operations required to remove information from the addressed location in memory and place it into the MIR. The write cycle refers to the time interval and operations required to insert the information contained in the MIR into the designated address in the storage element. MIR content will, of course, depend upon whether the write cycle is initiated to rewrite information or to store new information in the memory.

A variation of a full-cycle memory is a memory which requires only a read or a write cycle. This is referred to as a split-cycle memory. The more commonly used memories use the full-cycle operation; therefore, the functional and operational considerations presented will refer to the full-cycle memories.

FIG. 11·7 Full memory cycle.

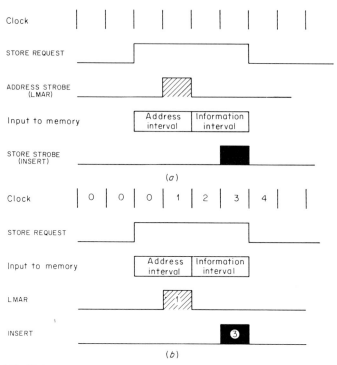

FIG. 11·8 Memory store operations. (a) Requester control of store; (b) memory control of store.

The output mixer gates the MIR information to the requester. This gating is under command of the operational controls.

Refer to Fig. 11·4 and note the sequence of events, movement of data, and interfaces which exist among the major sections of the memory system.

The store operation is performed in the following manner. A store operation from a requester is interpreted by the interface control, which results in the activation of the operational controls for a store. The address into which the information is to be stored appears on the input line from the requester. The period during which the input lines contain the address may be indicated by the interface controls, or internal memory timing may specify the period of availability. Figure 11·8a illustrates the timing sequence for interface control of timing, while Fig. 11·8b illustrates internally generated timing within the operational controls. In Fig. 11·8a, the address strobe is used to identify the address interval. It is sent to the operational controls from the requester via the interface controls for the generation of LMAR. Figure 11·8b illustrates how internally generated timing in the operational controls might be used to designate the address interval. The STORE REQUEST signal could be used to initiate the cycling of a timing

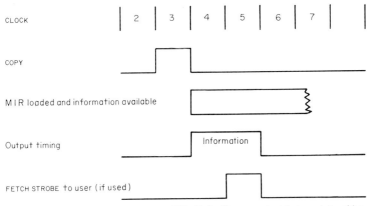

FIG. 11·9 Memory output timing relationships.

counter. At a count of 1, LMAR is generated. In either case, the generation of LMAR results in the loading of the designated address for the store operation into the MAR.

After the address has been specified, the IMC command is used to activate the read/write cycle on that location in memory. The information to be stored is present on the input lines. The information content of the memory location is being read. Since a store operation has been called for, the operational controls generate the STORE STROBE, which gates the information on the input lines into the MIR.

Since COPY is not generated at this time, the information read from the memory is not to be stored and is, therefore, lost. The specified location is now clear to receive and record information on the write cycle. Figure 11·8 illustrates the two possible timing sequences for the operation. The memory cycle continues, with the write portion of the cycle causing the MIR content to be reproduced in storage.

A fetch operation is performed as follows. The fetch operation from a requester is interpreted by the interface controls which activate the fetch operational controls. The address for the operation is provided on the input lines, as before, by the requester. LMAR causes the MAR to be loaded and IMC initiates the read/write cycle. The information readout from the designated location is gated into the MIR by the COPY command from the operational controls. After the MIR is loaded, the output mixer is enabled, making the information available to the requester. At the same time, the information is available for rewrite into the addressed memory location. In some memories a FETCH STROBE is transmitted to the requester via the operational and interface controls to indicate information availability from memory. Timing for this type of operation is illustrated in Fig. 11·9. An arbitrary timing has been assumed for convenience. The COPY signal is de-

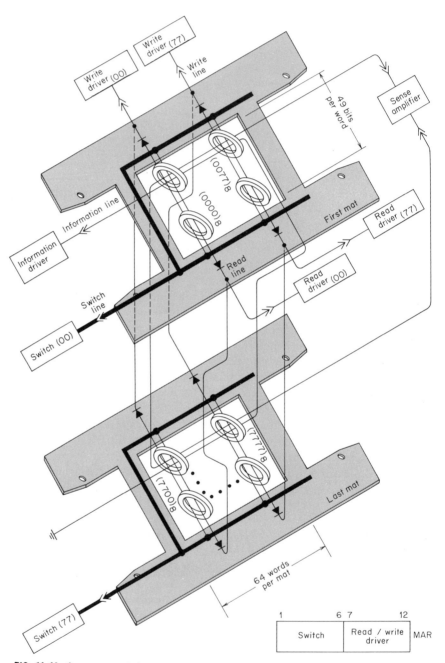

FIG. 11·10 Core memory stack.

veloped at *T*3, and the MIR is loaded at *T*4 time. MIR contains the requested data until the MIR is reset. Output timing generated makes the information available during timing periods 4 and 5. If a FETCH STROBE is used, it is usually positioned in respect to information availability as shown. Thus the information contained in a specific memory location has been made available to a requester and rewritten in the same location for future use.

Note the similarity of memory operation for the fetch and store operations.

Core Memory Storage Unit

A representative core memory storage unit referred to as a *core memory stack* is illustrated in Fig. 11·10. It is capable of storing 4096 forty-nine-bit words. It consists of 64 memory planes (mats), each containing 64 forty-nine-bit words (64 × 64 = 4096 words). Each mat is identical in construction and operation. For ease of explanation only the first and last words of the top and bottom mats are shown. Note also that only cores 1 and 49 are shown for each word.

A word is selected by the address contained in the MAR (0–4095 locations). The addressing of the location is performed by a decode of two groups of six bits each of the MAR. As shown in Fig. 11·11, bits 1 through 6 are decoded to select a memory switch, while bits 7 through 12 are decoded to select both a read and a write driver.

The switch is used to provide a partial current path for any of the 64 words on a mat. There is one switch for each mat. The decode of bits 1 through 6 is used to select the mat on which the desired memory location is contained. The driver pair selected through the decode of bits 7 through 12 selects the position of the word on the mat and when activated, provides the second half of the current path for memory read/write operations. It should be noted that only 64 read and 64 write drivers are associated with this

FIG. 11·11 Memory address decoding.

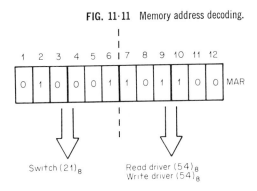

memory, one for each word location on a mat. The read/write drivers select the word position on the mat, the switch selects the mat on which the word is located. The read and write drivers, when activated, complete the current path as well as provide all or part of the current necessary for memory operations.

Word selection is accomplished as follows. Assume MAR content is 0000_8. The address decode results in the selection of switch 00_8 which provides a partial current path for any word on mat 1. The decode also selects driver pair 00_8. The result of MAR decode is that memory word 0000_8 has been selected and when memory cycling begins, the information content of this location will be read into the MIR. In a like manner an MAR content of 0077_8 would have resulted in the selection of the last word on the first mat. The decode of 7700_8 and 7777_8 would result in the selection of the words on the bottom mat, as illustrated in Fig. 11·10. The diodes in each line (read or write) are used for word isolation to ensure that the desired operation current is developed in only one word of the stack.

The remaining lines through the cores are sense and information lines and are bit-oriented. The sense line is used to detect information presence in a switching core during the read operation. It is threaded through the same bit position of every word within the stack. In this memory, 49 sense lines and sense amplifiers are required. The amplifier is used for signal amplification of the sensed data bit which is then passed to the MIR. Core switching upon readout results in a sensed 1, the absence of switching results in no signal or a 0 readout.

The information line, like the sense line, is threaded through the same bit position of every word within the stack. Forty-nine information drivers are required. The information line is connected to an information driver and is used to determine whether a 1 or a 0 is to be stored in a particular bit position during the store operation. It should be recalled that the MIR contains the information to be stored; hence, the information drivers are controlled by the MIR.

The memory presented is a full-cycle memory which means its cycle consists of both the read and write cycles. Assume an MAR content of 7777_8. The MAR decode for a read operation results in the selection of switch 77_8 and read driver 77_8. Under control of memory controls, the read driver is turned on and a read current of sufficient magnitude, duration, and direction to accomplish switching is passed through the selected word. Cores which were in the ONE state are switched to the ZERO state, causing induced voltages in the appropriate sense lines. These voltages are amplified, and the MIR is set to indicate ONE data bits in the proper positions. Memory content has been reproduced upon readout. It should be recalled that the readout is destructive and the information must be rewritten if it is to be retained in memory. Cores which are in the ZERO state at the time of read are unaffected by the switching read current. No output voltage is detected in the sense lines for these bits, and this condition is reflected in the MIR.

The write cycle begins at the completion of the read cycle. During the write cycle, the write driver 77_8 (in this example) is turned on. When it is turned on, it develops a current (write current) on the write line through word 7777_8. The write current is of the proper duration and direction to change any core within word 7777_8 to the ONE state; however, it is only two-thirds of the required magnitude. It alone is not capable of changing the cores to the ONE state. The information drivers are used to determine the digits to be stored within the word. The information drivers which require binary 1's to be stored in the cores of word 7777_8 will be turned on. The current through these cores is of the proper duration and direction to change them to the ONE state; however, it is only one-third of the required magnitude. The resultant effect at each core which is to contain a binary 1 will be a magnetic intensity (from the summation of the two-thirds and one-third currents) which will change it to the ONE state. The magnetic intensity at each core which is to contain a binary 0 will not be sufficient to change it to the ONE state because the information driver is turned off and does not provide the necessary additive current for switching. A binary 0 was established by the read line current during the read cycle, and the absence of information current through the core during the write cycle did not disturb this condition. The information drivers are turned on and turned off by the memory controls. This control is required to obtain the necessary coincidence in currents through the cores to store binary 1's. It should be noted that the information current, when on, is supplied to 4096 cores; however, its magnitude is not sufficient to cause a binary 1 to be stored in any core outside of the selected word. The basic timing relationships of the various currents considered are illustrated in Fig. 11·12. The sequence of events explained is the same for any operation (fetch or store) performed on any

FIG. 11·12 Current relationships in core memory.

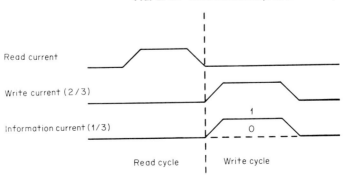

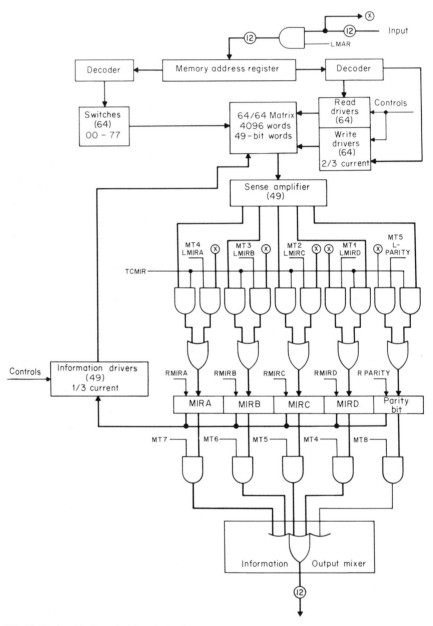

FIG. 11·13 Read/write and address logic of core memory.

location (word) within the stack. Note the coincidence of the write and information currents for the storing of a 1 and the absence of the information current for the storing of a 0.

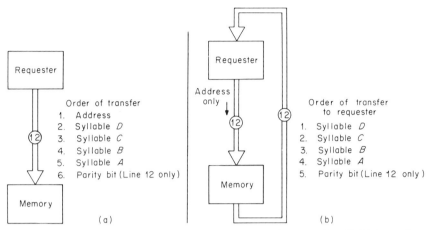

FIG. 11·14 Data flow for memory operations. (a) Store operation; (b) fetch operation.

Figure 11·13 illustrates a more detailed logical breakdown of the read/write and address logic associated with a memory system. The transfer of the 49 bit words between the memory and requesters is performed in a serial-parallel fashion. Transfers consist of four consecutive 12-bit transfers (referred to as syllables A, B, C, and D) and a single parity bit transfer. The 12-bit memory address is always transferred from the requester to identify the location in memory which is to be used in the operation. Gross data flow for the store and fetch operations for the memory of Fig. 11·13 are shown in Fig. 11·14.

On a store operation, the first 12 bits transferred from the requester are the address which is loaded into the MAR by the command LMAR. Bits 7–12 of MAR are decoded for read/write driver selection, and bits 1–6 for switch selection. During the period of address loading and decoding, MIR is reset by the RMIR-RPARITY signals. Memory controls initiate the read current in the selected address with the sensed outputs passed to the sense amplifiers. Since this is a requested store operation, the information to be stored is not the information read from memory. TCMIR remains "false" at this time so that the sensed outputs are not passed to the MIR and are therefore lost. The selected memory location is cleared by the destructive readout of information. While this read operation is in progress, the LMIR signals are generated, allowing syllables D, C, B, A, and parity to be loaded. The timing sequence for this load is shown in Fig. 11·15. The selected information and write drivers are activated to cause the selected core switching for the storage of 1's in the desired bits. The MIR content is available at the output mixer, but it is not sensed by the requester since a store operation is involved.

The fetch operation is performed in a similar manner. The differences which exist are that when bit sensing on read-from-memory takes place,

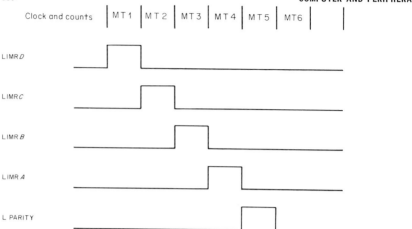

FIG. 11·15 Memory information input load timing.

TCMIR allows the data to be placed into the MIR. The information read is available to control the rewrite into memory as well as available to the output mixer for delivery to the requester. As shown in the timing of Fig. 11·16, the syllables are transferred to the requester. During this time period, rewrite into memory takes place.

The logical organization discussed is typical of that found in memory systems. Note the similarity in organization to the thin-film memory as it is examined.

FIG. 11·16 Memory information output timing.

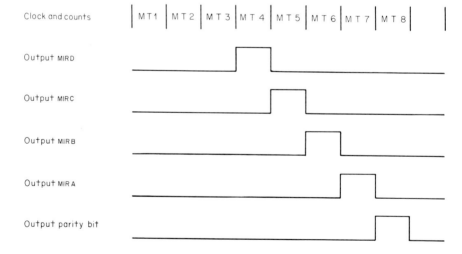

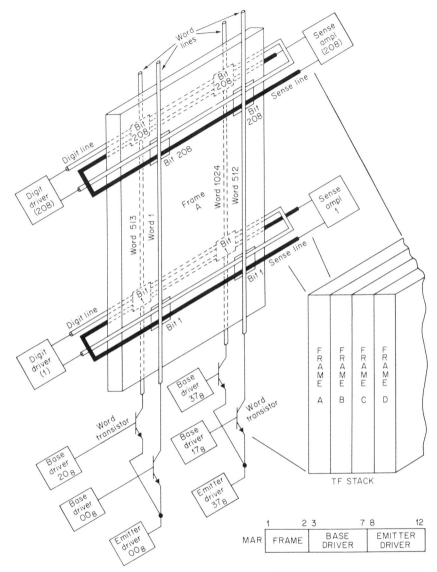

FIG. 11·17   Thin-film memory stack.

Thin-film Memory Storage Unit

The thin-film storage unit, referred to as a thin-film stack, is illustrated in Fig. 11·17 and is capable of storing 4096 (0–4095 address locations) 208-bit words. It is constructed of four frames, each capable of storing 1024

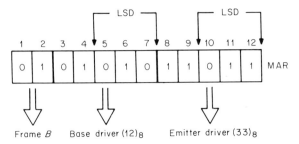

FIG. 11·18 Thin-film address decoding.

(0–1023) 208-bit words. Since each frame is identical, one frame has been separated from the stack and expanded for explanation purposes.

It would be useful at this point for the reader to review the action of the thin-film spot as a storage element (Chap. 5).

Each side of the frame is fabricated with a storage capacity of five hundred and twelve 208-bit words. Figure 11·17 illustrates the bit 1 and bit 208 of the first and last words on each side of the frame. Each word is identified with a word line which is associated with the 208 thin-film spots (bits) of each address.

Word selection (address) is determined by a decode of the contents of the MAR. As shown in Fig. 11·18, the MAR is decoded to select a frame (2 bits), a base driver (5 bits), and an emitter driver (5 bits). The base driver selected is used to divide the 1024 words into 32 groups of 32 words. The emitter driver is used to identify the word within the group (this is a 32×32 matrix). The selection of a base driver and emitter driver will allow the turn-on of only one word transistor. The word transistor is used to provide a current path through the word via the word line. Assume that the address 0000_8 had been loaded into the MAR. Bits 1 and 2 of the MAR indicate that the required word is on frame A. Base and emitter drivers 00_8 are selected from the respective decodes of the content of the MAR. This combination of base and emitter drivers allows the turn-on of the word transistor which provides the current path through word line 1 only. (The current in all other word lines is 0.) If the MAR were loaded with 1000_8 as the address, the drivers selected for frame A would be base driver 20_8 and emitter driver 00_8. In this case the word of the group is the same (emitter driver 00) but the group has changed (base driver 20). The two drivers together cause the turn-on of the word transistor which provides the current (word current) through word line 513 (word 513). Word current through word 1024 would require the selection of base and emitter drivers 37_8 and an address of 1777_8 within the MAR. The decoding technique employed may be summarized as follows:

1. Bits 1 and 2 of the MAR select one of four frames.
2. Bits 3–12 are used to select one of 32 base drivers and one of 32 emitter drivers which together allow the selection of one word on the frame (a 32 × 32 matrix).

The remaining lines through the words are bit-oriented. They consist of a sense line and a digit line. The sense line is provided to sense the rotation of the magnetic field of the TF spot (sense the binary digit stored). It is laid across the same bit position of every word on the frame (both sides). Two hundred and eight sense lines are required to sense the binary digits stored within any word of the frame. A sense amplifier is connected to each sense line for amplification of the digit sensed. If the digit sensed is a binary 1, a directional output current is generated; if the digit sensed is a binary 0, an opposite direction output current is sensed. The 208 sense amplifiers provide the information readouts for the MIR. The digit line is provided to store the digit in the TF spot. The digit line, like the sense line, is laid across the same bit position of every word of the frame (both sides). Two hundred and eight digit lines are required to store the binary digits within any word of the frame. A digit driver is connected to each digit line. The digit driver is used to control digit storage within the TF spot by developing the required current direction in the digit line. The 208 digit drivers are controlled by the content of the MIR as the information source for storage.

Note the similarity of functional operation within the thin-film and core memories. The MAR decoding provides the locations (address) of the word involved in the memory operation. The base and emitter drivers allow digit read in a single word to occur via the word line (switch and read/write drivers with switch line in core). The MIR is used to accept data on readout and provide the information for the store operation in both memories. The sense lines perform the same function in both memories. The information and write drivers of the core stack are replaced by the digit driver of the thin-film stack. In the core stack, information is sensed on readout of a 1; the lack of a 1 in a bit position results in no output. In the thin-film stack 1's and 0's are sensed as opposite-direction currents.

The operation of the thin-film memory is also divided into two cycles, read and write. The respective cycles are performed in the following manner on word location 512 (address 511). Base driver 17_8 and emitter driver 37_8 are enabled by the respective decodes of MAR 3–7 and MAR 8–12. Both circuits are turned on and off by the memory controls. When both drivers (base and emitter) are turned on in coincidence, word current is developed in word 512 via the word transistor. This current is of the proper magnitude and direction to rotate the magnetic fields of all the TF spots of the word into their "hard" direction. A current is induced into each sense line by the direction of rotation of the magnetic field, and current polarity (direction) indicates the original "easy" state of the TF spot (the binary digit stored). The sense amplifiers detect and amplify the sense line currents and load the MIR with the fetched information. This sequence is referred to as the *read cycle* operation of the TF memory. The digit drivers are then turned on by the memory controls to store the binary digits within the word. The digit drivers produce a current which is of the proper magnitude and direction to tip the magnetic field of the TF spot in the required "easy" direction (for storing a binary 1 or 0). If the digit to be stored is a 1, the current flow is in one direction (plus), while if the digit to be stored is a 0, the current is in the opposite direction (minus). The word current and digit line currents are then turned off, allowing the magnetic fields of the TF spots (word 512) to rotate to their required "easy" direction. The term used to describe the storing of the digits within the selected word of the TF memory is *write cycle*. The basic timing relationships of the currents considered is illustrated in Fig. 11·19.

The above sequence is the same for any operation (fetch or store) performed on any word location within the stack. Information is transferred in this system between the requester and memory in either of the following forms:

1. Single 52-bit word
2. Four 52-bit words

The thin-film stack is organized into 4096 two-hundred-and-eight-bit words; however, it is viewed by the requester in fetch or store operations as 16,384 fifty-two-bit words. The respective operations for either single-word or four-word movement are shown in Table 11·2.

The 208-bit TF word is divided into four 52-bit words in the following manner:

1. Bits 1–52, word A
2. Bits 53–104, word B
3. Bits 105–156, word C
4. Bits 157–208, word D

When a fetch or store operation is required of the memory, a four-word or single-word operation is specified by the requester. If the operation is a single word, the 52-bit word involved is indicated. The read cycle for either type of fetch operation causes the readout of four 52-bit words (208 bits), and they will be transferred to the MIR. In a single-word fetch only the 52-bit word required will be transferred to the requester, while a four-word fetch results in a serial-parallel transfer of four 52-bit words to the requester. The original 208 bits (four 52-bit words) are always rewritten into the TF stack during the write cycle of a fetch operation.

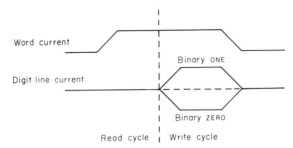

FIG. 11·19 Current relationships in thin-film memory.

The read cycle for either type of store operation will be used to sense the 208-bit TF word. The MIR is loaded with three 52-bit words from TF and a single word from the requester for a single-word store. Four 52-bit

TABLE 11·2 Single- or Four-word Memory Operations

		Fetch operation			*Store operation*
Single word	Read cycle	Sense four 52-bit words and transfer into the MIR	Single word	Read cycle	Sense four 52-bit words but only transfer three words to the MIR Load single 52-bit word into MIR from the user
	Write cycle	Copy (rewrite) four 52-bit words Output single 52-bit word to user		Write cycle	Copy (rewrite) three 52-bit words Insert new 52-bit word
Four word	Read cycle	Sense four 52-bit words and transfer into the MIR	Four word	Read cycle	Sense four 52-bit words but do not transfer any to MIR Load four 52-bit words into MIR from the user
	Write cycle	Copy (rewrite) four 52-bit words Output four 52-bit words to user		Write cycle	Insert four new 52-bit words

words from the requester are loaded into the MIR for the four-word store. The write cycle is always used to write 208 bits into the TF stack. In a single-word store, a write of 52 new bits and a rewrite of 156 bits (three 52-bit words) is involved. In a four-word store, a write of a new 208 bits (four 52-bit words) takes place.

The requester is required to transmit a memory control word (MCW) to the memory for each operation. For either type store operation (single or four word), the MCW precedes the transfer of information to the memory

FIG. 11·20 Information and control word movement in thin-film memory. (a) Single-word store; (b) four-word store; (c) single-word fetch; (d) four-word fetch.

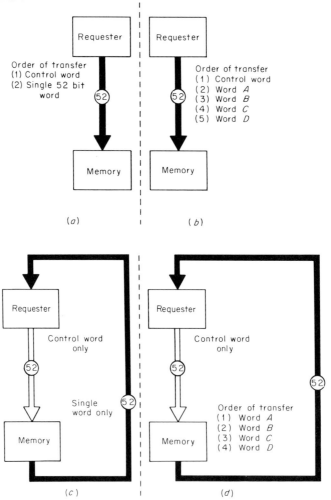

1	2	3	14 15	16 17		51 52
Fetch or store	Single or four word	Address	Word	Not used		P a r i t y

FIG. 11·21 Typical memory control word.

(Fig. 11·20a and b). The MCW is the only input transmitted to the memory by the requester for either type of fetch operation (Fig. 11·20c and d). The MCW is used to define the operation and address for the memory. See Fig. 11·21 for an example of an MCW.

Bits 1 and 2 of the MCW define the operation in the following manner (bit 2 is LSB):

1. 00 (single-word fetch)
2. 01 (four-word fetch)
3. 10 (single-word store)
4. 11 (four-word store)

Bits 3–14 specify the address of the 208-bit TF word and are loaded into the MAR for address decoding. Bits 15 and 16 define the 52-bit word for both single-word operations or the starting 52-bit word for both four-word operations. The configurations are decoded in the following manner by the operational controls of the memory (bit 16 is LSB):

1. 00 (word A)
2. 01 (word B)
3. 10 (word C)
4. 11 (word D)

Bits 17–51 are not used and contain binary 0's. Bit 52 is the parity bit of the MCW which allows checking of the information transfer from the requester.

The basic logical organization of the read/write and address logic used with this TF memory stack is shown in Fig. 11·22. The thin-film memory is organized into the MIR, TF stack, memory controls, and output mixer. The MIR is a 208-bit register which is organized into four 52-bit words (A, B, C, and D). The MIR is cleared at the beginning of each operation by the clear MIR command (CLMIR). Each word section may be loaded from either the TF stack or from the input lines (to the memory). The source of the load is dependent upon the command signal (COPY or INSER). The COPY command allows the 208 bits from the TF stack (sense amplifiers) to be loaded into the respective word portions of MIR. For example, COPY B will

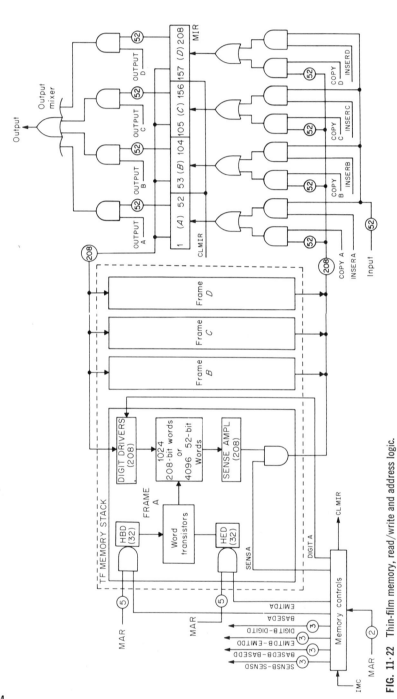

FIG. 11-22 Thin-film memory, read/write and address logic.

allow the load of word position B of the MIR from bits 53–104 of the TF stack. The insert (INSER) command allows the 52 or 208 bits transferred from the requester to be loaded into the respective word portions of the MIR. For example, INSERA allows the 52 bits received from the requester (via the input lines) to be loaded in word A of the MIR. The load commands are developed by the operational controls of the memory (refer to Fig. 11·4 as required) and are dependent on the operation specified within the MCW by the requester. The MIR content for the write operation may contain 208 bits of information read from the memory or 208 bits of information provided by a requester for a store or 156 bits of information read from memory and 52 bits provided by a requester for single-word store.

Refer to Fig. 11·22. The TF stack is fabricated as four frames. Each frame is a self-contained storage unit in that it contains the TF memory elements and all required circuits (drivers, sense amplifiers, digit drivers). Word selection is performed by turning on the required base and emitter drivers on the frame. The frame is selected by the signals EMITD, BASED. For example, if the desired word is on frame A, EMITDA and BASEDA will be "true." The respective decodes of the remaining MAR bits select the required base and emitter drivers on frame A. The base driver and emitter driver selected allow word current in the required word of frame A only. Readouts to the MIR may come from the 208 sense amplifiers on any of the four frames but only from one frame on a given operation. Each group of 208 bits is tied electrically in parallel to the MIR; however, only the readouts from the selected frame will act as the input stack source to the MIR. SENSA, for example, enables the readouts from the sense amplifiers on frame A to be transferred to the MIR. Information to be written is tied in parallel to the digit drivers of each frame from the MIR; however, only the selected frame will have its digit drivers enabled. DIGITA, for example, enables the 208 digit drivers on frame A to conduct. The controls for all frames are all developed by the memory controls.

Thin-film stack operation is initiated by the operational controls with the IMC command. MAR 1 and 2 indicate to the memory controls which frame is required. The memory controls develop the following commands:

1. SENSA–SENSD (sense A–D)
2. BASEDA–BASEDD (base driver A–D)
3. EMITDA–EMITDD (emitter driver A–D)
4. DIGITA–DIGITD (digit drivers A–D)
5. CLMIR

The sense signals (SENSA–SENSD) cause the readouts to be taken from the selected frame only. Only one sense command will be "true" at a time. BASED and EMITD enable the turn-on of word current only through the word

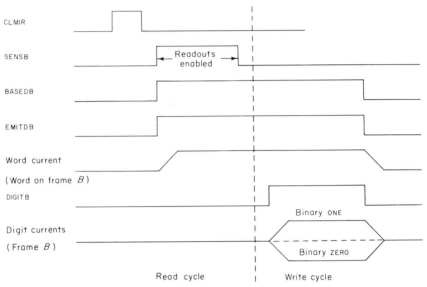

FIG. 11·23 Thin-film timing, frame B.

on the selected frame. DIGITD enables the turn-on of the digit drivers on the selected frame. The clear MIR command (CLMIR) is generated each time a new operation is begun (initiated by IMC). Figure 11·23 illustrates the timing relationships of the respective commands for selection of a 208-bit word on frame B.

The CLMIR command is developed and clears the MIR. BASEDB and EMITDB commands control the turn-on and turn-off of the selected drivers on frame B. Readouts are enabled from frame B during the read cycle by SENSB. In the write cycle the DIGITB command controls the turn-on and turn-off of the digit drivers of frame B. The timing relationships illustrated are the same for the selection of any word on any frame.

The output mixer is used to gate the output word or words to the re-quester. In a single-word fetch operation the operational controls gate the required 52-bit word to the requester. For example, if a single-word fetch is to be made of word D, the OUTPUT D command is the only command "true." This allows word D of the MIR to be gated through the output mixer.

If a four-word fetch operation is to be performed, the output commands cycle as illustrated in Fig. 11·24, allowing all four 52-bit words to be gated through the output mixer to the requester (starting word is word A).

Fetch operations (single or four-word) are performed in the following manner. The operational controls initiate the memory cycle with the IMC command. After the MCW is received, the memory controls generate CLMIR which clears the MIR. The memory controls then allow the turn-on of the word current through the selected address by enabling the drivers on the required frame (BASEDA–BASED, EMITDA–EMITDD). The SENSA–SENSD command allows the readouts from the selected 208-bit TF word to be transferred to the MIR. The operational controls generate all four copy commands simultaneously (COPYA–COPYD) and load the 208-bit readout into the MIR.

The digit drivers are turned on to allow a rewrite to be made on the selected TF word location. The digit drivers are controlled by the DIGITA–DIGITD command. The operational controls enable the output commands to allow the transfer of information to the requester. For a single-word fetch, the output command generated will gate the required 52-bit word through the output mixer. For example, if a single-word fetch of word *B* were requested, the OUTPUT B command would gate word B of the MIR through the output mixer. For four-word fetches, the output commands cycle as shown in Fig. 11·24, allowing the transmission of all four 52-bit words through the output mixer. The division of the content of the MIR as 52-bit words is performed by the operational controls when the gating of the requested words through the output mixer to the requester is accomplished.

Store operations (single or four-word) are performed in the following manner. The operational controls initiate the memory cycle with the IMC command after the MCW is received. The first command given by the memory controls is CLMIR. The memory controls then turn on the word current through the selected 208-bit TF word by enabling the drivers on the required frame. The sense command developed allows the readouts from the selected TF word to be transferred to the MIR. (Note that to this point the operation is identical with either fetch operation.) The operational controls load the MIR as directed by the MCW. If the operation

FIG. 11·24 Thin-film timing, output four-word fetch.

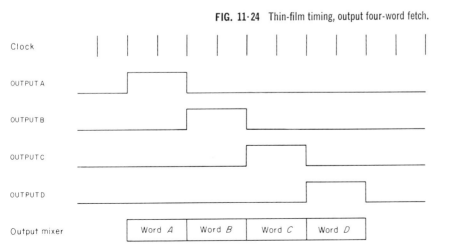

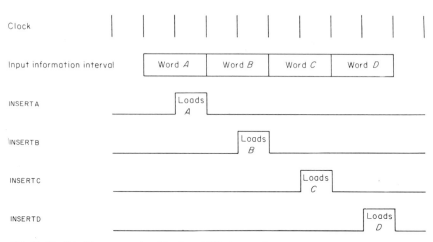

FIG. 11·25 Thin-film memory. Input loading of MIR, four-word store.

were a single-word store, the insert command developed would be used to gate an input 52-bit word into the required word position of the MIR; the copy signals would load the remaining word positions of the MIR from the TF readouts. For example, a single-word store of word C causes INSER C to load an input 52-bit word into the word-C position of the MIR. COPY A, B, D load the respective word positions of the MIR from the TF readout. For four-word store, all copy signals are inhibited, and the insert commands are cycled as illustrated in Fig. 11·25 to load the word positions of the MIR. During the write cycle the content of the MIR is written into the 208-bit TF word location. If the operation were a single-word store, the information written by the digit drivers would be one new 52-bit word and a rewrite of the three original 52-bit words. For a four-word store operation, the digit drivers write four new 52-bit words. The 52-bit division of the MIR is performed in the operational controls through the generation of the insert and copy commands as required.

Memory Growth

Continued development in internal memory systems seeks to achieve faster access time and larger bit densities for unit of space. Access times continue to decrease in present-day core and film memories.

Other techniques are under development for the production of memory systems. One such development is the plated-wire bit steering memory shown in Fig. 11·26. It consists of the conventional addressing, sensing, and associated circuitry but differs in the storage element itself.

Each storage element of the memory (bit position) occurs at the intersection of the copper strap and the plated wire. The plated wire is a copper beryllium wire which is electroplated with a Permalloy film. The word straps are used to define the words, and the bit lines define the number of bits per word. A digit is stored at each intersection of a strap and wire in the form of a directional magnetic field (one direction for a binary 1, the opposite for a 0). The digits are stored through the interaction of the strap current and bit line current. The strap current causes rotation of the magnetic field of the plated wire into its "hard" direction. The bit current, as determined by the bit driver, is used to direct the field toward either of its two rest positions. When the currents are removed, the magnetic field at the intersection moves to the directed rest position (for a binary 1 or 0). Sensing is accomplished by turning on the strap current through the required word, which produces a rotation of the magnetic field in the wires at each intersection. This produces a current whose polarity indicates the rest state (the digit stored) which is passed on to the sense amplifiers. This type of memory is considered capable of producing conventional-size memories of thousands of words at reasonable costs. The integrated circuit flip-flop and thin-film cryotron memories mentioned in Chap. 5 indicate other approaches being explored in the continued development of memory systems.

The memory system of a modern computer must be capable of storing vast quantities of data. In addition, to facilitate maximum computing speed, rapid access to each item of stored information is desirable. To meet these requirements, most memory systems employ two or more different types of storage units. Usually, a low-speed, high-capacity storage device is used as an external memory for bulk storage, and one or more high-speed, low-capacity memories are located internally to provide rapid access to stored information during data processing.

FIG. 11·26 Plated-wire bit steering memory.

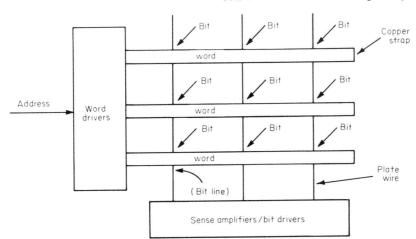

Many types of storage units using several different principles of storage are employed in modern computers. Devices utilizing magnetic principles, however, are most frequently used. Included in this category are magnetic-tape units, magnetic drums, magnetic disks, coincident-current magnetic-core arrays, and thin-film stacks. Tape units are used as external memories in cases where vast quantities of reference data are required. High-speed internal memory systems usually employ thin-film and ferrite-core arrays, used singly or in combination. These devices have a smaller storage capacity than tape units but provide much faster access to stored information.

Some of the factors that must be considered when selecting a storage unit for a given memory application are reviewed in the following list:

Storage capacity. Usually expressed in terms of the maximum number of characters or words that may be stored within the storage medium.

Mode of access. Refers to the method used to gain access to the storage locations or addresses of the storage unit. The mode of access may be either random or sequential.

Access time. The time interval between the instant information is requested and the instant it becomes available.

Permanence. Specifies whether or not information in storage may be erased.

Volatility. Specifies whether or not information is lost when power is removed.

Cost. Usually expressed in terms of cost per character of stored information.

Physical considerations. Bulk, air-conditioning requirements, and power consumption.

SUMMARY

The most commonly used internal memory systems are magnetic-core or thin-film stacks. These units offer rapid access, small physical size, and have relatively low power consumption characteristics.

The internal memory systems of a computer consist of the basic storage device (core or film spot), address and information registers, timing and control output gating, and interface logic with the requester. In addition, the necessary circuitry is provided to allow sensing and to provide the necessary drive currents for the read and write operations. These elements are organized to allow the read (fetch) of information or the write (store) of information within the memory. The address register indicates the particular word locations in memory involved in the operation. The information register receives the data readout of memory and is the information source of data to be returned to the memory. The output gating logic passes the information to the requester.

Information is stored as words which vary in length (number of bits) depending upon the processing system organization and requirements.

A "full memory" cycle is used in most internal memories and consists of a read followed by a write cycle. Readout is destructive, and the information must be rewritten if it is desired to retain the data. The timing for these operations is generated as a memory timing cycle which is coordinated with the operations external to the memory.

QUESTIONS

11·1 What are the two most important characteristics to be considered in the selection of a memory system?

11·2 What type of information is normally stored in the external memory of a computer? What type of information is stored in the internal memory?

11·3 Why do computers usually have an auxiliary memory?

11·4 How is storage capacity expressed? Explain.

11·5 List the different modes of access. Explain.

11·6 In a ferrite-core memory system, how is a 1 which is written into a selected core prevented from being written in the cores of adjacent planes in the same physical location?

11·7 State the purpose of each of the following elements in a memory system:
(a)   storage element
(b)   interface controls
(c)   memory controls
(d)   operational controls
(e)   memory information register
(f)   address register
(g)   output mixer

11·8 State the purpose of each of the following in a core-memory system:
(a)   read driver and line
(b)   write driver and line
(c)   switch and switch line
(d)   sense line and sense amplifier
(e)   information driver

11·9   In a core memory system, how is the required magnitude of current for switching achieved?

11·10   Draw a simplified block diagram of an internal memory system.

11·11   Describe the full-cycle operational sequence for a core memory read.

11·12   Discuss the operational differences for a store operation.

11·13   In the thin-film stack discussed, state the purpose of each of the following:

(a)   word line and word transistor
(b)   digit line and driver
(c)   emitter driver
(d)   base driver
(e)   sense line and amplifier

11·14   Discuss the thin-film stack operational cycle for a store-word-D operation.

11·15   In what way does the memory control word of thin film differ from the address transmitted to the memory address register of a core memory?

chapter twelve

Computer Organization

In Chap. 10 the basic functional areas of the computer were discussed, and a representative logical organization presented to illustrate how the required functions were performed. These basic functions are performed in all computers, but the manner in which the computer is organized to perform these functions has changed. This chapter is intended to show two stages of computer organization which have taken place in an attempt to optimize computer "production" or, rather, to increase throughput.

Because of the basic organization of the early computer, it could not easily adapt itself to the changing requirements of the user. Processing speeds were reduced because the computer was limited to the speed of the lowest-speed device with which it had to communicate. Even though the speeds of the peripheral devices were considered slow, communication with the human element (operator) further reduced operating speeds.

Program length was restricted by the limited memory size available. A program requiring more than the available memory space had to be performed in segments interleaved with input/output operations. These operations involved both slow I/O devices and operator intervention, which increased program execution time. The computer was not processing whenever input/output operations were in progress. It was a serially driven device — program in, execute, program out. As the volume of programs (work load) increased, the computer, although fast, eventually became a bottleneck. The processing rate was fixed. Although processing speeds continued to increase in later-model computers, replacement of older computers or multiple computer installations was costly, and the desired capability to meet an expanded future work load could not be achieved.

The need for a system which could be adapted to the changing needs of the user became apparent. The system required had to be characterized by the ability for efficient utilization under current and varied work loads and the ability to be adapted to the projected future processing needs of the user. This adaptability, of course, had to be achieved within realistic economic bounds. In the hardware area, this need is being met by the modularity concept which allows the addition of hardware elements to the system as required. Efficient computer utilization is achieved by the use of sophisticated programs which schedule the system work load (refer to Chap. 18). In addition, complete program rewrite or conversion is not necessary each time additional individual elements are added because of system expansion.

Modular processor organization. The modular processor system is a computing system which is organized into three basic hardware units (modules): a memory module, an input/output module (I/O), and a computer or central processor module (CPM). The number of each type of module in the processing system is tailored to meet the need of the individual user, and modules may be added to provide expanded system capability; however, there exist maximum system configurations. A minimum system consists of one memory module, one I/O, and one CPM. The maximum system might be defined as 16 memory modules, 10 I/O modules, and four CPMs. This range of system capability is different for each modular processing system, but it does indicate the growth capacity which modular systems exhibit.

This type of system may easily be expanded to meet increasing future needs of the user. In the modular organization, one significant advance is the ability of the system to perform computation and input/output operations simultaneously.

FIG. 12·1 Computer organization. (a) Block diagram of basic computer; (b) block diagram of modular processor; (c) modular processor organization 1.

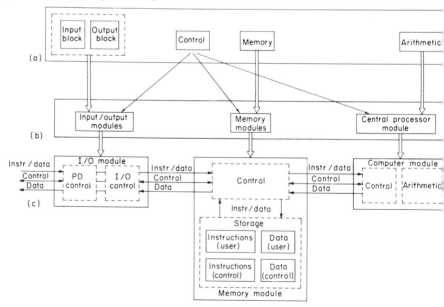

Figure 12·1 illustrates the reorganization of the basic computing system into a modular processing system. Figure 12·1a illustrates the five basic functional blocks (program is included as part of memory). Figure 12·1b shows the reorganization into the three modules of memory, I/O, and CPM. A further functional organization within each of the three modules is shown in Fig. 12·1c. Note that the control area has been decentralized, and each of the modules contains the function-related controls.

The logic and functional requirements of the input and output operations of the basic computer have been combined within the modular I/O unit. The frequency and level of inputting and outputting dictated by user requirements and programming determine the number of I/O units for the system configuration. Each I/O module is identical and is capable of communicating with any memory module, any CPM, or any peripheral device at the required speed or transfer rate.

Each I/O may be divided into two major areas, peripheral device (PD) control and input/output (I/O) control.

The PD control area of the I/O module controls information movement to and from any of the peripheral devices. It is capable of information transfer in either direction at the rate of the peripheral device. Each I/O is capable of information transfer with only one PD at any given instant.

The I/O control area is capable of communicating with any CPM in the system and of executing any input or output command. Control words which define the operation are transmitted from the memory to the I/O under CPM command. These control words are the operational link between the CPM and I/O. The control word specifies the operation, identifies the PD involved, establishes memory locations for fetching and storing, and indicates the quantity of information involved.

The I/O control area provides buffering between any of the I/O devices and the memory. It contains the necessary logic and storage for the information involved in the transfers.

The modular I/O concept provides flexibility of system operation by freeing the CPM from internal/external and external/internal data movements and allowing processing to continue during I/O operations. Simultaneous multiple I/O operations were made possible through the addition of I/O modules to the system.

The memory or storage function of the basic computer remains unchanged. It provides storage for program and data. The flexibility added through the modular memory concept allows the addition of modules to the system to meet expanding storage needs. The addition of these modules requires a minimum change in system programming.

The major advances in storage devices (memories) are centered about increases in operational speeds and higher packing densities of components which allow for greater storage capacities in smaller physical areas.

The memory module may be divided into two major areas, the control area and the storage area. The control area is responsible for interface or communication with the CPM and I/O modules. Since each memory module has communication with all CPMs and I/O modules, the control area is responsible for determining which module receives service first, should two modules request memory simultaneously. Service is granted on a priority basis in a specified order.

Within the storage area, controls exist which generate the necessary timing and commands for instruction and data fetch. These sequences are fully covered in Chap. 11.

The arithmetic and instruction execution functions of the basic computer have been mechanized into the central processor modules. This organization allows the use (or increase in number) of the required number of processor modules to meet users' needs.

The computer module is organized into two areas, control and arithmetic. The control area is responsible for all memory communications. This involves two-way movement of instructions and data between any memory module and any CPM. The control area also contains all the logic required to execute the instruction repertoire. An additional capability added to the control area allows the computer to respond to program interrupts. This capability allows suspension of a program already running to allow computer response to higher priority requests.

The arithmetic element of the CPM performs the same type of operations as the arithmetic section of the basic computer. Improvements in this area deal with increased speeds and packaging techniques. Packing densities of components were increased which allows the use of logical approaches requiring more logic to implement. The logic additions were possible, and in many cases a reduction in physical size of the unit was achieved. Chapter 9 provides a short history of the development of these packaging techniques.

The programs which control the processing system may be classed as control and object (user). The control program is used for efficient scheduling of the user programs and assignment of system elements. This scheduling allows multiple-user program execution simultaneously. The modular processor organization allows for this multiple processing capability. The control program, of course, is written to interleave user program execution. It schedules the users, handles all user I/O operations, allocates memory space, assigns systems elements, and is responsible for all related decisions involving the program queue. This scheduling occurs, of course, at internal processor speeds.

The control program handles all operations related to interrupts. It examines the interrupt condition and decides upon disposition of the interrupt. In some cases an immediate response is made, in others a delayed response, in others the condition is noted and may be indicated to the user at the time results are outputted.

The user programs consist of instructions and data required to perform the desired sequence or data manipulation operation. The user program is concerned primarily with sequence for problem solution, while the book-keeping and control functions for I/O operations, memory allocation, data movement etc., are taken over by the control programs.

Modular processor organization has resulted in increased system throughput and has been a big step in providing system flexibility and expansibility.

Modular processor organization, advanced. The basic organization in the second family of modular processors remains unchanged with the I/O, CPM, and memory as the three units from which the processing system is constructed. See Fig. 12·2. The functional capabilities of the units, however, have been greatly increased. The I/O was expanded and mechanized as a processor which allowed it to execute a program. Memory modules were capable of larger storage capacity and faster access times. The computer (central processor module) no longer had to execute the program related to input/output information movement. Additional flexibility in meeting user needs was achieved in that a processing system could consist of any combination of processor modules (CPM or I/O) which did not exceed 15. In this family of processors, the minimum system would again be one I/O module, one CPM, and one memory module. The maximum system could be 16 memory modules, and any combination (not exceeding 15) of CPMs and I/O modules. As may be seen from the discussion which follows, the combination possibilities provided could allow for heavy processing loads or increased speeds even in programs requiring many I/O operations for completion.

The I/O functions of the basic computer are still combined in the I/O processor module. The organization within the module changed with this family of I/O processors to include a data service unit, a communication unit, a local memory unit, and a processor unit.

The data service unit performs all communications with the peripheral devices. Each I/O processor module is capable of communication with every PD in the system. In this module, however, multiple simultaneous communications are possible with the peripheral devices. For example, one I/O processor module could communicate with 512 I/O devices at any given instant. The flexibility gained in I/O communications can be seen. As in other I/O areas, the communications with memory are at the internal timing rate, while outside communications are at the rates of the individual peripherals.

The communication unit is capable of interfacing with any of the memory modules within the processing system. It provides the necessary interfaces required by the data service and processor areas of the I/O

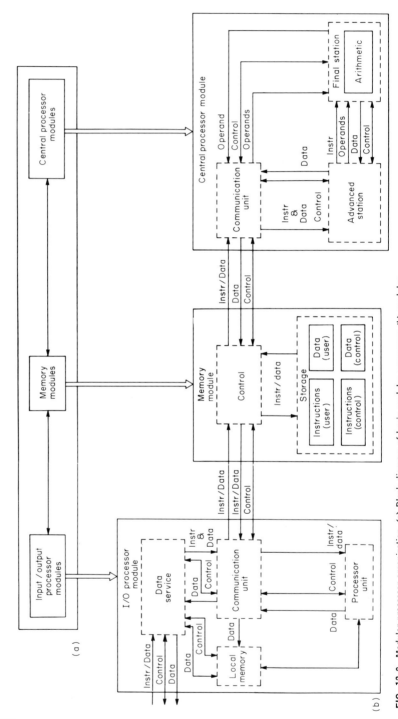

FIG. 12·2 Modular processor organization. (a) Block diagram of basic modular processor; (b) modular processor organization 2.

378

processor module. Also included is the logic for conflict resolution of requests between the two units on a priority basis. Parity error and no-access-to-memory conditions are sensed for. In addition, parity generation for information-transfers-to-memory takes place within the communication unit.

The I/O processor unit executes programs which are designed to control I/O input/output operations. This improvement in the area of the I/O module releases the CPM from execution of I/O related programs and increases the CPM availability for the running of user programs. The processor unit of the I/O module has its own instruction set which is designed for controlling input/output operations. This instruction set is not the same one used by the CPM. The CPM initiates input/output operations on the I/O module by specifying a type of data transfer to be performed. The I/O module then executes the transfer without further instruction by the CPM. The I/O processor initiates data service operations with the specified peripheral devices and requests "comm" service for all instruction or data transfers required for program execution.

The local memory unit provides storage areas for use by the I/O processor module. It is divided to provide a storage area for each channel (device) that is serviced by the I/O module. These areas are control locations and are used to store the base program information, control words, and termination information. Both the data service unit and I/O processor unit have access to local memory and use the control locations as a means of communication. Local memory provides buffering between internal memory and devices which transfer data in character form. Program information for each device is stored in its control location during the time that data service is controlling data transfers between memory and the device. During the same period, data service is using a part of the control location to store the control word while waiting for a request from the device. When a transfer is terminated for any reason, data service stores termination information in local memory for use by the I/O processor in completing the execution of a program.

The memory module remains unchanged in its organization from that of the first family of modular processing systems. Improvements in the state of the art allow faster access times and increased storage capacities. For example, a memory module exhibits a storage capacity for 16,384 fifty-two-bit words. Single (52 bits) or four (four 52-bit) memory word operations are completed in less than 1 μsec. The function of the control area remains in the areas of conflict resolution and interfacing of the memory with the CPM and I/O processor modules.

The CPM is organized into three areas, communication unit, advanced station (ADVAST), and final station (FINST).

The communication unit of the CPM is functionally similar to the communication unit of the I/O processor module. The communication unit performs the communication functions with memory, conflict resolution on a priority basis, parity-error and no-access-to-memory detections, and parity bit generation on information transfers to memory.

The advanced station provides fetching, via the communication unit, of the instructions in advance of their use. It stores the instructions in a memory within ADVAST referred to as a "local" memory. Since most computers fetch instructions only on a need basis, the time it takes to run a program always includes instruction fetch times. The technique employed within ADVAST of fetching instructions in advance of use allows a significant reduction in program run time.

ADVAST provides all operation codes (instructions) for FINST. It provides all operands fetched by instructions and is capable of requesting "comm" service to fetch an operand for FINST. ADVAST executes all program jumps and recognizes and services all interrupt conditions. In addition, ADVAST performs the memory address arithmetic.

All arithmetic operations are performed by FINST. It performs all logical operations, shifts, conversions, and comparison between operands. Final station is capable of storing operation codes (instructions) and operands within a local memory. This capability allows final station to hold instructions/operands in advance of their use. Final station has a "local" operand memory (stack) which allows accumulation of operands or results.

The two-station mechanization allows reduction in program run time. If FINST is involved in the execution of an instruction which requires a long time (3 μsec), ADVAST is capable of proceeding with program preprocessing. It places operation codes and operands in local memory in FINST in advance of their use. This allows the masking of communication and ADVAST execution times associated with the respective instructions. The reader is cautioned that ADVAST is not always ahead of FINST with respect to program execution. In some operational sequences, ADVAST must wait for response from FINST before it can proceed.

Program organization continues to be divided as control and object programs. Improvements in control programming have been made; some of the sophistication in these programs is exposed in Chap. 18.

Future developments in modular processors. The University of Illinois and the Burroughs Corporation are developing a large-scale processing system known as ILLIAC IV. ILLIAC IV is a further extension of the multiprocessing concept (use of more than one processor so that a number of problems or problem segments may be processed simultaneously). ILLIAC IV allows a problem to be segmented into as many as 256 parts with each part being simultaneously processed. This technique allows increased processing speeds to be reached, from 500 to 700 times faster than current computers. ILLIAC IV is organized into two parts, the ILLIAC IV complex and the I/O subsystem.

The ILLIAC IV complex is further divided into (1) four control units, (2) 256 processing elements, (3) 256 memory modules, and (4) an I/O switch. Each of the four control units is functionally capable of performing the control functions for a preassigned group of processing elements and memories. Each processing element is basically a "general purpose computer" without control logic. Each of the memory modules is capable of storing 1024 128-bit words (131,072 bits). The I/O switch provides the necessary control and data paths required for communications between the memory modules and the I/O subsystem.

The I/O subsystem controls the flow of all information into and from the ILLIAC IV complex. An idea of system capacity may be gained if one considers that the Burroughs B6500 processor, a large-scale computer, is one element of the I/O subsystem. The B6500 is intended to function as a control computer for the ILLIAC IV complex.

ILLIAC IV is currently one of the largest-scale processing systems under development within industry. It may certainly be considered a look to the future and another step in the continual evolution which is occurring in the computer organization.

SUMMARY

Early data processing systems were characterized by their fixed nature. The installation of a data processing system resulted in response to a particular "here and now" need. The early systems were characterized by a serial sequential operation which limited their productivity or output. In addition, little flexibility existed whereby system expansion to meet increased needs was possible without major financial outlays to procure new and faster equipment.

The advent of the modularity concept in processing systems provides an approach to overcoming the shortcomings of the earlier systems. The hardware organization in a modular processing system is so organized that individual areas of memory, processing, or input/output capacity could be added to the basic modular system without major expenditures for hardware or programming.

The input/output operational sequences were combined in an I/O processing module. The memory was segmented so that discrete blocks of storage capacity could be added to the system. Processing elements were separated from data movement and control functions and are responsible for program execution.

Although sophistication in system elements has resulted from the continued evolution of the data processor, the basic computer functions of input, memory, arithmetic, controls, output, and program are found in all data processing systems.

QUESTIONS

12·1   What was a disadvantage of the basic organization of the early computer?

12·2   Why was program length restricted in the early computer?

12·3   What is a modular processor?

12·4   What organizational change took place in going from the basic computer to a modular processing system?

12·5   What advantages were gained through modular organization?

12·6   In the modular system, can any I/O communicate with any memory or computer?

12·7   What are the two major areas of the modular I/O? Define each.

12.8   What are the two major areas of the modular memory? Define each.

12·9   What are the two major areas of the modular computer? Describe each.

12·10 What feature was added to the I/O in the advanced modular system?

12·11 How did the advanced I/Os program execution aid the computer?

12·12 Name the areas of the advanced computer. Define each.

12·13 Name the two types of programs and briefly describe each.

12·14 Is the ILLIAC IV capable of increased processing speeds compared with other systems? Explain.

chapter thirteen

Computer Peripheral Devices

In order to make use of the processing capabilities of a computing system, there must be an interface or communication link between the processing system and the human operator. The computer must be told what it is to do (through the program). It must be given the data upon which it is to perform its operation. During the computation, it may require inter- mediate storage areas, and it must provide to the outside world the results of its computations.

This communication takes place through the use of the computer input/output system. The input/output system consists of a software system (the program which controls the entry and output of user programs and data) and the mechanical/electrical devices used to format, provide data for entry, and record the outputs from the data processing system.

This discussion is concerned with the mechanical/electrical devices used to perform the communication function and which are usually referred to as *peripheral devices*. The devices used include punched-card equipment, punched-tape equipment, hard-copy devices, and various forms of mag- netic storage devices such as magnetic-tape units, magnetic drums, mag- netic cards, and magnetic-disk units. The magnetic storage devices may be used as extensions of the internal memory systems; however, they are treated here as I/O devices.

By today's standards the computer of yesterday is considered slow or obsolete. However, the problem then as now is to ensure that the computing system has rapid access to the data required for computation and has the ability to communicate with the user on a timely basis. These functions are performed by a combination of I/O devices. For example, punched paper tape and punched cards could be used as an input medium. Magnetic drums and magnetic disks could be used as an extension of the internal memory for instruction and data storage. The magnetic tape could be used as a file to store intermediate and updated records resulting from the computation. A line printer could be used to communicate the results of the operation in a form readily usable by humans, while a card deck could be prepared for records and subsequent use as computer inputs to indicate sales or reductions in inventory. In any event the human operator must communicate with the computing system via some input medium. The processing system response to the input data is the completion of the required instruction sequence and the communication of the result via an output medium to the human operator.

Input data in its original form is termed *external data* and is usually in a form which can be read and utilized by human beings rather than machines. In commercial applications this would include sales slips, conventional time reports, accounting records, and business reports. Since none of these forms can be fed directly into a computer, some form of conversion is necessary. The most obvious method is direct conversion. In such a case, the computer operator, using an input device similar to a teletypewriter transmitter, reads data directly from normal business forms and types it into the memory of the computer. This procedure, however, generally has decided disadvantages from the point of view of cost and time. Recall that some systems may not be processing data during the time period of inputting information. If the above procedure were utilized, only a small percentage of the total system time would be spent in the processing of data. However, the system use may dictate this type of operation. The use of an indirect input system could increase the time spent in computer processing by the use of a higher-speed input medium. For example, a card reader capable of reading 1400 cards per minute (cpm) provides faster communication with the system than the human operator is capable of providing. The time spent by the operator in card preparation is no less than he would spend in direct communication with the system. However, during the card preparation phase, the processing system can be executing other user programs. A 1500-card input, assuming a 300-card-per-hour preparation rate, would require 5 hr of input time if the direct input method were used. Preparing the data off-line and using the indirect input method would require only 1 min of input time.

Many computing systems are organized so that they can simultaneously perform input/output operations while continuing with the data processing operations.

The selection of the input/output devices is dependent upon such factors as device speed, capacity, cost, and intended usage. The original trend was to cater to the computer needs by minimizing the time spent on I/O operations to maximize system throughput. This development resulted in more diverse and faster devices and the removal of the human element from on-line system control. The computing system became almost independent of human intervention with sophisticated executive programs controlling computer operations. More effective scheduling of computation and I/O operations increased system throughput.

New uses for the processing system dictated the requirement for an increase in human interaction with the processing system. Computer organization allows this communication to take place by interrupting the processing, responding to external inquiries, and then resuming its interrupted computation sequence.

Peripheral equipment may function in on-line or off-line modes of operation. On-line peripheral operation is that which must be carried on concurrently with the computer's calculations in order to obtain the correct solution to the problem in the required time. Whether a particular piece of equipment is utilized in an on-line or an off-line capacity depends on the type of problem being solved and the characteristics of other types of equipment in the system. Some devices are used for input operations only, others for output operations only, while some devices are capable of functioning either as input or output devices.

Assume that the computer's memory has sufficient input-data space available for the contents of one or, at most, a few punched cards. In such a case, the input equipment will have to operate concurrently with the computer in order to solve the problem in a reasonable amount of time. This is on-line operation. If, however, the computer's memory can hold all the required data involved in the problem, the input equipment will be needed before the calculation rather than during it.

Off-line peripheral operation occurs either before or after the data processing phase and is not required during the actual computation periods.

Punched-card Equipment

The use of punched cards as input and output media in data processing systems is widespread. The punched card is perhaps the most widely used input medium with practically all data originally taken into the system being inputted in this manner. After a program has been written, it is usually prepared in a card deck, read into the computer, and executed. Once established within the system, the program is stored internally or transferred to a file tape or disk from where it may be retrieved more rapidly than from punched cards. The input data upon which the computations are to be performed is usually inputted via punched cards. In many commercial applications the punched card is used as an output from the processing system since the punched card will be used subsequently as an input.

Punched-card equipment consists of punched-card readers and card punches. Card punches may be further subdivided into automatic and manual. The automatic card punches are the devices used as output equipment and are controlled by the processing system. The manual card punches, referred to as keypunch, are the devices used by humans for preparation of original data in punched-card form.

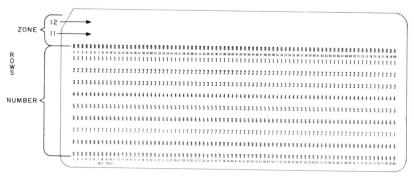

FIG. 13·1 80-column card.

Card formats. The punched card contains information in the form of discretely arranged punched holes in the card. The punched card is divided into 80 vertical columns and 12 horizontal rows. Each column of the card is used to represent a character(s) by the unique placement of the punched holes in the row portion of the column. Figure 13·1 illustrates a standard 80-column card. Note the vertical column numbering across the horizontal face of the card. The horizontal rows are designated nos. 12, 11, and 0 through 9, top to bottom. Rows nos. 12, 11, and 0 are referred to as the *zone portion* of the card, while rows nos. 0 through 9 are referred to as the *numeric portion* of the card. Note that row no. 0 is common to both the zone and numeric portions of the card. Row no. 0 is used as a numeric when it is the only punch in the column.

The two most widely used codes in card punching are the Hollerith and binary codes.

In the Hollerith code, characters are represented on a card by a combination of zone and numeric punches in a column. The characters and punch configurations which can be represented in a column of the card are

FIG. 13·2 Standard punched card Hollerith character set.

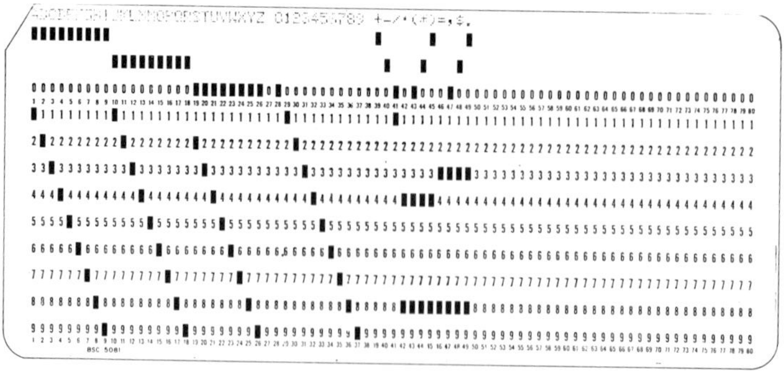

shown in Fig. 13·2. Note that in the use of the Hollerith scheme for character representation, only a single character is represented in each column of the card for a maximum storage capacity of 80 characters. For example, the letter D is represented by a hole in row no. 12 and row no. 4. This is shown in column 4 of the card illustrated in Fig. 13·2. The letter D may be represented in any card column by a punch in rows nos. 12 and 4. In a like manner, the card representation for the numeral 8 is a hole punched in row no. 8 (see column 36 in Fig. 13·2). Table 13·1 lists the zone combinations for the character representations.

TABLE 13·1 Zone-numeric Combinations for Hollerith Character Representations

	No zone	12	11	0
Zone only	*Blank*	+	−	
0	0			
1	1	A	J	/
2	2	B	K	S
3	3	C	L	T
4	4	D	M	U
5	5	E	N	V
6	6	F	O	W
7	7	G	P	X
8	8	H	Q	Y
9	9	I	R	Z
8–2				
8–3	=	.	$	,
8–4	'	)	*	(

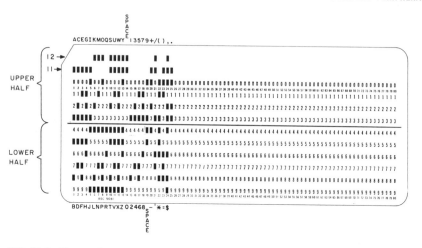

FIG. 13·3 Binary coded punched card character set.

Figure 13·3 illustrates a punched binary coded card and the configuration required to represent the available characters. Note that the same 80-column, 12-row card is used. In the binary coded scheme, each column is capable of storing two 6-bit characters. The card is not divided into row and numeric zones but is divided into an upper half and a lower half. Thus rows nos. 12, 11, 0, 1, 2, and 3 are used to represent a single character while rows nos. 4, 5, 6, 7, 8, and 9 are used to represent another character. The character is in a six-bit binary code representation. For example, an A is represented in column 1 (Fig. 13·3) by punches in rows nos. 11 and 3. These holes are in the second and sixth positions of the six-bit groupings. The same positional representation in the lower half of the card is rows nos. 5 and 9 for the representation of an A. The letter A could also be expressed as 21_8. To represent the same character in the lower half of the card as the upper, the same positional combinations are used with a punch in row no. 12 equivalent to a punch in row no. 4, 11 in 5, 0 in 6, 1 in 7, 2 in 8, and 3 in 9. Binary coded cards are usually generated as the output of the system. The information presented on the card is in system internal code and is an image of the memory data with a binary 1 represented by a hole and a binary 0 represented by no hole. Table 13·2 lists the hole punch combinations for the character range.

The codes presented will vary but the scheme of card division will hold true for alphameric and binary card coding.

Card reader. The card reader is an electromechanical device which is capable of reading punched cards at a rate in excess of 2000 cards per minute. Cards are placed in a stacker capable of holding approximately

TABLE 13-2 Hole Punch Combinations for Character Range in a Binary Coded Card

	7	Y	Z	*	,				
	6	Space	/	S	T	U	V	W	X
	5	Q	R		$				
	4	—	J	K	L	M	N	O	P
	3	H	I	+	.	)			
1st digit	2		A	B	C	D	E	F	G
	1	8	9			'	(	=	
	0	0	1	2	3	4	5	6	7
		0	1	2	3	4	5	6	7

2d digit

4000 cards. The stacker is adjusted to accept either 51-, 60-, 66-, or 80-column cards. These cards are the standard cards which have been scored to allow the customer to retain a portion of the card as a receipt. The major portion of the card is returned with the payment and is used as an input to the processor. The cards are moved past the read station where a column at a time is read. The reading is performed by detecting the hole, using a light source and a solar cell. The holes in the card allow illumination from the light source to pass through with the solar cell detecting this condition and generating an output signal. The read cards are then passed on to the stacker area.

It should be noted that the card reader may be mechanized to read either in the alpha or the binary mode. In the alpha mode, a conversion to the internal machine language is effected by the read and decode logic. Binary cards require no conversion and are passed directly to the storage areas of the computer. Figure 13-4 illustrates the card path from the input hopper area, through the read station to the output stacker area.

The three major operations performed in the card reader are card feeding, reading, and stacking.

Card feeding. There are two methods used to feed cards. One method uses a feed knife which, by moving back and forth, feeds one card at a time into

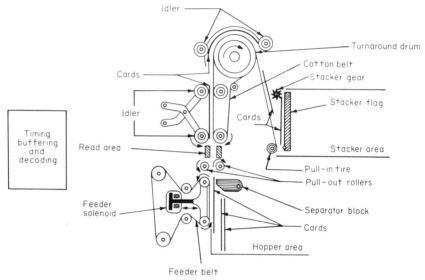

FIG. 13·4 Card path through card reader.

the read station. This method is illustrated in Fig. 13·5a. The throat is adjusted to allow only a single card to pass into the read station.

The second method utilizes a revolving belt which, when forced against the card, pulls it into the read station. Figure 13·5b illustrates the belt not in contact with the card, while Fig. 13·5c shows the action of the belt in moving the card into the read station. Once the card is in the read station the belt retracts until another card is to be read. The reader checks the card travel throughout to ensure against jamming. Both methods of card feed are controlled by the START signal from the I/O area of the processing system (see Chap. 10).

Reading. As the card passes through the read station, each column of information is read. The information is checked for validity, decoded (if

FIG. 13·5 Card feed methods. (a) Feed knife; (b and c) belt.

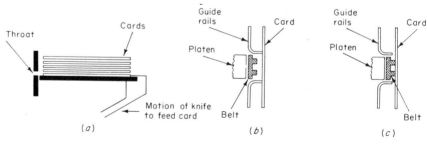

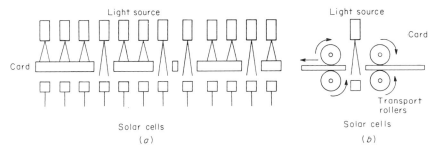

FIG. 13·6 Card reading with photocells. (a) End view; (b) side view.

necessary), and sent to the processor. The buffering action of the I/O area
of the processing system has been discussed previously. There are several
methods of reading cards; however, most high-speed readers use a photoelectric method for reading. In this method of reading, an assembly of 12
solar cell and light source pairs are located on the transport (Fig. 13·6a).
The path of the card is between the light source and the solar cell (see
Fig. 13·6b) so that a hole in the card will allow the solar cell to be activated
by the light beam. The absence of the hole in a particular row will, of
course, result in the solar cell being shielded from the light source and hence
generate no output. This sensing action occurs simultaneously for each of
the 12 row positions in the column. The outputs are sent to the decoding
networks (if required) to translate the data to internal machine formats.
Internal card reader timing is generated to ensure that information sensing
and transfer are properly synchronized. This timing is set to correspond
with the arrival of each column at the read station regardless of card speed.
The adjustment of the input card hopper to accept other than the 80-column
cards causes the necessary timing adjustments in the reader. Since 80
columns of information must be transmitted to the control area for every
card read, blanks are sent for each of the nonexistent columns on the shorter
punched cards (51, 60, and 66 columns).

Stacker.   After the card is read it is transported to the stacker. The stacker
must ensure that the cards are collected and held in the same order in which
they were read. This operation may be performed by gravity stacking or by
the use of a stacker gear. In the gravity stacking method, the stacker is
located lower than the read station. After the card is read, it falls into the
stacker on top of the preceding card. See Fig. 13·7. In this method the
cards are stacked vertically. Figure 13·4 illustrates the use of the stacker
gear. In this method the stacker gear contacts the trailing edge of the card
and bends it slightly so that it is bent toward the preceding card in the
stack. This allows the next card to ride over it as the new card enters the
stacker area. This method stacks the cards horizontally.

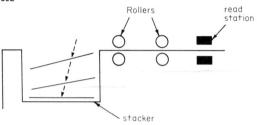

FIG. 13·7 Gravity stacking.

Card punch. The card punch is an electromechanical device capable of punching 80-column cards at rates up to 300 cards per minute. It is used as an output device from the processing system and operates under processor control. Program decks, inventory cards, and billing represent some of the uses of these output cards. The cards serve the function of customer billing as well as input media for subsequent operations. The card punch can be loaded with up to 3300 cards in a combination of input-card hoppers. After the punching, the cards, under computer control, can be directed into the main, or auxiliary stackers, or directed into an error stacker under internal card reader control. Cards are punched a row at a time with row-12 punching occurring first. This scheme requires a block of 80 parallel punch mechanisms controlled electronically by the processing system. Each row is punched, read, and compared for accuracy, and after the operations for all 12 rows are completed, the card is directed to the stacker areas. As in the card reader, the necessary timing, clocking, and error detection features are incorporated to detect card jams and other mechanical and electrical failures.

    Figure 13·8 illustrates the card punch action. To process a card, the

FIG. 13·8 Card punch cycles.

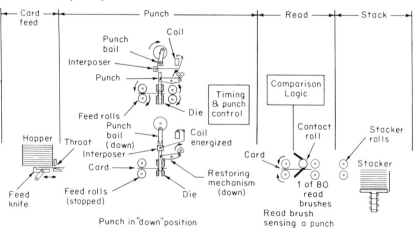

punch must pick a card from the input hopper, carry it through the punch and read stations, and place it in the output stacker. This process is accomplished through what is termed *four card cycles*, which are the card feed cycle, the punch cycle, the card read cycle, and the stacker cycle. Refer to Fig. 13·8.

Card feed cycle. After the input hopper is filled with cards and the cycle initiated, the card feed knives pick a card from the bottom of the deck and feed it into the feed rollers. As the feed knives complete their movement, the card has been moved into the punch-card-ready station. This action causes a signal to be generated to the computer indicating a punch-ready condition. The data to be punched in the row-12 position of the card is transferred to a buffer register which controls the punch action. The card passes between the punch and punch die. As shown in Fig. 13·8, the positioning of the interposer between the punch bail and the punch by the presence of a 1 allows the punch to be driven through the card. A 0 in a buffer position will not position the interposer so that no punching action takes place. One bit position of the register controls each of the 80 punch mechanisms. The feed rollers move the card with a feed-stop, feed-stop motion as the card moves through the punch station. This motion is synchronized to ensure that the data transfer which controls the punching action in each of the rows has taken place in the proper time frame. As the card moves through the punch station, it enters the card-read-ready station.

Read cycle. As the card passes through the read cycle, each row is passed in turn over a series of 80 read brushes. Holes in the card are read when the hole allows the brush to make electrical contact with the contact roll located above the brushes. The feed-stop action of the card controls the card movement through all the card cycles. The information read is compared with the original information held in a buffer for verification of correct punching. The card is then fed into the stacker area by another set of rollers.

Stacker cycle. The set of rollers feeding the card into the stacker area is controlled by the same feed-stop motion until the card passes through its last (row no. 9) read/comparison. The card is then in contact with the stacker rollers which draw the card into the stacker. The cards may be directed into the main or auxiliary stacker bins or into the error bin as directed by the control circuitry.

It should be noted that since the cards follow each other through each cycle and station by approximately $\frac{1}{4}$ in., four cards are in process at a given time. As one card is being stacked, a second is being read, a third is being punched, and a fourth is being picked out of the input hopper.

Punched cards have both advantages and disadvantages in comparison with other media. Probably the most important advantage of punched cards is that an individual card may be used to hold the data on a significant subdivision of the file. For example, data on a particular employee, customer, or inventory item is usually found on one card. For many purposes this is convenient. For example, if 10 names are to be added to an alphabetical payroll file, new cards may be conveniently punched and inserted. If the same operation is to be performed on a tape, for example, the situation may be more complicated. Even if spaces were left between names, several individuals with similar names may be employed. In this case, the alphabetical tape file would probably have to be rewritten. The advantages of punched cards can be listed as follows:

1. A file of punched cards is easily expanded, contracted, or revised.
2. A file of punched cards may be quickly sorted into subfiles, and cards with special characteristics may be conveniently removed. For example, the cards of "all employees with over 1 yr of tool and die experience" can be sorted out of a properly prepared employee file in a few minutes.
3. Punched cards conveniently carry names, numbers, or other visual tags which enable them to be identified quickly and handled manually when necessary. In general, punched cards are often employed whenever the ability to manipulate individual items conveniently in a data file is important.

Although punched cards are the most widely used input medium and find fairly widespread use for output operations, certain limitations to their use must be pointed out. Punched-card preinput equipment, namely card punches, is usually slower and more bulky than tape equipment of the same cost. This is especially true in high-data-volume applications. The punched cards themselves are heavier and take up more storage space per data bit. As a result, most computer applications which have a high data volume combined with minimum sorting and searching requirements utilize some form of tape in preference to punched cards.

Manual card punch. The punching of cards for subsequent use as computer input occurs in many cases under computer control. However, many applications require that punched cards be prepared manually off-line. This manual operation is performed by an operator with the use of a keypunch. The keypunch is a card-punching device which is controlled from a keyboard similar to that of a typewriter. The operator "types" the required data from specially prepared forms to initiate the punching action necessary to record the information. Some models of the keypunch, the IBM 26 series for example, have a printer capability which records the characters along the top edge of the card at the time the card is punched. The characters printed are aligned with the column in which the character is punched, thus facilitating the reading of the card without the necessity of punched-hole interpretation.

Cards are loaded into the input hopper and are advanced to the punching station so that a column at a time is available for punching. Each time a key is depressed, some combination of punching bails is activated to cause the character to be punched, and the card is advanced one column to the next punch position. When the eightieth column has been punched, the card is automatically advanced to the read station where a visual check may be made.

Duplication of a card can take place with a master card at the read station and a blank card at the punch station. The two cards are stepped through their stations in synchronization in order to maintain the column-to-column accuracy required. Sensing brushes are used at the read station to decode the holes that are punched in the columns. These brushes generate feedback signals to the punch station that automatically activate the proper punch bails. Corrections can be made to particular columns of a card by duplicating a card to the column where the error has been made and using the keyboard to activate the proper punch bails to punch the desired character.

The automatic functions of the keypunch can be used to facilitate the punching of cards in which a particular formatting or column skip convention is required. The automatic functions are controlled by a pre-punched card mounted on a cylinder called the *program drum*. This program drum can be used to automatically skip over the portions of the card where no data is to be punched. The card will automatically stop at the column where data is to be punched, then continue after the manual punching is completed. Additional features of the program drum enable automatic duplication of columns that are identical on all cards, the keyboard can be shifted from alphabetic to numeric characters, and on certain models the printing above the columns can be suppressed.

Punched Paper-tape Equipment

Punched paper tape is used as both input and output media in a computing system. Though not so widely used as cards, paper tape is used in smaller systems in specific applications. In accounting systems employed by banks, paper tape may be the preferred media since tapes may be punched simultaneously with the preparation and recording of other data such as deposit slips. The tape may then be used as a computer input for account updating.

Paper tapes are a permanent, nonerasable storage medium and may be used as data files or as program tapes.

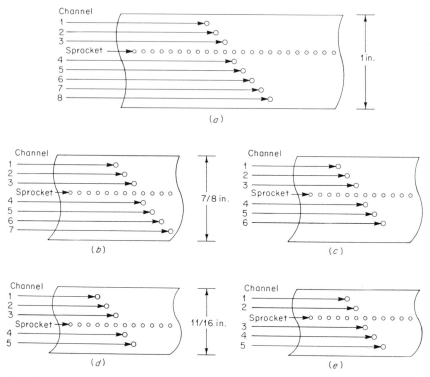

FIG. 13·9 Punched paper-tape formats. (a) Eight channel; (b) seven channel; (c) six channel; (d) five channel regular; (e) five channel teletype.

Paper-tape equipment consists of paper-tape punches and paper-tape readers. Both operate under the control of the computing system. In addition, paper-tape punches are available for off-line preparation of punched paper tape. This off-line punched paper-tape preparation capability may be provided by a separate unit or may be part of a combination keyboard device such as the Flexowriter discussed in a later section.

Tape formats.   Information is recorded on paper tape by punching holes in the tape in different configurations for character representation. Characters are punched across the width of the tape and may be represented either as 5, 6, 7, or 8 holes (channels). Figure 13·9 illustrates the various tape configurations in use. Codes are selected to provide the proper interfacing with the internal operations of the processing system selected. Note that each of the tapes has an additional hole of smaller diameter termed the *sprocket hole*. This hole is used for tape alignment and in some cases as part of the tape transport system.

Paper-tape reader. The paper-tape reader is an electromechanical device capable of reading punched paper tape at speeds of up to 1500 characters per second. Reading action may be by either mechanical or electrical means. In mechanical reading the holes are sensed by a star wheel or feeler pin which detects and indicates the hole by completing an electric circuit as described for brush sensing in card reading. As in other devices, mechanical operations limit operating speeds. Electrical reading of paper tape is performed with the use of a light source and photocells. The hole represents a binary 1, the absence of the hole a binary 0. Code selection for reading and tape alignment must be accomplished on the transport by the operator.

Reading data from paper tape is accomplished by moving the tape past the read station, sensing the data, and transferring it to the data processing system. The sprocket hole is also read to generate a timing pulse used to transfer the data.

Figure 13·10 illustrates a simplified front panel of a punched-tape reader. The left side of the panel contains the same linkages as the right side. The tape from the supply reel is threaded past the right tape sensor, through the dancer arm, over the capstan, through the read station, and in reverse order through the identical linkages contained on the right side of the panel.

During a read operation, the tape is moved in a forward direction past the read station by pressure exerted on the tape by the right capstan. The speeds of motors which drive the tape supply and takeup reels are controlled by a servo system mechanically linked to the dancer arms. A difference of

FIG. 13·10 Punched-tape reader front panels.

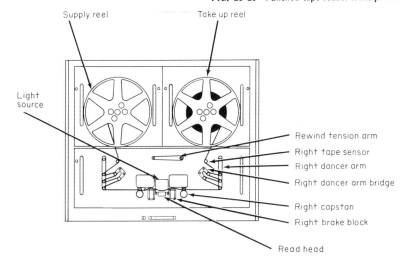

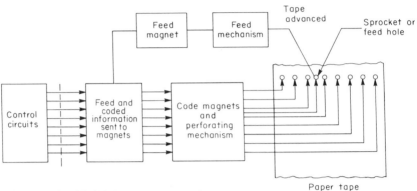

FIG. 13·11 Simplified block of paper-tape punch.

speed in either of the reels is sensed by movement of the dancer arms because of pressure changes on the arms due to too little tape or an excess of tape threaded through the arms. Either of these actions results in a change in the speed of the drive motors to compensate for the imbalance until the same rate of supply and tape takeup is achieved.

The tape sensors are used to detect the beginning and end of tape so that the unit may be stopped before the tape is pulled away from the reel.

Tape reverse is achieved by tape pull from pressure exerted by the left capstan resulting in tape movement in the opposite direction. A more rapid tape rewind may be achieved by "unthreading" the tape and passing it through the rewind tension arm.

Paper-tape punch. Perforated paper tape may be prepared at speeds in excess of 100 characters per second under computer control. The tape unit is basically able to perforate tape in the internal code of the system to which it is attached. It may, however, generate other codes through the use of a translator which provides conversion capabilities. Any tape width can be used with the punch. During the punch operation, simultaneous punching of all channels and the sprocket takes place.

Figure 13·11 illustrates the information flow in a tape punch system. Information is received from the processor system a character at a time and buffered internally until the punch mechanism is set up for punching. The data input controls a series of code magnets which control the punch pins. One character is punched for each operating cycle of the punch. The selected punch pins are driven through the tape to perform the perforating action. The pins are then mechanically withdrawn, and when the pins are clear of the tape, the tape is advanced to the position for next character punching. The buffer register receives a new character, and the cycle is repeated.

Paper tape is inexpensive and easy to handle, which makes it well-suited

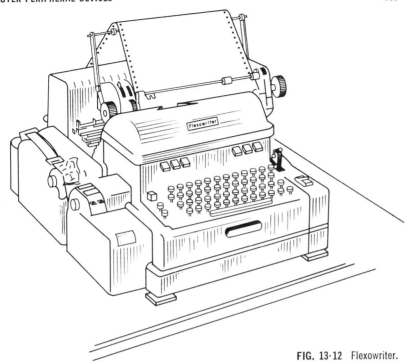

FIG. 13·12 Flexowriter.

for use in a small- or medium-size computer. It can be stored in considerably less space than punched cards, and if it is to be used as an auxiliary storage, it is probably superior in most respects to cards. During actual operation, a reel of paper tape is less likely to suffer damage than would a deck of cards in the same operation. Should physical damage occur, however, or should an error area be encountered, repair or correction of this area on paper tape is somewhat more difficult than it is in a deck of punched cards.

Keyboard devices. Under certain conditions it is desirable for the operator to interrupt the processing system to communicate with it. Such interruptions occur for the purpose of inquiry or control and may be responded to by the computer with short output messages. The means provided for this communication usually takes the form of a keyboard or typewriter. One such device is the Flexowriter illustrated in Fig. 13·12.

The operator may type various alphameric combinations which are interpreted by the program to initiate predetermined operations by the computing system. These operator communications may change the program sequence, initiate system checks, or cause the computer to respond to the interruption with a print of data. Because of the slow printing-speed capability of these units, a character at a time, the information transmitted is usually low volume.

The keyboard may be activated manually by the operator or it may be controlled automatically by the processor. A translator unit is located between the keyboard and the computer to effect the necessary conversions between the internal language of the computer and the keyboard.

The device illustrated in Fig. 13·12 is a combination device. Although the primary use of the keyboard is direct communication, it has the capability of performing paper-tape operations. The unit has a paper-tape reader which can be used as an input device. This input capability is used to insert small data or program patches. A paper-tape punch capability is also present in this device. Control of tape punching may be manually from the keyboard or automatically from a tape strip in the tape reader.

Magnetic tape. Magnetic tape is used as both an input and output storage medium in data processing systems. Magnetic tape is used as an external storage device rather than as an extension of internal memory. An advantage of tape is large storage capacity. A 10½-in. reel of ½-in. tape contains 2400 ft of tape and is capable of storing approximately 50 million characters. Since the tape reels are easily replaced on the transport, an almost limitless storage capacity may be achieved. This reserve of storage capacity makes feasible the storage of voluminous business records such as inventory, payroll, employment, and other similar data.

Tape speeds do not approach the internal memory speeds or the speeds of other bulk storage devices. A tape transport can move approximately 150 in. of tape per second. Assuming a bit-packing density of 800 bits per inch, 120,000 characters per second may be processed. The information on tape is stored sequentially; therefore, effective tape use dictates its use in data storage applications suited to sequential retrieval of data. Desired information cannot be accessed directly but must be searched for in a sequential manner.

The tape consists of a base of a thin ribbon of plastic, such as acetate or nylon, coated with a magnetic substance such as a ferrous oxide or chromium dioxide. A binder is employed to make the magnetic substance adhere to the base and to provide lubricants to reduce friction between the coating and the read/write heads. The two thicknesses of tape available are referred to as regular and thin tape.

Information is recorded in tracks across the width of tape and may be recorded as 7, 8, or 9 bits. One of the bits is usually designated as a parity bit. Each write operation causes one character to be recorded. Figure 13·13 illustrates a section of seven-track tape with a file consisting of two "one-word" records.

Information on the tape is organized in the form of records and files. A

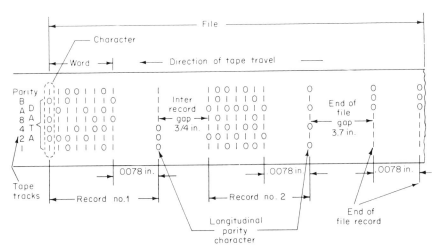

FIG. 13·13 Magnetic-tape format.

record may consist of from one word (a typical word length of eight characters is shown) to several thousand words, as determined by the system in
use. In the example, the records illustrated consist of a single word. The
last character of a record is the longitudinal parity (LP) character which is
an even parity for each track in the record. Parity is used in error checking
and is usually generated by the tape system and spaced about four character spaces beyond the last data character. This character is not transferred to the data processing system during the read operation.

An interrecord gap of approximately ¾ in. is written between records
to separate them. This gap contains no data. One method of producing this
gap is to allow the tape to move past the write head for a short period of time
after the unit receives an end-of-data indication. Since data characters are
no longer being received, only 0's are recorded, creating the record gap. The
end of record can be recognized regardless of the length of the record. The
gap also allows the tape to reach its operating speed before the reading or
the writing actually takes place. When the tape is brought to a halt, the
read/write (R/W) head will be positioned somewhere near the center of the
record gap. Groups of records are organized into files. A file contains a
variable number of records. The end of file (EOF) gap is the same as the
interrecord gap (void of data) except it is usually much longer (3.7 in.). At
the end of the gap, an end-of-file character is written and, four character
spaces later, a longitudinal parity character is written. These two characters are referred to as the end-of-file record. When the tape is commanded
to advance or backspace to an EOF position, it does so by recognizing the
bit configuration of the EOF character rather than the gap preceding it. In
this manner, the tape unit will pass over any number of records, including

all record gaps, until the EOF character is detected. Because of the bit pattern chosen for the EOF character, the parity convention of the remainder of the tape is not followed. Lateral parity is ignored when reading these characters.

During a read operation, each character (except LP and EOF) is checked for odd lateral parity, and then track parity is checked (for even) at the end of the respective record by comparing each bit of the LP character against the accumulated bit condition of each respective track. If either parity is found in error, the tape system usually sends a status code to the I/O control for proper action. Not shown in Fig. 13·13, two position markers (1-in. strip of aluminum-foil-like reflective material) are placed on the tape. A BOT (electrical beginning of tape) and an EOT (electrical end of tape) are placed on opposite ends of the tape to indicate the areas outside the normal recording areas. These markers will cause the tape to stop to prevent complete tape unwinding.

Separate read and write heads are provided for each track. Shielding between heads is employed to reduce cross talk. Data to be recorded on tape is usually presented serially in the form of characters to the tape transport from the input/output control. Data recorded on tape may be used to represent alphameric or binary information. The tape merely records 1's and 0's, and any data translation must take place within the processing system.

Data read is accomplished by passing the tape beneath the read head. Output sensing from the read head detects the 1's and 0's for transmission to the processing system. See Chap. 5 for a discussion of magnetic recording principles.

Although all tape systems do not have the same set of command operations, they usually perform the same basic operations. A typical tape system performs the following: read, write, advance N records, backspace N records, advance to EOF, backspace to EOF, and rewind to BOT. Of these operations, only the read and write involve data transfer between tape and I/O, while the others are used to position the tape to a desired point. These tape operations are controlled (initiated) by the computer system.

A typical tape handling unit (transport) contains the mechanical elements necessary to drive the tape past the read/write head for a read or write operation and the circuitry necessary to write and sense the data read. A tape transport is shown in Fig. 13·14.

In this system the tape movement is controlled by a pair of constantly rotating capstans and pinch rollers. One set is used for forward drive and the other for reverse. To drive the tape forward, the left pinch roller is energized, pinching the tape against the rotating capstan [always a counterclockwise (ccw) direction] so that the tape is pulled in a forward direction. Figure 13·14 shows the forward pinch roller deenergized, while the backward

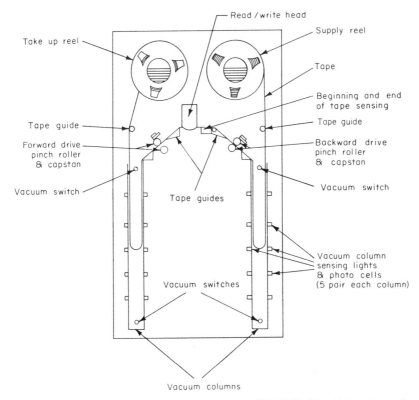

Read / write head
Supply reel
Take up reel
Tape
Beginning and end
of tape sensing
Tape guide
Tape guide
Forward drive
pinch roller
& capstan
Backward drive
pinch roller
& capstan
Vacuum switch
Vacuum switch
Tape guides
Vacuum column
sensing lights
& photo cells
(5 pair each column)
Vacuum switches
Vacuum columns

FIG. 13·14 Magnetic-tape transport.

roller is energized. Only one of the two pinch rollers can be energized at any one time.

Tape is looped into vacuum columns to control the tape drive system and provide several feet of tape to the pinch rollers for immediate movement without having to overcome the inertia of the tape reels. Separate servo drive circuits are supplied for each reel. The reel drives are independent of each other and of the pinch roller drive circuits. The speed of the respective reel motor and its direction is controlled by sensing lights and photocell assemblies (vacuum switches could also be used as the sensors) located in left and right vacuum columns. The center photocell assembly in each column serves as a reel direction control, while the other four photocells are used for speed control. When the tape is driven in either direction by the pinch rollers, the photocell system will ensure the proper speed and direction of the reel motors in order to maintain the proper tape loops in each vacuum column. The vacuum switches located at the top and bottom of each vacuum column are used to remove power in case the tape should either pull out of either column or drop to the bottom. Either of these conditions could cause damage to the tape. The various tape guides provide for smooth tape movement. The BOT, LOAD, and UNLOAD positions are sensed by the BOT/EOT sensing assembly. When the tape is under control of the computer I/O system and is commanded to move to the BOT mark, it will drive until the BOT reflective marker is sensed by the BOT sensor, at which time drive is removed and status transferred to the I/O. Usually the tape is not commanded to move to EOT, but instead this marker is used to signal the system (during an operation) that the tape is at its usable end. A REWIND command causes the tape to rewind to the BOT marker. The LOAD command positions the tape to the initial R/W point (BOT), while the UNLOAD command positions the tape so that the tape reel can be removed.

Magnetic drum. The magnetic drum is a storage device used as both an extension of main memory and as a bulk storage device. It consists of a nonmagnetic base cylinder coated through an electroplating process with a ferromagnetic material. The drum is usually formed directly on a shaft and is mounted so that it may be rotated by a drive motor at speeds in the several hundred to several thousand rpm range. The drum surface is divided into tracks with each track considered to be a circumferential ring around the drum. Each track has a read/write head associated with it to effect the information transfers. The heads are mounted and may come in direct contact with the drum surface or may be mounted several thousandths of an inch from the drum surface. Direct contact of head and recording surface produces the largest signal output; however, friction shortens the drum life. The heads are therefore positioned away from the drum after the drum has been brought up to speed and temperature. The space between the R/W heads and the drum surface is one of the factors determining the area occupied by the 1's and 0's on the surface. Bit packing densities (the number of data bits which may be written) vary from 50 to 500 bits per inch (bpi). Generally, it can be stated that the capacity of a drum depends on the surface area, but the head separation is a factor to be considered. In moving the heads slightly away from the surface, tightly spaced bits are caused to interact with each other, which in turn can cause erroneous readouts. Thus, head separation, bit-packing density, and drum speed are all factors in determining storage capacity of a given drum system. Drum capacities are considerably less than those of magnetic-tape systems. The drum selected for discussion has a storage capacity of approximately 600,000 characters.

Access time is the time required for a desired point to pass under the read/write head to effect the desired drum operation (read/write). When a drum is addressed for access, there is no way of knowing where the information is contained on the drum surface in relation to the read/write head. A best-case condition exists if the desired data is passing under the read head at the time of drum addressing. The worst-case condition exists if the desired data has just passed under the read/write heads. An entire drum revolution delay is involved before the data transfer operation can take place. Assuming a drum speed of 3600 rpm, the worst-case timing for access is 16 msec. The best-case condition described above provides immediate access. Drum access time is therefore stated as an average time which is equivalent to one-half the revolution time of the drum. In this example, the drum access time is 8 msec. This access time could be reduced by the use of multiple heads for each of the tracks.

Once the starting word/character point is reached, the speed at which the data is read/written is termed the *data transfer rate*. A typical data transfer rate is 600,000 characters per second. The data transfer rate is affected by the bit packing density (bits per inch) or drum speed, or both. For a constant drum speed, an increased packing density results in a faster data transfer rate because a greater number of bits pass under the R/W head per revolution. Of course a combination of the two can be used. It should be noted that there are certain limitations on controlling data rate by the above methods. Although the drum has far less storage capacity than the tape, it is usually much faster in both information transfer rate and in access time, which is a drum advantage. A disadvantage of the drum is that once the drum is "full," new information cannot be recorded without destroying the present data.

The information arrangement on drum tracks may vary. One method is to divide the drum surface into a certain number of channels with each channel consisting of a number of tracks. The number of tracks in a channel would be dependent upon the decision to either store an entire word or only a character in parallel. For example, a 25-bit word (24 data, 1 parity) could be stored in parallel in 25 drum tracks as a single word, or in a seven-track channel as four characters, one in each of four consecutive locations. Figure 13·15a illustrates the use of a seven-bit character channel to effect the storage. Note that seven separate drum tracks are used to form the channel. Characters 1 through 4 comprise a single word stored in four consecutive locations. Characters 5 through 8 comprise the second word, etc. Each time a read/write operation takes place, one character is recorded (or read). Note the one-to-one relationship of read/write heads to drum tracks.

Figure 13·15b illustrates the organization of the data on the drum for the 25-bit word channel storage scheme. Note that as the drum surface passes under the read/write heads, the entire word is recorded in 25 parallel tracks. Each time a read/write operation takes place, the transfer of an entire word is effected.

The use of either data arrangement scheme provides the same storage

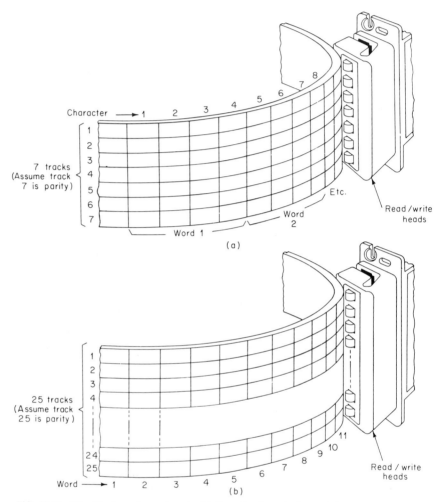

FIG. 13·15 Magnetic-drum storage formats. (a) Character channel; (b) word channel.

capacity. If it is assumed that in both methods the drum has 10,000 bit positions per track, the "word" channel method provides a capacity of 10,000 words per channel and assuming 6 data channels, the total drum capacity is equal to 60,000 twenty-five-bit words. In a character channel arrangement, since the same length word requires four consecutive characters for recording only, 2500 words per channel could be stored. However, with fewer tracks per channel, 24 channels are contained in the same surface area, thus providing the same total storage as the word type (24 × 2500 = 60,000 twenty-five bit words). The total tracks across the face of the drum are divided into the desired channel arrangement. Access time

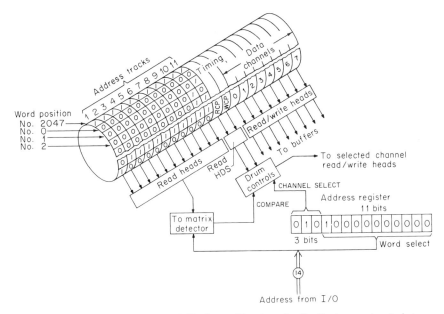

FIG. 13·16 Drum addressing using the direct-comparison technique.

in either arrangement is the same; however, the data transfer rate could be significantly faster for the 25-bit word channel. If the drum were word-organized, provisions would probably exist to allow the parallel transfer of data to the I/O. A single transfer completes the operation. The character-organized drum would be implemented for character transfer between the drum and I/O. In this instance a serial transfer by character would be necessary; hence four 25-bit words (word-organized) could be transferred in the time required for one 25-bit word (character-organized) to be transferred.

In order to initiate a read/write operation on the drum, the area which contains the information must be reached and recognized. This recognition process is termed *addressing the drum*. Drum addressing may be accomplished in several ways.

One method utilizes a number of address tracks with an address written in each of the possible word positions on the drum. Figure 13·16 illustrates a drum with 11 address tracks which allows identification of word positions 0 through 2047. As the drum rotates, the address R/W heads read the address and pass it to a matrix detector. A comparison is made with the desired word address from the address register. If a successful comparison takes place, a COMPARE signal is sent to the drum controls. The drum illustrated contains eight channels. In addition to specifying the word position, the address register uses three bits to select the desired channel at that word position. This selection allows the drum controls to direct the read clock pulses and write clock pulses (RCP/WCP) to the selected channel read/write heads. The read clock and write clock pulses are prerecorded on separate drum tracks and are read from the drum as each word position of the drum comes under the read/write heads. The RCP/WCP tracks use "read only" heads since the clock tracks are usually prerecorded at the factory.

The drum illustrated contains 2048 word positions (0 through 2047) with eight channels for word position for a total of 16,384 word storage locations. These words are stored at locations identified by locations 0 through 16,383. Thus channel 0 contains location 0 through 2047, channel 2 contains 4096 through 6143, etc., with channel 7 containing locations 14,335 through 16,383. The addresses specified for both the word and channel fields have the most significant bit to the left, least significant bit to the right.

The address contained in the address register indicates access to location 1024 in channel 2. This is equivalent to word 5120 of the 16,383 possible locations. The beginning location in channel 2 is 4096 + 1024 (indicated word location) = word location 5120.

Figure 13·17 illustrates a character channel-type drum utilizing a different addressing technique. The drum is organized into 64 data channels with 1024 word positions, with each word consisting of 8 six-bit data characters plus a longitudinal parity character. Recall that for this format, six drum tracks are available for character representation, with eight characters written sequentially. A 48-bit word is assumed for this example. A parity bit is not written with each character; instead, a longitudinal parity bit (as used in the magnetic tape) is written for each word. Although the parity bit is not written with each character, the parity bit is checked on each seven-bit character received from the I/O and a parity bit is generated for each character sent to the I/O.

One track is designated an address track (AT) and has a clock pulse recorded for each of the 1024 word positions. As in the previous method this clock applies to all the character positions of the particular word location. A second track designated the drum mark pulse (DMP) has a single clock recorded on it. This pulse is read once per drum revolution and is the reference for all address counting. A 10-bit address counter is reset to 0 by the DMP and is advanced through its maximum count by the AC pulses. When a read or write operation is to be performed, the address counter output is compared with the address register (which contains the desired starting word location) in a matrix detector. When the two match, signal COMPARE is generated and sent to the drum control block, which in turn allows the RCP or WCP to be fed to the read/write circuits. Words are now read/written (in consecutive characters) until the word counter (WC)

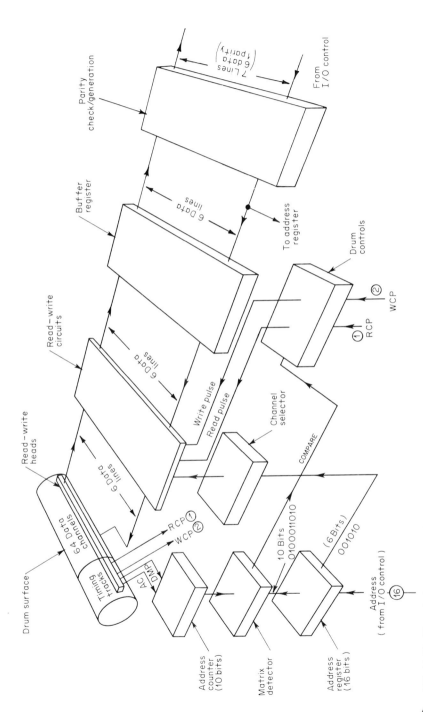

FIG. 13·17 Magnetic-drum functional diagram.

equals 0 and the I/O terminates the operation. The WC in the I/O indicates the number of words involved in the operation. This address method, as in the previous method, requires that the channel be selected independently of the word location. For example, assume that it is desired to read/write X number of words beginning at word location 10,522. Since the total storage capacity is 65,536 words, 16 bits of address are required. The 16-bit configuration (binary) for word 10,522 is 0010100100011010 with the left-most bit being most significant. The address is divided into channel selection and word selection, with the MS six bits selecting one of 64 channels (0–63). The remaining 10 bits select one of 1024 word locations (0–1023) within the selected channel (all other channels are disabled). The address specifies channel number 10 (the eleventh of 64 channels) and word number 282 of that channel. Since the first 10 channels (0–9) contain 10,240 words, then word 282 of the next channel (10) will be the 10,522d word (10,240 + 282). When the address counter has advanced to 282 (from DMP reference output), a successful comparison is made with the address register, and signal COMPARE initiates the R/W operation. The operation continues until terminated by the I/O at a WC of 0. It should be noted that although the RCP and WCP signals are constantly being generated, the drum control applies these signals only to the selected channel circuitry for the duration of an actual R/W operation.

Regardless of the drum organization and addressing methods used, the information flow is basically that shown in Fig. 13·17. Most drum systems are capable of generating terminating status codes to be sent to the I/O control, via the data lines. Typical status conditions include parity error from I/O detected, parity error from drum (longitudinal), data too slow (I/O not requesting or sending data at the required drum transfer rate), and write-lockout. The lockout is usually controlled by manual switch settings which protect certain channels from being destroyed by writing new information over the present information content. This data (program, for example) may be read from the drum since reading does not destroy the data.

Information storage may be in normal sequence or interlaced. In normal-sequence storage, consecutively numbered words are stored in consecutive word positions. This recording scheme allows all words of a given channel to be read/written in one drum revolution. A feature sometimes incorporated into drums is data word and/or address interlacing. In this mode, consecutively numbered words or addresses are not recorded in consecutive word or address positions on the drum surface, but are spaced (interlaced). This spacing may be at every other word position, or every three words, etc. For example, assume that the data words and addresses (word channel type) are interlaced every other word or address position. To read/write all words of a given channel requires two drum revolutions instead of one. This storage technique has the effect of cutting the data transfer rate in half (from 600 to 300 kHz, for example) which may be desirable in some drum/processor systems. This reduction in transfer rate might be used to prevent the drum (which is much faster than some other terminal devices) from monopolizing a commonly shared I/O bus (different I/Os sharing a common bus for concurrent operations). This constant use by the faster device (drum) would interfere with proper data movement from the slower devices sharing the same bus. The interlace mode may be inserted or removed by switch action at the drum unit. The decision for normal mode or interlace is dictated by system requirements.

Magnetic disk.   The magnetic disk is a storage device which may be used as an extension of the main memory system or as a bulk storage device. It consists of a circular metal plate which is coated on both faces with a magnetic substance. The disks may be mounted vertically or horizontally and vary in diameter from about 10 to 26 in. Rotation of the disk is at speeds up to approximately 1800 rpm. Reading and writing is accomplished by a single head which moves across the disk face in the manner of a phonograph pickup arm, or by the use of fixed heads on a head-per-track basis similar to that used in the magnetic drum.

Magnetic disk systems may consist of a single disk with the capacity for recording on each of the two disk faces or may contain up to 800 disks with a 1600-face recording capability. A single-disk face is considered in the subsequent discussion.

One recording arrangement uses a read/write head for each track on the data face. This scheme allows for single-track or multiple-track operations similar to those discussed for the drum. The parallel read/write capability naturally provides for an increase in the data transfer rate over serial recording methods.

Another recording method used allows a single read/write head to service all data tracks on the disk face. The single read/write head must be moved and positioned over the desired data track prior to each operation. This physical head movement and positioning increases access time and limits the recording process to serial recording. If, for example, each disk face consisted of 150 tracks, the positioning range of the head is approximately 3 in. (roughly 50 tracks per inch).

A third method is similar to the second. However, the 150 tracks would be divided into three zones with 50 tracks in each zone. A read/write head would be used for each zone, with the maximum movement range for head positioning reduced to 1 in., thereby reducing access time.

The head-to-recording-surface relationships and problems discussed for the drum apply to disk face recording. Most disks employ the flying head technique for head-to-disk positioning. This term is used to indicate that the heads (because of their shape) tend to ride on a cushion of air created by

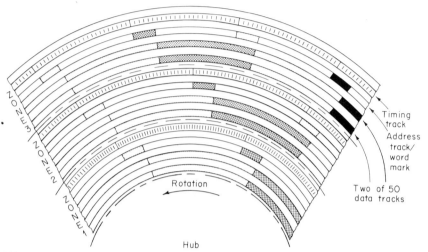

FIG. 13·18 Data organization on magnetic-disk face.

the rotation of the disk. During the disk "power-up" sequence, the head assembly is held in a retracted position by spring tension until the disk reaches its proper speed. Once proper operating speed is reached, the heads are forced into their operating position by a piston-type actuator assembly, which is usually controlled by an applied air pressure. This air pressure is removed when retraction of the heads is desired. Head-to-disk-surface separation is about 100 μin. Some type of monitor protection circuit is usually employed to retract the heads in case of reduced rotation speed or if a head actually "touches" the disk surface. As in the drum, this head-to-surface separation prevents wear on the magnetic surface, providing longer disk life. Bit-packing densities reach 3800 bits per inch (bpi) in some systems. Single disk faces are capable of storing 1.2 million six-bit characters. In the track-per-head systems access times are in the order of 16 msec.

The face of the disk is divided into zones, each zone containing a number of recording tracks (Fig. 13·18). The tracks in the outer zone are able to store more data than those in the inner zone because of the circumferential difference in track length. Figure 13·18 illustrates a section of a disk face which is organized into three zones. Each zone consists of a timing track, an address track, and data tracks. The timing track contains prerecorded clock pulses which are used to synchronize the read/write operations. A single-address track contains a prerecorded address for each word length or an address for each segment (groups of words) of all tracks in that zone. Since only a single track is used for addressing, addresses are recorded serially. To initiate the data transfer action, the entire address must be made available for comparison prior to the disk surface with the desired

Disk	Face	Zone	Track	Word (segment)

FIG. 13·19 Disk address word.

information passing under the read head. This is accomplished by recording the data word (or segment) displaced by one word (or segment) from the address which describes that word. There is a lag in the information from the address which identifies it. The address can thus be read and compared with the desired location, and the R/W operation initiated on the next word-mark pulse. The word mark is a 1 bit usually recorded on the address track as the first bit of a given address. A means must be provided for track selection, zone selection, and face selection in multiple-disk systems.

An address word for a multiple-disk system might be formatted as shown in Fig. 13·19. The address word is used to select a particular disk, a face of that disk, a zone on the selected disk face, a track within the zone, and a word (or segment) on that track. Once the selected word has been located, the R/W action is initiated and continues until the operation is terminated by the I/O at a WC of 0.

As in drum and tape systems, most disk systems employ some type of error check for the bits recorded. Some disks record a longitudinal parity bit at the end of each word or segment. These bits are read and checked but are not transferred to I/O control. Another error-checking method is the check-sum method. Check sum utilizes a mod 8 counter which is incremented each time a 1 is recorded, and at the end of the word (segment) the bit configuration contained in the counter is written into three bit locations. Assuming a three-stage counter, the operation is as follows. At the beginning of the operation the counter is reset to 0. As each 1 is recorded, the counter is incremented from 0 through 7 and then recycled. For example, if a total of five 1's is recorded in a given segment, the bit pattern 101 is recorded as the check sum for that segment. When the segment is read, the 1's are counted using the same counter. At the end of the segment, the counter configuration is compared against the 3-bit pattern read from the disk. If the comparison is not valid, a check-sum error is detected, and status is sent to I/O control. The check bits are not transferred to the I/O as data.

The operations performed by the disk are read, write, and erase. The erase may be a separate action, or, as in most systems, accomplished by writing zeros. Typical terminating status codes generated by the disk system are "parity error from I/O," "longitudinal/check-sum error," "write-lockout," "data too slow," and "storage unit busy."

The disk system discussed has been of the fixed-disk type; that is, the disks are physically tied to the disk system. Once the disk has been fully recorded, additional data may be added only at the expense of losing data already recorded. The removable tape reel of the magnetic tape unit provides for almost unlimited storage capacity. This concept is applied in some disk systems with a package which, like a tape reel, can be inserted into or removed from the system.

As in the other peripherals many variations of recording techniques, addressing, and information formatting exist. Although the implementation changes from system to system, each of the devices performs a basic function.

Printers

The printer as an output device provides the means of computer output in a form usable without conversion by the operator. Modern high-speed printers are capable of printing over 1400 lines per minute and have the capability for alphabetic, numeric, and special-character printing. The number of character positions per line varies from 10 to 200 per line with the character set dictated by the requirements of the output contents and format.

There are two general categories of printers in use, the mechanical and the electrostatic. The mechanical printer utilizes physical contact of the typeface and paper for character recording, while the electrostatic printer utilizes electronic means for character formation and recording.

Mechanical printers. The drum printer is one type of mechanical printer in use. It consists of a drum with the character set embossed on its surface. Figure 13·20 illustrates the drum. Note that the characters are repeated in each column of a line to provide the capability of printing any of the symbols in the character set in any of the positions of the line. In a 132-column printer, for example, each of the characters appears 132 times on the drum

FIG. 13·20 Line printer. (a) Print drum; (b) print mechanism.

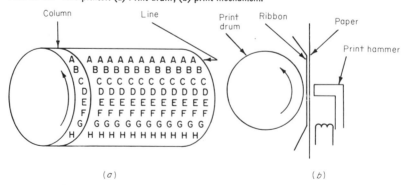

(a)   (b)

face. Up to 64 characters may be placed at equal intervals around the drum face.

Since intelligible data is produced by combinations of the characters in various ways, the ability to print in other than full-line, single-character fashion must be provided. For each column on the drum, an individually controlled print hammer is provided to cause the character on the drum to be transferred to the recording paper. Figure 13·20b illustrates the printer mechanism showing the print drum, ribbon, paper, and print hammer. The transfer action of the character is similar to that occurring on a typewriter. A 132-character printer is assumed for discussion purposes; hence, 132 individual print hammers are positioned to provide the print capability. The print drum is constantly rotating so that this type of printer is termed an *on-the-fly* printer. When the desired character to be printed is aligned with the paper, the print hammer is energized forcing the paper and ribbon against the print drum, causing the recording of the character.

Figure 13·21 is a block diagram of a printer system.

The data processing system initiates the printing operation by transferring 132 6-bit alphameric characters to the printer.

The data is gated into the 132-location memory by the control logic. As the data is brought in serially, it is loaded into consecutive memory locations starting with 001. When the last character is loaded into location 132, the control logic initiates a scan-print operation.

The print drum has 64 equally spaced rows of unique characters ar-

FIG. 13·21 Line printer block diagram.

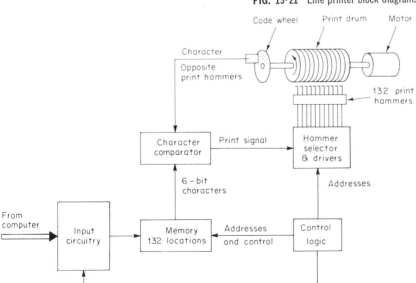

ranged into 132 columns. A code wheel containing the alphameric code equivalent of each of the 64 characters is mechanically fastened to the same shaft as the print drum. The code wheel consists of a thin opaque material with holes (clear areas) representing the 64 alphameric codes. A group of photocells detects light passing through these holes and thereby senses the drum character. The code wheel is aligned in such a way as to present the alphameric code of the character that is opposite the print hammers to the photocells.

When the scan-print cycle is initiated, the control logic gates the code of the character opposite the print hammers into the character comparator. The control logic then initiates the memory scan operation. A copy of the data in the 132 memory locations is read sequentially, one character at a time. The character from memory is compared with the code wheel character. If the comparison is unsuccessful, the character is returned to memory and the next sequential memory location is accessed. When a good comparison is made, a blank character is written into the memory location and a print signal is generated to energize the respective print hammer. Since there is a one-to-one relationship between the memory locations and the print hammers, the proper character is printed in its proper position. For example, if address 001 were read and a successful comparison made with the character from the code wheel, the character on the drum opposite the print hammer is printed in column 1. This sequence of memory read, comparison, and print is repeated for each of the 132 columns. At this point, only one character out of the 64 possible characters has been printed in the required positions of the 132 columns of a line. This memory scan occurs 132 times during the time period that each of the 64 different characters is under the print hammers. Figure 13·22 illustrates the development of a single line of print. In this instance, initial memory scan resulted in a successful comparison at the time the character H was under the print hammers. Character H is the first character printed. The entire sequence of line development occurs during a single drum revolution. The insertion of blank characters into memory for each character printed eventually results in a blank memory which indicates line print completion. An additional character may be transmitted to control paper movement. This character may specify single- or double-space movement of paper, or paper format control by the format tape. The format tape will result in paper movement to correspond to the desired printing operation. For example, in check printing, only particular areas are printed to indicate name, amount, etc. This special spacing or formatting is accomplished under the control of the format tape. While paper movement is in progress, the transfer of the next data line from the processing system to the printer is effected and the cycle repeats.

CODE WHEEL	PRINT DRUM					
H	H	H				
I	HI	I H	I	I	I	
L	HI	I H	LI	I	I	
N	HI	I H	LIN	I	IN	
0	HI	I HO	LIN	I	IN	
P	HI	I HO	LIN	I	P IN	
R	HI	I HO	LIN	I	PRIN	
S	HIS	IS HO	LIN	IS	PRIN	
T	THIS	IS HO	LIN	IS	PRINT	
W	THIS	IS HOW	LIN	IS	PRINT	
A	THIS	IS HOW A	LIN	IS	PRINT	
D	THIS	IS HOW A	LIN	IS	PRINT D	
E	THIS	IS HOW A	LINE	IS	PRINTED	

FIG. 13-22 Development of line of print.

Electrostatic printers. Increased printing speeds can be achieved by the elimination of the mechanical components associated with the printing operation. In the electrostatic printer, character formation is achieved through electronic means; thus, printing speeds are limited by paper movement and internal timing of the data processing system. It is possible in some systems to print the characters as they are received.

The electrostatic printer built by Stromberg Datagraphics, Inc., illustrates one of the techniques employed for character formation with this type of printer.

A CHARACTRON[R] shaped-beam visual display cathode-ray tube is utilized to form the desired character on special electrically charged electrostatic copy paper. A character image is formed on the paper by selectively discharging an area of the paper in the form of the desired character. The paper is then passed through a developing station where the character images are fixed and become permanent.

The CHARACTRON[R] tube displays alphabetic, numeric, and special characters on its phosphor screen by extruding an electron beam through a character matrix. The matrix is a thin metal disk with the character set etched in as in a stencil. The beam, passing through a particular character aperture, takes on the form of the character in a manner similar to the formation of a cookie as it is passed through a cookie press. As each character is transferred into the printer, it is converted to X and Y deflection voltages that select the proper character aperture on the character matrix. The shaped beam then passes through a second deflecting system that is under control of the printer control logic. This deflection system positions or formats the character for presentation. Figure 13-23 illustrates the sequence for electrostatic printing.

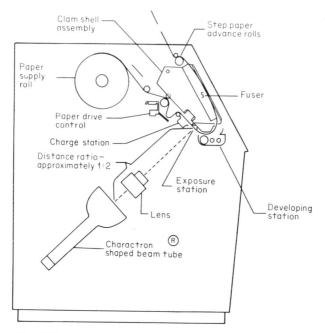

FIG. 13·23 Electrostatic printer. (Stromberg Datagraphics, Inc.).

As the paper is fed from the paper supply, it passes through a charge station that causes it to become positively charged on the uncoated side and negatively charged on the sensitive side that faces the CHARACTRON[R] tube. A lens system is used to project the displayed characters onto the sensitized paper. The projected characters reduce the negative charge on the paper where they impinge as a result of photon bombardment and form a latent electrostatic image in the shape of the character projected. The paper then moves to a developing station where the character images attract colloidal particles of a thermoplastic material. As the paper passes through the fuser station, heat causes the thermoplastic material to bond to the copy paper forming a permanent image. The method of character formation varies in electrostatic printers. Another method is the use of an arc discharge in the form of a character in close proximity to sensitized paper. An arc-discharge matrix exists for every column character position to be printed, and each is capable of forming the complete range of characters. The discharge pattern in the matrix is used to define the characters. A heat developing process is also used in this system to fix the image.

Optical Character Readers (OCR)

Optical character-recognition equipment is used to read typefonts directly from printed documents and to deliver its output either directly to the computer or to a computer data preparation device. Some readers are capable of on-line or off-line operation; some can interface with a limited number of systems, while others may be used with any system; some readers are capable of on-line operation only while others operate off-line only.

The optical character reader operates on the principle of recognizing the contrast difference between the character and the background. The element of human intervention is removed from the operation; hence, greater accuracy may be achieved than through the use of other conversion techniques such as going from the printed page to punched cards via the keypunch operation.

The character-reading capability varies from device to device. Some OCRs can read only a single typefont, while others are capable of multifont reading. The character sets vary, ranging from numerics to complete alphameric sets and special symbols. Most readers read characters produced by typewriters or printers; however, some are capable of reading hand-printed numbers. OCRs are capable of reading up to 3200 85-character lines per minute.

The optical character reader functions (as do other I/O devices) as the communication link between man and machine. It has the advantage, however, that its input medium is the same printed page which is used by its operator. Man and machine can use and interpret the same data form.

As in most other computer peripheral devices, the operational sequence involves a load operation, a read operation, and a collect or stack operation. These operations are tied together by the transport system of the device which moves the documents through the various phases of the cycle.

Document movement is performed via the transport system consisting of conveyer belts, vacuum feeders, drive rollers, or some combination of those methods. The input documents may be in printed page form, tab cards, or may take the form of a continuous tape such as cash register or adding machine tapes. Since document movement is by means of relatively slow mechanical means, the electrical reading ability of the unit is limited by the speed at which the documents can be made available.

When the document is moved into the read station, the contrast between the character and the background is noted through one of the optical scanning methods. The methods used in approximate relative order of speed are the mechanical disk, Vidicon scanner, flying-spot scanners, and the parallel-process photocell scanners.

As its name implies, the mechanical disk scanner uses a rotating disk, a lens system, and a photomultiplier for contrast sensing of the character outline. Its speed is limited by the fact that it is capable of only single-character sensing and either the sensing mechanism or the document must be repositioned prior to each new character read.

In the Vidicon scanning technique, an electron beam scans the face of a

Vidicon television camera tube onto which the characters to be read have been projected. The resulting signals are translated into blacks and whites which represent the characters sensed.

The flying-spot scanner employs a cathode-ray tube raster scanned spot which is projected onto the document through a lens system. A phototube senses the reflections from the spots and generates voltage signals which are proportional to the amount of reflected light. Since the characters contained on the document control the reflected light, the characters are sensed as the spot scans the document.

The use of parallel groups of photocells has increased the speed of scanning by allowing a number of points on the character to be sensed simultaneously. These points may cover a portion of the character or the entire character depending upon the number of photocells used. The photocell generated voltages indicate blacks and whites to describe the character sensed. The parallel-photocell scanning technique allows for the most rapid character reading.

Once the character has been scanned, an analysis of the resulting signals must be made to determine what character is represented (what character has been read). This recognition may be accomplished through optical matching, matrix matching, stroke analysis, or curve tracing.

In the optical-matching technique, the scanned character is compared with reference character masks. The mask which allows the least light to be passed constitutes the match and identifies the character read. Changes in the mask sets allow for reading of different typefonts.

In the matrix-matching technique, the scanner signals are stored in a digital register connected with resistor matrices. A single reference character is represented by each matrix. The opposite ends of the matrices are connected with a second digital register whose output voltages represent a "perfect character." Character recognition results from comparison of the output voltages. Changes in the resistor matrices allow for recognition of different character fonts.

Stroke analysis involves a comparison of the position and frequency of vertical or horizontal strokes or both, resulting from the scan operation with a truth table containing the stroke formation for each of the available reference characters. This comparison is performed by a special-purpose computer under program control. Changes from one character font to another require a reprogramming of the computer.

Character recognition in the curve-tracing technique is effected by following the character outline. Certain features such as line intersections and character splits are used to identify the characters.

The inability of the OCR to read a document can result in either display of the unreadable characters, marking of the document, or a rejection of the document completely. A retyping of the document may be necessary, or in some devices manual entry via keyboard of the unreadable character is possible.

Once identified, the character is made available to the selected device, either the computer or the selected data preparation device. The devices with which the OCR may interface include card punches, paper-tape punches, and magnetic-tape units.

Once read, the document is moved to the output stacker. Some devices have the capability of document sort at the output stacker area.

The optical character reader is expected to play an increasing role as a computer input medium.

QUESTIONS

13·1   What is the primary purpose of peripheral devices?

13·2   What are the three basic types of peripheral devices?

13·3   In what two modes do peripheral devices operate? Briefly describe each.

13·4   Name two types of card punches and describe how each is controlled.

13·5   Name the two most widely used card formats. What is the difference between them?

13·6   Name two advantages of punched cards.

13·7   How are punched cards verified for correct punching?

13·8   Are the cards usually punched by column or by row?

13·9   How are the automatic functions (skip, formatting, etc.) controlled on the keypunch?

13·10 In what two reading modes may a card reader operate?

13·11 Which of the two card reader codes is usually different from the computer's "internal language"?

13·12 Name two card feed methods utilized in card readers.

13·13 What is the most common method used for "reading" cards? Briefly describe the operation.

13·14 What is the function of the sprocket hole on the paper tape?

13·15 Name the two reading methods of paper-tape readers.

13·16 How is a difference in speed between the supply and takeup reels sensed by the paper-tape reader?

13·17 What enables the paper-tape punch to perforate tape in codes other than the internal code of the attached system?

13·18 What are the main advantages of paper tape and with what type computer system is it usually used?

13·19 What is the prime purpose of the keyboard (typewriter) input to a computer system?

13·20 Why is the information volume usually low when using the keyboard device?

13·21   Name two additional features that may be found on some keyboard devices.

13·22   How is information organized on magnetic tape?

13·23   What is a typical data transfer rate of a magnetic-tape system?

13·24   What is the main advantage of the magnetic-tape system? Disadvantage?

13·25   What method is used to indicate the end of a record on magnetic tape?

13·26   What is the last character of a record? Where does it originate?

13·27   How does the tape system recognize the EOF position?

13·28   What is the purpose of the tape loops in the vacuum columns?

13·29   What storage application is better served by a magnetic drum than by magnetic tape?

13·30   What is drum access time?

13·31   Name two drum addressing methods and give a brief explanation of each.

13·32   What is the purpose of the drum mark pulse (DMP)?

13·33   Define the term "drum lockout."

13·34   Name two methods of organizing information on the drum.

13·35   Name two disk R/W head arrangements. Give an advantage and disadvantage of each.

13·36   Why are the data and its associated address(es) usually displaced from each other in a disk system?

13·37   What is meant by the term "flying heads" in magnetic disks?

13·38   In regard to bit error checking, what is the advantage (if any) of the check-sum method over the longitudinal parity method?

13·39   Name the two types of printers. What is the main difference between them?

13·40   In the printer having the print drum, what is the maximum number of revolutions required to print one complete line?

13·41   How is the character image formed on the Stromberg Datagraphics, Inc., printer?

13·42   How does the optical character reader recognize the presence of a character?

13·43   What is the main advantage of the optical character reader?

13·44   Which of the various optical-scanning methods is the fastest and why?

13·45   Name the methods used for optical character recognition.

chapter fourteen

Display Systems

Communication between the computing system and the operator has been characterized by conversion delays. The operator speaks one language, the computer understands a different language. Each can perform efficiently only in terms of his own language. The keyboard and printer devices with the appropriate translators provided the first realistic method for man-to-machine communication on an understandable level. Externally the communications originated and received by the operator were in his own language terms. Internally the processing system received requests and supplied answers in its internal machine code. The translations were made by intermediate devices, and the operator received data in a usable form.

Information display systems provide another means of eliminating conversion delays. Each of the participants in the dialogue speaks his own language, and each of the participants hears in his own language. With information display systems, the operator's "hearing" is accomplished through the visual display of information. The display system may be used as an output device only or may have provision for two-way communication between operator and computing system.

Display systems may be used to perform monitoring or observation functions, or for direct on-line communication. Typical applications range from on-line editing and routing of data in message switching centers to observation of a process in steel production. Information display systems are employed in applications which require instant access to and simultaneous display of volume data.

A basic information display system is illustrated in Fig. 14·1. The computer provides control of the display as it would for any other I/O device. Instructions are required to initiate each function or operation of the display. The data to be displayed is passed from the computer to the display.

The interface block provides for level conversion and buffering between the computing system and the display device. The display generator provides the control signals and timing for symbol and character generation of the information to be displayed. The methods of the display generation vary with the system used.

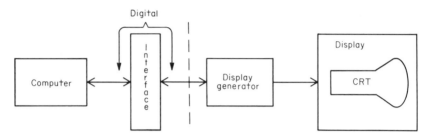

FIG. 14·1 Basic display system.

The display area contains the cathode-ray tube (CRT) and its associated circuitry. The alphameric characters and symbols are displayed on the face of the CRT. Special cathode-ray tubes allow for character and symbol generation within the tube itself. Other CRTs allow for the introduction of the data to be displayed by optical means.

Displays vary in the number of characters which can be generated, as well as in the information block which can be displayed. Some systems are capable of generating up to 200 different characters or symbols. The characters are displayed in printed-page format; the simultaneous display of 100 lines of 100 characters each is possible.

Display Elements

The most commonly used display element in the display system is the cathode-ray tube. The basic CRT and the CHARACTRON[(R)] CRT are used in most systems with special-purpose military systems using a picture window CRT. Each of the three is discussed below.

One other display element which enjoys fairly widespread use is the alphameric display tube. This tube is approximately 1 in. in diameter and

FIG. 14·2 Basic CRT.

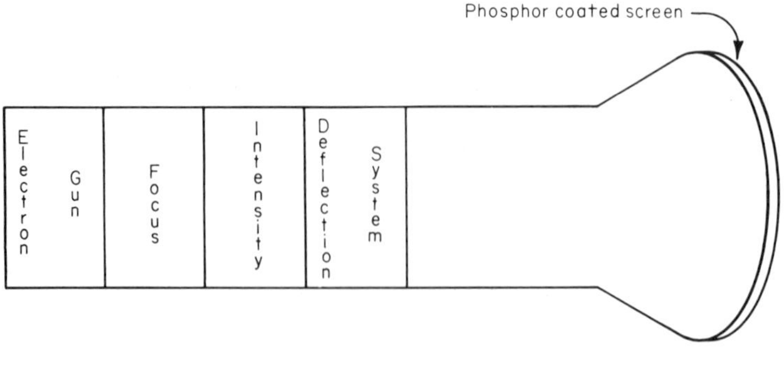

is capable of single-character representation at a given instant. The tube consists of 13 segments which, when energized in combinations, display a character in a red neon glow. The character representation is readily discernible even under high ambient lighting conditions.

Basic CRT. The cathode-ray tube produces an image on the face of the tube by directing an electron beam against a phosphor coating which emits light energy when struck by an electron beam. Figure 14·2 illustrates a basic CRT organized along functional lines.

The CRT consists of an electron gun assembly, focus control, intensity control, deflection system, and phosphor-coated screen. The electron gun produces a beam of electrons which is directed at the face of the screen. Control of the electron gun allows the beam to be turned off or allows "blanking" of the scope face.

The beam is formed or focused to achieve a highly concentrated spot or cross-sectional area which is desirable for clarity of the displayed image. The intensity control limits the amount of electrons allowed to reach the screen, and variations of the control provide different levels of brightness on the screen.

The deflection system is used to position the electron beam on the scope face. Positioning is performed both in the horizontal and vertical axes by separate circuitry. Deflection is accomplished by the use of electrostatically or electromagnetically generated fields. High-frequency applications generally employ electrostatic fields since they have the advantage of a better beam-positioning response, but they tend to enlarge the cross-sectional area of the beam. Electromagnetic deflection systems have less effect on electron beam shape, but the frequency response is not so good as in the electrostatic systems. The intended use is usually the deciding factor in the selection of the deflection system. It should be noted that CRTs are available which combine the advantages of both systems by the use of both deflection systems in a single CRT.

The phosphor coating is available to allow different color images to be produced; however, green is most commonly used since the eye is more sensitive to green than to any of the other colors. As the electron beam strikes the phosphor, light energy is created in the form of the electron beam spot. The phosphor type used determines the persistence or the period for which the screen will glow after being struck. This period is in the microsecond to millisecond range. In order to eliminate flicker (provide constant image), the beam must be allowed to impinge upon the image area at a 50- to 60-Hz rate, and this is termed the *refresh rate*.

Thus far a single spot has been projected onto the screen. This spot may be positioned at any point on the face of the scope. This positioning is termed the *random positioning technique* and is illustrated in Fig. 14·3.

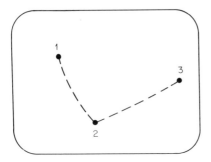

FIG. 14·3 Random positioning technique.

The spots numbered 1, 2, and 3 may be displayed using the deflection system for positioning. In this display only the dots illustrated are illuminated or visible. This occurs because the electron beam is blanked during the positioning periods and allowed to impinge on the scope face only during the desired display periods. The dotted lines would appear as solid connecting lines if the control signals applied did not cause CRT blanking during the beam movement periods. Thus in this positioning method any point on the scope face may be selected at random for the image display, hence the term *random beam positioning*.

Another method of beam positioning is the raster scan technique. In this method, the electron beam is positioned at the upper left of the tube face and the beam scans the tube face in line-reading fashion. This technique is used in a home television set and is illustrated in Fig. 14·4. Note that during the retrace period (dotted lines), the CRT is blanked so that the retrace is not visible.

This deflection technique is visible by turning to a TV channel not used in your area. A raster, or no-picture condition, exists. The application of control voltages for controlled beam blanking as the beam scans results in light and dark screen areas or picture. Thus in both deflection methods

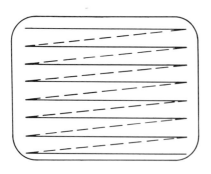

FIG. 14·4 Raster scan technique.

(random and raster scan), the application of blanking voltages describes the image to be presented.

The basic properties of the CRT horizontal and vertical positioning, intensity control, beam formation, and blanking (beam modulation) are used in various combinations for character generation. The two major methods of character formation are termed *beam forming* and *signal generator*.

CHARACTRON[(R)] *CRT*. The beam-forming technique of character generation uses a specially designed CRT. The CHARACTRON[(R)] CRT is illustrated in Fig. 14·5. Character formation involves the shaping of the electron beam by passing it through a stencil-like matrix which is contained in the neck of the CRT. The matrix contains an alphameric character set and special symbols. See the insert in Fig. 14·5. Matrices of up to 200 characters are available.

The electron gun generates an electron beam and shoots it toward the face of the tube. A series of selection plates bends the beam so that the electron beam floods the area of the selected character on the matrix. The stencil forms the electron beam into the shape of the selected character. The convergence coils direct the newly shaped beam to the reference plates which align the beam with the axis of the tube. Focusing of the beam takes place, after which the deflection yoke positions the beam for display. Increased brightness on the face is achieved by passing the shaped character beam through the helical accelerator. The formation and display of up to 10,000 characters per second are possible. The CRT may also be used as a conventional CRT device.

A variation of this tube (smaller size) allows the flooding of the entire matrix area by the electron beam for character formation. The desired character is selected by allowing it to pass through a masking aperture and then on to the face area of the tube.

Other variations of the CHARACTRON[(R)] include the two-gun tube and the special window tube illustrated in Fig. 14·6.

The two-gun tube of Fig. 14·6a uses the CHARACTRON[(R)] portion of the tube for character generation. Another tube neck is formed into the tube and shares a common tube face with the CHARACTRON.[(R)] This second-gun structure is used to display additional information which might not otherwise be displayed because of required character formation times. The two guns act independently of each other and on a noninterference basis.

The special-window tube illustrated in Fig. 14·6b allows optically generated images to be displayed on the face of the CRT. In the illustration, a camera system is used to project map outlines on the face of the scope. The gun structure of the tube is used to present changing data.

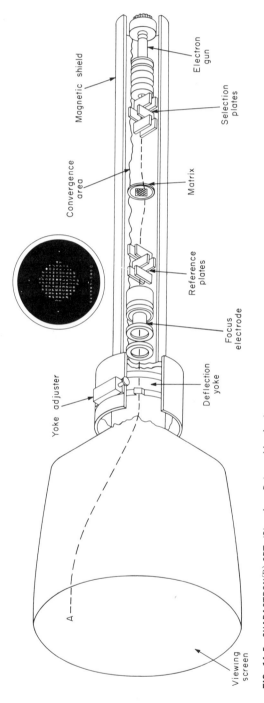

FIG. 14·5 CHARACTRON^(R) CRT. (Stromberg Datagraphics, Inc.)

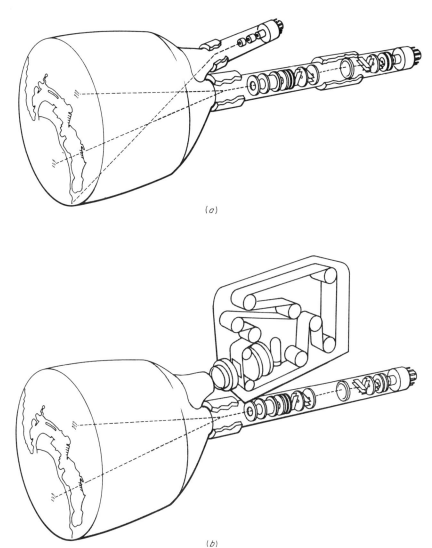

(a)

(b)

FIG. 14·6 Special-purpose CRTs. (a) Dual gun; (b) special-window tube. (Stromberg Datagraphics, Inc.)

Thus optical and electrical means are used to provide the composite "situation" at a given instant.

Signal generators. The second major classification of character generation techniques uses signal generators. Signal generators use a combination of blanking and control voltage application to the horizontal and vertical deflection systems for character formation. The deflection voltages are used for positioning, and the blanking voltages are used to allow image display. Signal generators are classed as either raster or function type generators.

Raster. In the raster technique of character generation the face of the display is divided into a series of blocks, each of sufficient area to display a single character. Raster formation may take place in each of these blocks on an individual basis. See Fig. 14·7a. The character can now be formed by the use of the blanking voltage. Character formation may be by either the dot or the line method.

In the dot method, a group of imaginary dots is arranged in a matrix with a certain dot pattern decided upon for character representation. As the beam scans the character area, the blanking voltage is used to control display of the desired dots, and the character is formed. Figure 14·7b illustrates a 5 × 7 dot matrix with the character A displayed.

The line method for character formation is similar to the dot character formation technique. In scanning the character area, a fixed number of raster lines are formed. The use of the blanking voltage in a predetermined manner allows part of the raster line to be displayed, and thus the character is formed. Figure 14·7c illustrates the formation of character A by the line technique.

It should be noted that during the raster scan, the raster trace pattern is blanked, and only the areas necessary for character formation are allowed to be "lighted" by the electron beam. The pattern of blanking may be controlled by a computer or may be controlled from an internal memory. Recall from earlier discussions that display refresh is necessary to present a flicker-free image.

The second technique used for character formation directs the beam to trace the character directly rather than employ a fixed scanning pattern.

FIG. 14·7 Display tube face. (a) Raster formation in individual character position; (b) dot matrix technique of character formation; (c) line technique of character formation.

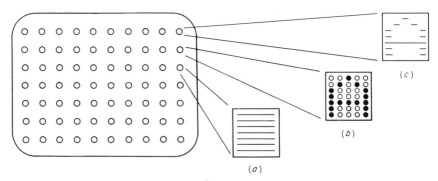

FIG. 14·8 Function character formation. (a) Programmed dot character formation; (b) Fourier character formation; (c) stroke character formation.

Characters may be traced by programmed dot, circular (Fourier), or programmed stroke methods.

The programmed dot method is similar to the raster dot method. Instead of horizontal scanning, however, the beam is directed in sequence to the position of the dots required to form the character. The beam is allowed to reach the display face only at the points of the desired dots. This is illustrated in Fig. 14·8a. Some systems do not blank the beam while it is moved from dot to dot, thereby allowing the character formation to take place as a continuous line.

The Fourier method of character formation utilizes the familiar Lissajous patterns of circle formation by the application of out-of-phase signals to the vertical and horizontal deflection system. The characters are then formed by the application of combinations of various frequencies and amplitudes to achieve the desired image. The character A formed by this method is illustrated in Fig. 14·8b.

A third method of character generation in the function technique is the stroke method. Beam movement is programmed in a series of straight-line strokes with each character or symbol resulting from a unique sequence of strokes. Character complexity determines the number of strokes required. The angle and length of each stroke are predetermined to give an accurate character representation. Figure 14·8c illustrates a stroke-formed character.

Display System

The basic display system (Fig. 14·7) has been expanded in Fig. 14·9 to illustrate the interface of the functional elements of a typical display system.

It was mentioned previously that every operation of the display is under computer control. The data to be displayed is contained in computer memory, and the controlling signals for display generation and display refresh originate in the computer. These signals are passed to the interface and controls area where the proper buffering and level conversion is effected.

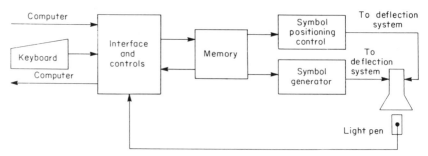

FIG. 14·9 Block diagram of typical display system.

In order to free the computer from direct control during the display cycle, an internal memory is added to the display system. This memory may be of the delay-line, magnetic-drum, or magnetic-core type. The communication periods between the display and the computer are limited to those periods of information transfer to set up the initial display conditions or to change the data to be displayed. The display refresh function is controlled by the memory.

The symbols to be displayed are stored in the buffer memory. The memory is organized so that each location contains the data associated with a particular position on the face of the display. A fetch of data from a memory location, therefore, provides the information necessary for positioning as well as data which, when decoded, results in the generation of the desired character.

The symbol positioning controls generate the necessary deflection signals to locate the symbol on the display face. These beam movements result from control signals which indicate the line and position in the line at which the character is to be displayed.

Symbol generation is effected through one of the previously discussed methods. Decoding of the binary data from memory activates the necessary control signals to the horizontal and vertical deflection systems and to the blanking circuitry for character formation. Thus the signals generated in the symbol positioning and symbol generation sections combine in the deflection system to form and position the image to be displayed.

The incorporation of a keyboard into the display system provides an added capability which allows the operator to compose, edit, and display information without a computer interrupt. The inputs from the keyboard are processed through the interface and controls in the same manner as data from the computer. To assist in message composition, the operator may use a cursor (▢) which is generated and displayed on the screen. The cursor is used to bracket the character position which is to undergo modification (by character insertion or correction). Movement of the cursor over the face of the display is controlled from the keyboard. Once entered, the data (message) may be transmitted to the computer. Communication between the display and computer is at internal computer speeds; hence, the use of the keyboard for message composition and editing minimizes computer communication time for manually inserted messages.

The addition of a light pen increases the flexibility of the display system. The pen consists of a photocell or fiberoptic element in a pen-shaped assembly. The positioning of the pen over a "lite" spot on the display generates an output which is sensed by the computer. Even though the display appears simultaneously, display formation is time-oriented and the signal generated is able to identify a position on the display for further action. Light pen action may be used, for example, to delete data or for line formation.

Certain applications make it desirable to display data in a dimension of 6 to 8 ft. Because of size limitations the CRT cannot respond to this need. Symbol generation and display are achieved in the conventional manner. Once displayed, the display is photographed, a high-speed film-processing cycle is initiated, and the completed film is projected by optical means on a screen. Large-size color as well as black and white displays are achieved through this means.

The use of display systems has greatly enhanced man's capability to communicate with computing systems on a meaningful basis.

QUESTIONS

14·1 What advantage do display systems provide over devices such as keyboards and printers?

14·2 In what type application do display systems find their greatest use?

14·3 Is the display considered an I/O device?

14·4 Name three types of cathode-ray tubes and briefly define how each produces an image on the tube face.

14·5 What are the two types of deflection systems used to position the electron beam on the scope face?

14·6 Will the screen brightness (intensity) increase or decrease if fewer electrons are allowed to reach the screen?

14·7 Define the term "persistence."

14·8 What determines persistence?

14·9 Define the term "refresh rate" and tell its purpose.

14·10 What are the two major methods of character formation?

14·11 What are the two types of beam positioning and which is the one used in home television?

14·12 What are the two types of signal generators? Give two methods used in each type.

14·13   Which of the character formation methods is similar to the Lissajous pattern method?

14·14   What unit of the display system frees the computer from direct control of the display during the display cycle?

14·15   What unit provides the operator the capability to modify display information?

14·16   What is the function of the cursor?

14·17   What is the main advantage of the light pen assembly?

III

PROGRAMMING AND SYSTEM CONCEPTS

chapter fifteen

Introduction to Programming

The computing system hardware has always been under the control of a program. A program is an orderly sequence of instructions which direct the hardware functions in the solution of a problem. In early computing systems, the system was self-contained; that is, the program was contained within the hardware elements as a "wired-in" set of instructions. The computing system was capable of a single problem solution. Any change in desired program execution could be achieved only by a physical wiring change in the instruction sequence. This wiring change, of course, again fixed the sequencing or problem solution capability of the computing system. In many cases, the process of wiring change resulted in hardware failure and reduction of system reliability. The process was a costly one, and system flexibility was still limited.

The introduction of the patch panel provided some flexibility in the programs which could be executed by a processing system. The patch panel consisted of a plugboard which could be interfaced with the processing system and which would control the sequencing in the processor in the same way as the wired-in program had previously done. Different programs could be prepared by wiring patches on the plugboard so that a program library could be built using the basic plugboard and jumper wires. The processing system program could be readily changed by the substitution of one program plugboard for another. This patching was generally performed by the programmer who was responsible for determining the operational sequences required for problem solution.

Hardware improvements added to system capability and flexibility. These advances were complemented by growth in programming techniques, and other methods of external program control were introduced. One means of external control was the use of punched cards. After the programmer had set up his sequence for problem solution, he translated the steps in the solution into an instruction sequence on a series of punched cards. Each of the cards contained an instruction which was read sequentially by the computing system. This action resulted in program execution. Multiple program possibilities existed for the system with the program library contained in card decks. Although this approach provided additional system capability in the type of program which could be executed, it had the disadvantage of slowing the system down. Recall that the early systems were characterized by serial operation — input, process, output. The system, therefore, was not processing each time it was inputting the next instruction. Multiple paper-tape units were also used for input of program data. Hardware and program developments were spurred by increasing demands by computing system users for greater capacity and more flexible processing systems.

To overcome the speed limitation of the slower peripheral devices, the magnetic-storage drum was introduced as a storage device for the program. The use of the drum allowed for a considerable reduction in time lost because of instruction transfer to the computer, and productive computer time was increased. In addition, the faster communication speed of the drum and the storage capacity available made it practical for the computer to use branching instructions. In branch instructions, the sequence of execution can be changed by the computer dependent upon the conditions which exist at some point in the execution phase. Manual intervention was required on branch instructions in earlier systems.

The use of the magnetic drum for program storage still required the problem solution by the programmer. The sequence decided upon is prepared as a card deck and transferred by the computer to the drum. The computer then communicates with the drum for all instruction movement and data manipulation.

Internal memory systems, such as magnetic-core and thin-film memories, have contributed further to the increased speeds at which programs may be executed. The program is stored internally, and program flexibility has been increased. Branching may be more easily achieved, and program segmentation is possible. Separate parts of a problem may be solved, intermediate results generated and checked, and decisions or branch operations performed.

Continued hardware developments have been matched by complementing developments in software in an effort to optimize system productivity. This growth has resulted in the division of programmers into application programmers and system programmers. The application programmers are directly involved in the analysis of the problem and in specifying the steps which are required for the solution of the problem. The system programmers create the overall system control programs and other tools used by the application programmer.

The communication with the computer must be in the language of the computer, *machine code*. Preparation of programs in machine code is a tedious and error-prone operation. Assemblers and compilers are tools which the system programmer has developed for use by the application programmer for more effective man-to-machine communication.

An *assembler* is a program which translates symbolic language into machine code, usually on a statement-for-statement basis. A *compiler* generates machine code from symbolic language, generally several machine instructions for each symbolic statement.

Other tools developed include executive programs, mathematical subroutines, and diagnostic programs.

Executive programs control the system and the execution of application (user) programs. See Chap. 18.

Mathematical subroutines include, for example, the instruction sequence required to perform a square-root computation. This sequence is stored as a subroutine which may be called upon by any user program. The same sequence may be used at any time in a program without requiring individual application programmers to develop the steps for the solution of this arithmetic operation. Other frequently used programs are available in the program library.

Diagnostic programs are used to establish confidence in both system hardware and software (program). Hardware diagnostics, for example, are executed to detect and isolate the probable causes of equipment failure.

The systems programmer develops programs which seek to optimize the system features to increase system throughput. The applications programmer applies these programs to the solution of problems.

Steps in Problem Solving

The applications programmer establishes the sequence of computer operation for problem solution. In arriving at his "ready to run" program there are certain steps or operations the programmer uses in this program development cycle. For purposes of this discussion, these operations have been divided into five steps.

1. Problem definition
2. Method of solution
3. Detailed problem analysis
4. Coding
5. Testing and debugging

Problem definition. During this phase, all facets of the problem are stated and explored. In so doing, the desirability of manual or automatic (computer) solution is also explored. This step serves the dual purpose of problem expression and feasibility investigation for data processing application.

The problem is stated in terms of input and output data requirements and format. The relationship of input data availability and output requirements timing are examined. The impact of required operational changes on the existing system, personnel requirements or displacement, and conversion costs are explored. Improvements to be gained by the conversion are stated.

This step is investigative in nature in that the results of this phase may be nothing more than the establishment of the fact that a problem exists or confirmation that present operations are satisfactory. If a problem has been established and defined, further action is usually necessary. Should the cost considerations indicate manual problem solution as the desired action, definition and solution have been accomplished. If problem resolution lies in the area of data processing, the programmer makes use of the data established in this phase in his program development cycle.

Method of solution. The type of problem involved will dictate to a great extent the methods employed in its solution. For example, methods which provide extreme accuracy (double-precision results) in calculations should not be used in payroll calculations. On the other hand, this type problem may lend itself to segmentation of the problem into a series of programs. Intermediate results of computations and updating of master records may be desirable.

This step to some extent defines the limits of the required hardware system, selects the programming language, and identifies some of the desired programming techniques to be used in problem solution. In addition, a flow chart of the major steps or operational sequences is generated for problem solution.

Detailed problem analysis. The problem analysis phase results in a finer breakdown of the flow chart into a more detailed sequence of program steps. The operations and their interconnections and interfaces are established. Identification of standardized library subroutines is accomplished. Program transfer points are indicated. The detail incorporated into the flow chart at this point is a matter of choice. It may be detailed to the point where an almost direct translation can be made to coding statements. The detailed problem analysis may, for some programmers, constitute nothing more than a mental examination of the problem and the alternatives for its solution. Documentation through flow charting may be desirable since it graphically illustrates the programming approach to problem solution.

Coding. After the analysis has been completed, the coding process takes place. Coding is the process of translating the problem solution into statements or instructions. The direct translation to machine language instructions is rarely used. In most cases, the programmer writes his program in the selected assembler or compiler language. Multiple-language systems allow the programmer to use several different compiler languages in the generation of a single program. (Compiler languages are discussed in Chap. 17.) During the coding process, the programmer may reference a language manual for the correct syntax to be used. Although the use of compiler languages simplifies the coding process, this particular phase of program generation presents the greatest probability for introduction of errors into the program. When the coding is complete, a card deck is prepared and the program is assembled or compiled. The result of the assembly or compilation is a machine language program for the solution of the problem. Although errors may be introduced into the program during any of the preceding steps, the compiler detects and indicates syntactical errors introduced in the coding process. These errors are the result of misuse of statements or improperly constructed statements. The program listing generated indicates these errors. The programmer corrects these errors by the use of correction cards and reassembles or recompiles. If all statements are syntactically correct, the object program is ready to run.

Testing and debugging. The ready-to-run status of the program established above does not guarantee a program capable of problem solution. The test of the ability of the program to achieve the desired result is the solution of a representative problem. The program is run and the results compared with a manually computed solution. These result comparisons are usually made at predetermined intervals in the problem so that any errors may be segregated to a smaller area of the total program. Should the program run and result checks prove positive, program execution may be initiated with actual data. A period of parallel operation of manual and automatic processing takes place, after which the manual system is discarded.

Should the attempt at program run prove unsuccessful, an error in the logic used in the solution of the problem is indicated. A single error may not be too difficult to uncover; however, multiple errors may react with each other to disguise the fault. There are several methods available for locating errors that do not involve the use of the processing system. Although time-consuming, these methods are usually used initially because of the costs involved in program debug on the processor.

The programmer may visually check the finished program statement by statement (desk check). This method has the disadvantage in that the programmer has a tendency to repeat all but the obvious errors since his approach to the solution of the problem is the same. This desk check could be performed by another programmer but this approach also has its disadvantages. It is time-consuming and the checker must usually be briefed on the details of the problem and program.

Another method of manual checking involves the translation of the program to flow charts. These charts are then compared with the original flow charts with logic or coding errors or both exposed. This approach is also time-consuming. After a reasonable manual check is made without success, the programmer may resort to machine error checking to accomplish program debug. These procedures involve the use of dump, monitor, or trace routines. Control cards are used to initiate these routines and are removed once the program debug is complete.

Dump results in the copying, on a line printer, of a specific data area in a format defined by DUMP. For example, DUMP NAME, FORMAT indicates the desired action. The location of data required is defined by NAME, while FORMAT specifies the form the information is to take (alphameric, decimal, octal). Dump may take place at various points during the execution of the program or at the completion of the program run. When the DUMP statement is used, the programmer may print data both before and after alteration depending upon the placement of the statement. The points at which the dump takes place may be used to segment the program so that the error area may be isolated for further analysis. Examples of DUMP statements are given below.

1. DUMP NAME for first X seconds of running.
2. DUMP NAME between sixth and twenty-third iterations.
3. DUMP NAME based on value of X (XPos, XNeg, XZero, etc.).

MONITOR results in the printing of a variable each time the value of the variable is altered.

MONITOR A results in the printing of the content of location A after alteration of the value. This is sometimes referred to as a "snapshot." Some MONITOR statements allow the programmer to specify the format for printing.

If the DUMP and MONITOR statements fail to locate error, the programmer may use the TRACE routine. The TRACE statement calls a program which executes and interprets each of the instructions while recording the instructions, the memory location of each, the content of various registers, and the status of various console indicators. This routine results in a detailed map of "computer sequencing" for each instruction as it is executed. The use of TRACE is expensive since the time for running the program may be increased by a factor of 20 or more.

Program debugging is probably the most time-consuming and hence most expensive phase in the overall program generation sequence. It has been estimated that 75 to 90 percent of the total time is spent in this operation.

An example of the problem solving sequence is given below. It is assumed that a decision has been made to use a data processing system to automate a payroll system.

Sample Problem

A decision has been made to convert the manual payroll system of a manufacturing firm to automatic processing. The present system requires that each employee complete a weekly time report for use by the accounting department in the calculation of wages. A master employee record contains rate of pay, number of dependents, and other information relating to deductions. After the calculations have been completed, a check is prepared and sorted by department for issue to the employee, a record of the check is made for file, and the employee record is updated.

Step 1.   This system requires the preparation of an employee master file suitable for inputting to the processing system and the weekly preparation of time report data for system input.

The system output will be in the form of printed checks sorted by department and a file copy of the checks issued. In addition, the employee master file will be updated.

Step 2.   The system flow diagram of Fig. 15·1 is generated to illustrate the gross flow of the operations. The employee time reports are trans-

FIG. 15·1   System flow diagram for payroll system.

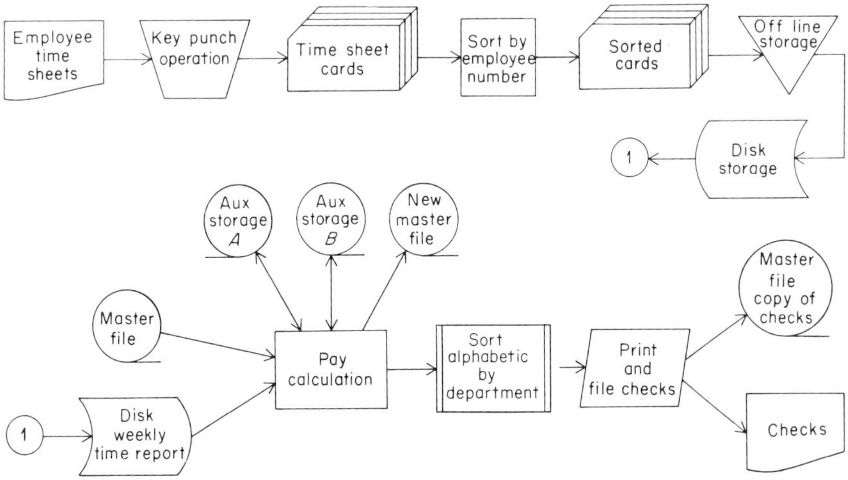

lated to punched cards in the keypunch operation. Since the time sheets are received from various departments, a sort of the cards by employee number is performed. The card deck data is then transferred to magnetic disk storage to allow for a more rapid data retrieval during the payroll calculation.

The master employee file is prepared in a similar manner (not shown on diagram). The employee master file is placed on cards via the keypunch operations and then transferred to magnetic-tape storage. The updating of the file will result in a current master employee file at the end of each pay period.

The processing system has as its inputs the current employee master file and the reported work time by week. The translation of master-file data from the manual record to the magnetic tape is a one-time operation. The weekly time report translation, of course, is performed weekly on the then-current reports. The payroll program is executed, and an updated master file is generated. An alphabetic sort by department is performed, and the employee check and file check copy are produced.

Step 3.   Each of the major functions illustrated in the system flow diagram is translated into a detailed flow chart. The pay calculation, for example, may involve straight time hours, overtime hours, shift premium, withholding tax and FICA deductions, insurance, stock plan, credit union, union dues, and other considerations. Figure 15·2 illustrates a detailed flow for the FICA calculation. Note the flow in this operation. To follow the operational sequence, follow the direction of the arrow. Note that certain symbols represent decision points. A YES results in the operational sequence continuing in one direction, while a NO causes a different path to be followed. As can be seen from Fig. 15·2, the detailed flow charting exposes the possibilities present in the calculation and allows for analysis and correction of approach prior to the coding phase.

Step 4.   The use of assembler or compiler statements to express the steps shown on the detailed flow charts constitutes the program writing. As was mentioned previously, syntactical errors will be indicated by the assembler or compiler.

Step 5.   The test and debug phase is used to prove the program. In a segmented program, individual portions may be tested and debugged. The final step connects all sections and checks for proper interaction of the program segments. Actual data is used with concurrent processing using both the manual and the automatic payroll systems. Satisfactory program performance during the trial period results in the adoption of the automated system.

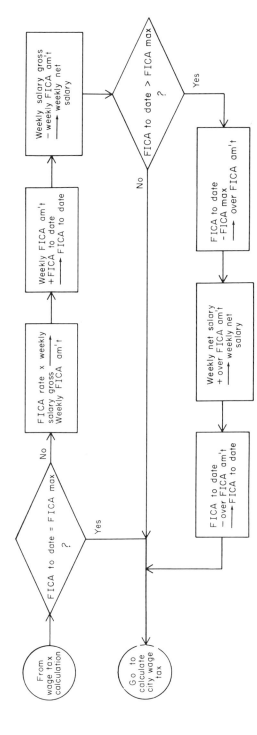

FIG. 15-2 Detailed flow charting for payroll problem.

445

It is well to mention another phase of the programming effort at this time. This phase is referred to as *program maintenance* and involves the changing or updating of the program. This program modification may be necessary because of changes in the payroll procedure, expansion, rate changes, etc. These changes are usually performed by the staff programmer at the data processing facility.

Flow charting. Flow charting is a pictorial representation of a problem and the sequence of operations or approach to its solution. Flow charts are usually referred to as *problem* flow charts or *computer* flow charts.

The problem flow chart is concerned with the problem and how it is structured and is a gross type of representation. It is useful in establishing the overall requirements and considerations for problem definition.

The computer flow chart is a more detailed representation of the problem solution and, in many cases, assumes such detail that an almost direct translation can be made in the coding process.

Although a standard set of flow-charting symbols has not been accepted by industry, there have been attempts at standardization. The symbols given in Fig. 15·3 on page 448 are those recommended for use by the American Standards Association. The flow chart of Fig. 15·1 illustrates the use of many of the symbols presented.

FIG. 15·3 Flow charting symbols. (a) Input-output symbol; (a1) punched card; (a2) magnetic tape; (a3) perforated tape; (a4) document; (a5) on-line keyboard; (a6) display; (a7) communication link; (a8) disk drum; (a9) off-line storage; (b) processing; (b1) decision; (b2) predefined process; (b3) manual operation; (b4) auxiliary operation; (c) flow; (d) annotation; (e) connector, (f) terminal.

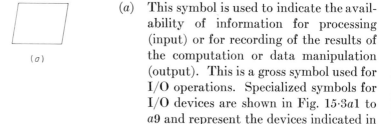

(*a*)
(*a*)   This symbol is used to indicate the availability of information for processing (input) or for recording of the results of the computation or data manipulation (output). This is a gross symbol used for I/O operations. Specialized symbols for I/O devices are shown in Fig. 15·3*a*1 to *a*9 and represent the devices indicated in the legend.

(*a*1)
(*a*1)   This symbol is used to represent input or output functions where punched cards are used for the operation.

(*a*2)
(*a*2)   The use of magnetic tape as the I/O device is represented by this symbol.

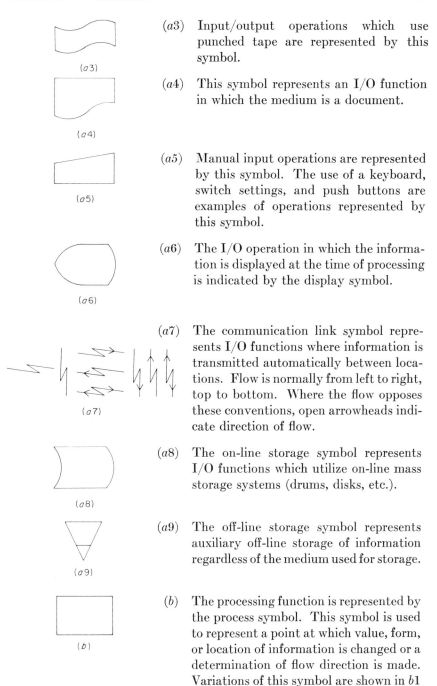

(a3) Input/output operations which use punched tape are represented by this symbol.

(a4) This symbol represents an I/O function in which the medium is a document.

(a5) Manual input operations are represented by this symbol. The use of a keyboard, switch settings, and push buttons are examples of operations represented by this symbol.

(a6) The I/O operation in which the information is displayed at the time of processing is indicated by the display symbol.

(a7) The communication link symbol represents I/O functions where information is transmitted automatically between locations. Flow is normally from left to right, top to bottom. Where the flow opposes these conventions, open arrowheads indicate direction of flow.

(a8) The on-line storage symbol represents I/O functions which utilize on-line mass storage systems (drums, disks, etc.).

(a9) The off-line storage symbol represents auxiliary off-line storage of information regardless of the medium used for storage.

(b) The processing function is represented by the process symbol. This symbol is used to represent a point at which value, form, or location of information is changed or a determination of flow direction is made. Variations of this symbol are shown in b1 through b4.

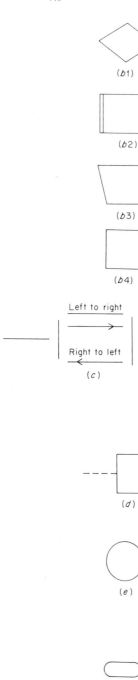

(*b*1) The decision symbol is used in those operations in which a choice of a number of alternate paths may be taken depending upon the results of the process.

(*b*2) The predefined process symbol represents a process consisting of program steps or operations that are specified elsewhere, e.g., subroutine.

(*b*3) The manual operation symbol is used to indicate an operator-performed off-line process.

(*b*4) The auxiliary operation symbol is used to indicate off-line equipment operations not under the control of the processing unit.

(*c*) The flow line is used to connect the flow diagram symbols and indicate direction of operation or sequence of flow. Normal flow is left to right, top to bottom. Where this convention is not followed, arrow-heads may be used to indicate direction flow. Bidirectional flow may be shown by single or double lines with direction shown by the use of arrowheads.

(*d*) The annotation symbol is used to facilitate the addition of descriptive comments at the appropriate point in the flow. The dotted line is connected to the symbol to which the comment applies.

(*e*) The connector symbol is used to represent a junction in a flow line. If the flow is broken by a limitation of the flow chart, the break and reentry point to the flow are shown. The symbol may also be used to show the junction of a single flow line with several other flow lines.

(*f*) The terminal symbol indicates a terminal point in a system at which data may be inserted or removed, e.g., start, halt, interrupt.

The programming process involves the generation of the instruction sequence for the data processing system.

The program-writing process includes problem definition, method of solution, detailed program analysis, coding, and testing and debugging. Each of the steps becomes progressively more detailed with a ready-to-run program resulting from the sequence.

The use of flow charting, which is a graphic presentation of the problem, facilitates program writing. Flow charts are translated to instructional sequences through coding statements using an assembler or compiler. Assemblers and compilers translate the statement sequences to machine language instructions.

The assemblers and compilers provide indications of syntactical errors in the coding process. Logic errors in the program must be detected by a manual desk check or with the use of dump, monitor, or trace routines on the operating system. After the final program debug is accomplished, the transition to an automated operation takes place.

QUESTIONS

15-1   Why is a program necessary?

15-2   What was the disadvantage of the wired-in program?

15-3   What gave the wired program some added flexibility?

15-4   Define applications programmer. System programmer.

15-5   What is an assembler? A compiler?

15-6   What is the purpose of diagnostic programs?

15-7   Name the five steps for problem solving.

15-8   Define desk checking of a program.

15-9   Why is programming in machine code undesirable?

15-10 Does a syntactically correct program guarantee an object program capable of problem solution?

15-11 Briefly describe dump, monitor, and trace routines.

15-12 What is flow charting?

chapter sixteen

Programming Elements

The earlier chapters of the text considered the basic hardware elements used by the logic designer in mechanizing the logic groupings called the arithmetic, memory, input/output, and control units of the data processing system. This chapter deals in a like manner with the basic elements used by the programmer in the creation of the program which directs the hardware in problem solution. Some of the basic tools used by the programmer include subroutines, loops, addressing techniques, assemblers, and compilers. Compilers are treated separately in Chap. 17.

The programmer is responsible for the creation of the program and the instructions that are interpreted by the control section of the computer to control the internal operations of the data processing system. The peripheral devices which are used for mass storage, input, and output operations are also under the control of the instructions written by the programmer. The program controls all phases of the operation of the computer system.

The program is written in response to a need for the solution of a particular problem on a data processing system. When a program is written, a particular instruction sequence is generated. This instruction sequence, when interpreted and acted upon by the computer, results in the solution of the problem. The instructions written by the programmer may take several forms and may be written in one of several different languages.

Programs may be written in machine language, which is a form used internally by the machine. More frequently programs are written in an assembler or compiler language, which requires translation into machine language before the computer can respond to the program.

Instructions

Computer systems are sometimes classified by the instruction formats used in the machine. A computer may be designated as a one-, two-, or three-address machine. This characteristic is decided upon during the design phase, and programs written for a particular equipment must follow the convention established for the equipment. Problem solution is possible using any of the address type machines, although each has its advantages over the others for a specific application.

The instructions written by the programmer are used to designate operations, to specify fetch and store memory operations, and to manipulate instructions and data. When an instruction designates a data fetch from memory, the data is usually placed in a predetermined hardware register. Data manipulation takes place in hardware registers which are predetermined by hardware mechanization and linked to particular operational sequences. Instructions which require memory store cause data transfer from hardware registers to internal memory. Each instruction specifies an operation to be performed by the computer and usually the memory location(s) of the operand(s) to be acted upon.

The ADD instruction (and other instructions) is considered to be a dyadic instruction; that is, the instruction requires two operands as inputs for execution. To complete the addition of two numbers residing in memory, each of two operands must be fetched from storage, the addition performed, and the sum returned to storage. Single- and two-address instruction machines require more than a single instruction to complete the operation. The three-address instruction machine, however, would perform the total operation under the control of a single instruction.

Single-address instruction format. A single-address instruction specifies an operation code (OP code) and one operand address. The address may specify the location of an operand, the location in which information is stored, or the location in which the next instruction is located (as in a BRANCH instruction).

The single-address instruction word is divided into an operation code, a variant, and an address, as illustrated in Fig. 16·1.

The OP code is used to specify the instruction which is to be performed by the computer. In the above instruction word, the six-bit OP code allows for decoding of an instruction set of up to 64 different instructions. Each OP code identifies a single instruction. For example, 000 111 (07_8) indicates load limit register 1, while a decode of 001 110 (16_8) would result in an ADD instruction.

The address points to a memory location which is associated with the operation specified by the OP code. For purposes of the early discussions in this chapter, all addresses are considered to be absolute addresses. The 12-address bits allow access to 4096 memory locations (0–4095). Relative addressing and other address modification schemes are covered later.

	1	6,7	12,13	24
	OP code	Variant	Address	

FIG. 16·1 Single-address instruction format.

The variant is considered as an extension of the OP code, or it may be used to indicate indirect addressing or indexing. For example purposes, assume a variant for the instructions of Table 16·1 as follows. For the majority of instructions, the variant is:

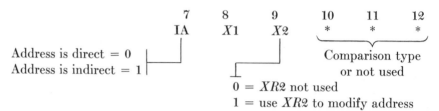

For the variant used with the MTX instruction refer to the MTX instruction listed in Table 16·1. For an example of how the variant may be used to extend the range of the OP code, consider the instruction: BRAB DDDD. This instruction is defined as: Branch to the location defined by DDDD after comparing the content of the A register with the B register. The instruction in this form might be mechanized for a comparison and transfer if the true condition ($=$), for example, exists. Depending upon the desired comparison condition, separate instructions might be defined to allow transfer on greater than, less than, or equal to, etc. The use of the variant allows the modification of the basic OP code to perform these variations without the need for separately defined OP codes.

Recall that upon the completion of the comparison, the next instruction in sequence is performed if an unsuccessful comparison (false) results. Successful comparison results in a branch to the instruction contained in the location specified in the address.

Although many instructions may be executed as variations of the basic instruction, the instruction set presented in Table 16·1 illustrates most instructions without this modification capability. The first column of the list indicates the octal machine code which represents the instruction, the second the mnemonics assigned to the instruction, the third the address, and the fourth a brief explanation of the operation performed by the instruction. All instructions listed in Table 16·1 can use indexing and indirect addressing unless specified otherwise.

Consider the addition of two numbers (operands) contained in memory and the return of the result to memory. This operation might be performed by the following sequence:

1. FETCH one of the operands (augend) from memory location MMMM and place into the A register.
2. ADD the contents of memory location NNNN (addend) to the contents of the A register; leave result in A. (Step 2 usually fetches the operand from memory into the B register and the addition takes place.)
3. STORE the contents of the A register (result) in memory location RRRR.

TABLE 16·1

Octal code	Mnemonic	Operand address	Explanation
	Control command		
00	HLT		HALT: Stop computer operation.
	Load commands		
01	LDA	DDDD	LOAD A REGISTER: Load the contents of memory location DDDD into the A register.
02	LDB	DDDD	LOAD B REGISTER: Load the contents of memory location DDDD into the B register.
03	LDX1	DDDD	LOAD INDEX REGISTER 1: Load the least significant 12 bits of the contents of memory location DDDD into index register 1.
04	LDX2	DDDD	LOAD INDEX REGISTER 2: Load the least significant 12 bits of memory location DDDD into index register 2.
05	LDX1A		LOAD INDEX REGISTER 1 FROM A: Load the least significant 12 bits of the A register into index register 1.
06	LDX2A		LOAD INDEX REGISTER 2 FROM A: Load the LS 12 bits of the A register into index register 2.
07	LL1	DDDD	LOAD LIMIT REGISTER L: Load limit register 1 with the contents of memory location DDDD.
10	LL2	DDDD	LOAD LIMIT REGISTER 2: Load limit register 2 with the contents of memory location DDDD.
	Index modify/branch command		
11 (Indexing and indirect addressing not allowed)	MTX	DDDD*	MODIFY AND/OR TEST INDEX: This instruction has several variations which are specified by variant bits 7–12. A representative group takes the general form of:
	$I(D)X_n$		INCREMENT (DECREMENT) specified index register. (n = 1 or 2)
	$I(D)TX_n$	DDDD	INCREMENT (DECREMENT) specified index and transfer control to location DDDD.

*Some variations of this instruction perform only increment or decrement functions and therefore do not use the address field.

TABLE 16-1 (continued)

Octal code	Mnemonic	Operand address	Explanation
	I(D)TX$_n$L$_n$E	DDDD	INCREMENT (DECREMENT) specified index and if new index value is equal to specified limit register, transfer control to location DDDD. ($n = 1$ or 2)
			NOTE: Other variations modify specified index and test against specified limit register for unequal, greater, less, equal or greater, equal or less, etc. If test is true, transfer to DDDD is executed. In assembly language X$_n$ is replaced by F (first) or S (second) and L$_n$ by F or S. For example: ITX1L2E would be ITFSE. D replaces I when index is to be decremented (DTX2L1E = DTSFE).

7	8	9	10	11	12	
INC	L	X	X < L	X > L	X = L	MTX variant

0 = XR1
1 = XR2
0 = L1
1 = L2
0 = increment
1 = decrement

Combinations
000 No compare, no transfer, increment or decrement only
001 X = L
010 X > L
011 X ≥ L
100 X < L
101 X ≤ L
110 X ≠ L
111 Unconditional transfer after index increment or decrement

Store commands

12	STA	DDDD	STORE A REGISTER: Store the contents of the A register into the memory location specified by DDDD.
13	STX1	DDDD	STORE INDEX REGISTER 1: Store the contents of index register 1 into memory location DDDD.
14	STX2	DDDD	STORE INDEX REGISTER 2: Store the contents of index register 2 in location DDDD.
15	STZ	DDDD	STORE ZERO: Clear (zero) the A register and store the zeros into memory location DDDD.

Table 16·1   (continued)

Octal code	Mnemonic	Operand address	Explanation
	Arithmetic commands		
16	ADD	DDDD	ADD: Perform an algebraic addition of the contents of memory location DDDD to the current contents of the *A* register. The results of the addition remain in *A*.
17	SUB	DDDD	SUBTRACT: Perform an algebraic subtraction of the contents of memory location DDDD from the current *A* register contents. Leave the result in the *A* register.
20	MUL	DDDD	MULTIPLY: Multiply the contents of the *A* register by the contents of memory location DDDD; place the most significant portion of the product in the *A* register and the least significant portion in the *C* register.
21	DIV	DDDD	DIVIDE: Divide the contents of the *A* register by the contents of memory location DDDD. The quotient is left in the *A* register and the remainder in the *C* register.
	Logical commands		
22	AND	DDDD	AND: Perform a logical AND between the contents of memory location DDDD and the *A* register contents, leaving the results in the *A* register.
23	OR	DDDD	OR: Perform a logical OR between the contents of memory location DDDD and the *A* register contents, leaving the results in the *A* register.
24	XOR	DDDD	EXCLUSIVE OR: Perform an exclusive OR between the contents of memory location DDDD and the *A* register contents, leaving the results in the *A* register.
	Branch/branch conditional commands		
25	BRUNC	DDDD	BRANCH UNCONDITIONAL: Unconditionally transfer control (BRANCH) to the location specified by DDDD.

Table 16·1   (continued)

Octal code	Mnemonic	Operand address	Explanation
26	BRAB	DDDD	BRANCH AFTER COMPARING A WITH B: This instruction has several variations specified by variant bits 7–12. The general form is BRAB. The instruction compares the A register contents with the B register contents and if the condition is true, transfers control to memory location DDDD. The conditions are as follows:

$$A = B \ (\text{BRAEB})$$
$$A \neq B \ (\text{BRANB})$$
$$A > B \ (\text{BRAGB})$$
$$A < B \ (\text{BRALB})$$
$$A \geq B \ (\text{BRAEGB})$$
$$A \leq B \ (\text{BRAELB})$$

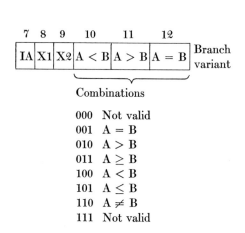

7	8	9	10	11	12	
IA	X1	X2	A < B	A > B	A = B	Branch variant

Combinations

```
000  Not valid
001  A = B
010  A > B
011  A ≥ B
100  A < B
101  A ≤ B
110  A ≠ B
111  Not valid
```

Input/output command

27	TI0	DDDD	TRANSMIT INPUT/OUTPUT: This instruction is used to control operations with the various terminal devices used by the processor system. Location DDDD contains a device control word that indicates the device to be used, number of words to be transferred, main memory starting address for data fetch (OUTPUT operation) or data store (INPUT operation), etc. The execution of the instruction causes the computer to fetch (READ) location DDDD and transmit same to I/O control. Once I/O control accepts the control word, the computer is free to continue normal execution sequence until notified by I/O of job completion, at which time the computer will take proper action.

Table 16·1 (continued)

Octal code	Mnemonic	Operand address	Explanation

Control word (general form)

	1	8 9	12 13	24

Word count (0–255)	Device†	Starting address (0–4095)

|0000|
|0001| —Magnetic tape

|0010|
|0011| —Magnetic disk (MD)

|0100|
|0101| — Flexowriter (FX)

|0110|
|0111| — Data display (DD)

| 1000 ⊢ Line printer (LP)
| 1001 ⊢ Card reader (CR)
| 1010 ⊢ Card punch (CP)
| 1011 ⊢ Paper tape reader (PTR)

|1100| Undefined: Could be
|1101| used to select a second
|1110| tape, drum, or card
|1111| reader, etc.

Register manipulation commands

| 30 | SHR‡ (Indexing and IA not allowed) | | SHIFT RIGHT: Shift the current contents of the specified register(s) right, in the manner described by bits 17–19 of the instruction word, the number of binary places indicated by bits 20–24. When |

†Bit 12 also serves as an INPUT or OUTPUT indicator.
‡See footnote on following page.

Table 16·1 (continued)

Octal code	Mnemonic	Operand address	Explanation

performing the double shift (A and C) the C register is considered an extension of the A register such as:

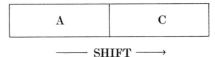

—— SHIFT ——→

31   SHL‡ (Indexing and IA not allowed)   SHIFT LEFT: Shift the current contents of the specified register(s) left, in the manner described by bits 17–19 of the instruction word, the number of binary places indicated by bits 20–24. When performing the double shift (A and C) the C register is considered an extension of the A register such as:

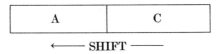

←—— SHIFT ——

NOTE: Because the shift instructions shift the current A register contents, they do not require an address field; therefore, for *these OP codes* only, the usual variant is ignored, and bits 13–24 are used to describe the shift as follows:

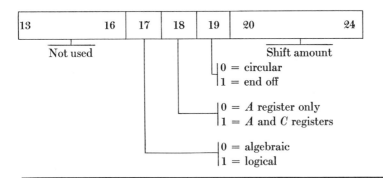

‡The assembly language for the shift instructions takes the general form SHR (or L) NN, S (or D), A (or L), C (or E).

NN = decimal number for shift amount   L = logical
S = single (A register only)   C = circular
D = double (A and C registers)   E = end off
A = algebraic

Table 16·1   (continued)

Octal code	Mnemonic	Operand address	Explanation
32	STZC		STORE ZEROS IN C: Store zeros in the C register by clearing C.
	Subroutine control		
33	SBJ	DDDD	SUBROUTINE JUMP: Store the contents of the program address register (PAR) into the A register, transfer the A register content into memory location DDDD, and transfer control (JUMP) to location DDDD + 1. The instruction address stored in DDDD will be the address of this instruction (SBJ) plus 1.
34	SRR	DDDD	SUBROUTINE RETURN: Fetch the contents of memory location DDDD and place them into the program address register. The next instruction executed will be fetched from the address that was stored in location DDDD.

Using the appropriate instructions from Table 16·1, the problem is expressed as follows:

1.	FETCH	LDA	MMMM	Load first number (operand) from memory location MMMM into the A register.
2.	ADD	ADD	NNNN	Add contents of location NNNN to A register contents (MMMM) and leave results in A register.
3.	STORE	STA	RRRR	Store contents of A register (result) in memory location RRRR.

Note that in this instruction sequence only a single-memory address is expressed with each instruction. Each of the operations is defined by a specific instruction in the instruction/address format defined for single-address instructions.

Two-address instruction format. The two-address instruction specifies an OP code and two address syllables and may be formatted as shown in Fig. 16·2.

FIG. 16·2 Two-address instruction format.

This format may direct the computer to perform the following operations:

1. Place the contents of the memory location specified by address 1 into the *B* register.
2. Perform the operation specified by the operation code (e.g., ADD operation) placing the results into the *A* register.
3. Store the contents of the *A* register (result) into the memory location specified by address 2.

In this format note that only one operand is fetched by the instruction. The second operand was assumed to be in the *A* register. The second operand could have been loaded by an instruction such as LOAD REGISTER (LDR) or could be the result of a previously performed operation.

Some instructions require two addresses while others (such as HALT, BRANCH, etc.) may not. There are several basic formats in use. In some systems, the operator syllable specifies only the instruction to be performed, while in others it may indicate both the instruction and possible variations of the instruction or addresses or both. The address syllables represent operand locations, store locations, branch locations, and in some instructions are used as special syllables. Typical special-syllable applications include shift amounts, type of shift (logical, circular, etc.) to be performed, and amount of increment or decrement for a particular index register. For test/compare index type instructions, the syllable could be used to select the desired index, limit register, and the type of comparison (equal, greater, etc.) to be performed. The bit length of the special syllable is determined by the

FIG. 16·3 Expanded address syllable, two-address instruction format.

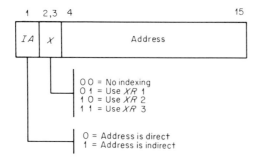

equipment in use. When the address syllable represents operand or store locations, a portion of the address syllable could be used to indicate indirect addressing or indexing or both and may take the form of Fig. 16·3.

The syllable length selected for the illustration contains 15 bits. Bit 1, when a 0, indicates that bits 4–15 form an address of an operand (or store location), and when a "1," indicates that bits 4–15 form the address of another address. Twelve bits of relative address can access 4096 separate memory locations (decimal 0–4095). The index field of two bits (assuming three index registers) indicates if indexing is required. A 00 configuration indicates that no indexing is to be performed, with the other configurations indicating indexing. For example, 10 would indicate that the contents of XR2 are to be added to the address (4–15) to obtain a final address (unless indirect addressing is also specified). The significance of the X field is dependent upon the system meaning. Some systems may have the index/ indirect control as part of the operator syllable in order to allow indexing of special syllables as well as addresses.

Table 16·2 illustrates a partial instruction set for a two-address ma-

TABLE 16·2 Partial Instruction Set for a Two-address Machine

Octal code	Mnemonic	Address	Address	Explanation
00	HLT			HALT: Stop computer operation.
01	ADD	DDDD	RRRR	ADD: Add (algebraic) the contents of location DDDD to the current contents of the A register, and store the result in location RRRR.
02	LDR	DDDD	SSSS	LOAD REGISTER: Load the contents of memory location DDDD into the register specified by special syllable SSSS. (Registers may be A, B, C, X, L.)
03	STR	DDDD	SSSS	STORE REGISTER: Store the contents of the register specified by SSSS into memory location DDDD.
04	IXR	AAAA	SSSS	INCREMENT INDEX: Increment the index register specified by the SSSS syllable by an amount that is specified by AAAA.
05	DXR	AAAA	SSSS	DECREMENT INDEX: Same as IXR except decrement.
06	TRX	SSSS	BBBB	TEST INDEX: Compare the index and limit registers specified by the SSSS syllable in the manner indicated by SSSS ($X = L, X > L, X < L$, etc.). If the comparison is true, transfer control to location BBBB (next instruction taken from address BBBB); otherwise execute the next instruction in sequence.

chine. The instructions presented are intended as a representative instruction set for a two-address format system.

The previous example of the addition of two numbers is stated in the two-address format as:

Mnemonic	Address	Address	Explanation
LDR	MMMM	SSSS	Load the contents of memory location MMMM into the A register (assumed).
ADD	NNNN	RRRR	Add the contents of location NNNN to contents of A register and store result (A) into memory location RRRR.

Note that only two instructions are required for the program. One instruction is used to fetch the first operand. The second instruction indicates the operation to be performed, the location of the second operand, and the location in memory into which the result is to be stored.

Three-address instruction format. A three-address instruction specifies an operation code (OP code) and three addresses and is generally formatted as illustrated in Fig. 16·4.

The instruction word may be considered as consisting of an operator syllable and three address syllables; some instructions use fewer than three addresses and may also use a syllable as a special syllable, such as SHIFT AMOUNT. When used with an arithmetic unit which contains two functional registers (A and B), the instruction format would be interpreted as follows:

1. Place the contents of the memory location specified by address 1 into the A register.
2. Place the contents of the memory location specified by address 2 into the B register.
3. Perform the operation specified by the operation code, placing the results in the A register.
4. Store the contents of the A register into the location specified by address 3.

Assuming that the operation specified by the OP code is an ADD, two operands must be fetched from the memory. At the completion of step 1, the A register contains the addend. The B register contains the augend at the completion of step 2. The summing of augend and addend takes place

FIG. 16·4 Three-address instruction format.

OP code	Address 1	Address 2	Address 3

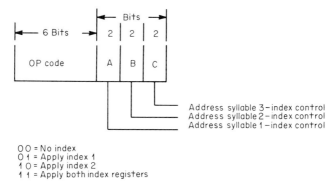

00 = No index
01 = Apply index 1
10 = Apply index 2
11 = Apply both index registers

FIG. 16·5 Expanded operator syllable, three-address instruction format.

during step 3 with the sum residing in the A register. Step 4 completes the operation with the store of the sum in the designated memory location. Thus in a three-address machine, a single instruction is used to specify the operation, the addresses of the two operands to be used, and the location into which the sum is to be placed.

The operator syllable may be used to indicate address modification (called indexing) on any or all three address syllables. Figure 16·5 illustrates the formatting of the operator syllable to indicate this modification.

Six bits of the operator syllable are used to specify the OP code. The remaining six bits, in groups of two, are used to indicate address modification on each of the three addresses. The binary configurations possible in the two-bit positions are used to specify the required action.

The operator syllable illustrated in Fig. 16·6 indicates that address 1 is to be modified by the content of index register 2, address 2 is to be modified by the content of index register 1, and address 3 by index registers 1 and 2. If no address modification is required, the 00 coding would appear in the appropriate positions of the operator syllable. In the example shown, two index registers are assumed; however, in systems which use many index registers, the significance of the bits in the A, B, and C fields would change. Address modification through indexing is covered more fully later in the chapter.

Each address syllable can designate indirect addressing (IA) as well as a memory location. The most significant bit of the address syllable is the IA bit. Formatting for an address syllable is shown in Fig. 16·7.

FIG. 16·6 Example of operator syllable defining address modification, three-address format.

FIG. 16·7 Expanded address syllable, three-address instruction format.

TABLE 16-3

Octal code	Mnemonic	Operand Address 1	Operand Address 2	Operand Address 3	Explanation
00	HLT				HALT: Stop computer operation.
10	LDX	SSSS	DDDD		LOAD INDEX: Load the contents of memory location specified by DDDD into the index register specified by special syllable SSSS.
11	LLR	SSSS	DDDD		LOAD LIMIT REGISTER: Load the contents of memory location specified by DDDD into the limit register specified by special syllable SSSS.
12	MTX	AAAA	SSSS	BBBB	MODIFY AND/OR TEST INDEX: Increment (decrement) the index register specified by special syllable SSSS by the amount specified by syllable AAAA. Then compare that index with the limit register that is also specified by syllable SSSS. If the comparison is "true," transfer control to location BBBB; otherwise, execute the next instruction in sequence. Syllables AAAA and SSSS take the general form of:

NOTE: An assembly language format for the MTX variations might appear as:

$$X = L \ I(D)TEQ \ X_n, \ NN, \ L_n, \ NAME$$
$$X > L \ I(D)TGR \ X_n, \ NN, \ L_n, \ NAME$$
$$X \neq L \ I(D)TUE \ X_n, \ NN, \ L_n, \ NAME$$

Example
ITEQ X1, 10, L2, LOOP
Increment index register 1 by 10 and compare new index value with limit register 2. If the comparison is "true" ($=$), transfer control to memory location LOOP; otherwise, execute next instruction in sequence.

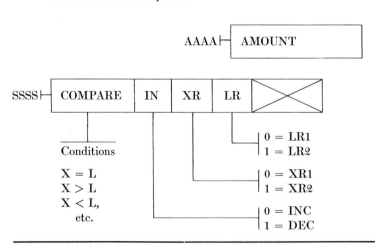

Table 16·3 (continued)

Octal code	Mnemonic	Operand Address 1	Operand Address 2	Operand Address 3	Explanation
20	ADD	DDDD	CCCC	RRRR	ADD: Perform an algebraic addition between the contents of the memory locations specified by DDDD and CCCC and store the result into the memory location specified by RRRR.
27	STZ	DDDD			STORE ZERO: Store 0's into the memory locations specified by DDDD.
30	SHR*	DDDD	SSSS	DDDD	SHIFT RIGHT: Shift the contents of memory location DDDD right the number of places specified by special syllable SSSS. Store the result in memory location DDDD. (The fetch and store locations are usually the same location, although they can be different if desired.)

*This instruction in assembly language may take the general form: SHR A1, A3, D, L, C, N, where A1 is the address of the operand to be shifted, A3 the address at which the result is to be stored, D indicates double (A and C registers) if present and single (A only) if absent, L indicates logical if present and algebraic if absent, C indicates circular if present and end off when absent, and N is the decimal shift amount. For example, SHR JOE, JOE, L, 10 indicates that the contents of memory location JOE should be shifted end-off logical 10 places and the results of the operation returned to location JOE.

A zero IA bit indicates that the 11 address bits specify the location of an operand. A one IA bit indicates that the 11 address bits specify the location which contains the address of the operand. Indirect addressing was discussed in Chap. 10.

Table 16·3 presents a partial instruction set for a three-address machine.

Examination of the instruction set indicates the use of three addresses for some instructions while others (such as LDX) use fewer than three. Others such as the shift (SHR) use both address and special syllable forms. Note that although three-address format is specified, not all instructions require three-address syllables nor is it required that all syllables specify addresses.

The basic ADD example discussed previously would be stated in three-address format as:

ADD   MMMM   NNNN   RRRR

This "program" sequence requires but a single instruction, while the single-address machine required three instructions, and the two-address machine required two instructions for execution.

Instructions such as HLT, STZ, etc., are executed in a single step regardless of the address format in use. Thus two- and three-address machines may or may not use the complete format defined for the machine type. Different instructions require fewer addresses specified to allow execution. Special syllables provide flexibility and more clearly define the operations. Equipment capability and instruction definitions provide many variations of the representative one-, two- and three-address formats presented.

Memory Addressing

The memory is a storage device which contains the program. Program is divided into data and instructions. The data is the information which is manipulated in the manner specified by the instructions.

Memory is divided into numerous locations which are identified by numerical addresses, each of which usually contains one data element or one program instruction. The addresses are usually assigned at the time of fabrication and begin at 0 and progress to the end of memory in ascending order of numerical sequence. In some systems, memory may contain over a million words. The programmer must be aware of the location of his program in memory and indicate to the processing system the location of data, instructions, or both. The computer must be made aware of the location of the program before the program can be executed. Some computers require that a program begin at location 0. The computer selects the first instruction from location 0, performs the operation specified, and goes to location 1 for the next instruction.

The programmer has several means at his disposal for addressing memory and calculating memory addresses. Four types are discussed in the following paragraphs, absolute addressing, relative addressing, indexing, and indirect addressing.

Absolute addressing. The absolute address is the designator assigned to the particular memory location at the time of construction. It is a physical location within the memory which will always be read each time that designator is addressed. For example, the address 0077_8 would always cause a read of the last word on the first mat of the memory illustrated in Fig. 11·10.

When a programmer is writing a program for a system that requires him to specify a physical memory location, he is using absolute addressing techniques. Consider the following single-address instruction sequence for the equation $(X + Y)/Z = D$:

Memory
location

0	LDA	4	Load A register with value X
1	ADD	5	Add memory location 5 (value Y) to A register
2	DIV	6	Divide A register by memory location 6 (value Z)
3	STA	7	Store A register content in memory location 7
4	Value	X	
5	Value	Y	
6	Value	Z	
7	Location reserved for result		

Note that the instruction sequence is located in memory addresses 0, 1, 2, 3. The example assumes a computer whose program must begin at location 0. These memory locations will be addressed sequentially, and the operations indicated will be performed. Note also that the absolute address of the operand involved in each data manipulation is specified. Locations 4, 5, and 6 contain the data, while location 7 is reserved for the result of the computation. Some problems would be involved in the hardware implementation of this method of memory location designation for the million-word memory, however.

In the example given, the problem solution is correct; however, the programmer did not instruct the computer to halt at the completion of the program. This oversight results in the continued sequencing of the program through steps 4, 5, etc., with the processor erroneously interpreting the data areas as instructions. The addition of a HALT instruction at the appropriate point results in the new instruction sequence below:

Memory
location

0	LDA	8
1	ADD	5
2	DIV	6
3	STA	7
4	HLT	
5	Value	Y
6	Value	Z
7	Location reserved for result	
8	Value	X

Note that the instructions are now contained in locations 0 through 4, the value X is placed in location 8, and the new location of value X is indicated in the LDA instruction. In a larger program where variable X is referred to numerous times, the changes necessitated by the original error increase, with the possibility of introduction of additional coding errors.

In a system that requires the program (instructions) to begin at location 0 of memory, it is almost impossible to multiprogram (Chap. 18). Multiprogramming requires that more than one program reside in main memory at the same time, and of course, both may not begin at location 0. A method was devised that allows a program to be moved from point to point within memory and still appear as though it begins in location 0. This method provides a reference point, and all addresses coded by the programmer are relative to this point. The reference point is termed the *base register*, and the method of memory addressing is termed *relative addressing*.

Relative addressing. Relative addressing allows a program to be placed anywhere in main memory and executed from that point. A base register is used to define the starting point of the program (program instruction base) and a base register is used to define the starting point of the data (data base). This allows the data and the program to be considered disjointed objects. The program base register (PB) contains the address of the starting point of the program, and the data base register (DB) contains the address of the starting point of the data area. Both registers indicate the displacement of the respective starting points from physical location 0 of memory. Figure 16·8 illustrates two programs and two data areas in main memory. A 16K memory is assumed. Note that the numbering is in an unbroken sequence, even though four physical memory units might be required to achieve this total storage capacity.

If multiprogramming is considered, at some time it will be required that program A be suspended and program B be initiated. When this condition occurs, the base registers must be reloaded to reflect the positioning of program B and the data for program B. Displacement B is placed in the PB register and displacement D is inserted into the DB register. The com-

FIG. 16·8 Simplified example of relative addressing.

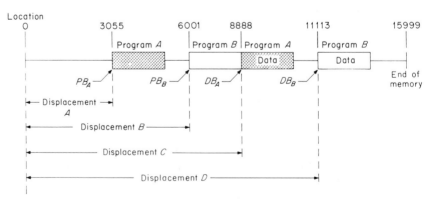

puter may now begin execution of program B. Figure 16·8 shows several places in the memory that are not allocated to program or data. A third and a fourth program may be placed in these areas; the central processor base registers would be altered to reflect their position during execution.

The addresses and instructions written by the programmer reflect the address of a memory location relative to the appropriate base register. Consider the following instruction sequence that directs the computer to solve the equation $(X + Y)/Z = D$:

Relative address (PB)		Relative address (DB)
0	LDA	0
1	ADD	1
2	DIV	2
3	STA	3
4	HLT	

Relative address (DB)	
0	Value of X
1	Value of Y
2	Value of Z
3	Location reserved for result

Assume that the above program is program A of Fig. 16·8. Displacement A is equal to 3055, as indicated by the program base register. To initiate the program, 0 is placed in the program address register (PAR). PAR + PB$_A$ are added to form an absolute address which will cause the initial program instruction (address 3055) to be fetched from memory. LDA 0 is fetched from memory. Relative address (RA) 0 is indicated for the data. The relative address 0 is added to the DB$_A$ (data base register value) of 8888 which is interpreted by the processor as LDA 8888 or load A from absolute address 8888. Upon the completion of this instruction, PAR is incremented to a count of 1. The next instruction (ADD 1) is fetched from the absolute address formed by adding the new PAR value to PB$_A$. An operation and relative address are specified. To the contents of A, add the contents of memory location 1 + 8888 (RA + DB$_A$). The program continues in sequence with the fetching of the instruction, computation of data address and data fetch operation execution, stepping of PAR, and repeating of the sequence.

When the programmer wrote the instructions, he assumed they were located in sequence from location 0; he also assumed that the data was located in sequence from location 0. When the program and data are loaded into memory, the executive program sets the base registers to the proper value. Note that the data or the program can be located anywhere in main memory; all that is required is that the base registers contain the absolute address of the starting point.

If the program designated to be run were program B, RA + PB_B indicate an initial address of 6001 (0 + 6001) as the beginning address for program B. Initial data location for program B data is RA + DB_B or 11113 (0 + 11113). Since both program and data were initially placed in sequential locations, the absolute addresses of program and data would be formulated during program execution.

Some problems may require that the address be further modified. Modification of addresses may be accomplished by inserting another variable into the equation (BA + RA = AA) for calculating the absolute address. The new equation for address calculation is BA + RA + IV = AA. IV (index value) is a value that can be incremented or decremented, allowing the programmer an additional amount of control over the address calculation.

Indexing. Indexing is the process of address modification which allows for the performance of repetitive operations or sequences without the requirement for a continual restatement of the instruction sequence.

Assume that a program is required to sum 100 numbers. If there were no method of address modification, the program might appear as follows:

	RA			RA	
PB → 0	LDA	0	DB → 0		first number
1	ADD	1		1	second number
2	ADD	2		2	third number
3	ADD	3		3	fourth number
	.			.	
	.			.	
	.			.	
99	ADD	99		99	one hundredth number
100	STA	100		100	reserved for result
101	HLT				

All data is assumed to be relative to DB. It is also assumed that the total of the 100 numbers will not cause an arithmetic overflow.

To complete the desired calculation required 102 instructions. The ADD instruction had to be repeated 99 times. It should be noted that each ADD instruction was stored in a separate memory location; thus 102 locations were required to store the instruction sequence.

Address modification by indexing allows a reduction in the number of instructions (and memory locations) required to complete the sequence. Address modification requires that the equation describing the absolute

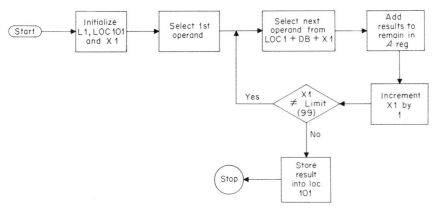

FIG. 16·9 Flow-chart solution of 100-sums problem.

address be modified to appear as $BA + RA + IV = AA$. The first number
is contained in memory location $DB + 0 + 0$, the second is contained in
memory location $DB + 0 + 1$, and the last in location $DB + 0 + 99$. In
this case the relative address remains constant, and the index variable is
altered. The following instruction sequence accomplishes the same function
as the preceding 102-instruction sequence.

RA			DB	
$PB \rightarrow 0$	LL1	100	$\rightarrow 0$	first value
1	STZ	101	1	second value
2	LDX1	101	2	third value
3	LDA	0	3	fourth value
4	ADD	1	.	
5	MTX*	4	.	
6	STA	101	99	one hundredth value
7	HLT		100	value = 99
			101	reserved for total

*(ITX1L1U)

Figure 16·9 illustrates the program flow.

The instruction LL1 is used to initialize the limit register to the value
contained in location 100 (value 99). STZ is used to initialize location 101
(value 0), while LDX1 is used to initialize index register 1 to 0. LDA
fetches the first operand from location specified by (RA) $0 + DB + 0$ (X1).
ADD fetches the second value from location (RA) $1 + DB + 0$ (X1) and
sums it with the value in A and returns the sum to the accumulator. The
MTX(ITX1L1U) increments the index register and compares the index
value with the limit register value. Since $X1 \neq L1$, the instruction sequence

branches to location 4. The next value is fetched from the specified address (RA) $1 + DB + 1$ (X1). The summing takes place, the index register is incremented by 1, the comparison of X1 and L1 values is made, and the sequencing continues. The index value is used for address modification, and it is also used to control the number of iterations through a portion of the program. The value of 99 that was loaded into the limit register acts as a loop control for the required number of additions. When the value of the index register reaches 99, the addition of the 100 numbers is complete. It should be noted that two values had already been added prior to incrementing the index register. After the index is incremented to 99, the comparison L1 is equal to X1; therefore the branch is not executed, and the next instruction in sequence is performed. (Recall that the check for branch is the $\neq$ condition.) STA 101 stores the accumulator in location 101, the PAR is stepped, and the computer halts.

The two important functions of address modification and loop control through indexing are shown in this example. The summation of 100 values may be expressed as

$$S = \sum_{i=0}^{99} a_i$$

where i is the subscript value representing each element.

$$S = a_0 + a_1 + a_2 + \cdots + a_{98} + a_{99}$$

The value i (index register 1) was initialized to 0 and incremented to select each variable in turn. The value i could have been initialized to 99 and decremented toward 0 with the same results.

Under certain conditions the data array may be contained outside the limit of the relative address, for example, if the numeric address of the first location of the data array is too large to be expressed by $RA + DB$. The

FIG. 16·10 Example of single-level indirect addressing.

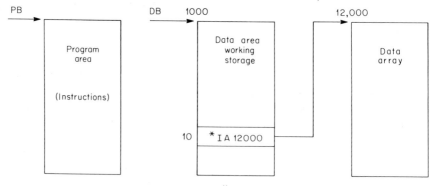

* IA = Indirect address

programmer may manipulate the data even though it cannot be addressed relative to DB. This method is termed *indirect addressing*.

Indirect addressing. Indirect addressing (IA) provides the programmer with the ability to control data that is not contained within the normal working storage area (relative to the data base register). Indirect addressing also provides a means of connecting data objects together allowing one data object to be found from within another. Figure 16·10 illustrates this relationship.

Location DB + 10 contains the address of the first location of the data array (i.e., the displacement of the first location of the data array from location 0 in main memory). This address is termed an indirect address and in the example is address 12000 absolute. The absolute address specified in indirect addressing may be modified by the use of index registers in a manner similar to that previously described. Note that in the previous example, the index register allowed the sequential addressing of locations in memory relative to the DB. In the above example, when indexing is used, the sequential addressing of memory locations takes place in another portion of the memory.

The programmer notifies the hardware through the use of the instruction and index bit that location 10 contains the absolute address and that it is to be modified by the index registers. Recall that this location is indicated by the programmer as a relative address. The IA in this example is contained in location 1010 (absolute). It is possible to use several levels of indirect addressing (Chap. 10).

An indirect-address operation initiates at least two memory operations, a fetch to obtain the indirect address and a fetch (or store) from (into) the specified memory location, depending upon whether data is being retrieved or stored.

The following instruction sequence illustrates the use of indirect addressing in the solution of the problem discussed in indexing.

	RA			Data array RA	
PB → 0	LL1	0	IA → 0		first value
1	STZ	2	1		second value
2	LDX1	2	2		third value
3	LDA	10	3		fourth value
4	IX1		.		.
5	ADD	10	.		.
6	MTX*	5	.		.
7	STA	2	98		ninety-ninth value
8	HLT		99		one hundredth value

*(ITX1L1U)

RA

DB → 0   value equal to 100

     2   reserved for result

    10   indirect address (IA)

DB + 10 = absolute address of location 0 of data array

DB + 0 = index control variable

As in the previous example, the LL1, STZ, and LDX1 instructions are used to initialize, which sets up the initial conditions of the limit and index registers. The LDA instruction requests a fetch from location 10. Recall that the location specified is equal to DB (1000 in our example) + RA 10 or 1010. This location has been designated as containing an indirect address which must be modified by an index value. The IA specifies location 12000 (absolute) and, as a result of initialization (LDX1), the index register contains a 0. The absolute address of the data required is 12000 (IA 12000 + IV 0). The first operand is brought from this location into the accumulator.

IX1 steps the index register (to 1), and the next instruction in sequence is decoded. The ADD instruction again addresses DB + 10 which contains the IA. The address modification in this instance results in an operand address of 12001 since the IV is 1. The second value in the array is fetched and added to the content of the accumulator. MTX(ITX1L1U) causes the index register to be stepped to 2, causes the comparison of the index register and limit register contents, and returns to instruction location PB + 5 (since comparison ≠). Program steps 5 and 6 are repeated with the IA address being modified by the increasing order of IVs, the data fetches occurring, and the addition, the incrementing of the index register, and the comparisons taking place. When the index value reaches 100, it indicates that the summing of the one hundredth value has taken place. The comparison will result in an equal condition, and instead of a branch to location PB + 5, the next instruction in sequence is decoded. The result is stored in DB + 2, and the computer halts.

Note that the indirect address contained in location DB + 10 was not changed but was allowed to serve as a base register to identify the starting point of the array. Each element in the array was addressed by IA + IV to allow the sequential selection of the variables.

The instruction sequences used in the indexing and indirect addressing examples used loops as a technique in problem solution.

Decision-making and loop control. The computer usually executes the instructions in the step-by-step sequence in which the programmer has written them. This characteristic provides limitations in the generation of programs. The use of branch or decision instructions allows the programmer to alter the sequence of instruction execution. Jump and comparison instructions have been mentioned previously. The comparison instructions provide the means whereby the computer can exercise decisions based on one or the other of the alternatives available from the comparison. Examples of comparison were given in the summation problem. The alternatives available as a result of the comparison allowed the program either to continue in the normal instruction sequence or to vary from the normal sequence.

Decision-making instructions usually take the form:

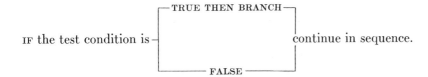

IF the test condition is   continue in sequence.

The symbolic representation for flow-chart use is illustrated in Chap. 15.

The test condition asks a question, and the path taken depends upon the answer to the question. It should be noted that only one of two possible conditions is allowed to occur (yes or no). This test condition operation is illustrated in Fig. 16·9. This decision-making capability of the comparison instructions forms the basis for loop control and other phases of program writing.

As a problem is being analyzed, redundancy in operations and procedures may be detected by the programmer. To effectively use the available memory space and save coding time, redundant operations and coding are decreased by the use of a loop. A *loop* may be defined as a sequence of instructions or operations that is executed repeatedly by the computer. Problems may be repetitious because calculations are performed repeatedly on a block of information or because the result of the problem is arrived at in an iterative manner. All loops have several characteristics in common:

1. Entry and reentry point
2. Initialization phase
3. Performance of a function
4. Loop control
5. Test for termination
6. Exit point

Figure 16·9 illustrates a flow chart for the summation of 100 numbers and possesses all the characteristics of a loop. The entry point into the loop is the first instruction. The first three instructions of this sequence perform the initialization of the loop, loading of a control value into the limit register, zero into the index register, and zero into the result location. The ADD instruction is repeated several times and may be considered the primary function of the loop. The incrementing of the index register and the comparison of the index with the limit performs the functions of maintaining loop control and testing for termination. If the test fails, the loop is terminated, and the exit path to the STORE instruction is taken. If the results of the test are "true," control is transferred to the loop reentry point which is the ADD instruction. Loops are used when it is desirable to repeat a sequence of instructions several times and are generally part of the in-line coding.

Subroutines. In any computer application, there are many logical and mathematical processes that occur again and again, such as computing a square root or character conversion. The same sequence of instructions is required to perform the process no matter where the process is required in the program. To decrease the tedium of coding and to conserve memory space, the necessary instructions are written once and then permanently stored and recorded in such a way that any programmer can insert them into his program wherever needed. These specialized programs are called *subroutines* and are so labeled because they are subordinate (nested) routines within the main program. A subroutine may be defined as a program designed to perform one specific function independently of any other program.

Since a subroutine can be called from any point in the main program, it must be standardized. In order to standardize a subroutine, parameters required by the subroutine must be established. Parameters required by subroutines are used to direct or control the operation of the subroutine and are generally of two types, values or addresses. A value may indicate the number of characters that are to be converted by the subroutine or may indicate a control variable. An address is used to indicate to the subroutine where the data to be manipulated is located. If the instruction sequence for a summation of 100 numbers is changed to a more general form, it appears as follows:

$$S = \sum_{i=0}^{N} a_i$$

Three parameters must be supplied to the summation subroutine. The quantity N which will be the same as the size of the data array must be given. The starting address of the data array must be indicated, and the address of the location where the result could be stored must be provided. In order to provide flexibility for use of the subroutine, the program is written independent of the main program and is able to solve for any value

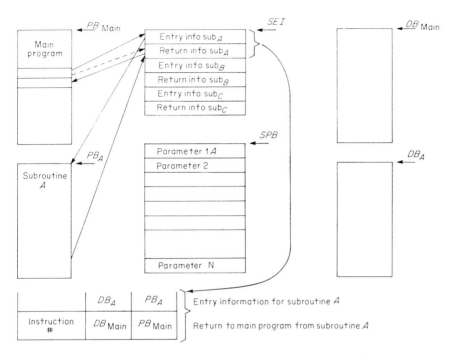

FIG. 16·11   Main program subroutine interface.

of N. The subroutine must be told what is to be manipulated, how much is to be manipulated, and where the results are to be contained.

Standardization of subroutines implies a standard method of passing the parameters to the subroutine. Figure 16·11 illustrates an interface which may be used to control the passing of parameters, entry to, and exit from a subroutine. The subroutine program base register (SPB) is added.

The parameters required for the subroutine are stored relative to SPB. The subroutine may remove the parameters for use by addressing the required memory location. The number of parameters varies in accordance with the requirements of the subroutine. The summation subroutine requires three parameters.

If the main program is able to reference several subroutines, a subroutine entry information base register is required. Subroutine entry and return information is stored relative to the subroutine entry information (SEI) base value.

Subroutine entry information is the program base register value (PB_A) which locates the subroutine in main memory and the data base value (DB_A) which locates the subroutine data area in main memory. In this referencing technique, the first instruction of the subroutine must be located in location 0 relative to PB_A.

Return information is also stored relative to the SEI register. The return information is the information required to return control from the subroutine to the main program at the completion of the subroutine. The return information consists of the program base (PB) of the main program, the data base (DB) of the main program, and the address of the next instruction of the main program to be executed ($PAR_{MAIN} + 1$).

Subroutine entry values are placed into areas identified by SEI as the subroutine is loaded into main memory. These locations are usually located from tables controlled by the executive program. Return information is placed into locations relative to SEI at the time the subroutine is entered.

In Fig. 16·11 the main program is executed sequentially until an instruction calls for a subroutine, e.g., subroutine A. The DB_{MAIN}, PB_{MAIN}, and $PAR_{MAIN} + 1$ are stored relative to SEI as return information for subroutine A. The subroutine entry information is brought from the entry information area and is loaded into the PB and DB areas to identify the subroutine locations relative to PB and DB. The instruction sequence of the subroutine is executed. At the completion of the subroutine, the subroutine return instruction is executed. The location of the subroutine A return information is addressed (relative to SEI) and the DB_{MAIN} and PB_{MAIN} values are inserted in the respective registers. In addition the word address of the next instruction in the main program sequence is specified. The main program reinitiates the execution of instructions in the normal sequence.

Assemblers. The instruction sets and sequences used in the illustrations throughout the chapter use the mnemonic names of the instructions instead of the machine code representation. This form is used to allow the reader to more easily identify the operations involved. The memory addresses and variants are noted in octal rather than binary for ease of representation. Although the octal notation is useful, locations expressed in octal may lose their meaning and make program writing more difficult. The machine can respond only to instructions it can decode, and these instructions must be in machine code. The programmer can write his instructions in machine code, but this procedure is time-consuming. The use of an assembler (assembly program) allows the programmer to write in an intermediate language (assembler language) readily understandable by himself and have the assembler convert it to the language of the machine. Thus the programmer specifies operations using mnemonics, uses names instead of numeric addresses, and uses certain specified symbols to indicate desired sequences or operations. The assembler program translates operation codes, address names, and variant names or symbols to the correct octal representation in machine language.

Symbols have special meanings in assembler language. For example, a slash (/) may mean INDEX BY. A name such as RESULT may indicate the memory location into which the result of an operation is to be stored. The names selected by the programmer have meaning to him, and thus he is able to more easily develop his program sequences. TEMP1 and TEMP2 may identify the locations containing temporary or intermediate variables. A three-address instruction in assembler language might be written as:

MUL PRICE, QUANTITY, TOTALDOL

and mean "Multiply price by quantity and store the result in location total dollars." The programmer is not concerned with the numeric address of each of the operands. The assembler will assign addresses to each of the names and associate the name and the specific address each time the name is repeated in the program. Symbols such as plus (+) and minus (−) are used to allow the programmer to reference locations relative to a previously named location. For example,

SUB TOTALDOL, DISCOUNT, TOTALDOL + 1

specifies that the discount is to be subtracted from the total dollars and placed into the location following total dollars. This eliminates the requirement of naming each memory location.

Machine operation mnemonic codes may change to allow the assembler mnemonic codes to define the operation more clearly.

The single-address instruction:

MTX DDDD

may appear as several unique codes in assembly language. For example,

ITFFE NAME

indicates an increment of the first index register with a transfer to the instruction in location NAME. The transfer is to be made if the comparison with first limit register is successful (=).

An increment of the second index register and a transfer to location NAME1, if the comparison with the first limit register is successful (≠), is expressed as:

ITSFU NAME1

In like manner, "Decrement the first index and transfer to NAME3 if the comparison with the second limit is successful (= or >)" is indicated by

DTFSGE   NAME3

It should be noted that the MODIFY INDEX instruction assumes many forms in various assembly languages for different machines. For example, "Increment index 2 by 3 and transfer if X2 does not equal limit 1," might appear in three-address format as:

ITUE   X2, 3, L1, NAME

It should be recalled that for the comparisons above, the index register value is compared with the associated limit register value after incrementing or decrementing. Note also that in the assembly language form, the variant symbol is not indicated. The machine variant(s) is developed by the assembler after decoding the symbolic operation code.

Indexing and indirect addressing. The assembly language allows the content of the base syllable to be specified more easily. Assume the instruction

STA DDDD B

There may be many variations of this instruction. Some of them may appear as follows:

STA JOE, DB

Store the contents of the accumulator in location JOE relative to the DB register, or:

STA JOE/X1, DB

An address presented to memory consists of RA + BA + IV. JOE is the relative address RA, DB is the data base, and /X1 specifies the index register that contains the index value IV. The first variation specifies that the content of the accumulator is to be stored into the memory location JOE which is relative to the data base (DB). The second symbolic representation indicates that the content of the accumulator is to be stored into location JOE plus the content of first index register. The location specified is relative to the data base (DB).

Indirect addressing may be designated with an asterisk (*). The instruction to store information with indirect addressing appears as:

STA *JOE, DB

This statement indicates that JOE contains an indirect address that specifies the actual data location. The combination of indexing and indirect addressing may be designated as:

ADD *JOE/X2, DB

This instruction may be interpreted as "Fetch the indirect address from location JOE relative to the DB, add the contents of the second index to the indirect address, and present the modified address to the main memory; fetch the data word from this location and add this value to the current contents of the accumulator."

Assembler languages are governed by rules which must be followed to ensure that statements are translated into the proper machine code. Some of these rules are stated in the following paragraphs.

It should be noted that symbolic names such as JOE, NAME, TEMP, and TEMP1 are meaningful only to the programmer. They are selected to allow him to more readily identify or develop his program sequences. However, the mnemonic identifiers used in place of the machine octal code may not change since they are used to identify a specific machine operation. The special symbols (*, /, +, −) also have precise meanings and may not be changed. The letter X followed by a number (X1, X2) identifies index registers and may not be used in this form to identify values. The letter L followed by an integer (L1, L2) represents limit registers and cannot be used to represent any variables.

Separators are used to enable the assembler to recognize the end of a term. For example, spaces are required between the name, the operation code mnemonic, and the specification.

JOE   ADD   INITIALVAL

The space between JOE and ADD separates the name from the operation code. The space between ADD and INITIALVAL separates the operation code mnemonic from the operand. Commas may also be used as separators. For example,

JOE   DEC   10, 19, 111

means that the operation DEC will convert the decimal numbers 10, 19, and

111 into equivalent machine code. In this example, the commas are used to separate the three values that are to be converted. The assembler will assign a memory location to each of the three converted values, the first of which will be called JOE. Using the symbol plus (+), the two locations which follow JOE can be obtained. The example below is used to illustrate how the three values can be added together although only one location was originally assigned a name.

```
LDA   JOE
ADD   JOE + 1
ADD   JOE + 2
```

Most assemblers have some operation codes that are not translated to the machine language by the assembler. The term applied to these operation codes is *pseudo-operator*. Pseudo-operators are used to direct the assembler operation or to cause the assembler to perform operations requested by the programmer. The pseudo-operators are reserved words that have special meaning. For example, the word COMMENT indicates that the following statement is a comment and is not to be translated into machine code. A comment may appear as:

COMMENT   THIS PROGRAM SOLVES FOR THE SINE OF X,
          WHERE X IS GIVEN IN RADIANS. END

or

COMMENT   DATA WRITTEN 1 JAN 69 END

The pseudo-operator COMMENT acts as a bracket to tell the assembler that machine code is not to be generated for the statement that follows. Special symbols (spaces, commas, etc.) and letters (X, L) are to be treated as English-language elements. The comment may be of any length; therefore, a closing bracket (END) is used to indicate the end of the statement. After the end of the statement has been recognized by the assembler, the assembler resumes normal translation of statements and special symbols. The COMMENT pseudo-operator is used to provide descriptive information on the program. Other pseudo-operators that direct the assembler may be:

START PROGRAM
START DATA

The first statement indicates that the statements which follow are to be treated as program statements. Program statements are statements that require translation into machine instructions.

The second statement identifies the statements which follow as data statements. Data statements are used by the programmer to initialize memory locations to specific values. Data statements used in conjunction with pseudo-operators cause the assembler to translate the specifications into machine code. For example,

```
START       DATA
INITIALVAL  DCFL    396 × 10 ↑ -6
```

The operation DCFL directs the assembler to convert the decimal value 396×10^{-6} to floating-point binary format and insert the equivalent value into location INITIALVAL. A statement such as this allows the programmer to express constants and data in the decimal form as he develops his program.

The upward-pointing arrow (↑) used in the statement indicates a superscript.

Additional data statement pseudo-operators may appear as:

```
DATE ALPH  25  FEB   68**
VALUE  OCT  73164532
```

These two pseudo-operators are used by the programmer to construct messages for printout or octal data constants. The conversion of the data statements into machine code is accomplished by the assembler program. The ALPH pseudo-operator causes the assembler to generate memory locations with the equivalent machine code for the specified alphameric characters. The double asterisk (**) specifies the end of the ALPH statement. Using the character set of Table 13·2 in Chap. 13, the conversion of the ALPH data statement for a 24-bit word system appears octally as:

```
02   05   60   44
21   70   60   06
77   77   77   10
```

There are nine characters, two of which are spaces contained in the ALPH statements. Since a 24-bit word can contain four 6-bit characters, two memory words are packed solid while the third word contains only one character. For partially filled words, the assembler right-justifies and adds leading delete characters (77), which are ignored by hard copy output terminal devices. It should be noted that the first word is referenced as DATE, and simple address arithmetic can obtain the other two locations of the message.

The OCT pseudo-operator causes the assembler to generate a memory location, identified as VALUE, to be initialized to the octal equivalent of 73164532. In this instance there is a one-for-one correspondence between the octal value specified by the programmer and the memory contents generated by the assembler. Like the DEC pseudo-operator, strings of octal values can be specified using the comma separator. Octal values that do not require a complete memory location are right-justified with leading 0's. An example of stringing octal characters and their equivalent memory locations appears as:

```
VALUE     OCT     701, 4232, 72544372
          00000701
          00004232
          72544372
```

It sometimes becomes necessary for the programmer to set aside memory locations that may be used as a buffer area for input messages, or to contain a table of numbers developed during the execution of a program. The statement

```
NUMBTBL    RESV    63
```

causes 63 locations, the first of which is identified as NUMBTBL, to be initialized as 0's. These 63 locations are reserved in the program data area so that they can be used during the execution of the program.

The program written by the programmer in the symbolic code is called the *source program*. The assembler translates the source program into its line code (binary). This object program is run by the computer to solve the problem.

Assembler language syntax has been discussed to illustrate that certain rules or conventions must be followed by the programmer in the generation of the source language program. Assume at this point that a program has been written and is ready for assembly.

Normally the source program is written on specially formatted coding sheets which allow easy interpretation by the key punch operator for translation to a source program punched-card deck. Each card contains one statement and comments. Information format on the card may either be fixed or free-form.

In fixed format, names, operators (instruction or pseudo), specifications (operands or data), and comments must occupy predefined columns on the cards. The fields are not defined for a free-form format, but the proper use of separators allows the assembler to differentiate between the various fields. Fig. 16.12 illustrates a flow for an assembly operation.

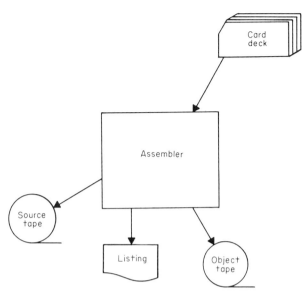

FIG. 16·12 Initial assembly functional block diagram.

The card deck containing the source program statements is accepted by the assembler program as the data which is to be manipulated (translated to machine language). The assembly takes place in the following sequence:

1. Each source statement is checked for syntactical errors by the assembler program.
2. Each card image in memory is assigned an item number.
3. The memory image is placed on magnetic tape. The source tape contains the image of the complete card deck with the assigned card numbers.
4. As each error-free card is encountered, it is translated into binary machine language and recorded on the object tape. The object tape contains the assembled program in machine language.
5. If no errors are encountered in the assembly, the operator may use the object tape as the computer input and execute the program.
6. Should an error be encountered during assembly, the generation of the object tape could be halted under certain conditions, but steps 1 through 4 continue so that the result of the assembly will be a source language tape of the card deck and a listing with program error points listed. The programmer must then correct the errors and reassemble.

The reassembly takes a slightly different form from the original assembly. Figure 16·13 illustrates the flow for the reassembly (and subsequent reassemblies, if required).

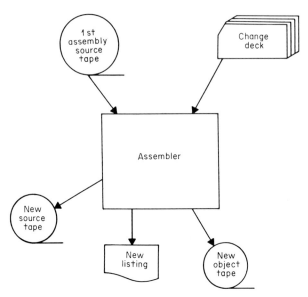

FIG. 16·13 Reassembly functional block diagram.

For reassembly the assembler accepts as inputs the previously generated source tape and the change card deck. Each change card contains the type of change, the new information, and the item number of its corresponding image on the source tape. Three different format change cards may appear as follows:

DELETE STARTING ITEM NO, END ITEM NO.
INSERT ITEM NO., NO. OF CARDS TO INSERT (N10)
REPLACE ITEM NO, INFORMATION

The DELETE change card directs the assembler to remove the specified item numbers from the program. The INSERT change card directs the assembler to insert into the program the specified number of cards (in decimal) after the specified item number. The programmer must ensure that the cards to be inserted follow the insert card. These first two change cards may cause the item numbers and address of the source tape and object tape to change as a result of the reassembly. The third type change card REPLACE directs the assembler to replace the specified item number with the information that follows. This is a one-for-one replacement and will not change the sequence of item numbers or assigned addresses. Note that the comma separator is used between the elements of the specification field.

The reassembly flow is illustrated in Fig. 16·14 and proceeds as follows:

1. The assembler reads a change card and a source image from tape. The item numbers are compared.
2. If the item numbers are not the same, the source image is stored on the new source tape, and the binary translation is stored on the new object tape.
3. If the item numbers are the same and a REPLACE change card is sensed, the information on the card is stored on the new source tape, and the binary translation is stored on the new object tape.
4. If the item numbers are the same and an INSERT change card is sensed, the information on the specified number of change cards is accepted and sequentially stored on the new source tape, and the binary equivalents are stored on the new object tape.
5. If the item numbers are the same and a DELETE change card is sensed, the source card images (from tape) are discarded and the tape is advanced until the end source item is detected.
6. The reassembly continues with the generation of new source and object tapes until the change cards are exhausted. A new listing will be generated.

The generation of the source tape during the original assembly results in a faster execution time for reassembly. Only the changes are submitted as card inputs, while the remainder of the data is available from the source tape at the faster tape transfer rates.

Table 16·4 illustrates the listing that is obtained for the loop problem previously discussed. The listing of the program is formatted by the assembler for ease of reading by the programmer. The format has columns for tags, operations, specifications, comments, relative memory addresses (octal), memory contents (octal), and item numbers (decimal). The content of memory locations is supplied by the object tape, while the remainder of the information is available from the symbolic tape. Between items 0014 and 0015 there are 50 locations. The assembler will print only the first location; however, the next memory address assignment will be location LIST + 50.

NOTE: If a syntactical error had been detected, the assembler would have indicated the error condition by printing an error message above the statement. For example, if item number 0007 had been incorrectly coded, the listing would appear as:

ILLEGAL OPERATION
IFFU   LOOP   IF NOT DONE GO TO ADD   0004 0000 0000 0007

FIG. 16·14   Detailed reassembly flow diagram.

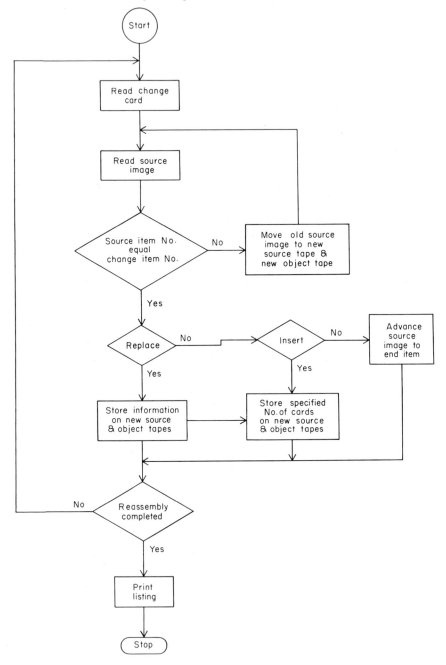

TABLE 16-4

Tag	Operation	Specification	Comments	Octal relative address	Octal memory content	Item no.
	COMMENT	THIS PROGRAM SUMS FIFTY INTEGERS END				0001
	START	PROGRAM				0002
	LDX1	ZERO	INIT. FIRST INDEX TO ZERO	0000	0300 0007	0003
	LDL1	C4T9	INIT. FIRST LIMIT TO 49	0001	0700 0010	0004
	LDA	LIST	FIRST NO. TO ACCUM.	0002	0100 0011	0005
LOOP	ADD	LIST+1/X1	ADD SUCCESSIVE OPERANDS	0003	1620 0012	0006
	(*)				0000 0000	
	ITFFU	LOOP	IF NOT DONE GO TO ADD	0004	1106 0003	0007
	STA	ANSW	STORE ACCUM. INTO ANSW.	0005	1200 0073	0008
	HLT		STOP PROGRAM	0006	0000 0000	0009
	COMMENT	DATA AREA END				0010
	START	DATA				0011
ZERO	OCT	0	CONSTANT ZERO	0007	0000 0000	0012
C4T9	DEC	49	CONSTANT 49	0010	0000 0061	0013
LIST	RESV	50	FOR NO. TO BE ADDED	0011	0000 0000	0014
ANSW	RESV	1	FOR RESULT	0073	0000 0000	0015
	FINI		END OF SYMBOLIC PROGRAM			0016

*See note on page 487 on syntactical error.

In this instance the generation of the binary tape need not have been aborted since a memory location containing 0's could be assigned to the instruction. This would not affect the assignment of the following addresses.

ITEM 16 in the assembly listing is a pseudo-operation that is used to specify to the assembler that the source program is at an end.

QUESTIONS

16·1   Define the programmer's responsibility.

16·2   Name the three instruction formats and briefly describe each.

16·3   Define a dyadic type instruction.

16·4   What does an instruction specify?

16·5   Draw a single-address format.

16·6   What is the purpose of the variant?

16·7   On a BRANCH instruction (condition), when is the branch not taken?

16·8   Do all instructions require an address? Explain.

16·9   Define the single-address instruction indicated by the following: 30000045_8.

16·10   Using the instruction set found in Table 16·1, multiply two operands (located in memory) and store the results into either operand location.

16·11   In the two-address format, what does the address syllable 43010_8 indicate?

16·12   Can indexing be used with the HALT instruction? Explain.

16·13   In the two-address format, if $XR1$ contains a value of 2 and $XR2 = 6$, what is the memory location specified by the following address syllables: 13010_8, 03010_8, 23010_8, 33010_8.

16·14   In the one-address instructions listed below, what does memory location 3010_8 contain at the completion of step 2?

Step 1   LDA 3010_8 Memory location 0600 = 00000000_8
     2   ADD 3010_8 3010 = 00000001(original)
     3   XOR 3010_8
     4   ADD 3010_8
     5   STA 3010_8
     6   BRUNC 0600_8

16·15   In the instruction in Question 16·14, at the completion of step 2, what does the A register contain?

16·16   In the instruction in Question 16·14, at the completion of step 5, what do the A register and location 3010_8 contain?

16·17   In the instruction in Question 16·14, how many instructions are executed after the BRUNC? Define the instruction(s).

16·18   What does a three-address format operator syllable of 2052_8 specify?

16·19   What does a three-address format address syllable of 4506_8 specify?

16·20   What type of information is supplied by a special syllable?

16·21   Define the following instruction: SHR JOE, JOE, D,L,C,10.

16·22   A program is divided into what two basic parts?

16·23   What four methods does the programmer have at his disposal for addressing?

16·24   Define absolute and relative addresses.

16·25   Will the following instruction sequence produce possible error conditions? If it will, how could the sequence be made correct?

Memory location 0   LDA   4
                         1   ADD   5
                         2   DIV   4
                         3   STA   5
                         4   data constant
                         5   data constant

16·26   Can multiprogramming be performed using a system that requires all programs to begin at location 0 of memory? Explain.

16·27   What is the purpose of the program base (PB) and data base (DB) registers?

16·28   Give the PB and DB settings to execute program B of Fig. 16·8.

16·29   Name the two basic uses for indexing.

16·30   How can a data constant outside the DB+ relative area be addressed without indexing?

16·31   Perform the summation problem illustrated by Fig. 16·9 using the instruction set of Table 16·1 (use machine language).

16·32   What general form defines decision-making instructions?

16·33   Name the six common characteristics of loops.

16·34   Define a subroutine.

16·35   Perform the summation problem of Fig. 16·9 using the instructions in Table 16·3. (Use assembler language and generate desired assembler format.)

16·36   When is a base register such as the SEI required?

16·37   What is usually the last instruction of a subroutine?

16·38   What advantage does an assembler provide a programmer?

16·39   Define the following assembler language statements:
ADD LIST/XR1, LIST/XR2, RESULT and ADD*START, *START + 1, RESULT.

16·40   In most assemblers, what code is used to direct assembler operations without causing the generation of machine language?

16·41   In reference to Question 16·40 give several examples.

16·42   What is meant by a source program and an object program?

16·43   What is the difference between fixed-form and free-form coding sheets?

16·44   What is contained on the object tape?

16·45   How does a reassembly operation differ from the normal assembly?

16·46   What is the purpose of the statement in item 16 in Table 16·4?

16·47   The statement in item 14 in Table 16·4 will perform what function?

16·48   What value is loaded into $XR1$ in Table 16·4?

16·49   If the instruction in memory location 0004 in Table 16·4 is changed to DTFF, what additional changes will be required to solve the problem?

16·50   If, through some malfunction, memory location 0004 in Table 16·4 becomes 000 000 73$_8$, what effect will this have on the program?

chapter seventeen

Programming Languages

One of the most significant innovations within the computer industry was the advent of compilers and problem-oriented languages. A *compiler* is a program that translates symbolic-language statements into machine code. A *problem-oriented language* is a rigidly defined language that allows the programmer to state his problem in the manner most familiar to him. Mathematicians write programs in mathematical languages such as ALGOL (ALGOrithmetic Language) or FORTRAN (FORmula TRANslation). Business people use a language such as COBOL (COmmon Business Oriented Language). Each of the languages has special constructs that aid in solving particular types of problems.

The compiler also allows the programmer freedom from the details of the computer system. The source language should be similar for all computer systems; the programmer should not be concerned with which computer system executes the program. Since compilers generate machine code for a particular system, the programmers are not forced to know the individual machine operations. Programmers are allowed to concentrate on the problem being solved.

A problem-oriented language deals with the formation of rules for calculation of a value or values by means of a computer. The languages also provide the means required by a programmer to communicate with the computing equipment.

To a computer user, the problem-oriented language offers the advantages of expeditious means of program implementation, accelerated programmer training and simplified retraining requirements, reduced conversion costs when changing from a computer of one manufacturer to that of another, significant ease of program modification, standardized documentation, and efficient object program code.

This chapter provides a brief description of COBOL as implemented for use on Burroughs electronic data processing systems. An attempt is made only to introduce the reader to the language and not to provide a detailed coverage.

A program written in COBOL, called a *source program*, is accepted as input by the COBOL compiler. The compiler verifies that all rules of the language are satisfied and translates the source program language into an object program language capable of communicating with the computer and directing it to operate on the desired data. Should source corrections become necessary, appropriate changes can be made and the program recompiled. Thus, the source deck always reflects the object program being executed.

All compiler languages employ a vocabulary of reserved words and symbols. These reserved words and symbols may not be used in a program for any purpose other than that defined by the language description.

In addition, to provide control over the computational process and external communication for a program, certain additional statements are defined. These statements provide iterative mechanisms, conditional and unconditional program control transfers, and input/output operations. In order to provide control points for transfer operations, statements may be labeled.

Declarations are provided in the language to provide information to the compiler about the constituents of the program such as array sizes, the types of values that variables may assume, or the existence of subroutines. Each such construct must be named by an identifier.

A COBOL source program is always divided into four parts or divisions in the following order: identification division, environment division, data division, and procedure division.

The purpose of the identification division is to identify the program and to include an overall description of the program.

The environment division consists of two sections. The configuration section specifies the equipment being used. The input-output section associates files with the hardware devices that will be used for their operation.

The data division is used to describe the data fields which the object program is to manipulate or create. These data fields may be files, records, fields within records, word areas, and constants.

The procedure division specifies the program steps necessary to accomplish the task desired by operating on data defined in the data division.

This chapter describes the general characteristics and makeup of COBOL, beginning with the identification division and considering the environment, data, and procedure divisions in turn. The discussion encompasses significant statement formats as well as portions of the rules governing their use.

NOTE 1:   Brackets are used to indicate statements that are optional.

NOTE 2:   Braces are used to indicate that the programmer is to make a selection of one of the entries between the braces.

The first division of the source program, the IDENTIFICATION DIVISION, identifies the source program and the output of a compilation. Other information, such as the date the program is written and the date the compilation is accomplished, may be included. The structure of this division is as follows:

IDENTIFICATION DIVISION.
PROGRAM-ID. Any entry.
[AUTHOR. Any entry including appropriate copyright statement.]
[INSTALLATION. Any entry.]
[DATE-WRITTEN. Any entry.]
[DATE COMPILED. Any entry. — the date supplied by the programmer is replaced by the current date (TODAYS-DATE) and TIME]
[SECURITY. Any entry.]
[REMARKS. Any entry.]

The following rules must be observed in the formation of the IDENTIFICATION DIVISION:

1. The IDENTIFICATION DIVISION must begin with the reserved words IDENTIFICATION DIVISION followed by a period and a space.
2. The entries must conform to the rules for the creation of COBOL words.
3. In addition to the IDENTIFICATION DIVISION entry, the only other required entry is PROGRAM-ID. It can be followed by any word or literal of up to 30 characters in length.
4. When DATE-COMPILED is included, the compiler automatically inserts TODAYS-DATE in the form of MMDDYY and TIME in the form of HHMM.
5. An entry is defined as any string of characters and blanks ended by a period.

An example of IDENTIFICATION DIVISION coding is illustrated in Fig. 17·1.

The ENVIRONMENT DIVISION is the second division of a COBOL source program. Its function is to specify the computer being used for the program compilation; to specify the computer to be used for object program execution; to associate files with the computer hardware devices; and to provide information to the compiler about the files used within the program.

The ENVIRONMENT DIVISION consists of two sections. The configuration section contains the overall specifications of the computer. The input-output section deals with files to be used in the object program.

Burroughs COBOL CODING FORM

PAGE NO.	PROGRAM									REQUESTED BY		PAGE	OF
1 3	PROGRAMMER									DATE		IDENT. 73 80	

LINE NO.	A	B													Z
4 6	7 8 11	12 16 20 24 28 32 36 40 44 48 52 56 60 64 68 72													

```
01    IDENTIFICATION DIVISION.
02    PROGRAM-ID. SALES-PERFORMANCE-CURVE.
03    AUTHOR. JOHN DOE.
04    INSTALLATION. MARKETING COMPUTER FACILITY.
05    DATE-WRITTEN. FEB 15, 1968.
06    DATE-COMPILED.
07    SECURITY. COMPANY CONFIDENTIAL.
08    REMARKS. THE FIRST PART OF THE PROGRAM PRINTS ACTUAL SALES AND
09          SALES QUOTA FIGURES IN STATEMENT FORM; THE SECOND PHASE
10          EXPRESSES THESE IN BAR GRAPH FORMAT.
11
12    ENVIRONMENT DIVISION.
13    CONFIGURATION SECTION.
14    SOURCE-COMPUTER. B3500.
15    OBJECT-COMPUTER. B3500.
16
17    INPUT-OUTPUT SECTION.
18    FILE-CONTROL.
19          SELECT DAILY-TAPE ASSIGN TO TAPE.
20          SELECT MASTER-TAPE ASSIGN TO DISK.
              SELECT ERROR-TAPE ASSIGN TO TAPE.
```

Printed in U. S. America.

FIG. 17·1 Sample coding form—IDENTIFICATION and ENVIRONMENT DIVISIONS.

The general structure of this division is as follows:

```
ENVIRONMENT DIVISION.
CONFIGURATION SECTION.
[SOURCE-COMPUTER ...]
OBJECT-COMPUTER ...
INPUT-OUTPUT SECTION.
FILE-CONTROL ...
```

The function of SOURCE-COMPUTER is to allow documentation of the configuration used to perform the COBOL compilation. The format of SOURCE-COMPUTER is:

SOURCE-COMPUTER. computer-name.

The function of OBJECT-COMPUTER is to allow documentation of the configuration used for the object program. The general format of this paragraph is as follows:

$$\text{OBJECT-COMPUTER. computer name, } \left[\text{MEMORY SIZE integer } \begin{Bmatrix} \text{WORDS} \\ \text{CHARACTERS} \end{Bmatrix} \right]$$

The actual name of the computer system is inserted by the programmer, in place of the words "computer name," when the statement is written.

The lowercase word "integer" is replaced with an integer by the programmer. The programmer also designates whether the integer refers to WORDS or CHARACTERS by making a selection of one of the entries between the braces.

The INPUT-OUTPUT section contains information concerning files to be used by the object program. The function of FILE-CONTROL is to name each file, to identify the file medium, and to allow a particular hardware assignment. The format of FILE-CONTROL is:

FILE CONTROL.
SELECT file-name ASSIGN to hardware-name.

All files used in a program must be the subject of a SELECT statement only once. The programmer must replace the words "file-name" with the actual file name.

The ASSIGN clause must be used in order to associate the file with a hardware-name. The allowable hardware-names are: TAPE, DISK, READER, PUNCH, PAPER-TAPE-READER, PAPER-TAPE-PUNCH, PRINTER, SORTER, and LISTER.

An example of ENVIRONMENT DIVISION coding is illustrated in Fig. 17·1.

When constructing the ENVIRONMENT DIVISION, the reserved words ENVIRONMENT DIVISION must appear first, followed by a period and a space.

The configuration section follows and contains information concerning the system to be used for program compilation (SOURCE-COMPUTER) and the system to be used for program execution (OBJECT-COMPUTER).

The third part of a COBOL source program is the DATA DIVISION. This division describes the data that the object program is to accept as input, to manipulate, to create, or to produce as output. The data to be processed falls into three categories:

1. Data which is contained in files and enters or leaves the internal memory of the computer from a specified area or areas.
2. Data which is developed internally and placed into intermediate or WORKING-STORAGE or placed into specific format for output reporting purposes.
3. Constants which are defined by the programmer.

The DATA DIVISION, which is one of the required divisions in a COBOL source program, may be subdivided into two sections. These are:

1. The FILE SECTION which defines the contents of data files stored on an external medium. Each file is defined by a file description followed by a record description or a series of record descriptions.
2. The WORKING-STORAGE SECTION which describes records, constants, and noncontiguous data items which are not part of an external data field but are developed and processed internally.

The general structure of the DATA DIVISION is as follows:

```
DATA DIVISION.              .
FILE SECTION.               .
*FD file-name-1† ...        .
‡01 record-name-1 ...       .
  [02 data-name-1 ...]      .
  [02 ...]                  .
  [03 data-name-2 ...]      .
  etc.
*[FD file-name-2† ...]      .
WORKING-STORAGE SECTION.
  [77 data-name-3 ...]      .
  [77 data-name-4 ...]      .
‡01 record-name-2 ...       .
  [02 data-name-5 ...]      .
  [02 data-name-6 ...]      .
  etc.
‡[01 record-name-3 ...]     .
etc.
```

   *FD indicates the beginning of a file description.
   †The file names must be the subject of a select clause in the ENVIRONMENT DIVISION.
   ‡Record names in the FILE SECTION are chosen by the creator of the file. WORKING STORAGE word names are chosen by the writer of this program. The phrase "data name-1" is used to represent an identifier chosen by the programmer. It should be noted that the line FILE CONTAINS 100 RECORDS shown on Fig. 17·2 is for example purposes only. This statement is required for disk files but is optional for all other files.

Record Description Structure

A record description consists of a set of data description entries which describe the characteristics of a particular record. Each data entry consists of a level-number followed by a data-name, followed by a series of inde-

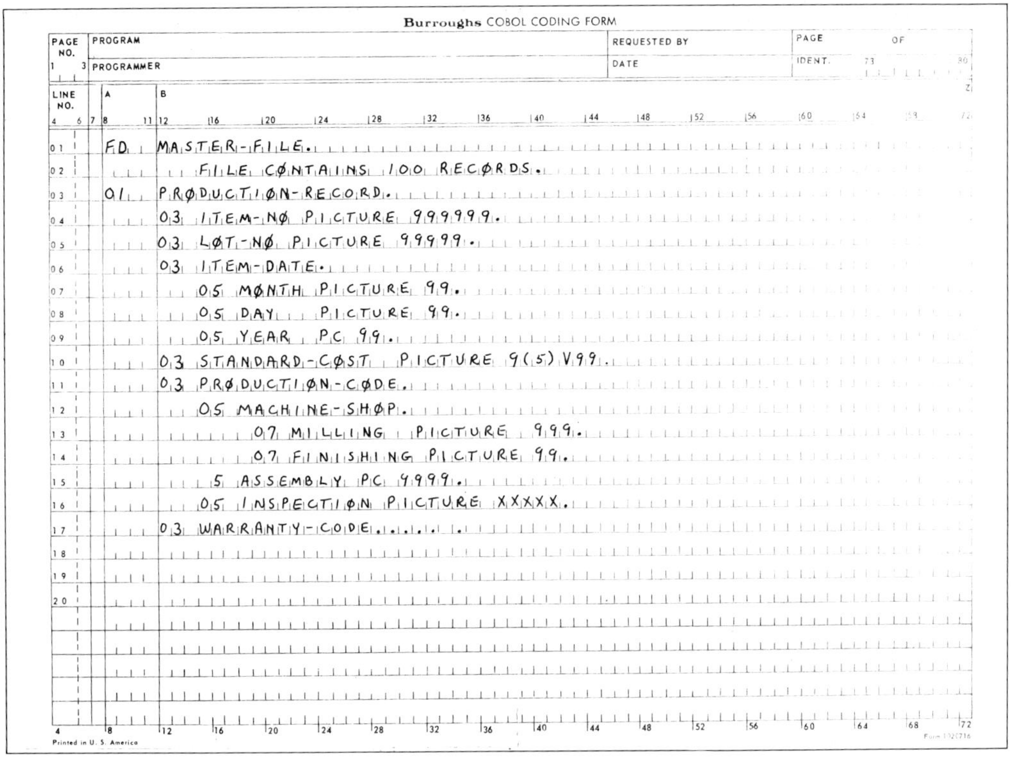

```
                              Burroughs COBOL CODING FORM
PAGE   PROGRAM                                      REQUESTED BY        PAGE        OF
NO.
                                                    DATE
       PROGRAMMER                                                       IDENT.  73        80

LINE   A   B
NO.
01    FD.   MASTER-FILE.
02               FILE CONTAINS 100 RECORDS.
03    01    PRODUCTION-RECORD.
04          03  ITEM-NO  PICTURE 99999.
05          03  LOT-NO  PICTURE 9999.
06          03  ITEM-DATE.
07              05  MONTH  PICTURE 99.
08              05  DAY    PICTURE 99.
09              05  YEAR   PC 99.
10          03  STANDARD-COST   PICTURE 9(5)V99.
11          03  PRODUCTION-CODE.
12              05  MACHINE-SHOP.
13                  07  MILLING  PICTURE 999.
14                  07  FINISHING  PICTURE 99.
15              5  ASSEMBLY  PC 9999.
16              05  INSPECTION  PICTURE XXXX.
17          03  WARRANTY-CODE.
18
19
20
```

FIG. 17·2 Sample coding form—DATA DIVISION.

pendent clauses, as required. A record description has a hierarchical structure, and therefore the clauses used with an entry may vary considerably,
depending upon whether or not it is followed by subordinate entries.

Level-number Concept

The level-number shows the hierarchy of data within a logical record. In
addition, it is used to identify entries for noncontiguous constants and
WORKING-STORAGE items.

Each record of a file begins with the level-number 01 (or 1). This number is reserved for the record name only, as the most inclusive grouping for a
record. Less inclusive groupings are given higher numbers but not necessarily successively. The numbers can go as high as 49. Figure 17·2 illustrates the use of level within a record.

For an item to be elementary, it cannot have subordinate levels, which
means that it is not to be further subdivided. Therefore, the smallest
elements of the description are called *elementary items*. In Fig. 17·2,

MONTH, DAY, YEAR, MILLING, and FINISHING are names of elementary items. Since ITEM-NO, LOT-NO, STANDARD-COST, ASSEMBLY, INSPECTION, and WARRANTY-CODE do not have subsidiary clauses, they also represent elementary items.

A level that has further subdivisions is called a *group item*. In Fig. 17·2 ITEM-DATE, PRODUCTION-CODE, and MACHINE-SHOP represent items on a group level. A *group* is defined as being composed of all group and elementary items described under it. A group item ends when a level-number of equal or lower numeric value than the group item itself is encountered. In Fig. 17·2, group item PRODUCTION-CODE ends with INSPECTION.

Apart from level-numbers 01 through 49, additional level-numbers exist in COBOL. These numbers are 66, 77, and 88. They represent special-purpose elements. Level 66 RENAMES previously described levels in a different grouping, level 77 is used for noncontiguous WORKING-STORAGE, and level 88 defines condition names.

A level-number is the first required element of each record and data description entry. In value it can range from 01 through 49, plus special numbers 66, 77, and 88.

Picture

The function of PICTURE is to describe the size class, general characteristics, and editing requirements of an elementary item. The word PICTURE may be abbreviated as PC. See Fig. 17·2. The format of a picture statement is:

$$\begin{Bmatrix} \text{PC} \\ \text{PICTURE} \end{Bmatrix} \text{ IS (any allowable combination of characters)}$$

In Fig. 17·2 ITEM-NO has a PICTURE of 999999. The six 9's indicate that the size of field ITEM-NO is 6 characters long. A field of all 9's indicates a numeric data item. MONTH with a PICTURE of 99 indicates that a two-character numeric field is used to define the months from January through December.

STANDARD COST on Fig. 17·2 has a PICTURE stated differently. Its PICTURE is 9(5)V99; again it is a numeric data item. The V represents the assumed position of the decimal point. In this case there are five numeric character positions preceding the decimal point and two numeric characters following the decimal point.

INSPECTION has a PICTURE of XXXXX. It could have been stated as X(5). Again a five-character field is represented; however the X indicates that each character position may contain any alphameric character.

A(5) or AAAAA would be a PICTURE that represents a five-character alphabetic field.

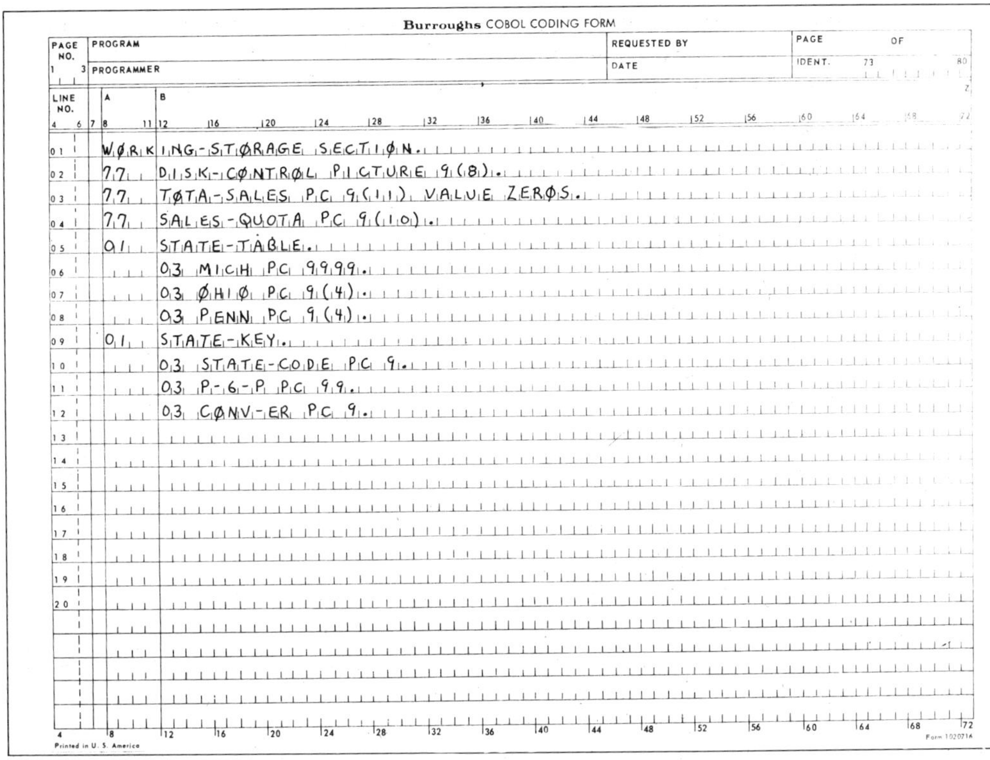

Burroughs COBOL CODING FORM

PAGE NO. | PROGRAM | REQUESTED BY | PAGE OF

PROGRAMMER | DATE | IDENT.

```
01  WØRKING-STØRAGE SECTIØN.
02  77  DISK-CØNTRØL PICTURE 9(8).
03  77  TØTA-SALES PC 9(11) VALUE ZERØS.
04  77  SALES-QUOTA PC 9(10).
05  01  STATE-TABLE.
06      03 MICH PC 9999.
07      03 ØHIØ PC 9(4).
08      03 PENN PC 9(4).
09  01  STATE-KEY.
10      03 STATE-CODE PC 9.
11      03 P-6-P PC 99.
12      03 CØNV-ER PC 9.
```

Printed in U. S. America Form 1020714

FIG. 17·3 Sample coding form—WORKING-STORAGE SECTION.

COBOL contains many additional types of PICTURE clauses that are not illustrated here.

WORKING-STORAGE SECTION

The WORKING-STORAGE SECTION is optional and is that part of the DATA DIVISION set aside for intermediate processing of data. The difference between WORKING-STORAGE and the FILE SECTION is that the working storage section deals with data that is not associated with an input or output file.

Whereas the FILE SECTION is composed of file description entries and record description entries, the WORKING-STORAGE SECTION is composed only of record description entries and noncontiguous data items (individual variables). The WORKING-STORAGE SECTION begins with a section-header and a period, followed by item description entries for noncontiguous working-storage items, and then by record description entries for working-storage records. Working storage record description entries describe the data area that is used during the manipulation of the data contained in the record. The record description in the FILE-SECTION describes the data record contained in the file. A typical WORKING-STORAGE SECTION could be:

WORKING-STORAGE SECTION.

```
77   data-name-1
77   data-name-n
01   data-name-2
     02 data-name-3
     etc.
01   data-name-4
  02 data-name-5
    03 data-name-n
```

Data names are names selected by the programmer to represent data fields

Noncontiguous Working-Storage

Items in working-storage which bear no relationship to one another need not be grouped into records, provided they do not need to be further subdivided. Instead, they are classified and defined as noncontiguous items. Each of these items is defined in a separate description entry which begins with the special level-number 77. The following description clauses are required in each entry:

Level-number.
Data-name.
PICTURE clause or equivalent

Working-Storage Records

Data elements in working-storage which bear a definite relationship to one another must be grouped into records according to the rules for the formation of record descriptions. All clauses which are used in normal input or output record descriptions can be used in a WORKING-STORAGE record description. Each WORKING-STORAGE record name (01 level) must be unique. (Duplication of names at this level is not allowed.) Subordinate data-names need not be unique if they can be made unique by qualification. Qualification is accomplished by following the data-name to be qualified with either IN or OF (use either for readability) and the qualifying data-name or record-name. In the example below, all item descriptions, except the data-name PREFIX, are unique. In order to refer to either PREFIX item, qualification must be used. Otherwise, if reference is made to PREFIX only, the compiler would not know which of the two is desired. For example, in order to move the contents of one into the other, the PROCEDURE DIVISION should read: MOVE PREFIX OF ITEM-NO TO PREFIX IN CODE-NO.

```
01 TRANSACTION-TAPE.....          01 MASTER-FILE.....
     03 ITEM-NO.....                   03 CODE-NO.....
        05 PREFIX.....                    05 PREFIX.....
        05 CODE.....                      05 SUFFIX.....
     03 QUANTITY.....                 03 DESCRIPTION.....
```

The initial value of any item in the WORKING-STORAGE SECTION is specified by using the VALUE clause of the record description. If VALUE is not specified, the initial values are unpredictable. An example of initial value is TOTA-SALES on Fig. 17·3. VALUE may be abbreviated with VA. The VALUE clause may set a field to a string of alphameric characters (literal). The literal must be enclosed in quotes.

The fourth part of the COBOL source program is the PROCEDURE DIVISION. The previous divisions have identified the program and described the system and the data. The PROCEDURE DIVISION contains the procedures needed to solve a given problem. Statements within the PROCEDURE DIVISION will manipulate the data defined in the previous divisions. These procedures are written as sentences, which may be combined to form paragraphs, which in turn may be combined to form sections.

COBOL procedures are expressed in a manner similar to (but not identical with) normal English prose. The basic unit of procedure formation is a sentence or a group of successive sentences. A procedure is a paragraph, a group of successive paragraphs, a section, or a group of successive sections within the PROCEDURE DIVISION. The sentence structure is not governed by the rules of English grammar but dictated by the defined syntax for the COBOL compiler.

Statements

There are two basic types of statements: imperative statements and conditional statements. Statements are the executable elements of a COBOL program.

Imperative Statements

An imperative statement is any statement that is not a conditional statement. An imperative sentence may consist of a sequence of imperative statements. A single imperative statement is made up of a verb followed by its operand. A sequence of imperative statements may contain either a GO TO statement or a STOP RUN statement which, if present, must appear as the last imperative statement of the sequence. The imperative verbs are: WRITE, SUBTRACT, STOP, PERFORM, OPEN, MULTIPLY, MOVE, GO, DIVIDE, DISPLAY, COMPUTE, CLOSE, ADD, ACCEPT.

Conditional Statements

A conditional statement specifies that the truth value of a condition is to be determined and that the subsequent action of the object program is contingent upon this truth value. The basic conditional statement is an IF statement. The following is an example of an IF statement.

IF condition statement-1 ELSE statement-2

Statement-1 or statement-2 can be either imperative or conditional. If conditional, it can in turn contain conditional statements to an arbitrary depth (nested).

Sentences

There are two basic types of sentences, imperative and conditional. A sentence consists of a sequence of one or more statements, with the last statement of a sentence terminated by a period.

Imperative Sentences

An imperative sentence is an imperative statement terminated by a period followed by a space. An imperative sentence can contain either a GO TO statement or a STOP RUN statement which, if present, must be the last statement in the sentence. Examples would be:

ADD MONTHLY-SALES TO TOTAL-SALES.

or

SUBTRACT MINUSES FROM PLUSES; ADD NEW-PLUSES TO PLUSES THEN STOP RUN.

Conditional Sentences

A conditional sentence is a conditional statement optionally preceded by an imperative statement terminated by a period followed by a space. For example:

IF SALES EQUAL TO QUOTA THEN ADD NEW TO OLD; ELSE SUBTRACT NEW FROM MINUSES.

Control Relationship between Procedures

In COBOL, imperative and conditional sentences describe the procedure that is to be accomplished. The sentences are written successively to establish the sequence in which the object program is to execute the procedure. In the PROCEDURE DIVISION, names are used so that one procedure can reference another by naming the procedure to be referenced. In this way, the sequence in which the object program is to be executed may be varied simply by transferring to a named procedure.

In executing procedures, control is transferred only to the beginning of a paragraph or section. Control is passed to a sentence within a paragraph only from the sentence written immediately preceding it. If a procedure is named, control can be passed to it from the sentence immediately preceding it or can be transferred to it from any sentence which contains a GO TO or PERFORM, followed by the name of the procedure to which control is to be transferred.

Paragraphs

So that the source programmer may group several sentences to convey one idea (procedure), paragraphs are included in COBOL. In writing procedures in accordance with the rules of the PROCEDURE DIVISION, the source programmer begins a paragraph with a name. The name consists of a word followed by a period, and the name precedes the paragraph it names. A paragraph is terminated by the next paragraph-name. The smallest grouping within the PROCEDURE DIVISION that can be named is a paragraph. The last paragraph in the PROCEDURE DIVISION is terminated by the special paragraph-name END-OF-JOB which must be the last card in the source program. In Fig. 17·4 OPENER, READING, SKIPPER, HEADER, FINISH, and END-OF-JOB are paragraph names.

Sections

A section consists of one or more successive paragraphs and must be named. The section-name is followed by the word SECTION and a period. Under all other circumstances, a sentence may not begin on the same line as a section-name. The section-name applies to all paragraphs following it until another section-name is found. It is not required that a program be divided into sections. The only section shown in Fig. 17·4 is the one named DISK-BACK SECTION.

Each sentence, paragraph, section, and procedure of the PROCEDURE division uses verbs to direct the operational sequence of the program.

Verbs

A portion of the verbs available for use with the COBOL compiler are categorized below. Although the word IF is not a verb in the English language, it is utilized as such in the COBOL language. Its occurrence is a vital feature in the PROCEDURE DIVISION.

1. Arithmetic:
   ADD
   SUBTRACT
   MULTIPLY
   DIVIDE
   COMPUTE
2. Data manipulation:
   MOVE
3. Ending:
   STOP
4. Input-output:
   WRITE   CLOSE
   READ   ACCEPT
   OPEN   DISPLAY
5. Logical control:
   IF
6. Procedure branching:
   GO TO
   PERFORM

A general definition of some of the verbs previously described is given in the following pages. The arrangement of the verbs is in alphabetical sequence.

ADD FUNCTION

The function of ADD is to add two or more numeric data items and store the result in a receiving field. The general format of ADD is as follows:

ADD data-name-1   TO data-name-2 [ROUNDED]

Data-name-1 and data-name-2 are the names of fields that have been described in the DATA DIVISION. ROUNDED is an optional statement that indicates that the results of the operation are to be rounded under the conventional rules of rounding.

CLOSE

The function of CLOSE is to indicate that processing of a particular file has been completed. The general format of CLOSE is:

$$\text{CLOSE file-name-1} \quad \left[\text{WITH} \left\{ \begin{array}{l} \text{LOCK} \\ \text{RELEASE} \\ \text{NO REWIND} \end{array} \right\} \right]$$

The CLOSE statement generally indicates that a program is finished with the file named file-name-1. The programmer may select the WITH RELEASE option, meaning he is completely finished with the file, and it is being released to the executive for disposition. The NO REWIND indicates that the program is not finished with the file and intends to reopen the file again. The LOCK option removes the file from the executive control and indicates to the operator that a file is no longer in use.

NOTE: The file must have been opened before a CLOSE statement can be executed (see OPEN statement) and the file must have been described in the FILE CONTROL section of the ENVIRONMENT DIVISION and the FILE SECTION of the DATA DIVISION.

GO TO

The function of GO TO is to provide a means of breaking out of the sequential, sentence-by-sentence, execution of code, and to permit continuation at some other location indicated by the procedure-name. The format of GO TO is

GO TO procedure-name

Each procedure-name is the name of a paragraph or section in the PROCEDURE DIVISION of the program.

IF

The function of the IF is to control the sequence of commands to be executed depending upon either a condition or the relative value of two quantities. The purpose of a condition is to cause the object program to select between alternate paths depending on the passing or failing of a test. There are several variations of the IF statement; however, only one is illustrated at this point:

$$\text{IF} \left\{ \begin{array}{l} \text{data-name-1} \\ \text{arithmetic-} \\ \text{expression-1} \end{array} \right\} \text{IS[NOT]} \left\{ \begin{array}{c} = \\ < \\ > \\ \text{EQUAL TO} \\ \text{LESS THAN} \\ \text{GREATER THAN} \end{array} \right\} \left\{ \begin{array}{l} \text{data-name-2} \\ \text{arithmetic-expression-2} \end{array} \right\} \ldots$$

MOVE

The function of MOVE is to transfer data from one area of memory to another area of memory (receiving field). The format of MOVE is:

MOVE   data-name-1   TO   data-name-2

A common usage of a move is the movement of a data item from an input record to an area in WORKING-STORAGE for manipulation.

OPEN

The function of OPEN is to initiate the processing of both input and output files. The general format of OPEN is one of the following:

OPEN   INPUT   file-name
OPEN   OUTPUT   file-name

The use of the file (input or output) determines which of the above options may be used. An OPEN statement must be executed prior to the first READ or WRITE statement for that file. A second OPEN statement for a file cannot be executed prior to the execution of a CLOSE statement for that file.

PERFORM

The function of PERFORM is to depart from the normal sequence of execution in order to execute a procedure either a specified number of times or until a specified condition is satisfied. Following this departure, control is returned to the normal sequence. The format of PERFORM has four options, only one of which is illustrated.

$$\text{PERFORM}\quad \text{procedure-name-1} \quad \left\{ \begin{array}{l} \text{integer-1} \\ \text{data-name-1} \end{array} \right\} \quad \text{TIMES}$$

PERFORM is the means by which subroutines are executed in COBOL. The subroutines may be executed once or a number of times, as determined by a variety of controls. Subroutines are not unique parts of a program. A given paragraph may be PERFORMed by itself or in conjunction with another paragraph; control may pass to it in sequential operation, or it may be the object of a GO TO statement, all in the same program.

READ

The READ statement makes available the next logical record from an input file and allows performance of a specified imperative statement when the end-of-file is detected. The format of READ is:

READ   file-name   RECORD   [INTO   data-name]
    AT END any imperative-statement [ELSE statement]

The INTO option may be used only when the input file contains records of one type. The data-name must be the name of a WORKING-STORAGE record area or output record area.

If, during execution of a READ statement with AT END, the logical end-of-file is reached and an attempt is made to read that file, the statement specified in the AT END phrase is executed. After the execution of the imperative statement of the AT END phrase, a READ statement for that file must not be given without prior execution of a CLOSE statement and an OPEN statement for that file. The optional statement following the ELSE is executed each time a record is read and the end of file has not been reached.

STOP

The function of STOP is to terminate execution of the object program. The format of STOP is:

STOP RUN

When the STOP RUN is executed, all OPEN files are CLOSED, all storage areas are released, and the job is removed from the job mix.

WRITE

The function of WRITE is to release a logical record for an output file. It can also be used for vertical positioning of a printer. The general format of WRITE is as follows:

WRITE   record-name [FROM data-name-1]

$$\left[\left\{\begin{matrix} \text{AFTER} \\ \text{BEFORE} \end{matrix}\right\} \text{ ADVANCING} \left\{\begin{matrix} \text{integer-1} \\ \text{data-name-2} \end{matrix}\right\} \text{LINES}\right]$$

An OPEN statement for a file must be executed prior to executing the first WRITE statement for that file. The record-name must be defined in the DATA DIVISION by means of a 01 level entry under the FD entry for the file.

The field specified by data-name-1 is an 01 level defined in WORKING STORAGE.

The ADVANCING option allows the control of vertical positioning of each record on the printed page. If the ADVANCING option is used, any automatic advancing is overridden. When data-name-2 or integer-1 is used, it must have a positive integral value of 0, 1, or 2, specifying no spacing, single space, or double space.

Figure 17·4 is an example of the coding format for the PROCEDURE DIVISION. All data names must have been defined in the DATA DIVISION in

FIG. 17·4   Sample coding form—PROCEDURE DIVISION.

```
PROCEDURE DIVISION.
DISK-BACK SECTION.
OPENER.
    OPEN INPUT DISK-OUT, OUTPUT PRINT-OUT.
    MOVE 1 TO DISK-CONTROL.
    PERFORM HEADER.
READING.
    READ DISK-OUT INTO DISK-PART. AT END GO TO FINISH.
    ADD 1 TO DISK-CONTROL.
    MOVE RELEVANT TO CARD IMAGE.
    IF FINAL-CARD = "ENDER" GO TO FINISH.
    IF COUNTER > 37 MOVE 1 TO COUNTER GO TO SKIPPER.
    WRITE PRINTS FROM NEW-PRINT BEFORE ADVANCING 2 LINES.
    ADD 2 TO COUNTER GO TO READING.
SKIPPER.
    WRITE PRINTS FROM NEW-PRINT BEFORE ADVANCING 2 LINES.
    GO TO READING.
HEADER.
    MOVE SPACES TO PRINTS WRITE PRINTS BEFORE ADVANCING 1 LINE.
    WRITE PRINT FROM TITLE, BEFORE ADVANCING 2 LINES.
    MOVE 3 TO COUNTER.
FINISH.
    CLOSE PRINT-OUT, CLOSE DISK-OUT.
    STOP RUN.
END-OF-JOB.
```

either the FILE SECTION or the WORKING STORAGE SECTION. All files must have been associated with a SELECT and an ASSIGN clause in the ENVIRONMENT DIVISION.

QUESTIONS

17·1   What is the purpose of a compiler?

17·2   What advantage does the problem-oriented language offer a programmer over the machine language?

17·3   Which language(s) is (are) suited for business problems and which to mathematical problems?

17·4   Name the four divisions of COBOL and briefly describe each.

17·5   In Fig. 17·1 (IDENTIFICATION DIVISION), which statements are actually required?

17·6   How many times must a file of a program be the subject of a SELECT statement?

17·7   What does the level number 01 identify?

17·8   What is the difference between elementary items and group items?

17·9   Explain the following:

(a)   PICTURE 9(3)V999

(b)   PC 999V999

(c)   PC XXXX

(d)   PC A(7)

17·10   If two data items located in different records are not unique (they have the same name), how must they be referenced?

17·11   What are the two types of statements? Sentences?

17·12   Name the paragraphs on Fig. 17·4.

17·13   What statement(s) is (are) used to break out of sentence-by-sentence sequential program execution?

17·14   How are subroutines executed in COBOL?

chapter eighteen

System Control Concepts

The concept of complete system control is a recent innovation in the data processing industry. Complete system control is an attempt to remove time-consuming manual operations from the data processing system or at the very least mask with program execution.

Complete system control is accomplished through an executive program that yields more than masking and elimination of manual operations. Frequently an executive program will control all input-output operations, schedule the use of memories, control processors, and schedule the entry of programs into the system. In this case a system should be considered to be both the hardware and the executive program combined in a manner that will provide the maximum system throughput per unit of time.

The features of an executive program are more readily understood by an examination of the evolution of the executive program in relation to some of the data processing systems that do not use executive control concepts.

Synchronous I/O Processing System

Figure 18·1 illustrates the operations of a synchronous I/O processing system. The symbols to the left and right of the processor block represent programs into and out of the system. Consider a program A being executed by the system; at some point in time the program must execute an I/O operation either to output the results of computation or to receive data for input to the computation process. The synchronous I/O processing system requires that computation be interrupted to allow the input or output operation to be executed. At the completion of the input or output operation the computation process is resumed. After a period of execution, the program will be completed and deliver its final output. At the completion of the final output, the processor is stopped, allowing the operator to "set up" for the execution of the next program. At this point, program A is shown to be completed, and program B is started.

The manual operations performed by the operator may include the

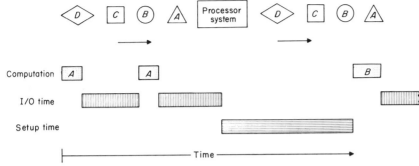

FIG. 18·1 Synchronous I/O processing system.

mounting of magnetic tapes, the loading of punched cards, and the setting of console switches. The time required to perform even minimal manual operations is considerable, compared with the number of instructions a processor might execute during the same period of time if the processor were active.

The programs that are serially initiated by the operator on the synchronous I/O processing system might be several parts of the same application. Applications might be large when compared with the memory size of the system. In overcoming the limitation of memory size, applications are divided into several independent programs that require separate initiation by the operator. These independent programs initiated by the operator may be called *runs*. If these runs are part of one application, the operator requires a run chart or run book to designate the order of runs and the manual operations required by the application.

The speed of the synchronous I/O processing systems is relatively slow, with instruction execution speeds in excess of 100 μsec. Memory speeds in the millisecond range are not uncommon because some systems use drum memories for instruction and data storage. The access time of the storage device becomes a restraint on system speed.

Input and output operations for this type of system are slow because the low-speed mechanical operation and small memory capacity inhibit the movement of large amounts of data quickly. The arithmetic unit of the synchronous I/O processing system controls the flow of data to the input-output media, which constantly interrupts the primary task (computation) of the arithmetic unit. This method of controlling input-output operations does not allow computation during an input-output operation; thus a large amount of computation time is wasted.

In a synchronous I/O processing system the operational sequence is totally serial in implementation. The input, output, and computation function of the computer are serially combined with operator intervention in program execution. Only one of the functions is being performed during any one time period; hence, the processor is idle during the periods of input, output, or operator setup time. These periods of processor nonuse (for program execution) are many times longer than the periods during which computation is taking place.

Asynchronous I/O Processing System

The asynchronous I/O processing system attempts to alleviate some of the problems of the synchronous I/O processing system. The primary improvement in functioning of the asynchronous over the synchronous is the method of controlling input-output operations. The operation of the synchronous I/O processing system required that computation be suspended during an input or output operation because the arithmetic unit was required to monitor the input-output operation. The asynchronous I/O processing system provides both an arithmetic unit for computation and an independent I/O control unit for controlling the input-output operations. Both units are allowed to function at the same time, overlapping input-output operations with computation. As in the synchronous I/O processing system, a considerable time period is devoted to setup between different program runs.

An example of overlapped operation is shown in Fig. 18·2. Computation is suspended for a short period of time to allow an input operation to be initiated. After the input operation is initiated, computation is resumed. The input operation continues without intervention by the computation element. After a period of computation the program execution may require data to be delivered to an output device. Computation is suspended, an output operation is initiated, and computation is resumed. Note that this system allows both input and output operations concurrent with processing. Many data processing systems have several input and output channels which are allowed to operate in parallel with the arithmetic unit, which results in greatly reduced time periods for program execution. The example shown in Fig. 18·2 shows a two-segment program in which the input/output

FIG. 18·2 Asynchronous I/O processing system.

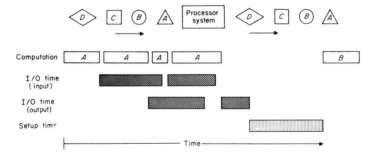

operations are so scheduled that only minor time periods of interruption of computation are necessary to initiate the I/O operations.

Even with the overlapping of input-output operations, the computation element may have to wait for data to be received or wait for data to be delivered to the output media before it may continue with the program. This wait is due to the low speed of peripheral devices. It is possible for complete program sequences to be executed during the time required to read one punched card; thus program suspension may occur while waiting for the next card. The computation speed of the asynchronous system may still be limited by the speed of the slowest peripheral device.

The asynchronous I/O processing system is probably the first instance in which a simple input-output executive program is implemented. The input-output executive provides standard procedures for handling input-output operations. These procedures are activated each time a computation process requires an input or output operation. This executive controls access to all the peripheral devices and coordinates the allocation of memory space. In addition, the executive causes instructions for tape loading, for example, to be transmitted to the operator during the program execution periods.

Total time required for program execution was reduced with the advent of the asynchronous I/O system. However, setup time and the speed of the I/O devices themselves remained as a limiting factor to effective processor utilization.

Satellite Systems

In an attempt to minimize the effects of the low-speed I/O devices on the processing system, a second system is combined with the high-speed processing system. This second system is called a *satellite system* and is concerned with the low-speed peripherals in data preparation and output operations. Normally, the high-speed processor system is a tape-oriented system (uses magnetic tape for most input-output operations). Using high-speed tape and disk for input-output operations reduces the input-output time for the high-speed system, leaving more time for processor program execution. All information to be printed is placed on magnetic tape for output to the printers by the satellite system.

The satellite system is independent of the high-speed processor and serves the high-speed processor system in such tasks as card-to-tape operations. The satellite reads information from the low-speed card reader, formats this information, and places the information on magnetic tape. The tape is mounted on tape units of the high-speed system, and the high-speed system reads the tape to obtain the information. Output information is removed from the high-speed system tape units and placed on the satellite

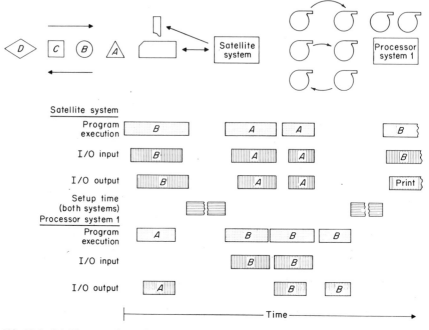

FIG. 18·3 Satellite processing system.

system tape units. The satellite system arranges the output information into the desired format for transfer to the line printers, card punches, and paper-tape units, thus removing low-speed functions from the high-speed processor system.

Figure 18·3 illustrates the operations of high-speed and satellite processing systems.

While processor system 1 is engaged in the execution of program A, the satellite is engaged in program execution of data preparation sequences involved with program B. It should be noted that both systems are oriented to the asynchronous I/O operating mode previously discussed.

Assume that the execution of program A on processor system 1 resulted in a print tape. The result of the data preparation program on the satellite system resulted in input tapes for program B to be executed on processor 1. The tapes are shifted between systems and processor system 1 begins program B execution while the satellite system engages in the conversion of the results of program A from magnetic tape to printed form.

It should be noted that setup time still remains for each of the systems, although it has been shortened from that encountered in the previous systems discussed. The delay because of I/O device speed is minimized since the I/O operations of processor 1 are limited to interface with the high-speed I/O devices. The example also indicates that there may be periods of downtime in processor system 1 since it may complete its program prior to the completion of the data preparation phase of the satellite. The order in which the runs are executed is controlled by the operator. The run book provides the operating instructions for proper execution of the sequence of runs on both the satellite and high-speed systems.

Master-Slave System

By connecting two systems through common peripheral devices, some of the setup time can be eliminated because the physical movement of tapes is minimized. Many of the functions performed by the operator under guidance of the run book can be programmed and executed by a master system. The automatic assignment of jobs to the slave processors by the master reduces periods of processor downtime.

The slave systems are a different type from the master and perform most of the processing because of their speed and capability. The master transfers programs and data to the higher-speed slaves through a high-speed peripheral device, such as magnetic tape or disk. The intermediate peripheral device can be accessed by either the master or the slave processing system for an input or output operation. An output to a common peripheral device by the master (slave) becomes an input operation (from the same device) to the slave (master).

Figure 18·4 illustrates the operations of a master-slave system consisting of a master system and two slave systems.

The master places job A on the peripheral device that is between system 2 and the master. Slave system 2 executes an input operation to bring job A into system 2 main memory. System 2 then begins execution of job A.

During the execution of job A by system 2, the master is set up as required by job B. The master executes a scheduling program and determines that program B should be activated on slave system 1. While system 1 is performing an input operation for job B, the master is being set up with job C. The scheduling program being executed by the master determines that program A, running on system 2, will soon be completed and delivering outputs. Job C is placed on the intermediate peripheral device between the master and system 2. System 2 will deliver its output to the master by means of an intermediate peripheral device and receive its next input by means of another intermediate device. System 2 begins execution of program C, while the master places the results of program A on an appropriate output device.

In a system of this type, the two slaves can be scheduled efficiently. However, with programs that require long processing times, the master may be used very inefficiently because it is frequently waiting for the slaves. If

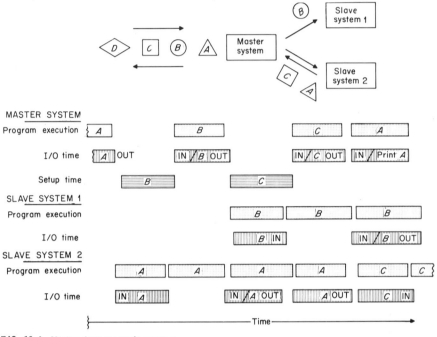

F IG. 18·4 Master-slave processing system.

programs require a large amount of input and deliver a large amount of output while doing relatively little processing, the slaves may waste time waiting for the master to deliver the inputs or remove the outputs. If the programs are of a type that will produce an efficient running mix of processing and input-output operations, the master should absorb the setup time and the low-speed input-output time. Data files and programs are collected by the master before they are required, and they are available when they are requested by the slave system.

Expansion of this type of system may require redesign of the complete system or the addition of a single processor system such as one of those previously discussed.

In the master-slave system any failure of the master results in the loss of all processing capability. However, if one of the slaves fails, processing can continue at a reduced rate through the other slave system.

Modular System

The modular system overcomes many of the disadvantages of the other types of systems while maintaining the better characteristics of these systems. A modular system is one in which the system capacity can be increased by the addition of individual "boxes," e.g., memory elements, processors, or input/output modules.

In the same way that the slaves are operated remotely from the master system, the I/O modules of a modular system are independent of the computation elements. The computation element only specifies the operation to be performed by the I/O module. Information that is to be passed to peripheral devices is passed from high-speed, main memory through the I/O modules. Data that is entered into the system is placed in the high-speed, main memory by the I/O module. This independent operation of the I/O module eliminates the lower-speed transfer that exists between the master and the slaves discussed in the previous example.

Scheduling and controlling input-output operations were the primary functions of the master in the master-slave system. It was stated that in some input-output operations this task could result in inefficient use of the system. In a modular system, through a scheduling and control program that resides in main memory, all the central processor modules can schedule themselves and specify which operations are to be performed by the I/O modules. The need for a master processing system and most of the scheduling inefficiencies due to external run selection are thus eliminated.

When the scheduling program is allowed to select the programs from a job list on a predetermined priority basis, the system can control the order of program execution. The scheduling and control program can make a determination of the most efficient combination of programs to be run and the order in which they are to be run much more efficiently than an operator with a run book.

All the system components are independent of each other and, in most installations, are duplicated. Each central processor can execute the scheduling and control program to initiate operations on all the I/O modules

FIG. 18·5 Modular processing system

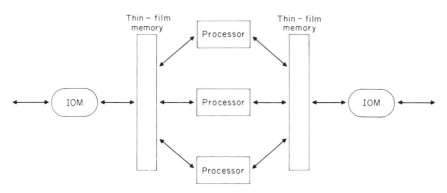

and control the allocation of peripheral devices and memory storage. If any single module fails, the processing is continued by the remaining modules; however, it is at a reduced rate. The system can be expanded by adding more modules in a combination tailored to the needs of a particular installation. The scheduling and control program is written to accept this expansion with little change.

The modular system shown in Fig. 18·5 consists of three identical central processors, several main memory modules, and two identical I/O modules. Each of the I/O modules controls the simultaneous flow of data between the peripheral device channels and any of the main memory modules. The data contained within the memory modules is accessible to all central processor modules. The ability of the central processors and I/O modules to communicate with main memory eliminates the bottleneck which exists between the master and the slave systems. In a modular system, the hardware and programs interface to a great degree in maximizing processor use and reducing downtime.

Multiprogramming

Multiprogramming may be defining as the interleaved execution of two or more programs by the same computer. The modular system (Fig. 18·5) lends itself to the concept of multiprogramming as a natural extension of the system's capabilities. A modular system has all the elements required for multiprogramming: independent I/O modules, common main memories, and central processors that can execute instructions from any location in main memory. Programs are written to be relocatable in main memory. Also, programs can be executed by any of the central processors.

Figure 18·6 shows a queue or list of three programs to be executed by a single processor under control of an executive and scheduling program (ESP)

FIG. 18·6 Multiprogramming mode of program execution.

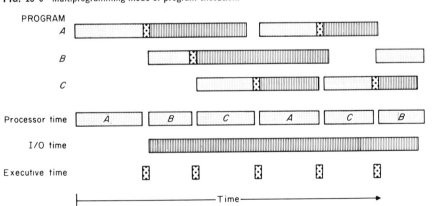

that schedules the programs and I/O operations. Program A is the first program scheduled on the processor; it is executed until it requires an I/O operation. When the program requests an I/O operation, the execution of the program is suspended and the required I/O operation is initiated on an available I/O module. ESP then scans the programs contained in the program queue and selects the highest priority ready-to-run program (a program not waiting for completion of an I/O operation). Then ESP initiates the execution of program B in the central processor. Program B is executed until it requires an I/O operation, at which time the execution of program B is suspended, and ESP initiates the required I/O operation. The internal scheduling function of ESP selects program C to be executed next, because the I/O operation required by program A has not been completed. (Program A not ready to run.)

The execution of program C continues until it requires an I/O operation. After the I/O operation for program C is initiated, program A is selected by ESP to resume its execution because it is the highest priority ready-to-run program (its I/O operation is completed). When execution of program A is in need of an I/O operation, it is interrupted, and ESP is invoked to initiate the desired I/O operation, to suspend program A, and to start the processor on program C. Program C is selected because the I/O operation required by B has not been completed. When program C is suspended, program B is resumed.

A survey of the processor time expended shows that the central processor is almost totally occupied with the execution of user programs. ESP is activated only when required to provide a function to the user or to select the next logical program to be executed for efficient system operation.

Note that because of the scheduling technique, the elapsed time required to execute program B is longer than if program B had been the only program executed by the system; however, the slight lengthening of time on program B allows the execution of at least part of program A and of program C. This time delay is insignificant since in a normal system, program B would not have begun processing until program A had been completed.

The I/O time required by a program is completely overlapped by execution of other programs. Many I/O operations are performed at the same time through the use of a multichannel I/O module. The overlapping of I/O operations increases the effective I/O time and provides for more efficient use of peripheral devices such as line printers and disk units.

Multiprocessing

Multiprocessing may be defined as the interleaved or simultaneous execution of two or more programs or sequences of instructions by a computer network (two or more processors).

A single processor modular system can be expanded into a two-

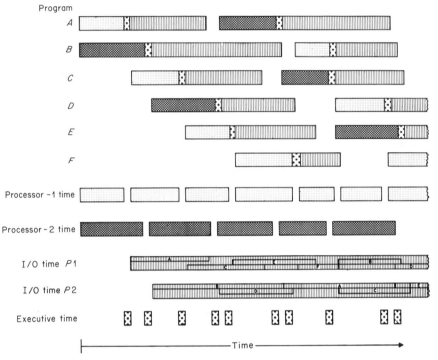

FIG. 18·7 Multiprocessing mode of program execution.

processor modular system merely by adding a second central processor module. This addition results in the changes in capability suggested on Fig. 18·7. The most obvious changes are the number of programs in the program queue and that the modular system is now multiprocessing.

In Fig. 18·7 the two central processors are initially assigned to programs A and B. When program A requires an I/O operation, processor 1 reverts to ESP and initiates the required I/O operation. The I/O operation required is designated by parameters passed to ESP when the operation is called for (call time). After the I/O is initiated, the scheduling function selects program C to be executed because it is the highest priority ready-to-run program of all programs in the mix. Processor 1, which is executing ESP, then assigns itself to execute program C.

When program B (being executed on processor 2) requires an I/O operation, processor 2 starts execution of ESP, which initiates an I/O operation and selects program D as the next program to be executed by processor 2. When program C (being executed by processor 1) requires an I/O operation, processor 1 starts processing ESP, which initiates the I/O operation and schedules processor 1 to begin execution of program E, because there is no higher priority program that is ready to run. Next, when program D (processor 2) requires an I/O operation, processor 2 starts processing ESP to initiate the I/O operation; however, the scheduling portion of ESP selects program A to be executed by processor 2, because program A is the highest priority ready-to-run program.

Programs are completely independent of the central processors. The programmers are not concerned with which central processor module executes their programs. At the second execution of programs B and C, both programs are completed at the same time, and both processors start execution of ESP at the same time. ESP is written to allow simultaneous execution by two processors. Safeguards are designed in the program to ensure that the processors do not interfere with each other. Note also the total amount of processing accomplished by allowing the interleaved execution of programs, rather than assigning a program to a processor and executing the entire program. The multichannel I/O module allows full overlapping and simultaneous I/O operations, thereby minimizing the time that an individual program must wait for I/O completion. ESP time is minimal considering that it controls all the user I/O operations and contributes to the high throughput of the modular system.

Sharing of Common Processing Elements

In a multiprogramming and multiprocessing system, there are many processing elements that must be shared by the many users of the system. All the programs that are in different states of execution share the central processor modules by their interleaved execution. A portion of each pro-

FIG. 18·8 Sharing of common hardware elements.

FIG. 18·9 Sharing of common software elements.

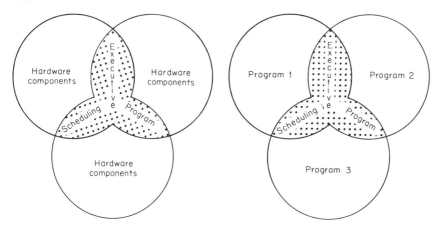

gram in the program queue is residing in main memory, which means that the many programs that can be executed are sharing main memory during their residency. All programs that can be executed will, at one time or another, require the use of the I/O module. Each I/O module is a multichannel device capable of controlling many different I/O operations simultaneously. Thus, if a program requires an I/O operation, it will almost certainly share the I/O module with another program.

The control over the sharing of the hardware elements is effected by ESP (Fig. 18·8). ESP controls the assignment of processors, I/O modules, and peripheral devices to a task. ESP also controls the allocation of main memory and disk storage as well as the processing of hardware interrupts.

The sharing extends further than the sharing of hardware. The software is also shared in a manner similar to the hardware sharing. The functions of a program that are normally contained in all programs are shared by all programs in the queue regardless of the source language used to write them. For example, I/O control functions, file handling, and standard error-processing routines are items that are shared by all programs (Fig. 18·9). To make use of the various common procedures provided by ESP, the user program passes control variables to ESP at the time a procedure is called on for execution.

As a part of multiprocessing and multiprogramming, the user programs do not control their own I/O operations. ESP must control the scheduling of the peripheral devices to avoid having more than one of the programs in the queue attempt to output to the same printer or input from the same magnetic tape at the same time. A necessary part of a multiprogramming and multiprocessing system is that all programs executed by the system must be independent of peripheral devices in the same way that they are independent of the central processors. A programmer is not concerned with the physical tape unit upon which a tape file is mounted or with the printer that will contain his print information at the end of his program. By allowing ESP to control all I/O operations, the programmer need only say, for example, READ FILE FUZZY RECORD LOST or PRINT CHECK, and ESP will designate the physical unit on which the data will appear.

ESP may substitute a similar peripheral unit for one that is not ready or hold the information on an alternate type of device until the desired type becomes available. In any situation, ESP determines what course to follow by determining the elements of the hardware and software that can be shared.

Totally Modular System Equals ESP Plus Hardware

A totally modular information processing system such as the Burroughs B8500 is a combination of hardware elements and an executive and schedul-

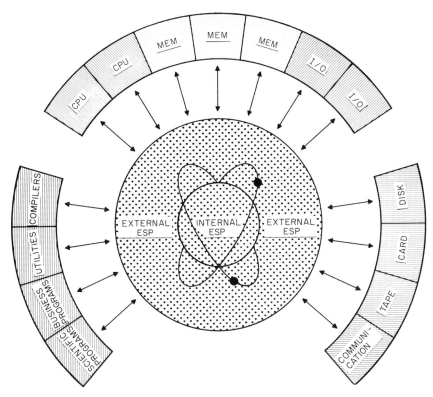

FIG. 18-10   Totally modular system equals ESP plus hardware.

ing program. The computers, memories, and I/O modules are molded into an efficient information processing system under control of the powerful executive program.

As illustrated in Fig. 18-10, ESP consists of two major parts, internal ESP as the nucleus of the system and external ESP as the innermost orbits. Internal ESP is composed of those functions that are concerned with the actual processing of user programs after they have been established for execution. Internal ESP functions include such things as file control, I/O programs, memory allocation, and internal scheduling and control. Programs are established for execution by external ESP, which is composed of those functions that communicate directly with the external environment, such as the operator, the file library, and the external scheduler programs.

External scheduling selects programs from a queue of programs and schedules them for execution by the system. Internal scheduling schedules the computers, memories, I/O modules, and peripheral devices used to execute the programs selected by the external scheduler. Together, internal and external ESP control the environment under which the user program operates. ESP controls all elements that constitute the modular information processing system.

Programs to be executed by the system are allocated space in main memory and are scheduled for execution. Central processor modules are shared by the programs. I/O operations are queued for the I/O modules and balanced between the I/O modules under control of ESP. The terminal devices are allocated to a program only for the time required for reading or writing the information; e.g., print information may be held until the job is complete, then printed all at one time, or the contents of a tape reel may be moved to the disk, and the tape unit may be reassigned to another task. All programs executed and all equipment units used during the execution of a program queue are controlled by ESP.

The totally modular system responds to the overall processing requirement in the most efficient manner possible. The combination and sharing of the programs and the hardware minimize the human intervention necessary in achieving maximum system throughput.

Executive Program

The concepts of system control including multiprocessing and multiprogramming have been presented. The scheduling functions for sharing of programs and hardware were performed by an executive system. Among the names applied to executive systems, by Burroughs for example, are master control program (MCP), automatic operating and scheduling pro

FIG. 18·11 Major executive procedures.

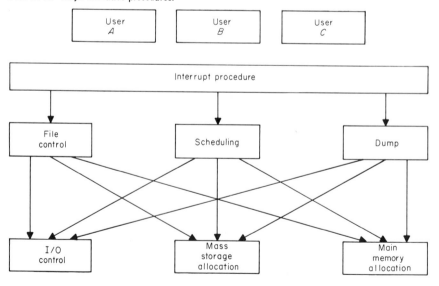

gram (AOSP), and executive and scheduling program (ESP). Regardless of
the name given to this program, many functions are performed by the executive system. Some of these functions and relationships are shown in Fig.
18·11. These relationships are discussed below.

User program. User programs are problem-solving programs rather than
system control programs and are written in one of the problem-oriented
languages (COBOL, ALGOL, FORTRAN) that are supplied with a data
processing system. A user program is not part of the executive system;
rather, the executive system is designed to provide services to the user
programs.

It is the function of the problem-oriented compilers to interface the user
program with the executive system in a manner that makes programming as
easy as possible. All compilers must generate a machine code program
structure that is easily manipulated by the executive system. The executive
system establishes the user program structure in main memory and controls
its execution. Therefore, the executive system requires a specific program
structure regardless of the language used to code a problem.

During user program execution, the program will execute statements
that make calls on the executive system for functions normally supplied by
the executive. The user program has two methods of calling for an executive
function, explicit and implicit. Under both calling methods the user program is suspended until the called function is completed by the executive.
See Fig. 18·7 for an example of the user-executive program relationship.

An *explicit call* is a call on the executive as a direct result of a source
language statement coded by the problem-solving programmer. An example
of an explicit call would be a read or write file call. Each time a read or write
statement is executed, the executive suspends the calling program to locate
its file buffer and determine if the buffer contains the desired record. If the
buffer is empty, the executive must obtain the record from file. The executive is aware which record is required by the user through the type of file
and the parameters supplied by the user at the time of the call.

An *implicit call* is a call on the executive that may or may not be made,
dependent upon conditions that exist at the time a statement is executed.
For example, an ALGOL statement to solve part of a quadratic equation
may look like this:

$$R \leftarrow (-B + SQRT)(B \times B - 4 \times A \times C)/(2 \times A);$$

SQRT is a call on the square root procedure. One function of the executive is to obtain, attach, and disconnect procedures for the user programs.
Each time this statement is executed, a call on the procedure SQRT is made.

A call on the executive may or may not be made, depending upon the connection of the SQRT procedure to the user program.

The first time this statement is executed there may be a call on the executive to locate the SQRT procedure and connect it to the user program. Subsequent executions of the same statement may not call the executive because the SQRT procedure is already connected to the user. The programmer is not aware of when the call is made because he does not know if the SQRT procedure is currently connected to his program.

Each time either type of call is made, the executive is involved. However, there is only one entry point to the executive system, the interrupt procedure. The interrupt procedure controls entry to other executive procedures by interpreting the requirements of either the explicit or implicit call. Any type of call on the executive system is a call on the interrupt procedure.

Interrupt procedure. The interrupt procedure is the part of the executive system that coordinates the actions of the user programs with those of the executive. The interrupt procedure interprets calls on the executive and activates the proper section of the executive system. The interrupt procedure has five primary functions: (1) suspension of user programs, (2) executive function selection in response to an explicit or implicit call, (3) reinstatement of user programs, (4) error handling, and (5) special interrupt handling.

The suspension of the user program implies that the program will be resumed at a later point in time. To enable the resumption, the suspension phase stores an image of the processing element in main memory. The image that is stored in memory contains all registers and control values contained within the processing element that pertain to the program being suspended. The interrupt procedure adds information to the image for subsequent statistical evaluation of this program's execution (e.g., accumulated run time, amount of memory in use, and number of errors). In the multiprocessing environment there may be several processor images in main memory (one for each suspended program).

After a program is properly suspended, the interrupt procedure determines the reason for the executive call and selects the proper executive function to cope with the call. Figure 18·11 illustrates three major procedures (functions that may be called from this point. The file control procedure may be called to perform the actual reading or writing of the file as a result of a user's read or write statement. If the interrupt was caused by an abort condition, the dump procedure is called to produce information about the error. When a user program completes normally or because of an abort, the scheduling procedure is called to perform file disposition and space deallocation. Each of the three major procedures may in turn call upon other procedures such as I/O control, mass storage allocation, and main memory allocation. As can be seen in Fig. 18·11, all the procedures interface with each other.

A user may call some functions that are completely handled by the interrupt procedure and do not result in user program suspension. Examples of these are the time function, how much memory space is available, and what is the equipment configuration.

Reinstatement of a user program is accomplished by a section of the interrupt procedure called *internal scheduling*. This section of the interrupt procedure controls the assignment of programs to central processor modules. Internal scheduling must examine each of the suspended program images and select the highest priority ready-to-run program. The image is then loaded into the central processor module, and the program is initiated. Upon reinstatement, the program resumes and completes as though no suspension had occurred.

Error interrupt conditions may be caused by a hardware failure or program error. In all cases of error interrupt, the interrupt system may respond to the error condition or call upon another executive procedure. Executive procedures exist for diagnostic and corrective action as well as for error recovery and automatic system restart.

The user program has two methods of calling the executive program functions, through the interrupt procedures, both explicit and implicit. However, these two types of calls are not the only methods of activating executive functions. A third method of activating the executive is through a special interrupt condition. Special interrupts may be external to the user program. Special interrupts may be caused by the executive scheduling program or by operator inquiry. An example of an interrupt caused by ESP would occur when the executive requires a table from disk for its own use. The executive may initiate the I/O operation and suspend itself, requiring the I/O module to notify the proper executive procedure when the operation completes. When the executive procedure suspends itself, the interrupt procedure may activate a user program, knowing that the user program will be suspended to allow reactivation of the executive procedure at the termination of the I/O operation. When the operation completes, the I/O module generates an I/O complete interrupt which causes the interruption and suspension of the user program that is being executed by the central processor. Since each interruption invokes the interrupt procedure for interpretation of the interrupt, the interrupt procedure may activate the section of the executive that is awaiting the completion of the I/O operation.

The operator may interrupt the system to make inquiries such as "What tasks are running?" The operator may want to initiate the scheduling of tasks, to abort jobs, and to respond to system messages. When a user program is running, it must be suspended so that the inquiry message can be interpreted.

There are several reasons for, and methods of, activating the procedures of the executive system. Each of them involves activating the interrupt procedure to suspend the user program and transfer control to the desired procedure. The interrupt procedure coordinates the operation of the users and the executive through internal scheduling and interrupt interpretation.

File control procedure. The file control procedure controls user access to all files. The file control procedure may be activated from two places, from the interrupt procedure due to a user read or write statement or from the scheduling procedure which requests transfer of files from off-line storage media to high-speed disk storage. The file control procedure in turn calls on the I/O control procedure for the actual data movement.

A user program has commands for file manipulation, such as READ, WRITE, OPEN, CLOSE, and BACKSPACE. Serial or random files may be manipulated by these commands, with the exception of the BACKSPACE command, which is used only with serial files.

Serial files may be contained on several different devices such as card readers, paper tapes, magnetic tapes, or disks. Random files are contained on such random-access devices as disks or drums. The placement of the file at run time is determined by the scheduling procedure.

With either type file, the user's first functional call must be an OPEN command. The OPEN command connects the file to the user program structure and allows access to the file. The file control procedure refers to the active file directory to locate the file so that it may be connected to the caller.

The next functional call on the file control procedure is the result of a READ or WRITE command, depending on whether the file is an input or output file. For serial input files the file control procedure calls on the main memory allocation procedure to find space for two file buffer areas. When control is returned from the memory allocation procedure, a call is issued to the I/O control procedure to remove two blocks from the file and fill the two file buffers. The file control procedure provides the user with pointers (addresses) to the first logical record in the first block (or buffer). Control is returned to the interrupt procedure so that internal scheduling may activate the correct user.

Two buffers are filled with data to enable the user program to communicate with one buffer through file control repositioning pointers during the time the second buffer is being filled, thereby masking the low-speed device operation. When the first block (buffer) is exhausted, the user pointers are moved to allow access to the second buffer. The file control

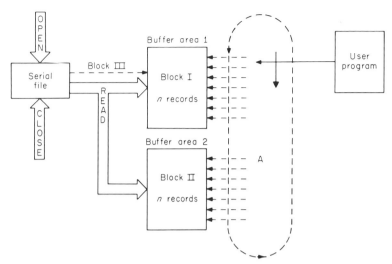

FIG. 18·12   Data manipulation in serial file-read.

procedure calls the I/O control procedure to insert the third block into buffer 1. The file control procedure is always one block ahead of the user in a manipulation of a serial file. Figure 18·12 illustrates this data manipulation.

When the user executes a read statement in a random type file, the number of the record desired by the user must be supplied to the file control procedure as a parameter. The file control procedure calculates the position of the record within the file (base plus record number times record size) and calls main memory allocation to locate space for the record in main memory. The I/O control procedure is called with the absolute disk address of the record to be read. When control is returned to the file control procedure, pointers are set to reflect the position of the record in memory, and control is transferred to the interrupt procedure so that internal scheduling may activate the user. During the time the data is being moved, control is passed to the interrupt procedure, and another user is selected for activation. This action allows other user processing during the data movement from the file to main memory.

When a user executes a write statement during the manipulation of a serial file, the function of the file control procedure is very similar to the serial read. File control moves the record from the working storage area of the user into a write buffer and passes control to the interrupt procedure for user activation. After several write statements, the buffer is full of logical records, and the file control procedure writes the buffer into the file. To write in random file, the user specifies a record number to the file control procedure. The file control procedure calculates the record-starting address and calls the I/O control procedure to insert the record into the file. Appropriate calls are made on the memory allocation procedure to allocate buffers as a result of the first WRITE command.

The BACKSPACE command is not applicable to the random access file. However, for the serial file the BACKSPACE command causes the file to be positioned backward one logical record, allowing the record to be read a second time. An attempt to backspace across a block boundary will require the retrieval of the data block into which backspacing is desired. Refer to Fig. 18·12. When the pointer advances to point A (the first record in data block II), data block III replaces data block I in buffer area I. A backspace at this time will require that data block I be retrieved from the file in order to provide the desired data record.

The CLOSE command is the last functional command for any file type. A CLOSE causes the file to be disconnected from the user, all memory buffers to be released, and access to the file not to be granted until the user issues an OPEN command.

When files are to be moved from off-line storage media to disk, the scheduling procedure calls on the file control procedure to move the file to disk. The file control procedure makes appropriate calls on the other executive procedures to allow the movement to take place. Initially, checks are made on the file to ensure that it is the correct file. Some of the checks made are tape label, reel number-label, and file label. At the completion of the file movement, control is returned to the scheduling procedure.

The file control procedure controls all reading, writing, opening, closing, backspacing, requests for memory allocation, and I/O control for files that are to be manipulated by a user program. File placement at run time is controlled by the scheduler and file control procedures, making the user program completely independent of devices. The user program need not specify where his files are to be located. The file control procedure ensures timely availability of data to satisfy user needs.

Main-memory allocation. One of the primary resources of the system which is controlled by the executive in the multiprogramming, multiprocessing environment is the main memory. Space is allocated to the users as required and when this space is no longer required by a user, it is reassigned to another user. The main-memory management procedure which accomplishes the allocation and deallocation of space is divided into the allocator and overlay routines.

Allocator routine. When a user program issues an explicit or implicit call on the interrupt system, main-memory space may be required as a result of the call. The SQRT procedure, for example, may have to be moved from disk

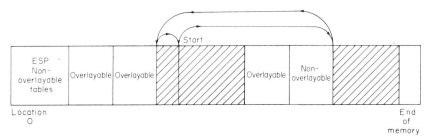

FIG. 18-13 Linking of available memory space.

to main memory, or buffers may be required to contain records obtained from files.

The allocator maintains tables and scans available space links to determine if there is space available. All blocks of available space are connected, with the largest connected to the next largest, through the smallest. The smallest is in turn connected to the largest so that all available space is connected in a closed loop. This is illustrated in Fig. 18-13.

When space is requested, a comparison of the size of the requested space with each of the available spaces in the available space link is made. This comparison begins with the largest available space link and continues in the descending order of size of the available areas until the smallest available area which satisfies the requested space size is reached. The allocator removes that area from the available space link and assigns the area to the requester. If the allocator determines that space is not available to meet requester needs, the overlay routine is called upon to find presently assigned memory space which may be made available.

Overlay routine. All memory area which is not available contains either alterable or nonalterable data. Alterable data may consist of, for example, intermediate results of a computation of a suspended user. If this space is declared overlayable, the data will have to be transferred or "rolled out" to some secondary storage area (disk, for example) from where it may be retrieved on user demand. Nonalterable information is data contained in the main memory and is duplicated in some secondary storage medium. The memory space occupied by this type of data may also be declared overlayable. However, it is not necessary to "roll out" this data since the original data is available for recall at any time. Nonoverlayable memory space could consist of, for example, the memory allocator and overlay routines.

Overlayable objects are linked together in the same manner as available space, in descending order of size, largest to smallest, and smallest to largest in a closed loop. The overlay routine scans the overlayable object link and selects the smallest overlayable area that is large enough to fulfill the size request, delinks the object, copies the object to disk, if required, and assigns the newly available space to the requester.

In the event that the allocator and overlay routines are unable to provide the requested space as a single block, the user is suspended until space becomes available. During the allocator routine, the user continues his normal processing. However, during the overlay routine, all users are suspended until overlay is complete. This suspension ensures that a current user and a user newly assigned are not attempting to manipulate the same space at the same time.

When a user program completes, the executive is activated to perform clean-up functions. One of the clean-up functions involves the return of no-longer-needed memory space to the availability status. This involves space deallocation from completed users and the return of the memory areas, by size, to the available space link.

Mass storage allocation. Data movement from low-speed storage devices to disk storage is accomplished by the file control and scheduling procedures to allow the user to take advantage of disk speed. The file control procedure maintains the records of file position, size, etc. Before any data transfer can take place, space allocation on the disk must be made by the mass storage allocation procedure.

Each time a file is to be placed on disk, the file control procedure requests space from the mass storage allocation procedure. The mass storage allocation procedure checks disk maps to find contiguous storage of the size requested, marks the map to indicate that the space is in use, and provides the starting address of the area to the requester. The requester (in this case file control) may manipulate the area as desired.

If the mass storage allocation procedure cannot find physically contiguous space, the requester is informed that no space is available. The requester may then request logical allocation. In logical allocation, several smaller areas may be connected to appear contiguous. The disk allocation procedure will pass the starting address of each small area to the requester and mark the disk map to indicate that the areas are not available. As each data file is removed from disk and placed on an external storage device by the file control procedure, the mass storage procedure marks the disk map to indicate that the space previously allocated to that file is now available.

If the mass storage allocation procedure cannot provide space, the request is queued until space becomes available. Mass storage allocation may receive space requests from the I/O control and scheduling procedures and respond, generally, in the manner described above.

I/O control. The I/O control procedure controls and coordinates all input and output operations. Each time a user requests a read or write operation, the interrupt system is activated, and the user is suspended. The interrupt procedure then passes control and parameters to the file control procedure, which locates the file, reformats the parameters, and calls the I/O control procedure.

The I/O control procedure interprets the parameters and selects a program to be executed by the I/O control module. Parameters are passed to the I/O module program, and the program is activated. At least one program exists for each type of device that is connected to the I/O module. There may also be a set of file movement programs such as card to disk, disk to printer, disk to tape, disk to punch, or tape to disk.

The parameters passed to the I/O module programs may indicate where the input-output buffers are located, how much data is to be moved, type of operation to be performed, and type of data movement (record or file). The I/O module program uses the parameters to construct descriptors that control the operation of the I/O module. The I/O program initiates the data movement and suspends itself until it is reinitiated. The I/O program may be reinitiated by a call to activate a device on another channel or by a data-transfer-complete indication from an I/O device. Thus the I/O program is not active or tied to a single device but rather initiates data movement on a channel and becomes available to schedule I/O operations on other channels.

When the I/O operation on a channel is completed, the I/O program is reactivated to check status or reason for completion. This reactivation may be due to completion of data movement or to error indication. The I/O control procedure is then notified of I/O program completion. This program-complete status also indicates the reason for the completion of the I/O operation. If the data movement was completed properly, control is passed to the file control procedure. If there was an error in the data movement, the proper error recovery action is taken. The error recovery action may be to reread the data, notify the operator, abort the user program, etc.

The I/O control procedure maintains tables of device status and lists alternate devices (if applicable) to be used in event of device failure. For example, if the supervisory typewriter has been removed from the system for preventive maintenance, the device tables will indicate that the supervisory typewriter is not available. The alternate device list indicates which other typewriter, display console, or combination of devices should be used in place of the supervisory typewriter.

The I/O control procedure has the capability of queuing operations.

If two operations require the use of the same I/O channel, the I/O control procedure activates the I/O module program to initiate the first operation. The second operation is queued for execution at the completion of the first operation. At the completion of the first operation, the I/O control procedure is notified of status, and the I/O module program selects the second operation from queue and initiates the operation without I/O control procedure intervention. At the completion of the second operation, control is passed to the user via the I/O control procedure, file control procedure, and interrupt procedure.

Scheduling procedure. Automatic system scheduling is an attempt to provide more efficient system utilization by removing operator intervention and control and placing the scheduling function under the control of the executive system. In either event, operator or internal scheduling, a set of rules must be followed which allow the definition of work and execution order. Automatic system control allows for a more effective control since the system can be made aware of and respond to the dynamically changing environment much more readily than an operator can.

The parameters within which the scheduling takes place are defined by estimated program execution time, file arrival time, program completion time, desired program start time, and program priority. This data is prepared in a scheduling language. The scheduling program ensures a timely execution of the task program within the total system work load for the scheduling period.

In a system employing automatic scheduling, it is possible to initiate or request task scheduling by manual intervention. The routines involved in scheduling include collection, task introduction, and file disposition.

The collection stage ensures the availability of data required by the task that is being scheduled. The data files required for running of this task are defined in the scheduling language with the DEFINE statement. The scheduling language DEFINE statements are interpreted by the collection section of the scheduling procedure, and the file names are presented to the file librarian (operator). The librarian responds with file status. If the requested files are not available, scheduling on this task is discontinued and a new task is scheduled. If all files are available, they are made ready at the input tape station. After a period of time the collector designates tape reels to be mounted in specific tape units. Control is passed to the file control procedure. The file control procedure controls the movement of the file from the tape unit into disk storage. The file control procedure communicates with main memory allocation to schedule space for temporary buffers, mass storage allocation for space to place the file on disk, and the I/O control procedure to control the device operations. It should be remembered that the instructions to the librarian and the tape station must also be passed through the I/O control procedure.

When control is returned to the collector from the file control procedure, an active file directory is constructed to reflect the current position of the files. After all files required by this task have been collected and are available to the system, control is passed to another section of the scheduling procedure called *introduce*.

The introduce section acquires the space in main memory required by the task, reads the program from disk, and establishes it in main memory. The introduce section controls the introduction of jobs into main memory under the guidelines of memory availability and central processor utilization. If the central processors are not fully occupied with computation and there is space available, a new task is introduced.

After a task is established and the introduce section has determined that another task cannot be introduced and there are no scheduling and collection functions to be performed, the introduce section calls the interrupt procedure and provides parameters that indicate the introduce section wishes to be suspended. Suspension will continue until a task aborts, reaches normal completion, or a program requires one of the scheduling procedure functions.

The scheduling procedure will be reactivated by the interrupt procedure. Each time a task completes, the scheduling procedure is called to dispose of the files of that task and introduce a new task.

File disposition consists of moving files to their permanent residence (e.g., tape, cards, paper tape, or line printers). Operators are notified to prepare the appropriate output devices (tapes, cards, printers) to receive the files. The librarian is directed as to file location in the library.

The order of scheduling is designated by the programmer through a scheduling language. Either automatic or manual activation of the task may be specified. The programmer's statements are interpreted, and appropriate action taken or requested by the scheduler for task completion. As in the other executive system functions, the scheduling procedures closely interface with the previously discussed executive procedures during program execution.

Dump procedure. A program abort is generally characterized by a dump or printing out of the main memory image. The programmer would then employ various techniques to analyze and interpret memory content in an attempt to establish the reason for the failure.

The task of interpreting an error dump is made less difficult by allowing the executive program to interpret the memory image of the program before placement on the line printer. An error condition generates an interrupt condition which activates the interrupt procedure. The interrupt procedure stores information to record the error condition and position of the processor within the program at time of interrupt (processor image). The interrupt procedure activates the dump procedure and indicates the error condition information as parameters.

The dump procedure consists of dump and edit routines. The dump routine copies the aborted program from main memory to disk. This action frees main memory for reallocation to other programs.

The edit routine analyzes the memory image and the parameters and converts the error portion of the aborted program to a symbolic form that is easily interpreted outside of the system. The edit procedure is able to convert machine-language to source-language statements and print source language rather than machine code.

After the edit routine completes printing the symbolic information about the error, control is returned to the interrupt procedure. The interrupt procedure then notifies scheduling that the program aborted. Scheduling may introduce a new program for execution or return to the interrupt procedure for activation of a different user.

System Application

The development of data processing hardware and programs has broadened the total range of application far beyond the initial application of data processors to the repetitive processing and data manipulation tasks. Although much of the available processing time is devoted to this type of operation, the "computing machine" is serving the scientific, business, educational, and military communities in a multiplicity of tasks, and the potential for expansion of these services into new fields is unlimited.

In the growth of the data processing industry the attempt to increase the productivity of the machine was keyed to the elimination of the bottleneck in the overall process, the human operator. This approach was fairly successful, and the result is a generation of supercomputers which, through sophisticated programs, can exercise control and scheduling over their operations with a minimum of human intervention. However, many present-day applications require that the operator have the ability to communicate more directly with the processing system. This is possible through the use of inquiry devices ranging from typewriters to visual display units.

To meet the ever-increasing needs and demands of the system user, the modern data processor may function in four different modes of operation. Two of the modes of operation allow interaction with the human operator and are termed the *conversational* mode and the *time-sharing* mode. Of the remaining two modes, *batch-processing* and *real-time*, the real-time mode may be considered interactive although not with the human operator. The real-time mode, rather, is interactive with a mechanical or electrical system. The batch processing mode is the most widely used mode of operation. Each of the operating modes is considered below.

Batch-processing mode. The batch-processing mode may be defined as the sequential running of a queue of programs on a periodic basis. For example, a business may use a data processing system to perform payroll calculations and recording, inventory level control, and invoicing and billing operations. At specified intervals, under the control of an executive, the programs would be run and the results delivered as outputs. In the payroll application, the results would be printed checks ready for delivery to the employee. In inventory control, the result may be a purchase order to replenish stock which has dropped below a predetermined level.

In a system using batch processing, the response time is, of course, related to system load. A priority order for the programs is specified so that the "deadline" type programs are run before the normal processing jobs. An operator or operators may be authorized to enter programs into the scheduling queue. The operator(s) may be located at a console at the central facility or at a remote terminal hundreds of miles away. In either case, the results of the program run are delivered to the initiating activity. The economics of such an operation can be seen in that multiple locations may be serviced by the same processor at little additional cost over the basic system cost. In the batch mode of operation the operator communicates with the system. Additional flexibility could be gained if the operator had the ability to communicate with the system programs.

Conversational-mode processing. The capability to communicate with the system program mentioned above is provided in the conversational mode of processor operation. In this mode, the operator is able to initiate a program and "talk" to it during the execution phase. The program must, of course, be written to support this type of operation. It must be remembered, however, that the program is executed at a speed dependent upon the slowest peripheral device, which in this application is the human operator. The reduced operating speed at which the computer must operate in this mode may be justified by the application. Conversational-mode programs are usually written for those applications which require human intervention to control, instruct, or provide the program with information to accomplish a task.

Computer-assisted instruction is an example of the use of the conversational-mode processor operation by the educational community. Instruction in a particular subject is possible in a student-teacher relationship between the processor and the student(s). The computer can "converse" only in the subject matter which it knows (is programmed for).

The medical community may use the conversational mode, for example, to retrieve from data banks information on the success of various drugs or procedures in treating specific symptoms. It may also use data bank information to assist in diagnosing an illness or establishing possible causes for symptoms observed. The final diagnosis will, of course, be provided by the doctor.

A salesman may, from a remote location, query the availability of a product in inventory. The availability for delivery may be instrumental in making the sale. At the instant the sale is made, the salesman may so indicate to the computer. The result could be the generation of shipping invoices by the computer and the adjustment of the inventory level. In addition, data could be stored which, during the billing period, results in printout of customer invoices for billing purposes.

The scientific community is relieved of hours of tedious error-prone mathematical calculation with the scientist receiving his intermediate results on which to build further exploration and experimentation.

As in batch processing, the conversational-mode processing capability can be made available to numerous remote users. The timeliness of the result in a given application will determine the economics of the use of conversational-mode processing.

Real-time processing mode. A real-time system is driven by the demands of a device that is external to the system. In real-time processing, the computer is part of a loop which is controlling and continuously interactive with an in-process operation.

An example of real-time processing in a military application is missile guidance and control. The entire process from countdown through the final commands is computer-controlled. The nature of the device involved requires rapid and continuous sampling of position, speed, and acceleration, coupled with the rapid and continuous data outputs from the processor in the form of corrective control signals. The operation requires an almost instantaneous response from the processor; the processor is part of "what is developing" here and now. The slightest delay in the generation of controlling signals could spell the difference between success and failure in the mission.

The control of a chemical process is an example of a real-time commercial application. Normally, the process is controlled by sample taking, testing, and tolerance checking by a human operator, who, on the basis of his analysis, initiates an action to bring the process within tolerance. Such a procedure detects a trend or drift in the process and, in fine-tolerance manufacturing, is a problem because of the time involved. A computer used in process control can make almost immediate adjustments in the operation and can exert the required control for extremely sophisticated and close-tolerance operations. Real-time processing can, therefore, be considered as interactive, although with a device or system rather than with the human operator.

Time-sharing mode. The time-sharing mode of operation is similar to multiprocessing and multiprogramming in that the system capabilities are shared by a number of "customers." In a multiprocessing or multiprogramming environment, the limited hardware and program elements are available to all users of the system. The executive, of course, provides the overall control of what user is assigned specific system elements, the period of the assignment, and the priority of the users. In the time-sharing mode of operation, a reasonable response time is assured each user through a set of ground rules under which the executive runs.

The development of computing machines has been characterized by innovations designed to improve system throughput and remove the time-consuming human intervention in system operation.

The initial data processing system was a serial type operation in that only a single function could be performed at a time. The system was either in the process of computation or was engaged in input/output operations.

Some of the shortcomings of the basic system were overcome in the asynchronous I/O processing system. In this arrangement, the I/O operations were able to be conducted somewhat independent of the processing element.

The satellite-system concept was adopted in an attempt to minimize unproductive processor time while system setup and data preparation operations were performed. This approach provided for time savings in setup by allowing one processor to be used for data preparation and the other to be used for computation.

In the master/slave system, the use of intermediate devices between several systems allowed for reduction in operator setup times.

Each of the improvements allowed for an increase of system throughput; however, considerable time was still involved in system setup, and the expansion of system work load required the addition, in most cases, of complete systems.

The concept of modularity allowed for system expansion through the addition of "black box" elements of memories, processors, or I/O units and extended further the possibilities for the number of input/output units which could be connected to the system.

Multiprogramming techniques were introduced whereby the processing element of the system could operate on more than a single program. The control function of program selection and execution came under program control.

The addition of multiple processing units to a system allowed for the execution of user programs with a corresponding increase in system throughput.

Hardware and software designs became more closely related and complemented each other in providing flexibility in responding to user needs.

Executive or master program control of the system removed further the need for operator intervention in system operation. Hardware and software sharing optimized the use of available devices and provided greater program flexibility. The executive system assumed the responsibility for user program scheduling, data movement, device scheduling, input/output operations, bookkeeping functions, and allocation of available storage areas.

Computing systems now reach into every facet of human endeavor and look to an even brighter future.

QUESTIONS

18-1   Define the concept of complete system control.
18-2   How is the objective of complete system control realized?
18-3   Briefly describe the operation of a synchronous I/O processing system.
18-4   Briefly describe the operation of an asynchronous I/O system.
18-5   What advantage does the asynchronous I/O have over the synchronous I/O system?
18-6   In what way was the satellite computer system an improvement over the synchronous and asynchronous I/O types?
18-7   Describe the master/slave relationship in a computing system.
18-8   Describe the concept of modularity.
18-9   In the modular type system, what unit parallels the master of the master/slave computer system?
18-10   Define multiprogramming.
18-11   In multiprogramming, what is meant by a ready-to-run program?
18-12   In Fig. 18-6, when program A is suspended for the second time, why is program C initiated ahead of program B?
18-13   Define multiprocessing.
18-14   Define the basic concept of executive programs.
18-15   In multiprocessing and programming where common elements are shared (hardware and software) by various "users," why can not the "users" control their own I/O operations?
18-16   What does the ESP do when a desired peripheral device is not ready when required?
18-17   Name the two components of the ESP and briefly define the function of each.
18-18   What is the major advantage of the totally modular system?
18-19   Name the two methods used by a user program to call for an executive function and briefly define each.
18-20   Name the five primary functions of the interrupt procedure.
18-21   What is meant by the expression "stores an image of the processing element in memory"?
18-22   What is a third method (it can be external to user program) of activating executive functions? Explain.

18·23 Briefly define the two methods of activating the file control procedure.

18·24 What are the two types of files? Name the devices used with each.

18·25 With either type file, the user's first functional call must be what type command? Explain.

18·26 What does the file control procedure ensure?

18·27 What are the two routines used by the main-memory management procedure?

18·28 Are any user programs running during an overlay routine? Explain.

18·29 What is meant by the term "logical allocation"?

18·30 What type information is specified by the parameters passed from the I/O control procedure to the I/O module program?

18·31 What action is taken by the I/O control procedure when two operations require the use of the same I/O channel?

18·32 Is manual intervention possible in a system employing automatic scheduling?

18·33 Define the three routines involved in scheduling.

18·34 How is the order of scheduling determined?

18·35 What usually activates the dump procedure and what are the routines involved?

18·36 Define the four modes in which data processors may function.

18·37 Which of the modes allows manual intervention (by human operator), and which is the most widely used?

18·38 Place the following applications in the proper mode:
(a) Payroll and inventory control
(b) Missile control
(c) Computer-assisted instruction
(d) On-line banking

Answers to Odd-numbered Questions

CHAPTER ONE

1·1 The advantages that computers offer over conventional methods of problem solving are speed and accuracy.

1·3

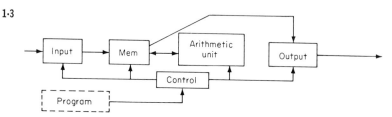

Input: Accepts input data from input peripheral devices; entry point of information into system.

Memory: Stores instructions and data (intermediate and final).

Arithmetic unit: Performs the mathematical and logical manipulations.

Output: Delivers results of data manipulations to output peripheral devices; exit point for problem results from system.

Control: Controls data flow and operation sequencing within the computer.

Program: Step-by-step operational sequence required for problem solution.

1·5 Computers are used in such applications as:
- (*a*) On-line and off-line banking
- (*b*) Airline reservations systems
- (*c*) Process control and scheduling
- (*d*) Payroll and accounting
- (*e*) Research
- (*f*) Medical diagnosis
- (*g*) Education
- (*h*) Space probe control
- (*i*) Communications systems

1·7 Data is applied to the digital computer in the form of signals of two discrete levels, high or low.

1·9 Blaise Pascal invented the first desk calculator. This machine performed both addition and subtraction, with later modifications allowing multiplication to be performed.

1·11 Perhaps the greatest advance in automatic computing was the ability to internally store the computer instructions.

CHAPTER TWO

2·1 The decimal system was the system of numeration used in the first electromechanical computers. Its use created a problem in implementation in that it required 10 separate storage devices per order or a device capable of 10 distinct level representations. Its implementation resulted in an unreasonable space requirement to house a modest-size computing capability.

2·3   The two basic logical gates used in digital computers are the AND gate and the OR gate. The AND gate is used in decision-making, while the OR gate functions as a mixer. The truth tables for two-input AND and two-input OR gates are shown below:

AND gate: $C = A \cdot B$				OR gate: $C = A + B$		
A	B	C		A	B	C
0	0	0		0	0	0
0	1	0		0	1	1
1	0	0		1	0	1
1	1	1		1	1	1

2·5   A bit is a binary digit which may be either a 1 or a 0. A character is the basic unit of intelligible machine information, usually of fixed length. Characters may be decimal digits (0–9), letters (A–Z), or special symbols. A word is a larger segment of information consisting of a number of characters. A block is a group of words, the information content of which is usually related to a given problem or information grouping.

2·7   A logical diagram is used to describe or illustrate computer organization and operation.

2·9   The most commonly used bistable element in digital computers is the flip-flop.

2·11   As a storage device, thin-film spots offer the advantage over magnetic cores of smaller physical size and faster switching speeds.

2·13   The equation $C = \overline{A} \cdot B + A \cdot \overline{B}$ will be satisfied by an exclusive OR (XOR) gate.

2·15   The equivalent circuit for a NAND gate is an AND gate feeding an inverter.

2·17   The logical diagram used to show the generation of a 1-μsec pulse delayed by 50 μsec is shown below:

CHAPTER THREE

Section 1

3·1   The radix of a number system may be defined as the number of different symbols which can be used in any digit position.

3·3   The advantage of the use of the binary number system in computers is the ease with which the allowable symbols may be represented (0, 1).

3·5   Alphameric characters consist of number symbols, letter symbols, and special symbols.

3·7   The modulo sum of 7 and 8 is 5 and the modulus is 10.

Section 2

3·9   The method used to convert decimal to binary integer is the repeated-division-by-2. The repeated-multiply-by-2 method is used to convert decimal to binary fraction.

3·11   The decimal equivalents of the binary numbers in question are:

Binary	Decimal
110101	= 53
111.101	= 7.625
010110	= 22
1111111.011	= 127.375

3·13 Binary addition

(a)	1010	(b)	1000	(c)	110101	(d)	11111
	0101		1001		000011		00001
	1111		10001		111000		100000

3·15 The advantage of the use of octal over the binary system is the ease of reading and interpreting long strings of binary numbers.

3·17 The octal representations of the decimal numbers in question are:

Decimal		Octal
7	=	7
322	=	502
88	=	130

3·19 The results of the conversion of the octal numbers to binary are shown below:

Octal	Binary
263	= 010110011
776	= 111111110
22	= 010010
544.321	101100100.011010001

3·21 The binary coded decimal system is a method of assigning a group of four binary digits to represent the decimal symbols 0 through 9 in any position of the number.
Weighted code: The sum of the bits is equal to the number represented. Example: In the 8421 code, $10_{10} = 1010$ BCD $= 10_{10}$, or in the 2421 code $5_{10} = 1011$ BCD $= 5_{10}$.
Nonweighted code: The sum of the bits does not equal the number represented. Example: Any excess-3 number.

3·23 The results of the conversion of the decimal number to hexadecimal are shown below:

$$57_{10} = 39_{16} \qquad 421_{10} = 1A5_{16} \qquad 5_{10} = 5_{16}$$

3·25 The results of the binary-to-Gray conversions are shown below:

Binary		Gray code
1101	=	1011
10111	=	11100
10001	=	11001
10101	=	11111

Section 3

3·27 The relationship between the 9's and 10's complement of a number is that the 9's complement is 1 less than the 10's complement.

3·29 The subtraction of 225 from 300 using the 10's complement add method is:

0000000300
9999999775 = 10's complement of 225
——————————
10000000075

Carry is ignored in sum but can be used to indicate that the sum is positive.

3·31 In a machine with the binary point to the left of the MSB of the word, the range of values which may be represented is that between plus and minus 1.

3·33 Overflow is possible during addition. The machine will accept number values which in themselves are within the capacity range of the machine. However, the addition of numbers can produce a sum outside the range of values which may be represented by the the machine. In this case, overflow has occurred since the represented sum is not a correct indication of the value of a valid addition.

3·35 (a) $0.0001(+1/16) = 0.0001$ (true form)
          $0.0100(+1/4) = 1.1011$ (1's complement of 1/4)
          —————————————————————————
                sum 1.1100 ($-3/16$ in 1's complement form)

(b) $1.1001(-9/16) = 1.0110$ (1's complement of 9/16)
      $1.0110(-3/8) = 0.0110$ ($+3/8$)
      ———————————————————————————
            sum 1.1100 ($-3/16$ in 1's complement form)

(c) $1.1000(-1/2) = 1.0111$ (1's complement of 1/2)
      $0.0101(+5/16) = 1.1010$ (1's complement of 5/16)
      ———————————————————————————
                  $1\ 1.0001$
          carry 1
                  ———————————
                  1.0010 ($-13/16$ in 1's complement form)

(d) $0.0101(+5/16) = 0.0101$ (true form)
      $1.1010(-5/8) = 0.1010$ (sign complemented)
      ———————————————————————————
            sum 0.1111 ($+15/16$)

(e) $1.110(-3/4) = 1.001$ (1's complement of 3/4)
      $0.101(+5/8) = 0.010$ (1's complement of 5/8)
      ———————————————————————————
                  $1\ 0.011$
          carry 1
                  —————————
            sum 0.100 ($+1/2$) overflow

3.37 DIVIDE operations by the machine method are shown below:

$$3/8 \div 1/2 = 3/8 \times 2/1 = 6/8 = 3/4 = 0.110$$
$$0.100(1/2)\overline{)0.011(3/8)}$$

Initial step

Dividend $= 0.011 = +3/8$
Divisor-subtract $= 1.011 = +1/2$ in 1's complement

Remainder $= 1.110 = -1/8$
Shifted remainder $= 1.101 = -5/8$ $\Big\}$ magnitude in 1's complement

Quotient sign positive
Q bits generated $= 0$
                  └indicates next step adds divisor to remainder

Second step

Remainder $= 1.101 = -5/8$ 1's complement magnitude
Divisor-add $= 0.100 = +1/2$

                   1   $\overline{0.001}$
          carry └⟶1

Remainder $= 0.010 = +1/4$
Remainder shifted $= 0.100 = +1/2$

Q bits generated $= 01$
                    └indicates next step subtract divisor from remainder

Third step

Remainder $= 0.100 = +1/2$
Divisor-subtract $= 1.011 = +3/8$ in 1's complement

Remainder $= 1.111 = -0$
Remainder shifted $= 1.111 = -0$ $\Big\}$ 1's complement magnitude

Q bits generated $= 010$
                    └ indicates next step adds divisor to remainder

Fourth step

Remainder $= 1.111$ -0 magnitude in 1's complement
Divisor-add $= 0.100$ $+1/2$

                   $\overline{0.011}$
                   └⟶1

Remainder $= 0.100$ $+1/2$
Remainder shifted $= 1.000$ $+1$ (sign bit has 2^0 value)

Q bits generated $= 0101$
     sign bit ⟶┘ └indicates next step subtracts divisor from remainder

Fifth step

Remainder   = 1.000 +1 (sign has 2^0 value)
Divisor-subtract   = 1.011 $-1/2$ in 1's complement

$$\overline{\quad 1 \quad 0.011 \quad}$$

carry $\longrightarrow 1$

$$\overline{}$$

Remainder   = 0.100
Remainder shifted   = $\Big(1.000$ = +1 (sign has 2^0 value)

Q bits generated   = 0.1011

sign $\longrightarrow\rfloor$ $\lfloor$roundoff bit

Final step

Unrounded quotient = 0.101
Roundoff bit   = 0.001

$$\overline{\quad 0.110 \quad = +3/4}$$

Section 4

3·39 A normalized number in a fractional machine is a number in which the first nonzero digit appears immediately to the right of the binary point.

3·41 The results of the scaling and normalizing of the given numbers are shown below:

Original	*Scaled*	*Normalized*
1 2 3 4 5 6 7	Sign 1 2 3 4 5	Sign 1 2 3 4 5
1 1 0.3 6	0.1 1 0 3 6 $\times 10^3$	0.1 1 0 3 6 $\times 10^3$
0.0 0 2 5	0.0 0 2 5 0 $\times 10^0$	0.2 5 0 0 0 $\times 10^{-2}$
3.5 2	0.3 5 2 0 0 $\times 10^1$	0.3 5 2 0 0 $\times 10^1$

3·43 The addition of two numbers after rescaling is shown below:

$$0.360 \times 10^2 + 0.250 \times 10^4 = 36 + 2500$$
$$= 2536_{10}$$

Rescaled
0.0036 $\times 10^4$
0.2500 $\times 10^4$

$$\overline{0.2536 \times 10^4 = 2536_{10}}$$

3·45 The most common system of error checking is parity checking.

3·47 A three-bit error correction code using the format $C1\ C2\ D1\ C3\ D2\ D3\ D4$ and an information value of 7 is as follows:

Bit 1 2 3 4 5 6 7

$$\overline{C1\ C2\ D1\ C3\ D2\ D3\ D4} \qquad (D1\ D2\ D3\ D4)$$
$$\ 0\ \ 0\ \ 0\ \ 1\ \ 1\ \ 1\ \ 1 = 7_{10} = (\ 0\ \ 1\ \ 1\ \ 1)$$

$C1\ C2\ C3 = 001$

$C1$ = modulo sum $C1 + D1 + D2 + D4 = 0$
$\quad =$ $\qquad 0 + \ 0 + \ 1 + \ 1 = 0$
$C2$ = modulo sum $C2 + D1 + D3 + D4 = 0$
$\quad =$ $\qquad 0 + \ 0 + \ 1 + \ 1 = 0$
$C3$ = modulo sum $C3 + D2 + D3 + D4 = 0$
$\quad =$ $\qquad 1 + \ 1 + \ 1 + \ 1 = 0$

CHAPTER FOUR

4·1   Boolean algebra provides a method of describing a complex function in terms of equations that provide a "big picture" of circuit operation.

4·3   Boolean algebra is based on the premise that a statement will be either true or false.

4·5   The equation $AB(C\overline{D} + E) = ABC\overline{D} + ABE$ illustrates Postulate 7 of the distributive law.

4·7   The proof for De Morgan's second theorem is:

Postulate 13: $\overline{A \cdot B} = \overline{A} + \overline{B}$
$A \cdot B$ is the complement of $\overline{A \cdot B}$
Proof: $(A \cdot B)(\overline{A \cdot B}) = 0$ (Postulate 10)
First prove that $A \cdot B$ is also the complement of $\overline{A} + \overline{B}$
Stated condition 1: $(A \cdot B) + (\overline{A} + \overline{B}) = 1$
Stated condition 2: $(A \cdot B)(\overline{A} + \overline{B}) = 0$
To prove the first condition:

$$(A \cdot B) + (\overline{A} + \overline{B}) = 1$$

$\overline{A} + (A \cdot B) + \overline{B} = 1$	rearrange expression (Postulate 5)
$(\overline{A} + A)(\overline{A} + B) + \overline{B} = 1$	(Postulate 8)
$1 \cdot (\overline{A} + B) + \overline{B} = 1$	(Postulate 9)
$\overline{A} + B + \overline{B} = 1$	(Example 6)
$\overline{A} + 1 = 1$	(Postulate 9)
$1 = 1$	(Example 13)

To prove the second condition:

$(A \cdot B)\,(\overline{A} + \overline{B}) = 0$	
$A\overline{A}B + AB\overline{B} = 0$	(Postulate 7)
$(0 \cdot B) + (A \cdot 0) = 0$	(Postulate 10)
$0 = 0$	(Example 5)

Since $(A \cdot B) + (\overline{A} + \overline{B}) = 1$ and $(A \cdot B)(\overline{A} + \overline{B}) = 0$, then $(A \cdot B)$ is the complement of $(\overline{A} + \overline{B})$ (Postulates 9 and 10). Therefore, if $(\overline{A} + \overline{B})$ and $\overline{A \cdot B}$ are both the complement of $(A \cdot B)$, then $\overline{A \cdot B} = \overline{A} + \overline{B}$.

4·9 $G = [(\overline{A} + B)(C + D)]\,[E + F] = [(A\overline{B} + \overline{C})(\overline{D} + \overline{E})][\overline{F}]$

4·11   If the NOT-side output of a flip-flop were "true," the flip-flop would be in the "reset" or ZERO state.

4·13   The logical diagram for the equation $(A + \overline{B}C)(\overline{A} + B + C) = F$ is

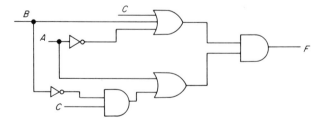

4·15 A truth table is useful for logical analysis because it shows all possibilities of the variables of an equation and their effect on the output or result of the equation.

4·17 A truth table for the equation $(\overline{A}\,\overline{C} + B)(A + \overline{B}C) = F$ is:

A	B	C	F
0	0	0	0
0	0	1	0
0	1	0	0
0	1	1	0
1	0	0	0
1	0	1	0
1	1	0	1
1	1	1	1

4·19 $(A + \overline{AB})(AB + C) = F$

CHAPTER FIVE

5·1 The right-hand rule states that if a conductor is held in the right hand so that the thumb points in the direction of current flow, the fingers of the closed hand will indicate the direction of magnetic flux.

5·3 Permeability is the reciprocal of reluctance, or the ratio of the flux in a material to the flux that would exist in the same area if the material were replaced by a vacuum.

5·5 The strength of the magnet is described in terms of magnetic flux density per square centimeter. The unit of measure is the gauss, and the symbol is B.

5·7 Residual magnetism may be defined as the level of magnetic flux remaining in a material after the magnetizing force has been removed.

5·9 Hysteresis is the energy lost (in the form of heat) when domains are aligned first in one direction and then in the opposite direction. Hysteresis loss occurs because the magnetization of the core does not reverse at the same time that the magnetizing force does.

5·11 Material with a rectangular hysteresis loop is preferred for magnetic information storage devices because it can discriminate against small switching currents and has a high signal-to-noise ratio during read.

5·13 Information is stored and retrieved from a ferrite core as follows:
Write: A full select current H is applied to switch the core into the ONE state.
Read: A full select current H is applied in the opposite direction to switch the core to the ZERO state. A sense winding detects the flux change that occurs.

5·15 The advantage of thin-film memory over ferrite-core memory is usually faster switching speeds due to a $90°$ flux change in film compared with the $180°$ of cores for the basic relationship of the magnetic domains.

5·17 A binary 1 is stored in a thin-film device as follows: After the internal field has been rotated to the "hard" state ($90°$ cw or ccw dependent upon whether a 1 or 0 had been stored) by a "read" (word) current, a perpendicular information current is applied in the proper direction, so that the resultant field tips the internal field to a position between the hard and 1 "easy" state. When the magnetizing currents are removed, the internal field "falls" to the 1 "easy" state.

5·19 Sensing of a binary 1 in a cryotron is accomplished as follows: A critical magnetic field is applied to a leg of the storage loop. This field causes that leg to return to a normal resistance. The resistance increase in the loop causes a voltage to be generated (by the interruption of the circulating current) which is sensed on the digit line as a 1 bit.

5·21 If a 1 is read from a cryotron cell, a 0 is stored in that cell by not reestablishing the circulating current.

5·23 Three commonly used magnetic recording techniques are return-to-zero, return-to-bias, and non-return-to-zero.

5·25 A 1 is recorded with each flux change in the non-return-to-zero recording technique.

CHAPTER SIX

6·1 Some factors to be considered in the selection of a transistor for switching applications are transistor delay time, rise time, storage time, and fall time.

6·3 At turn-off time the overdrive capacitor discharges, providing additional series aiding drive current to speed up the transistor turn-off time.

6·5 Nonsaturating techniques improve turn-off time by preventing the transistor from going into saturation and holding storage time to a minimum.

CHAPTER SEVEN

7·1 Five basic transistor gate configurations are:

(a) Direct-coupled transistor logic: The output of one amplifier is connected directly to the input of a following stage.

(b) Resistor transistor logic: A resistor current-summing network followed by an inverting amplifier.

(c) Resistor-capacitor transistor logic: A resistor current-summing network, with each of the resistors shunted by a speedup capacitor, followed by an inverting amplifier.

(d) Hybrid logic: A combination of diode gates followed by a frequency-compensated transistor amplifier.

(e) Current-mode logic: A system where a constant current is switched into either a transistor base or a diode (single transistor); current switching between separate transistors.

7·3 The common-emitter configuration is commonly used because of the low input drive requirements and high power gain characteristics.

7·5 There is no physical difference between a positive-input AND gate and a negative-input OR gate. The same hardware is used to implement either gate, with the polarity of the inputs used to determine the logical use of the gate.

7·7 Circuit "loading" is undesirable because of signal deterioration and instability which result in unreliable circuit operation.

7·9 Timing oscillators are used to generate the clock pulses required for synchronization and control of the operations within the data processing system.

7·11 Three essential sections of the feedback oscillator and their functions are:

(a) Frequency-determining element limits oscillation to a single frequency and supplies this frequency to the power amplifier.

(b) The power amplifier increases the amplitude of the signal applied to its input.

(c) The feedback element takes a small portion of the output power and returns it in phase with the oscillations originating in the frequency-determining element to sustain oscillations.

7·13 The operating frequency of an LC oscillator is determined by the value of L and C since $F = 1/(2\pi\sqrt{LC})$.

7·15 In a free-running blocking oscillator with fixed B+ and transformer, the frequency of the output can be varied without changes in pulse width by changing the $R1$ $C1$ network values.

7·17 The output frequency of a triggered blocking oscillator is determined by the frequency of the input trigger, provided the frequency of the input trigger is slightly higher than the natural oscillating frequency of the oscillator.

7·19 Three classes of multivibrators and their uses are:

(a) Astable: Used as a timing generator.

(b) Monostable: Used as a pulse stretcher, pulse shaper, and delay element.

(c) Bistable: Used as a temporary storage device and counter element.

7·21 Frequency stability is achieved in the free-running multivibrator (Fig. 7·39) by returning the base resistor to V_{cc} instead of to ground.

7·23 Complementary outputs may be obtained from a monostable multivibrator by taking outputs from both collectors.

7·25 The coupling resistors are bypassed with capacitors in the bistable flip-flop to increase switching speed.

7·27 Flip-flops are used as control elements, counters, storage registers, and shift registers.

7·29 Complementing serves to direct the input pulses to the proper transistor (pulse steering) for a state change. This is accomplished by connecting the ONE-side output to the AND gate associated with the ZERO-side input and connecting the ZERO-side output to the AND gate associated with the ONE-side input. When the flip-flop is in the ZERO state, complementing renders the ONE-side AND gate permissive and inhibits the ZERO-side input gate. When the flip-flop is in the ONE state, the ZERO-side AND gate becomes permissive, and the ONE-side input gate is inhibited.

7·31 The major areas of a power regulation and control system and their functions are:

(a) Relay assembly: Controls the sequence of system power application and removal.

(b) Rectifier assembly: Converts the ac input to pulsating direct current.

(c) Capacitor assembly: Filters the pulsating direct current.

(d) Fault control: Controls power shutdown in the event of alternating current or direct current failure.

(e) Regulator: Senses for output voltage variations and provides control signal to the heat sink assemblies.

(f) Heat sink assemblies: Regulate the output voltage over normal variations.

CHAPTER EIGHT

8·1 A binary counter is a device composed of appropriately connected flip-flops and gates, which perform the function of counting in the binary number system.

8·3 A serial counter has a low-order stage connected to the next higher-order stage while a parallel counter has lower-order stages connected to all higher-order stages.

8·5

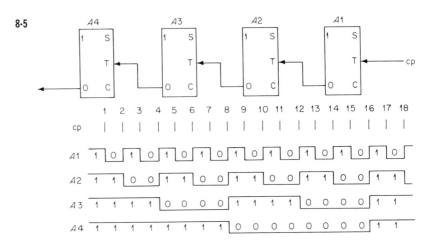

8·7 Mod 3 counter and timing diagram:

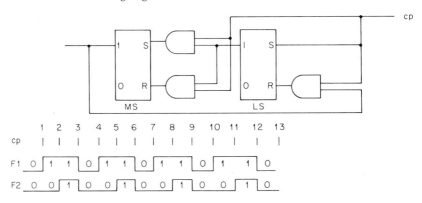

8·9 Storage registers may be composed of flip-flops, ferrite cores, thin-film spots, and other bistable devices.

8·11 The parallel shift register offers the advantage of speed over the serial shift register.

8·13 The barrel switch offers the advantage of multiple shift capability over the conventional shift register.

8·15 Arithmetic operations in a processor may be performed by the use of adders or subtractors.

8·17 A half-adder can generate a carry but does not consider a carry from a previous order. A full adder handles the possible carry from a previous order and consists of two half-adders.

CHAPTER NINE

9·1 Integrated circuits are the physical realization of a number of circuit elements inseparably associated on or within a continuous body to perform the function of a circuit.

9·3 The major improvement of diode transistor logic over resistor transistor logic is the requirement for a lower base-drive current.

9·5 A disadvantage of LSI memories is that they are dynamic in nature and therefore volatile.

CHAPTER TEN

10·1

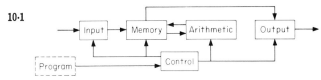

10·3 In order to be executed by the computer, the program must be in machine language.

10·5 Data is defined as anything which is not an instruction and is used within the instruction execution. An operand is data referenced with respect to the arithmetic unit.

10·7 The computer can communicate with a device faster than itself through the use of additional buffering in the input or output areas or both.

10·9 The START signal goes "true" to initiate an input operation, remains "true" during the operation, and goes "false" to terminate the operation.

10·11 The STORE MEMORY signal goes "true" when the eighth character is loaded into the word buffer.

10·13 The major subdivisions of the arithmetic unit and their functions are:

(a) Control: Indicates the operation to be performed and provides various LOAD and SHIFT commands.

(b) Registers: A register functions as both an operand register and as the accumulator for the results of an operation.

B operand register stores the second operand (if any).

C serves as an extension of the A register for certain instructions.

(c) Adder: Performs the addition of the operands.

10·15 During a MULTIPLY operation, an addition is performed if the least significant bit (LSB) of the multiplier is a 1.

10·17 Subtraction is performed in a machine which is mechanized with adders by complementing one of the numbers and then adding.

10·19 Two methods of address modification are indexing and indirect addressing.

10·21 Shift variations include single or double, left or right, circular or end-off, arithmetic or logical.

10·23 A conditional (decision) type instruction where the condition is met may cause an instruction execution sequence change.

10·25 An instruction word specifies the operation to be performed, possible variations, and address of operands or instructions.

10·27 The advantage of advance instruction fetch while another instruction is in the execution phase is the reduction of program run-time.

10·29 The signal INSTR COMPLETE indicates that the instruction register is available for loading.

10·31 The two-character buffer in the output area allows an increased memory transfer rate for operation with higher-speed peripheral devices. When the sixth character (OUTPUT 5) is being outputted, characters 7 and 8 are transferred from the word buffer to the character buffer. This frees the word buffer for loading.

10·33 The drum output interface differs from that of other devices in that the drum must be given the starting address of the data desired for the operation.

CHAPTER ELEVEN

11·1   Two important characteristics to be considered in the selection of a memory system are storage capacity and access time.

11·3   Computing systems usually employ auxiliary memories because of the limited capacity of the internal memory system.

11·5   Memory mode of access can be expressed as:
Random: Immediate access to any memory location without regard to its physical position.
Sequential:
  Cyclic—A sequential mode in which each memory location is available at periodic intervals, such as the magnetic drum.
  Progressive—Sequential in nature, but where the cyclic system implies constant movement in one direction. The progressive system is usually associated with stops and starts. Examples are magnetic tapes and punched cards.

11·7   The purposes of the various elements of a memory system are stated below:

(a)   Storage element: Stores the information (core, thin film).
(b)   Interface controls: Interpret requests as either fetch (read) or store (write). Indicate when information is available on input or output lines.
(c)   Memory controls: Perform control of interfacing between memory and requester; resolve conflicts, etc.
(d)   Operational controls: Provide gating and timing.
(e)   Memory information register: Provides storage for information which is either fetched from or to be stored in the memory.
(f)   Address register: Contains the address of the desired word(s) to be fetched or stored.
(g)   Output mixer: Gates the MIR information to the requester.

11·9   In a core memory system the required current magnitude for switching for read is provided by the read driver as a full switching current and for a "1 write" is provided as a 2/3 current from the write driver and as a 1/3 aiding current from the information driver.

11·11 The operational sequence for a core memory read is:

(a)   Decode address.
(b)   Enable proper switch and R/W driver pair.
(c)   Turn on read driver first.
(d)   Gate 1's from switched cores into MIR.
(e)   Rewrite copy of MIR back into cores (write driver ON and information drivers if 1's).
(f)   Transfer MIR word to requester.

11·13 In a thin-film stack memory system, the purposes of the elements are:

(a)   Word line and word transistor: Provide current path for one word only.
(b)   Digit line and driver: Two hundred and eight digit drivers provide required current direction to store the 1 or 0 in thin-film spot.
(c)   Emitter driver: Used to identify one word within a 32-word group.
(d)   Base driver: Used to select one of 32 groups on a frame.
(e)   Sense line and amplifier: Two hundred and eight sense line/amplifiers to sense and amplify the 1's and 0's.

11·15 The thin-film control word differs from the address of the core memory in that the thin-film control word has additional bits to indicate single or four-word fetch or store and the desired single word (A, B, C, or D) on a single-word operation.

CHAPTER TWELVE

12·1 A disadvantage of the basic organization of the early computer was that it could not easily be adapted to the changing requirements of the user.

12·3 A modular processor is one which is organized to allow the addition of discrete elements of hardware as the system requirements increase. These systems are organized as computer, memory, and I/O hardware elements.

12·5 Some advantages of modular organization are:

(a) System may be tailored initially to meet the need of the individual user.

(b) Modules may be added to provide expanded system capability.

(c) Only minor program modifications are usually required each time a system is expanded.

(d) A significant advance is the ability of the system to perform computation and input/output operations simultaneously.

12·7 The two major areas in a modular I/O are:

(a) Peripheral device (PD) control: Controls information movement to and from any device at the rate of the device.

(b) I/O control: Controls internal communication between the I/O unit and the memory and between I/O and computer at the internal speed of the processor.

12·9 The two major areas of a modular computer are:

Control: Responsible for all memory communications which involve two-way movement of data and instructions. Contains the logic required to execute the instruction repertoire.

Arithmetic: Performs the arithmetic operations such as logical, shifts, conversions, and comparisons.

12·11 The program execution capability of the I/O freed the CPM from the execution of programs related to I/O operations.

12·13 Two types of programs and descriptions of them are:

Control: Used for efficient scheduling of the user programs and assignment of system elements.

Object: The user programs consist of instructions and data required to perform the desired sequence or data manipulation operation.

CHAPTER THIRTEEN

13·1 The primary purpose of peripheral devices is to provide interface between the operator and the processing system.

13·3 Peripheral devices can operate:

(a) On-line: Operation carried on concurrently with the computer's calculations.

(b) Off-line: Operation occurs either before or after the data processing phase but is not required during actual computation.

13-5 The two most widely used card formats are the Hollerith and binary. In the Hollerith scheme, one character is represented in each column of the card, while the binary format allows two characters to be represented in each column.

13-7 If cards are punched on a manual keypunch they must be visually checked by the operator. If they are punched on automatic punches, a read-compare check is made that verifies the card with the original data transferred to the punch.

13-9 Automatic functions such as skip and formatting are controlled by the program drum on the keypunch.

13-11 The alpha card code is different from the internal computer language.

13-13 The most common method of reading cards is the photoelectric technique. An assembly of solar cells and light source pairs is mounted on opposite sides of the card path. A hole in the card allows the solar cell to be activated by the light beam and produce an output while the absence of the hole will block the light from reaching the cell, thus generating no output.

13-15 Paper-tape readers use mechanical reading mechanisms such as star wheels and electronic reading mechanisms such as photocell detectors.

13-17 A translator may be connected between the processing system and the paper-tape punch to enable punching in any desired code.

13-19 A keyboard input device allows real-time communication with the computer system.

13-21 Additional features which may be found on some keyboard devices are paper-tape punch and reading capabilities.

13-23 A typical data transfer rate of a magnetic-tape unit is 120,000 characters per second.

13-25 The end of a record on magnetic tape is indicated by an interrecord gap (a section of tape void of data).

13-27 The EOF position is recognized by the bit configuration of the EOF character.

13-29 The magnetic drum may be used as an extension of internal memory, while the magnetic tape is not used for this purpose.

13-31 Two drum-addressing methods and descriptions of them are:

  (a) Several address tracks with an address recorded for each of the possible word positions on the drum. The addresses are read and compared with the desired address; when the two match, the desired operation (R/W) begins.

  (b) One address track with a pulse recorded for each word position. From a reference mark (DMP) the address pulses advance an address counter. The address counter is compared with the desired address and if the same, the operation begins.

13-33 Drum lockout is a section(s) of the drum upon which write operations cannot normally occur. This section(s), however, may be read.

13-35 Disk R/W head arrangement may be:

  (a) Head-per-track: Advantage, faster access time; disadvantage, requires a large number of R/W heads.

  (b) One head per face: Advantage, fewer heads required; disadvantage, access time is slower because of head-positioning delay.

13-37 Flying heads are R/W heads that ride on a cushion of air during disk operation. The cushion of air acts as a spacing device that allows for proper head-to-disk spacing.

13-39 Two types of printers are:

  (a) Mechanical printer, which utilizes physical contact of the type face and paper for character recording.

  (b) Electrostatic printer, which uses electronic means for character formation.

13·41 Character formation on the Stromberg-Datagraphics electronic printer is by selective electric discharge on an area of treated paper.

13·43 The main advantage of the optical character reader is its ability to read typefonts directly from printed documents.

13·45 Methods used in optical character recognition equipment include optical matching, matrix matching, stroke analysis, and curve tracing.

CHAPTER FOURTEEN

14·1 Display systems offer faster access and communication between man and machine than do keyboards and printers.

14·3 The display system is considered an I/O device.

14·5 Electron beam positioning on the face of the CRT may be by electromagnetic or electrostatic deflection systems.

14·7 Persistence is defined as the period of time for which the screen glows after the electron beam that struck it is removed.

14·9 Refresh rate is the rate at which the beam is allowed to impinge on the image area. Refresh is usually at 50 to 60 Hz and is necessary to eliminate flicker from the image presented.

14·11 Two types of beam positioning are the random beam positioning and raster scan (used in home television sets).

14·13 The Fourier method of character formation is similar to the Lissajous pattern method.

14·15 The keyboard may be used by the operator to modify display information.

14·17 The advantage of the light pen assembly is that it can be used to identify a particular position on the display screen for further action.

CHAPTER FIFTEEN

15·1 A program is necessary to direct the required hardware functions in the step-by-step solution of a problem.

15·3 The wired program achieved some degree of flexibility by the use of a prewired patch panel which enabled a rapid change in program without a major rewiring of the computer.

15·5 An assembler is a program that translates symbolic language into machine code, usually on a statement-for-statement basis. A compiler is a program that translates symbolic statements into machine code but usually converts one symbolic statement into multiple machine instructions.

15·7 The five steps for problem solving are:

(*a*) Problem definition
(*b*) Method of solution
(*c*) Detailed problem analysis
(*d*) Coding
(*e*) Testing and debugging

15·9 Programming in machine code is a tedious and error-prone operation.

15·11 Dump: The printing of a specific data area in a format defined by DUMP.
Monitor: The printing of a variable each time the value of the variable is altered.
Trace: A program which executes and interprets each of the instructions; results in a detailed map of "computer sequencing."

CHAPTER SIXTEEN

16·1 The programmer is responsible for the creation of the program to be executed by the computer hardware.

16·3 A dyadic type instruction is an instruction that requires two operands for execution (such as ADD).

16·5 A single-address format is illustrated below:

OP code	Variant	Address

16·7 On a BRANCH instruction, the branch is not taken when the condition being tested is not true. For example, BRANCH ON $X = L$ will cause a transfer only when the values of X and L are equal. All other conditions cause the next instruction in sequence to be executed.

16·9 Shift the A register right five places algebraic end-off is the instruction indicated by 30000045_8.

16·11 In the two-address format, the address syllable 43010_8 indicates that memory location 3010_8 contains an address rather than an operand.

16·13 In the two-address format, if $XR1$ contains a value of 2 and $XR2 = 6$, the memory locations specified by the following address syllables are:

Address syllable	Memory location
13010_8	3012_8
03010_8	3010_8
23010_8	3016_8
33010_8	3020_8

16·15 For the specified instructions at the completion of step 2 the A register contains 00000002_8.

16·17 After BRUNC, the HALT instruction is executed.

16·19 A three-address format address syllable of 4506_8 specifies that memory location 0506_8 contains an address rather than an operand.

16·21 The instruction SHR JOE, JOE, D, L, C, 10 means place the contents of memory location JOE into the A register and then shift both the A and C registers logical and circular 10 places; place result into JOE.

16·23 The four methods which a programmer can use for addressing are: absolute, relative, indexing, and indirect.

16·25 The possibility of an error exists in the given instruction sequence. The data constant in location 4 will be treated as an instruction and thus an error may result. A HALT instruction could be placed after the STA instruction to correct the sequence.

16·27 The PB register contains the starting point for program instructions, while the DB register does the same for the data area. Both registers indicate the displacement of the respective starting points from physical location zero of the memory system.

16·29 Two basic uses for indexing are address modification and loop control.

16·31 The summation routine of Fig. 16·9, using the instruction set of Table 16·1 and machine language representation, would be performed as shown in Fig. A·16·31.

	1 6	7 12	13			24
Memory location 0000_8	000111	000000	000	000	001	000
0001_8	001101	000000	000	000	001	001
0002_8	000011	000000	000	000	001	001
0003_8	000001	000000	000	001	000	000
0004_8	001110	010000	000	001	000	001
0005_8	001001	000100	000	000	000	100
0006_8	001010	000000	000	011	001	000
0007_8	000000	000000	000	000	000	000
0010_8	000000	000000	000	001	100	011
0011_8	000000	000000	000	000	000	000
0100_8	←——————— FIRST VALUE ———————→					
THRU	SECOND VALUE					
0307_8	ONE HUNDREDTH VALUE					
0310_8	←——————— RESULTS ———————→					

FIG. A·16·31

16·33 Six common characteristics of loops are:

  (a) Entry and reentry point
  (b) Initialization phase
  (c) Performance of a function
  (d) Loop control
  (e) Test for termination
  (f) Exit

16·35 The summation routine of Fig. 16·9, using the instruction set of Table 16·3 and assembler language representation, would be performed as shown in Table A·16·35.

Table A·16·35

Tag	Operation	Specification	Comments	Item no.
	COMMENT	THIS PROG. SUMS	100 NUMBERS END	0001
	START	PROGRAM		0002
	STZ	RESULT	INITIALIZE RESULT LOCATION	0003
	LXR1	ZERO	START INDEX AT ZERO COUNT	0004
	LLR1	LIMIT	NUMBERS TO BE SUMMED	0005
LOOP	ADD	RESULT, LIST/XR1, RESULT	SUMMATION	0006
	ITUE	X1, 1, L1, LOOP	INC.X1 BY 1, IF NOT = L, GO TO LOOP	0007
	HLT		SUMMATION COMPLETE	0008
	COMMENT	DATA AREA END		0009
	START	DATA		0010
ZERO	OCT	0	CONSTANT ZERO	0011
LIMIT	DEC	100	CONSTANT 100	0012
LIST	RESV	100	FOR NO. TO BE ADDED	0013
RESULT	RESV	1	FOR RESULT	0014
	FINI		END OF PROGRAM	0015

NOTE: LXR1, LLR1, and ITUE are assumed assembler formats for Table 16·3 instructions LXR, LLR, and MTX. For example, if the registers had been XR2 and LR2 with a desired increment amount of 3, the format would have been: ITUE X2, 3, L2, LOOP.

16·37 The last instruction of a subroutine is usually the subroutine return instruction.

16·39 Both assembler language statements are in three-address form and are interpreted as follows:

ADD LIST/XR1, LIST/XR2, RESULT: This instruction adds the contents of memory location LIST modified by index register 1 to the contents of location LIST modified by index register 2 and stores the results in memory location RESULT.

ADD*START, *START +1, RESULT: Add the contents of the memory location specified by the address contained in location START to the contents specified by address contained in location START +1 (indirect addressing) and store the result in location RESULT.

16·41 Several examples of pseudo-operators are:

Comment	Data Area
NAME OCT	0
NAME RESV	50

16·43 In fixed format, names, operators, specifications, and comments must occupy predefined columns. In the free-form format, the fields are not defined, and the proper use of separators allows the assembler to differentiate between the various fields.

16·45 On reassembly, only the "change" cards are inputted to the assembler with the other input coming from the previously generated source tape. On the original assembly, the entire card deck (program) was inputted as the only input.

16·47 The item 14 statement of Table 16·4 causes the assembler to reserve 60 memory locations starting at location LIST.

16·49 If the instruction in memory location 0004 in Table 16·4 is changed to DTFF, the new program could be as shown in Table A·16·49.

Table A·16·49

Tag	Operation	Specification	Comments	Item no.
	START	PROGRAM		0001
	LDX1	CT49	START INDEX = 49	0002
	LDL1	ZERO	LIMIT TO ZERO	0003
	LDA	LIST +49	LOAD 50TH VALUE	0004
LOOP	ADD	LIST−1/XR1	ADD VALUES 49, 48, 47, etc.	0005
	DTFFU	LOOP	DEC.XR, IF ≠ 0, REPEAT ADD	0006
	STA	ANSW	STORE RESULTS	0007
	HLT		SUMMATION COMPLETE	0008
	COMMENT	DATA AREA END		0009
	START	DATA		0010
ZERO	OCT	0	CONSTANT ZERO	0011
CT49	DEC	49	CONSTANT 49	0012
LIST	RESV	50	FOR NO. TO BE ADDED	0013
ANSW	RESV	1	FOR RESULT	0014
	FINI		END OF PROGRAM	0015

NOTE: This is one of several solutions. Another example might be: LDA   LIST
                                                                    ADD   LIST/XR1
Remaining portion is the same. This method would load A register with the first value, as in Table 16·4, and would then add the fiftieth value to A register, then the forty-ninth value to A register, etc. Also the octal address and memory contents are not shown here but can be the same as appear in Table 16·4.

CHAPTER SEVENTEEN

17·1 A compiler translates symbolic-language statements into machine code.

17·3 ALGOL and FORTRAN are best suited for mathematical problems, while COBOL is oriented toward business problems.

17·5 In Fig. 17·1, the statements IDENTIFICATION DIVISION and PROGRAM ID are required; the others are inserted at the programmer's option.

17·7 Level number 01 is reserved for the record name only. Less inclusive groupings are given higher numbers but not necessarily successively.

17·9 (a) PICTURE 9(3)V999: Three numeric character positions preceding the decimal point and three following the decimal point.

      (b) PC 999V999: Same as a.

      (c) PC XXXX: Four-character alphameric field.

      (d) PC A(7): Seven-character alphabetic field.

17·11 Statements and sentences can be imperative or conditional.

17·13 Sentence-by-sentence sequential program execution can be broken by the use of statements GO TO or PERFORM.

CHAPTER EIGHTEEN

18·1 Complete system control is an attempt to automate all functions of a data processing system, thereby eliminating time-consuming manual operations.

18·3 A synchronous I/O processing system operates serially. Computation must be interrupted to allow for input/output operation execution.

18·5 The advantage a system with an asynchronous I/O has over one with a synchronous I/O is a reduction in the time required for program execution, since I/O operations are somewhat independent of the processing element.

18·7 The master/slave computer system employs two types of computers, a master and several slaves. The master schedules jobs for the higher-speed slaves to execute and outputs the results of those jobs.

18·9 In a modular system, each I/O module can perform the functions of the master in a master/slave system.

18·11 A ready-to-run program is a program not waiting for completion of an I/O operation.

18·13 Multiprocessing is the interleaved or simultaneous execution of two or more programs or sequences of instructions in a computer system.

18·15 In a multiprocessing and multiprogramming environment where common elements are shared, the users cannot control their own I/O operations because more than one of the programs in the queue might attempt to output to or input from the same peripheral device at the same time. To prevent this, the scheduling of peripherals is performed by the ESP.

18·17 The two components of the ESP and their functions are:

(*a*) External ESP: Establishes programs for execution by the internal ESP.

(*b*) Internal ESP: Concerned with the actual processing of user programs after they have been established by the external ESP.

18·19 The two methods by which a user program may call for an executive function are:

(*a*) Explicit call. A direct result of a source language statement of a user program.

(*b*) Implicit call. Dependent upon conditions that exist at the time a statement is executed.

18·21 In the interrupt procedure, when a user program is suspended, all registers and control values pertaining to the program being suspended are stored in main memory. This allows resumption of this program at a later time. This procedure is known as "storing an image of the processing element."

18·23 The file control procedure may be activated by the interrupt procedure due to a user READ or WRITE statement or by the scheduling procedure when files are to be moved from off-line storage to high-speed disk storage.

18·25 The first functional call for the use of a file is the OPEN command. This command connects the file to the user program structure and allows access to the file.

18·27 The main-memory management procedure employs the allocate and overlay routines.

18·29 Logical allocation is a routine (in mass storage allocation) whereby several smaller memory areas (separate areas) may be connected to appear contiguous. This mode is available when physically contiguous space cannot be found.

18·31 When two operations require the use of the same I/O channel, the I/O module program is activated to initiate the first operation, and the second is queued for execution at the completion of the first operation.

18·33 The three routines involved in scheduling are:

(a) Collection: Ensures the availability of data required by the task being scheduled.

(b) Task introduction: Controls the introduction of jobs into main memory under the guidelines of memory availability and central processor utilization.

(c) File disposition: When a task is completed, moves the files of that task to their permanent residence (tape, cards, etc.).

18·35 The dump procedure is activated by program aborts caused by error conditions. The routines are the dump and edit.

18·37 The conversational and time-sharing modes are characterized by manual operator intervention. Batch processing is the most widely used.

Index

Index

This book was set in Scotch Roman, printed on permanent paper and bound by The Maple Press Company. The designer was Richard Paul Kluga; the drawings were done by Textart Service, Inc. The editors were Alan W. Lowe and Albert Shapiro. Morton I. Rosenberg supervised the production.